DANA'S

MANUAL OF **M**INERALOGY

By the late JAMES D. DANA

SYSTEM OF MINERALOGY. *Seventh Edition.*
Rewritten and enlarged by the late Charles Palache, the late Harry Berman, and Clifford Frondel.

Vol. I. 1944.
Vol. II. 1951.
Vol. III. In preparation.

MANUAL OF MINERALOGY. *Seventeenth Edition.*
Revised by Cornelius S. Hurlbut, Jr.

By the late EDWARD S. DANA

A TEXTBOOK OF MINERALOGY. *Fourth Edition.*
Revised by the late William E. Ford. 1932.

MINERALS AND HOW TO STUDY THEM. *Third Edition.*
Revised by Cornelius S. Hurlbut, Jr. 1949.

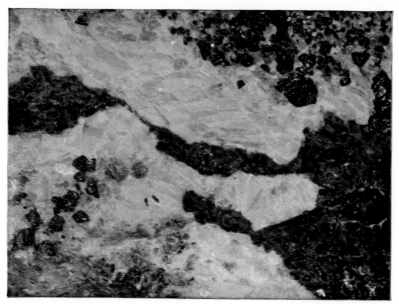

Specimen in White Light Showing White
Calcite, Red Zincite, Pale Green Willemite and
Blue-black Franklinite.

Fluorescent Specimen from Franklin,
New Jersey. *Natural size*

Same Specimen as above in Ultraviolet Light,
Showing Fluorescence.

DANA'S

MANUAL OF

17TH EDITION

MINERALOGY

REVISED BY

CORNELIUS S. HURLBUT, JR.

Professor of Mineralogy
Harvard University

New York · John Wiley & Sons, Inc. · London

SEVENTEENTH EDITION
Third Printing, March, 1963

Copyright, 1912, 1929, by Edward S. Dana and William E. Ford
Copyright, 1912, 1929, in Great Britain
1912 Copyright Renewed 1940
Copyright, 1941, 1952 © 1959 by John Wiley & Sons, Inc.

Library of Congress Catalog Card Number: 59-11820

Printed in the United States of America

▼

PREFACE

In the sixteenth edition of *Dana's Manual of Mineralogy* published in 1952, it was stated that ". . . the increasingly close relationship between mineralogy and chemistry and physics has been manifested by many new mineralogical techniques and, more important, new points of view." This statement applies as well to the last seven years as it did to the previous decade. The resulting changes in the science of mineralogy have been to make it more quantitative, and the new material added in this edition reflects these changes. Quantitative methods have been introduced wherever possible but in such a way as not to impair the usefulness of the descriptive portions which must remain in any elementary treatment of mineralogy.

The chapter "Crystallography" has been expanded to include a discussion of (1) the stereographic projection, (2) the thirty-two crystal classes, (3) the calculation of axial ratios, and (4) x-ray crystallography. All of these combine to give a more rigorous treatment of crystallography and introduce the elementary student to quantitative thinking as a better basis for advanced study.

The major change in the book is in the broad use of the crystal-chemical approach throughout. This serves as a basic and unifying force relating the properties of minerals through fundamental structural and chemical considerations. The section on "Crystal Chemistry" has been enlarged to include enough of the general principles to serve as a basis for a better understanding and interpretation of mineral groups. In the section on "Descriptive Mineralogy" a short discussion of the crystal chemistry of each class precedes the description of the individual species of that class.

The classification of minerals, with the exception of the silicates, is that used in Volumes I and II of the seventh edition of the *System of Mineralogy*. Both the major subdivisions of the silicates and the arrangement of the individual species follow the classification used by Hugo Strunz in *Mineralogische Tabellen*, which is essentially the one to be used in Volume III of the *System of Mineralogy*.

In preparing the manuscript for this edition, I have been most ably assisted by Dr. Henry E. Wenden, Assistant Professor of Mineralogy at Ohio State University.

I am indebted to Professor B. M. Shaub of Smith College for the photographs of the crystal models.

CORNELIUS S. HURLBUT, JR.

July 1959

CONTENTS

1
▼

INTRODUCTION

Although the emergence of mineralogy as a science is relatively recent, the practice of mineralogical arts is as old as human civilization. Tomb paintings in the Nile Valley executed nearly 5000 years ago show busy artificers weighing malachite and precious metals, smelting mineral ores, and contriving delicate gems of lapis and emerald. Minerals and products derived from minerals have figured largely in the growth of our present technologic culture, from the prized flints of Stone Age man to the uranium ores of the present-day atomic scientist. Mineral substances and products are indispensable to the welfare, health, and standard of living of modern man and are the most valued and jealously guarded of the natural resources of a nation.

In view of the age-old dependence of man on minerals for his weapons, his comforts, his adornments, and often for his pressing needs, it is surprising that many persons have only a vague idea about the nature of minerals and are unaware of the existence of a systematic science concerning them. Yet anyone who has climbed a mountain, walked on a sea beach, or worked in a garden has seen minerals in their natural occurrence. The rocks of the mountain, the sand on the beach, and the soil in the garden are completely or in large part made up of minerals. Even more familiar in everyday experience are the products made from minerals, for all articles of commerce that are inorganic, if not minerals themselves, are mineral in origin. All the common materials used in a modern building such as steel, cement, brick, glass, and plaster had their origin in minerals.

1

In general, we may think of minerals as the materials of which the rocks of the earth's crust are made, and, as such, minerals constitute the most important physical and tangible link with the earth's history. Because one of the goals of mineralogy is the elucidation of the physical, chemical, and historical aspects of the earth's crust, the term *mineral* and the study of mineralogy are limited to materials of *natural occurrence.* Thus, steel, cement, plaster, and glass are not regarded as minerals themselves, since they have been processed by man. A synthetic ruby, although it is chemically, structurally, and physically identical with naturally occurring ruby, is thus not a mineral. A further limitation imposed on minerals is that they be of *inorganic* origin. Thus coal, oil, amber, and the bones of animals are excluded even though they occur naturally in the earth's crust. Also the pearl of the oyster and the shell itself, although chemically and structurally identical with the minerals aragonite and calcite, are not classed as minerals.

Perhaps the most important and significant limitation placed on the definition of a mineral is that it must be a *chemical element or compound.* This restriction arises from the consistent picture of the structure of a crystalline solid as an indefinitely extended framework of atoms, ions, or groups of atoms arranged in regular geometric patterns. Such a solid must of necessity obey the laws of definite and multiple proportions and be as a whole electrically neutral; hence it must have a composition expressible by a chemical formula. Thus all mechanical mixtures, even if quite uniform and homogeneous, are eliminated.

Now that we have determined what shall be included and what excluded, we may frame a definition of a mineral as *a naturally occurring chemical element or compound formed as a product of inorganic processes.* This definition sets logical limits for the sphere of activity of the mineralogist and permits the construction of a consistent classification of minerals.

The science of mineralogy is an integrated field of study intimately related to geology on the one hand and to physics and chemistry on the other. The mineralogist may in the field map rock formations, mineral deposits, and structural features of the earth's crust, and then subject the specimens he collects to scrutiny in the laboratory, using the techniques of the chemist and physicist. It is neither necessary nor desirable to view mineralogy as compartmented into definite divisions, for the chemical, physical, and crystallographic properties are closely related and interdependent. However, to make for easier treatment in this book, the following arbitrary divisions are used: *crystallography, physical mineralogy, chemical mineralogy,* and *descriptive mineralogy.*

Although modern mineralogists share in the scientific disciplines of the physicist and the chemist and use physical and chemical techniques to construct a truer and more exact picture of the intrinsic nature of crystalline minerals, they have never forgotten that they are natural scientists whose primary purpose is the search for keys to the problems of earth history. Nor have mineralogists, in their concern with atoms and space lattices, become insensitive to the imaginative appeal of the world of ordered beauty beneath their feet.

The history of mineralogy shows that techniques and philosophy have been repeatedly and profoundly changed by the introduction of new tools and new concepts. Mineralogy today is a living growth, and we may expect similar drastic revisions of viewpoint and method in the future.

CRYSTALLOGRAPHY

A. INTRODUCTION

Minerals, with few exceptions, possess the internal ordered arrangement characteristic of the solid state. When conditions are favorable, they may be bounded by smooth plane surfaces and assume regular geometric forms known as *crystals*. Most crystallographers today use the term crystal in reference to any solid with ordered internal structure, whether or not it possesses external faces. Smooth bounding faces are largely an accident of growth, and, since their destruction in no way changes the fundamental properties of a crystal, this usage is reasonable. We may thus frame a broader definition of a *crystal* as *a homogeneous solid possessing long-range three-dimensional internal order*, which, under favorable conditions, may express itself externally as smooth plane bounding surfaces. The study of these solid bodies and the laws that govern their growth, external shape, and internal structure is called *crystallography*. Although crystallography was developed as a branch of mineralogy, it has today become a separate science which deals not only with minerals but with all crystalline matter. Thus, crystallography has become a powerful tool in chemistry, physics, metallurgy, and ceramics and has been used to solve problems connected with refractories, pharmaceuticals, semiconductors, alloys, soaps, synthetic gems, and a host of other man-made substances.

In this chapter the elements of crystallography are presented in a brief and elementary manner to introduce the reader to the more essential facts and principles of the subject that are useful in elementary mineralogy. The discussion will be concerned primarily with the external geometry, or *morphology*, of well-formed crystals, since a systematic discussion of the internal structure is beyond the scope of this book. However, one is better equipped for the understanding of crystal structures if a solid foundation has been laid in crystal morphology. Further, the characteristic crystal habit of many minerals is a valuable aid in their identification.

The general term *crystalline* will be used in this book to denote the possession of an ordered arrangement of atoms in the structure, whereas the term *crystal*, without a modifier, will be used in its traditional sense of a regular geometric form bounded by smooth plane surfaces. The term crystal may be used in its broader sense with modifiers indicating perfection of development. Thus, a crystalline solid with well-formed faces is said to be *euhedral;* if it has imperfectly developed faces, it is *subhedral;* and without faces, *anhedral.*

Certain crystalline substances are in such fine subdivisions that the crystalline nature can be determined only with the aid of the microscope. These are designated as *microcrystalline.* For crystalline aggregates that are so finely divided that the individuals cannot be resolved with the microscope yet give a diffraction pattern with x-rays, the term *cryptocrystalline* is used.

Although most substances, both natural and synthetic, are crystalline, a few lack any ordered internal structure. These are said to be *amorphous.* The naturally occurring amorphous substances are designated as *mineraloids.*

Crystallization. A better idea of the fundamental laws of crystallography will be obtained if we consider first the three prominent modes of crystallization. Crystals are formed from (1) solution, (2) fusion, or (3) vapor.

The first, crystallization from solution, is the most familiar in our ordinary experience. Consider, for example, a solution of sodium chloride (common salt) in water. Suppose that by evaporation the water is slowly driven off. Under these conditions the solution will gradually contain more and more salt per unit volume. Ultimately the point will be reached where the amount of water present can no longer retain all the salt in solution, and the salt must begin to precipitate out. In other words, part of the sodium chloride, which up to this point has been held in a state of solution by the water, now assumes a solid form. If the conditions are so arranged that the evaporation of the water goes on very slowly, the separation of the salt in solid form will progress equally slowly and definite crystals will result. The ions of sodium and chlorine as they separate from the solution will group themselves together and gradually build up a definitely shaped solid which we call a crystal.

Crystals can also be formed from solution by lowering the temperature or pressure of the solution. Hot water will dissolve slightly more salt, for instance, than cold; and, if a hot solution is allowed to cool, a point will be reached where the solution becomes supersaturated for its temperature and salt will crystallize out. Again, the higher the pressure to which water is subjected the more salt it can hold in solution. So, with the lowering of the pressure of a saturated solution, supersaturation will result and crystals will form. Therefore, in general, crystals may form from a solution by the evaporation of the solvent, by the lowering of the temperature, or by a decrease in pressure.

A crystal is formed from a fused mass in much the same way as from a solution. The most familiar example of crystallization from fusion is the formation of ice crystals when water freezes. Though it is not ordinarily considered in this way, water is fused ice. When the temperature is sufficiently lowered the water can no longer remain liquid, and it becomes solid by crystallization into ice. The particles of water which were free to move in any direction in the liquid now become fixed in their position and arrange themselves in a definite order to build up a solid crystalline mass. The formation of igneous rocks from molten magmas, though more complicated, is similar to the freezing of water. In the magma there are many elements in a dissociated state. As the magma cools the various ions are attracted to one another to form crystal nuclei of the different minerals. Crystallization proceeds with the addition of more ions in the same ratios to form the mineral particles of the resulting solid rock.

The third mode of crystal formation, that in which the crystals are produced from a vapor, is less common than the other two described above. The principles that underlie the crystallization are much the same. The dissociated atoms or molecules, through the cooling of the gas, are brought closer together until at last they form a solid with a definite crystal structure. The most familiar example of this mode of crystallization is the formation of snowflakes: air laden with vapor cools, and snow crystals form directly from the vapor. Another example of this type of crystallization is seen in the formation of sulfur crystals about the mouths of fumaroles in volcanic regions, where crystals have been deposited from sulfur-bearing vapors.

The Internal Structure of Crystals

The most fundamental and important fact concerning a crystalline substance is that the particles of which it is composed are arranged in an orderly manner. A crystal must, therefore, be pictured as built up of a very large number of exceedingly minute units arranged in a repetitive three-dimensional array. The keynote of crystal structure is repetition, and the repeat mechanisms of the internal arrangement of crystals have been likened to those of patterns found in wall paper, floor tiles, or gingham prints. The geometry of arrangement of the units constituting a crystal may be described, like a wall-paper pattern, in terms of a motif or fundamental pattern unit and the rules according to which the motif is repeated.

These identical units of pattern are arranged at points on a three-dimensional lattice in such a way that all have identical environments. The lattice is defined by the three directions and by the distances along these directions at which the motif is repeated. Trial has shown that it is geometrically possible to have only fourteen types of space lattices; other combinations of points destroy the lattice requirement that the environment about every point be identical with that about all other points. This was demonstrated by Bravais in 1848, and hence the lattices are known as the *14 Bravais space lattices*. (Fig. 1.)

The simplest unit of a lattice is a parallelepiped known as the *unit cell*. In Fig. 1 it will be noted that some of these have points only at the corners and are called *primitive*, each containing one unit of pattern. They differ from one another in the lengths of the various edges and the angles (α, β, and γ) between the edges. Others have additional points at centers of faces or along body diagonals and are multiple cells.

The structural units that are marshalled in space on the lattice framework to form the crystals that we can hold in the hand and make tests upon are atoms or groups of atoms. In some, as in the native elements, these atoms are uncharged, but more frequently they carry electrical charges and are called *ions*. Ions are atoms that have become electrically charged. Positively charged ions are called *cations* because they move to the *cathode* in an electrolytic cell; negatively charged ions or *anions* are so called because they migrate to the anode during electrolysis. Most minerals are made of ions or clusters of ions held together by the electrical forces that arise between oppositely charged bodies. The arrangement in space of these ions and ionic groups and the nature and strength of the electrical forces that hold them together comprise the *structure* of the crystal. Just as educators often refer

to "bricks and mortar" in speaking of the actual buildings and instal-
lations of a college, so we lump together under the term *structure* the

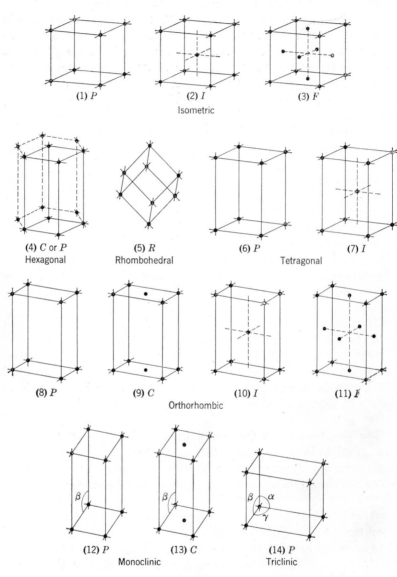

Fig. 1. 14 Bravais Space Lattices.

"bricks," that is, atoms, ions, and ionic clusters, and the electrical
"mortar" that holds them together.

Symmetry Angles Edges	Lattice-Type Figure No. and Symbol	Lattice Points*	Points per Cell
Isometric			
$\alpha = \beta = \gamma = 90°$	(1) P	Points only at corners	1
$(a = b = c)$	(2) I	Points at corners plus point at cell center	2
$a_1 = a_2 = a_3$	(3) F	Points at corners plus points at centers of all faces	4
Hexagonal			
$\alpha = \beta = 90°$	P	Points only at corners	1
$\gamma = 120°$	(4) or	or	
$(a = b \neq c)$		Hexagonal cell with points at	
$a_1 = a_2 = a_3 \neq c$	C	corners plus points at centers of ends	3
Rhombohedral			
$\alpha = \beta = \gamma \neq 90°$	P		
$a = b = c$	(5) or	Points only at corners	1
	R		
Tetragonal			
$\alpha = \beta = \gamma = 90°$	(6) P	Points only at corners	1
$(a = b \neq c)$	(7) I	Points at corners plus	
$a_1 = a_2 \neq c$		point at cell center	2
Orthorhombic			
$\alpha = \beta = \gamma = 90°$	(8) P	Points only at corners	1
$a \neq b \neq c$	(9) C	Points at corners plus points at centers of two opposite faces	2
	(10) I	Points at corners plus point at cell center	2
	(11) F	Points at corners plus point at centers of all faces	4
Monoclinic			
$\alpha = \gamma = 90° \neq \beta$	(12) P	Points only at corners	1
$a \neq b \neq c$	(13) C	Points at corners plus points at centers of ends	2
Triclinic			
$\alpha \neq \beta \neq \gamma$	(14) P	Points only at corners	1
$a \neq b \neq c$			

* Although there are points at the eight corners of a unit cell of a primitive lattice, the table shows but one point per cell. This is because each point is shared by eight adjoining cells and only one-eighth of it belongs to any individual cell. A point at the center of a face is shared by two cells, one half belonging to each.

The unit cell can never be as small as the individual atom, since the relations of the atoms to each other and the forces binding them together are important factors in determining the properties of the crystal. The number of atoms in a unit cell is generally some small whole number or a multiple of the number shown by the simplest chemical formula. Thus, in quartz the structural unit has been shown to be $3(SiO_2)$, in halite to be $4(NaCl)$. Any smaller subdivision would not have the properties of the mineral species.

The atoms, ions, or ionic groups that make up crystals may be thought of as being clustered or packed, according to geometrical rules, around the *nodes*, or points, defining the Bravais lattice. However, it has been shown that the various ways of packing, combined with the fourteen different lattice types, give rise to only **230** possible ways of arrangement. These are known as *space groups*.

Evidence of Regular Internal Structure of Crystals

Evidence that crystals do possess regular internal structure is found in the regularity of their external form, in the presence of cleavage, and in the reaction of crystals to light, heat, and x-rays.

Outward form. If crystals are considered to be made up by the repetition in three dimensions of a unit of structure, the unit cell, the limiting surfaces depend both on the shape of the units and on the environment in which they are brought together. Environment as used here includes all the external influences such as temperature, pressure, nature of solution, speed of crystal growth, surface tension, and direction of the movement of the solution.

As a simple illustration, consider a pile of ordinary bricks of identical size and shape. If they are stacked together according to a regular plan, the form of the resulting mass will depend upon the shape of the individual bricks and the conditions that governed their arrangement. A cubic mass might result from one method of stacking, and a pyramidal mass might result from another. In any event, if a law of arrangement has been followed, the resulting pile will, as a whole, appear as a regular and definitely shaped solid. On the other hand, if bricks of different sizes and shapes were piled together in a haphazard fashion, the external appearance of the whole would be totally lacking in regularity. It is conceivable that piling the bricks without following a definite plan might fortuitously result in a regular outward form. If, however, one were to encounter hundreds of such piles all having the same outward appearance and all composed of bricks of the same size and shape, it would be impossible to assume that they resulted from chance: all must have been built according to a definite plan.

The same is true of crystals. The presence of a single solid body bounded by smooth plane surfaces could not in itself constitute logical proof of an ordered internal arrangement, but if hundreds or even thousands of crystals of the same substance have similar outward form, it can be argued that the form is the result of the same orderly internal structure in each crystal.

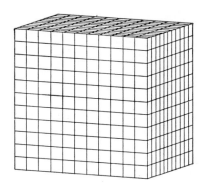

Fig. 2. Octahedron Built of Small Cubes.

Fig. 3. Large Cube Built of Small Cubes.

It is not uncommon to find at a given locality many crystals of the same mineral all having identical appearance. However, crystals of the same mineral from other localities may appear quite different. They are none the less constructed from the same building stones (unit cells) but stacked in such a way as to give a different outward shape.

Figures 2 and 3 show how it is possible for crystals of a given mineral to have different external forms as the outward expression of the same internal structure. As in the example of the bricks, the building units are identical in both the cube and octahedron, but the rate of growth in different directions varies. Such forms are common on the mineral galena, but the building units are so small that the resulting external faces are plane, smooth surfaces. Fluorite, however, is frequently in octahedrons built up of many small cubes, and resembles Fig. 2. It should be pointed out that each tiny cube is made up of many unit cells.

With a given internal structure there are, however, only a certain number of probable planes that serve to limit a crystal. It is to be noted, moreover, that only comparatively few occur commonly. In considering the distribution of faces on a crystal we are concerned only with the arrangement of the units of structure which can be represented diagrammatically by lattice points or nodes. The position of crystal faces is determined by those directions through the structure having a high density of these nodes.

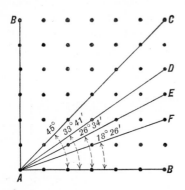

Fig. 4. Layer of Nodes in a Crystal Lattice.

The frequency with which a given face is observed on a crystal is roughly proportional to the number of nodes lying in it; the larger the number, the more common the face. Consider Fig. 4 which represents one layer of nodes in a cubic crystal lattice. The nodes are equally spaced from one another and have a rectilinear arrangement. It will be noted that there are several possible lines through this network that include a greater or lesser number of nodes. These lines would represent the trace on this section of possible crystal planes; and it would be found that of these possible planes those that include the largest number of lattice points, those cutting along *AB* and *AC,* would be most common.

The above rule, known as the *law of Bravais,* is generally confirmed by observations. Although there are exceptions to the law, as pointed out by Donnay and Harker,[1] it is usually possible to choose the lattice in such a way that the rule holds true.

Since the internal structure of any crystalline substance is constant and since the crystal faces have a definite relationship to that structure, it follows that the faces must also have a definite relationship to each other. This fact was observed long ago (1669) by Nicolaus Steno who pointed out that the angles between corresponding faces on crystals of quartz were always the same. This observation we generalize today as Steno's law of the constancy of interfacial angles which states that *the angles between equivalent faces of crystals of the same substance, measured at the same temperature, are constant.* For this reason crystal morphology is frequently a valuable tool in mineral identification. A mineral may be found in crystals of widely varying shapes and sizes, but the angles between pairs of corresponding faces are always the same.

Cleavage. Many crystals have *cleavage* which gives evidence of the internal order. Cleavage is the ability of a crystal to break along smooth plane surfaces everywhere parallel to each other throughout

[1] J. D. H. Donnay and David Harker, "A New Law of Crystal Morphology Extending the Law of Bravais," *Am. Min.,* Vol. 22, 1937.

the body of the crystal. In the latter part of the eighteenth century, the Abbé R. J. Haüy observed that calcite crystals, whatever their external form, always broke to yield rhombohedral fragments bounded by three directions of cleavage. On the basis of this observation, Haüy proposed the idea that all crystals are built of tiny structural units similar in shape to the cleavage fragments, to which he applied the name "integral molecules." This concept of the "integral molecule" was the direct forerunner of our modern picture of the *unit cell*. We have seen that the unit cell is the fundamental unit, which, repeated over and over according to the geometrical pattern of one of the Bravais lattices, builds up the crystal. If the internal structure of crystals were heterogeneous, cleavage would be inexplicable. It can be explained only by assuming some definite internal structure that permits and controls such a property.

Optical properties. Still another line of evidence indicating the regularity of the internal structure of crystals is to be found in the behavior of light in crystals. If crystals lacked orderliness of internal arrangement and were composed of atoms mixed together in haphazard and chaotic fashion, we should expect from the general rules of probability that light moving through crystals would find, on the average, the same atomic environment along any path. It would be, thus, slowed down an equal amount on any path regardless of direction. This is true of glasses, and we infer from this uniformity of behavior of light in glasses that they have a chaotic and disordered internal structure. In most crystals however, the speed at which light moves is a function of the direction in which it is vibrating.[1] In calcite the difference in speed between light vibrating in two planes at right angles to each other is so great that, when an object is examined through a transparent block of the mineral, a double image is seen. (See Fig. 369.) The separation of the two images is proportional to the thickness of the calcite block, and it may be established that each image is formed by light that is completely polarized, that is, has a definite plane of vibration related to definite crystallographic directions. Such a phenomenon cannot be accounted for except through the constraining influence of the crystal.

Properties of Crystals

Because crystals possess regular, orderly internal structure different planes and directions within the crystal have different atomic environ-

---

[1] Light vibrates at right angles to the direction of propagation, and in all crystals, except those of the isometric system, it is broken up into two rays vibrating not only perpendicular to the direction of movement but also at right angles to each other.

ments.   Consider Fig. 5, which shows a photograph of a model illustrating the packing of atoms in sodium chloride, the mineral halite. It will be seen that any plane parallel to the front face of the cubic model will contain alternating atoms of sodium and chlorine along directions parallel to the edges, and alternating strings of sodium and chlorine atoms parallel to the diagonals. On the other hand, a

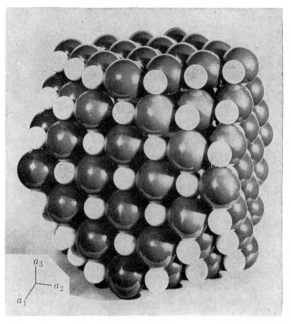

Fig. 5. Halite, NaCl, packing model, cubo-octahedron. Na white, Cl dark. Note that the (001) planes consist of sheets having equal numbers of Na and Cl ions, whereas the (111) planes consist of alternating sheets of Na ions and sheets of Cl ions. Na and Cl are both in 6-fold coordination in a face-centered lattice. This structure is also found in galena PbS, MgO and many other AX compounds.

plane cutting the corner from the cube, as shown in Fig. 5, will contain either all sodium atoms or all chlorine atoms, forming rather widely spaced sheets. Planes through the crystal cutting edges from the cube and inclined 45° to the cube faces contain rather widely separated strings of alternating sodium and chlorine atoms parallel to the cube edges. If crystals of more complex structure are studied, still more elaborate dependence of atomic arrangement on the cutting plane will be revealed.

   This condition gives rise to a regular variation in some of the properties of crystals depending on the plane or direction being considered. Properties that display variation with crystallographic direction are said to be *vectorial*. The property has both magnitude and direction; that is, for a given direction in the crystal it has a certain magnitude, different from the magnitude for other directions. Some of the vectorial properties of crystals are hardness, conductivity for heat and electricity; thermal expansion; the speed of light; growth rate; rate of solution; diffraction of x-rays, electrons, and neutrons; and many others.

Of these properties, some vary continuously with direction within the crystal; that is, any direction chosen at random can be said to have a characteristic magnitude for the property being considered. Such properties could be represented graphically by a smoothly rounded solid whose surface is everywhere at a distance from the center proportional to the magnitude of the property. Hardness, electrical and heat conductivity, thermal expansion, and the speed of light in the crystal are all examples of such *continuous* vectorial properties.

The *hardness* of some crystals varies so greatly with crystallographic direction that the difference may be detected by simple scratch tests. Thus, kyanite, a mineral which characteristically forms elongate bladed crystals, may be scratched with an ordinary pocketknife in a direction parallel to the elongation of the crystals; no scratch is produced when the blade of the knife is drawn across the crystals perpendicular to the elongation. The cutting and polishing of diamonds depends on the fact that some directions in the diamond crystal are much harder than others. Hence, when a powder of diamond dust is used for cutting or grinding, a certain percentage of the grains always presents the hardest surface and, hence, is capable of cutting along planes in the crystal of lesser hardness. If a perfect sphere cut from a crystal is placed in a cylinder with abrasive and tumbled for a long time, the softer portions of the crystal wear away more rapidly. The nonspherical solid resulting serves as a hardness model for the substance being tested.

The directional character of *electrical conductivity* is of great importance in the manufacture of silicon and germanium diodes, tiny bits of silicon and germanium crystals used to rectify alternating current. In order to obtain the optimum rectifying effect the small bit of semimetal must be oriented crystallographically, since the conduction of electricity through such crystals varies greatly with orientation.

Ball bearings of synthetic ruby sound very attractive, as the great hardness of ruby would cut down wear and give long life to the bearing. However, ruby, when heated, expands vectorially, and ball-bearing ruby balls would rapidly become nonspherical with the rise of temperature from friction during operation. However, since the *thermal expansion* figure of ruby is an ellipsoid of revolution with a circular cross section, roller bearings are practical. Most minerals have unequal coefficients of thermal expansion in different directions, leading to poor resistance to thermal shock and easy cracking with heating or cooling. Quartz glass, which has a much less regular internal structure than quartz itself, is more resistant to thermal shock than the mineral.

Discontinuous vectorial properties, on the other hand, pertain only to certain definite planes or directions within the crystal and may not be represented by a smoothly rounded solid. There are no intermediate values of such properties connected with intermediate crystallographic directions. An example of such a property is *rate of growth*. The rate of growth of a plane in a crystal is intimately connected with the density of points in the plane. We saw that a plane such as *AB* in Fig. 4 has a much greater density of points than plane *AD, AE,* or *AF*. Calculations of the energy involved indicate that the energy of particles in a plane such as *AB*, in which there is a high density of points, is less than the energy of particles in less densely populated planes such as *AF*. Hence, the plane *AB* will be the most stable, since in the process of crystallization the configuration of lowest energy is that of maximum stability. Planes *AF, AD, AE,* etc., will however be faster growing than *AB* since fewer particles need to be added per unit area. In the growth of a crystal from a nucleus, the early forms that appear on the juvenile crystal will be those of relatively high energy and rapid growth. Continued addition of material to these planes will build them out while the less rapidly growing planes lag behind. Thus, the edges and corners of a cube may be built out by addition of material to the planes cutting off the corners and edges, while little material is added to the cube faces. As growth progresses, the rapidly growing faces disappear, literally growing themselves out of existence, building the slower-growing, more stable forms in the process. After this stage is complete, growth is much slower, as addition is now entirely to the slower-growing, lowest-energy form. Thus, crystals themselves, if taken at various stages of their development, serve as models of the rate of growth for the compound being studied.

Rate of solution of a crystal in a chemical solvent that attacks it is likewise a discontinuous vectorial process, and solution of a crystal or of any fragment of a single crystal may yield a more or less definite solution polyhedron. A clearer illustration of the vectorial nature of the rate of solution is afforded by etch pits. If a crystal is briefly treated with a chemical solvent that attacks it, the faces are etched or pitted. The shape of these pits is regular and depends on the structure of the crystal, the face being attacked, and the nature of the solvent. Valuable information about the internal geometry of arrangement of crystals may be obtained from a study of such etch pits.

The *diffraction of x-rays, electrons, and neutrons* by crystals constitutes the most direct and powerful of all research techniques available to mineralogists. The diffraction phenomena are examples of discontinuous vectorial properties of crystals. (See page 126.)

Cleavage may be thought of as a discontinuous vectorial property and, like crystal form, reflects the internal structure, since cleavage always takes place along those planes across which there exist the weakest electrical forces. Those planes are generally the most widely spaced and the most densely populated.

B. SYMMETRY

All crystals show by the arrangement of their faces a definite symmetry which enables one to group them into different classes. The various operations that can be performed upon a crystal which result in bringing it into coincidence with the initial position are known as *symmetry operations*. The fundamental symmetry operations are: (1) rotation about an axis, (2) reflection across a plane, (3) rotation about an axis combined with inversion (rotary inversion). Inversion about a center alone is considered by some a distinct symmetry operation. Since it is equivalent to a 1-fold axis of rotary inversion, it is not here considered fundamental, although the term *center* is used for convenience.

Symmetry plane. A symmetry plane is an imaginary plane that divides a crystal into halves, each of which, in a perfectly developed crystal, is the mirror image of the other. The shaded portion of Fig. 6 illustrates the nature and position of such a plane of symmetry. For each face, edge, or point on one side of the plane there is a corresponding face, edge, or point in a similar position on the other side of the plane.

Symmetry axis of rotation. A symmetry axis is an imaginary line through a crystal about which the crystal may be rotated and repeat itself in appearance two or more times during a complete rotation. In Fig. 7 the line CC' is an axis of symmetry, for the crystal represented, when rotated about it, will have, after a rotation of 180°, the same appearance as at first; or, in other words, similar planes, edges, and solid angles will appear in the places of the corresponding planes, edges, and solid angles of the original position. Point A' will

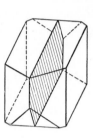

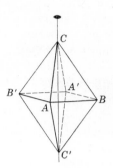

Fig. 6. Symmetry Plane.   **Fig. 7.** Symmetry Axis.

occupy the original position of A, B' that of B, etc. Since the crystal is repeated twice in appearance during a complete rotation, this axis is said to be one of 2-fold or binary symmetry. In addition to rotation axes of 2-fold symmetry there are axes of 3-fold (trigonal), 4-fold (tetragonal), and 6-fold (hexagonal) symmetry. The nature of crystals is such that no symmetry axes other than 1-, 2-, 3-, 4-, and 6-fold can exist.

Symmetry center. A crystal is said to have a center of symmetry if an imaginary line can be passed from any point on its surface through its center and a similar point is found on the line at an equal distance beyond the center. This operation is known as *inversion*. The crystal in Fig. 8 thus has a center of symmetry, for the point A is repeated at A' on the line passing from A through the center, C, of the crystal; the distances AC and $A'C$ are equal. Similar and parallel faces on opposite sides of the crystal indicate a symmetry center.

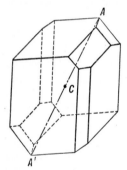

Fig. 8. Symmetry Center.

Symmetry axis of rotary inversion. This composite symmetry element combines a rotation about an axis with inversion through the center. Both operations must be completed before the new position is obtained. If the only symmetry possessed by a crystal is a center, the symmetry notation is usually given as a 1-fold axis of rotary inversion. There are also 2-, 3-, 4-, and 6-fold axes of rotary inversion. Let us consider the mechanism of an axis of rotary inversion. In the operation of a 4-fold rotation axis, four identical points will be located—one each 90° of rotation—all at the top or all at the bottom of the crystal. In the operation of a 4-fold axis of rotary inversion, four identical points will also be located but two will be at the top and two at the bottom of the crystal. The operation of such an axis involves four rotations of 90°, each followed by an inversion. Thus, if the first point is at the top of the crystal, the second is at the bottom, the third at the top, and the fourth at the bottom. Figure 9 illustrates a crystal with a 4-fold axis of rotary inversion.

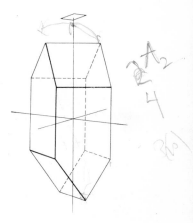

Fig. 9. Four-fold Axis of Rotary Inversion.

Another composite symmetry element combines a rotation about an axis with reflection across a plane at right angles to the axis (rotary reflection). By such an operation one can develop the same symmetry as with rotary inversion; but, since rotary inversion has been adopted by international agreement, it is given preference here.

Symmetry notation. The symmetry axis, plane, axis of rotary inversion (or rotary reflection), and center are known as the *elements of symmetry*. In describing the symmetry of a crystal, it is convenient to use a kind of shorthand notation of the symmetry elements. A rotation axis is indicated by A_n, where n is 2, 3, 4, or 6; a plane by P; and a center by C. Using these notations the symmetry of a crystal with a symmetry center, one 4-fold rotation axis, four 2-fold rotation axes, and five planes of symmetry would be written: C, $1A_4$, $4A_2$, $5P$. In this way it is possible to express all but two possible symmetry conditions. One of these is the case of no symmetry; the other, illustrated by Fig. 9, is an axis of 4-fold rotary inversion or rotary reflection. It is represented by the symbol $\mathcal{A}P$.

The above system of symmetry notation is one of many that have been proposed by crystallographers and is mentioned here because it is straightforward and easy for the beginning student to understand and use. However, the *Hermann-Mauguin symbols* have been accepted by international agreement and are given preference. By their use one can express not only the outward symmetry (point group) but also the far more complicated internal symmetry (space group). A brief explanation of the Hermann-Mauguin symbols follows:

1. Symmetry axes of rotation are denoted by numbers 1, 2, 3, 4, 6; and axes of rotary inversion by numbers with lines above, as $\bar{1}$, $\bar{3}$, $\bar{4}$, $\bar{6}$

(read bar one, bar three, etc.). Symmetry planes are indicated by m. An axis of symmetry with a symmetry plane normal thereto is given as a number over m, for example, $2/m$, $4/m$.

2. In the hexagonal, tetragonal, isometric, and monoclinic systems, the first part of the symbol refers to the principal axis of symmetry, as 4 in the symbol $4mm$.

3. In the tetragonal system the second and third symbols refer to the axial and diagonal symmetry elements respectively. For example, in the tetragonal scalenohedral class, $\bar{4}2m$, the 2 refers to a 2-fold axis coincident with the a crystallographic axes; the m refers to a symmetry plane in the 45° position.

4. In the hexagonal system the second and third symbols refer respectively to the axial and alternate axial symmetry elements. Thus in the dihexagonal-pyramidal class, $6mm$, there are three vertical symmetry planes in which lie the three crystallographic axes, and three additional vertical symmetry planes at 30° in the alternate axial positions.

5. In the orthorhombic system the symbols refer to the symmetry elements in the order a, b, c. For example, in the rhombic-pyramidal class, $mm2$, the a and b axes lie in vertical symmetry planes and the c axis is an axis of 2-fold symmetry. This order is more significant in denoting space groups than in denoting crystal classes.

6. In the isometric system the second and third parts of the symbol refer, respectively, to the 3-fold and 2-fold symmetry elements. The 2-fold element may be either an axis as in the gyroidal class, 432, or a plane as in the hextetrahedral class $\bar{4}3m$, or a combination of an axis and a plane as in the hexoctahedral class $4/m\bar{3}2/m$.

At first glance it may appear that the Hermann-Mauguin symbols do not express the symmetry completely. However, it should be pointed out that symmetry elements operate on one another as well as on crystal faces. Consider the symbol 622. The first 2 represents a 2-fold rotation axis coincident with a horizontal crystallographic axis, and the second 2 represents another horizontal 2-fold rotation axis at 30° to the first. Operating on these 2-fold axes with the 6-fold rotation axis generates from each two others making a total of three of each kind. Thus there are six 2-fold rotation axes.

The Hermann-Mauguin symbols used here are complete, but some crystallographers use more abbreviated symbols to express the same symmetry. For example, the symmetry 622 can be expressed merely as 62; for if there are three horizontal 2-fold axes, three others in the alternate positions are implied. The symbol $2/m\,2/m\,2/m$ may be shortened to mmm. The shorter symbol indicates three mutually perpendicular symmetry planes which implies 2-fold symmetry axes at their lines of intersection.

The Thirty-Two Crystal Classes

Crystal System	Crystal Class	Hermann-Mauguin Symbols	Symmetry
Isometric	**Hexoctahedral**	$4/m\,\bar{3}\,2/m$	$C, 3A_4, 4A_3, 6A_2, 9P$
	Gyroidal	432	$3A_4, 4A_3, 6A_2$
	Hextetrahedral	$\bar{4}3m$	$3A_2, 4A_3, 6P$
	Diploidal	$2/m\,\bar{3}$	$C, 3A_2, 4A_3, 3P$
	Tetartoidal	23	$3A_2, 4A_3$
Hexagonal — Hexagonal division	**Dihexagonal-dipyramidal**	$6/m\,2/m\,2/m$	$C, 1A_6, 6A_2, 7P$
	Hexagonal-trapezohedral	622	$1A_6, 6A_2$
	Dihexagonal-pyramidal	$6mm$	$1A_6, 6P$
	Ditrigonal-dipyramidal	$\bar{6}m2$	$1A_3, 3A_2, 4P$
	Hexagonal-dipyramidal	$6/m$	$C, 1A_6, 1P$
	Hexagonal-pyramidal	6	$1A_6$
	Trigonal-dipyramidal	$\bar{6}$	$1A_3, 1P$
Hexagonal — Rhombohedral division	**Hexagonal-scalenohedral**	$\bar{3}\,2/m$	$C, 1A_3, 3A_2, 3P$
	Trigonal-trapezohedral	32	$1A_3, 3A_2$
	Ditrigonal-pyramidal	$3m$	$1A_3, 3P$
	Rhombohedral	$\bar{3}$	$C, 1A_3$
	Trigonal-pyramidal	3	$1A_3$
Tetragonal	**Ditetragonal-dipyramidal**	$4/m\,2/m\,2/m$	$C, 1A_4, 4A_2, 5P$
	Tetragonal-trapezohedral	422	$1A_4, 4A_2$
	Ditetragonal-pyramidal	$4mm$	$1A_4, 4P$
	Tetragonal-scalenohedral	$\bar{4}2m$	$3A_2, 2P$
	Tetragonal-dipyramidal	$4/m$	$C, 1A_4, 1P$
	Tetragonal-pyramidal	4	$1A_4$
	Tetragonal-disphenoidal	$\bar{4}$	$1P_4$
Orthorhombic	**Rhombic-dipyramidal**	$2/m\,2/m\,2/m$	$C, 3A_2, 3P$
	Rhombic-disphenoidal	222	$3A_2$
	Rhombic-pyramidal	$mm2$	$1A_2, 2P$
Monoclinic	**Prismatic**	$2/m$	$C, 1A_2, 1P$
	Sphenoidal	2	$1A_2$
	Domatic	m	$1P$
Triclinic	**Pinacoidal**	$\bar{1}$	C
	Pedial	1	No symmetry

Classes of symmetry. It has been shown that there are only thirty-two possible combinations of the various symmetry elements, giving rise to the thirty-two crystal classes (point groups). These classes are further grouped into six crystal systems, the classes of each system having certain close relations to each other. Most of the common minerals crystallize in fifteen crystal classes. In the table on page 21 are listed all the crystal classes with their symmetry elements; those of most importance to the mineralogist are indicated in bold-face type.

Many different names have been used to designate each of the crystal classes. The names used here were proposed by Groth[1] and are derived from the name of the general form in each crystal class, i.e., the form whose faces intersect all the crystallographic axes at different lengths.

C. CRYSTAL NOTATION

Crystallographic axes. It is found convenient in describing crystals to assume, after the methods of analytic geometry, certain lines passing through the center of the ideal crystal as axes of reference. These imaginary lines are called the *crystallographic axes* and are taken parallel to the intersection edges of major crystal faces. In addition the positions of the crystallographic axes are more or less fixed by the symmetry of the crystals, for in most crystals they are symmetry axes or normals to symmetry planes.

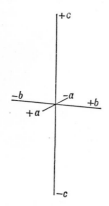

Fig. 10. Orthorhombic Crystal Axes.

All crystals, with the exception of those belonging to the hexagonal system (see page 62), are referred to three crystallographic axes. In the general case (triclinic system), all the axes are of different lengths and at oblique angles to one another; but for simplicity in describing their conventional orientation consider those illustrated in Fig. 10. Here the three axes are mutually perpendicular and when placed in the proper position for description are oriented as follows: One axis, called a, is horizontal and in a front-back position; another axis, called b, is horizontal and in a right-left position; the third axis, called c, is vertical. The ends of each axis are designated by either a plus or a minus sign; the front end of a, the right-hand end of b, and the upper end of c are positive; the opposite ends, negative.

Crystal systems. Certain of the thirty-two crystal classes mentioned above have symmetry characteristics in common with others which permit their assignment to larger groups called *crystal systems*.

[1] Paul Groth, *Physikalische Krystallographie,* Verlag von Wilhelm Engelmann, Leipzig, 1895.

The six crystal systems are listed below with the crystallographic axes and the characterizing symmetry for each.

Isometric System. All crystals in the isometric system have four 3-fold symmetry axes and are referred to three mutually perpendicular axes of equal lengths.

Hexagonal System. All crystals in the hexagonal system have either a single 3-fold or 6-fold symmetry axis. They are referred to four crystallographic axes; three equal horizontal axes intersect at angles of 120°, the fourth is of different length and perpendicular to the plane of the other three.

Tetragonal System. A unique 4-fold symmetry axis characterizes crystals of the tetragonal system. Crystals are referred to three mutually perpendicular axes; the two horizontal axes are of equal length, but the vertical axis is either shorter or longer than the other two.

Orthorhombic System. Crystals in the orthorhombic system have three 2-fold symmetry elements, i.e., symmetry planes or 2-fold symmetry axes. They are referred to three mutually perpendicular axes, all of different length.

Monoclinic System. Crystals of the monoclinic system are characterized by a single 2-fold symmetry axis or a single symmetry plane or a combination of a 2-fold axis and a symmetry plane. The crystals are referred to three unequal axes, two of which are inclined to each other at an oblique angle and the third of which is perpendicular to the plane of the other two.

Triclinic System. Crystals in the triclinic system have a 1-fold symmetry axis as their only symmetry. This may be a simple rotary axis or a 1-fold axis of rotary inversion. The crystals are referred to three unequal axes all intersecting at oblique angles.

Axial ratio. In all the crystal systems, with the exception of the isometric, there are crystallographic axes differing in length. If it were possible to isolate a unit cell and measure carefully the dimensions along the edges, which are parallel to the crystallographic axes, we would be able to write ratios between the edge lengths. The x-ray crystallographer cannot isolate the cell, but he can measure accurately the cell dimensions in angstrom units, (Å).[1] Thus for the orthorhombic mineral sulfur the cell dimensions are given as 10.48 Å along the a axis, 12.92 Å along the b axis, and 24.55 Å along the c axis (Fig. 11). Setting the b value equal to 1, we can write the ratios $a : b : c = 0.81 : 1 : 1.90$. The ratios thus express the relative, not the absolute, lengths of the cell edges that correspond to the crystallographic axes.

---

[1] An angstrom unit is 0.00000001 centimeter, i.e., 10^{-8} centimeter.

Axial ratios were calculated many years before x-rays made it possible to determine the absolute dimensions of the unit cell. By measuring the interfacial angles on the crystal and making certain calculations, it is possible to arrive at axial ratios that express the relative lengths of the crystallographic axes. It is interesting to see how closely the new axial ratios calculated from the dimensions of the unit cell compare with the older ratios derived from the morphological measurements. For example, the ratios for sulfur are:

$a : b : c = 0.8131 : 1 : 1.9034$ from morphological calculations
$a : b : c = 0.811 \ \ : 1 : 1.900$ from unit cell measurements

A brief discussion of the calculations of axial ratios in the higher-symmetry classes is given beginning on page 116.

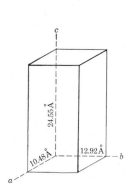

Fig. 11. Unit Cell of Sulfur.

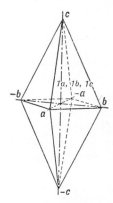

Fig. 12. Dipyramid of Sulfur.

Parameters. Crystal faces are defined by indicating their intercepts on the crystallographic axes. Thus in describing a crystal face it is necessary to determine whether it is parallel to two axes and intersects the third, or is parallel to one axis and intersects the other two, or intersects all three. In addition one must determine at what relative distance the face intersects the different axes. We have seen in the discussion of axial ratios that the ratios express the relative lengths of the axes. For sulfur the a axis is 0.8 of the b axis, and the c axis is 1.9 times as long as the b axis. For a crystal face that intersected the crystallographic axes at these relative distances (taken as unit distances), the intercepts would be given as: one on a, one on b, and one on c, or $1a$, $1b$, $1c$ (see Fig. 12).

A face that cuts the two horizontal axes at distances that are proportional to their unit lengths and cuts the vertical axis at a distance twice its relative unit length will have for parameters $1a$, $1b$, $2c$. It is to be emphasized that these parameters are strictly relative in their values and do not indicate any actual cutting lengths. To illustrate this further, consider Fig. 13, which represents a possible sulfur crystal. The forms present upon it are two dipyr-amids of different slope but each inter-secting all three of the crystal axes when properly extended.

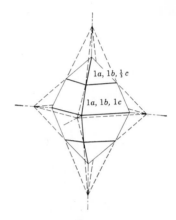

Fig. 13.   Sulfur.

The problem exists here, as in many crystals, of choosing which dipyramid to select as the unit form, i.e., which one shall be considered to cut all three of the crystallographic axes at unit lengths. Lacking other evidence, it is customary to select as the unit the form with the largest faces. This, in Fig. 13, is the lower dipyramid, and the parameters of the face of this form which cuts the posi-tive ends of the three axes would be $1a$, $1b$, $1c$. The upper dipyramid would cut the two horizontal axes, as shown by the dotted lines, also at distances which, although greater than in the lower dipyramid, are still propor-tional to the unit lengths. It cuts the vertical axis, however, at a dis-tance which, when considered in respect to its intersections with the horizontal axes, is proportional to one-third of the unit length of c. The parameters of a face of this form would therefore be $1a$, $1b$, $\frac{1}{3}c$. From this it will be seen that the parameters $1a$, $1b$ do not in the two examples represent the same actual cutting distances but express only relative values. The parameters of a face do not in any way determine its size, for a face may be moved parallel to itself for any distance without changing the relative values of its intersections with the crystallographic axes.

Indices.   Various methods of notation have been devised to express the intercepts of any crystal face upon the crystal axes, and several different ones have been used. The most universally employed is the system of indices of Miller.

The Miller indices of a face consist of a series of whole numbers which have been derived from the parameters by their inversion and, if neces-sary, the subsequent clearing of fractions. The indices of a face are always given so that the three numbers (four in the hexagonal system) refer to the a, b, and c axes respectively, and therefore the letters which indicate the different axes are omitted. Like the parameters, the indices express a ratio, but for the sake of brevity the ratio sign is also omitted. The face of the dipyramid illustrated in Fig. 13, which has 1a, 1b, 1c for parameters, would have (111) (read: one, one, one) for indices. The face, Fig. 14, which has 1a, 1b, ∞c for parameters and on inversion $\dfrac{1}{1}$, $\dfrac{1}{1}$, $\dfrac{1}{\infty}$ would have (110) for indices. Faces which have respectively the parameters 1a, 1b, $\tfrac{1}{2}c$ and 1a, 1b, 2c would on inversion yield $\dfrac{1}{1}$, $\dfrac{1}{1}$, $\dfrac{2}{1}$ and $\dfrac{1}{1}$, $\dfrac{1}{1}$, $\dfrac{1}{2}$. Thus on clearing of fractions the resulting indices would be respectively (112) and (221).

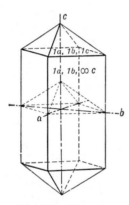

Fig. 14. Prism and Dipyramid.

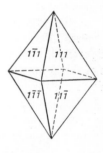

Fig. 15. Dipyramid.

It is sometimes convenient when the exact intercepts are unknown to use a general symbol (*hkl*) for the Miller indices; here h, k, and l each represents a simple whole number. In this symbol h, k, and l are respectively the reciprocals of rational but undefined intercepts along the a, b, and c axes. The symbol (*hkl*) would indicate that a face cuts all three of the crystallographic axes. If a face is parallel to one of the crystallographic axes and intersects the other two, the general symbols would be written as (0*kl*), (*h*0*l*), and (*hk*0). A face parallel to two of the axes is considered to intersect the third at unity, and the symbols would, therefore, be: (100), (010), and (001).

In the above discussion only those faces that intercept the positive ends of the crystallographic axes have been considered. To denote the interception at the negative end of an axis, a line is placed over the appropriate letter or number, as shown in Fig. 15.

Early in the study of crystals it was discovered that for given faces the indices would always be expressed by simple whole numbers. The ratios between them may be $1:2$, $2:1$, $2:3$, $1:\infty$, etc., but never $1:\sqrt{2}$, etc. This is known as the *law of rational indices*.

Form. In its most familiar meaning the term *form* is used to indicate general outward appearance. In crystallography external shape is denoted by the word *habit*, whereas *form* is used in a special and restricted sense. Thus, a form consists of a group of crystal faces all of which have the same relation to the elements of symmetry and display the same chemical and physical properties because all are underlain by the same atoms in the same geometrical arrangement.

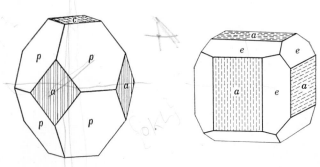

Fig. 16. Apophyllite.   **Fig. 17.** Pyrite.

Although faces of a form may be of different sizes and shapes because of malformation of the crystal, the similarity is frequently evidenced by natural striations, etchings, or growths as shown in Figs. 16 and 17. On some crystals the similarity of faces of a form can be seen only after etching with acid.

In Fig. 16 there are three forms each of which has a different physical appearance from the others and in Fig. 17 there are two forms. Including the faces not visible in the drawings, the forms have the following number of faces: Fig. 16, a—4, p—8, c—2 and in Fig. 17, a—6, e—12.

In a discussion of Miller indices we saw that a crystal face may be designated by a symbol enclosed in parentheses as (hkl), (010), or (111). Miller indices also may be used as form symbols and are then enclosed in braces as $\{hkl\}$, $\{010\}$, etc. Thus in Fig. 15, (111) refers to a specific face; whereas $\{111\}$ embraces all eight faces. In choosing a form symbol it is desirable to select, if possible, the face symbol with positive digits; $\{111\}$ rather than $\{1\bar{1}1\}$, $\{010\}$ rather than $\{0\bar{1}0\}$.

In each crystal class there is a form the faces of which intersect each of the crystallographic axes at different lengths; this is the *general form,* {*hkl*}. All other forms that may be present are *special forms.* In the orthorhombic, monoclinic, and triclinic crystal systems {111} is a general form, for the unit length along each of the axes is different. In the crystal systems of higher symmetry in which the unit distances along two or more of the crystallographic axes are the same, a general form must intersect the like axes at different multiples of the unit length. Thus {121} is a general form in the tetragonal system but a special form in the isometric system, and {123} is a general form in the isometric system.

In Fig. 15 is illustrated a single crystal form known as a dipyramid. In the symmetry class to which it belongs the three crystal axes are axes of 2-fold symmetry, and the axial planes are planes of symmetry. With this symmetry, if the presence of face (111) is assumed, there must be the seven other faces, for they all have the same relations to the elements of symmetry. These eight faces constitute a form, and, since they inclose space, it is called a *closed* form. Also see Figs. 33–42. The forms illustrated in Figs. 23–32 do not inclose space and, therefore, are called *open forms.*

A crystal usually displays several forms in combination with one another but may have only one, provided that it is a closed form. Since any combination of forms must inclose space, a minimum of two open forms is necessary. The two may exist by themselves or be in combination with closed forms or other open forms. Altogether there are forty-eight different types of crystal forms which can be distinguished by the angular relations of their faces. Thirty-two of these are represented by the general forms of the thirty-two crystal classes; ten are special closed forms of the isometric system; and six are special open forms (prisms) of the hexagonal and tetragonal systems. The various forms will be discussed under the symmetry class or classes in which they are found. Each form of the isometric system has a special name, but the same general names are used for the forms present in other systems; they are as follows:

Pedion. A single face comprising a form (Fig. 18).

Pinacoid. A form made up of two parallel faces (Fig. 19).

Dome. Two nonparallel faces symmetrical with respect to a symmetry plane (Fig. 20).

Sphenoid. Two nonparallel faces symmetrical with respect to a 2-fold or 4-fold symmetry axis (Fig. 21).

Disphenoid. A four-faced form in which two faces of the upper sphenoid alternate with two of the lower sphenoid (Fig. 22).

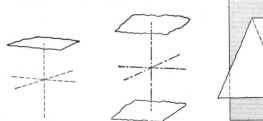

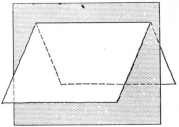

Fig. 18. Pedion.   **Fig. 19.** Pinacoid.   **Fig. 20.** Dome.

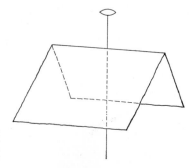

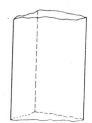

Fig. 21. Sphenoid.   **Fig. 22.** Disphenoid.   **Fig. 23.** Trigonal Prism.

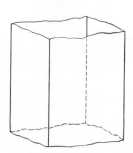

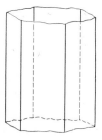

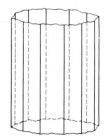

Fig. 24. Tetragonal Prism.   **Fig. 25.** Hexagonal Prism.   **Fig. 26.** Dihexagonal Prism.

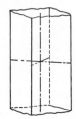

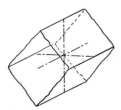

Fig. 27. Vertical Orthorhombic Prism.   **Fig. 28.** Horizontal Orthorhombic Prism.

Prism. A form composed of 3, 4, 6, 8, or 12 faces, all of which are parallel to the same axis. Except for certain prisms in the mono-clinic system, the axis is one of the principal crystallographic axes (Figs. 23–28).

Pyramid. A form composed of 3, 4, 6, 8, or 12 nonparallel faces that meet at a point (Figs. 29–32).

Fig. 29. Trigonal Pyramid. **Fig. 30.** Tetrag-onal Pyramid. **Fig. 31.** Hexagonal Pyramid. **Fig. 32.** Dihexag-onal Pyramid.

 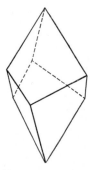 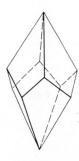

Fig. 33. Tetragonal Scalenohedron. **Fig. 34.** Hexagonal Scalenohedron. **Fig. 35.** Trigonal Trapezohedron. **Fig. 36.** Tetragonal Trapezohedron.

Scalenohedron. 8-faced (tetragonal, Fig. 33) or 12-faced (hex-agonal, Fig. 34) closed forms with the faces grouped in symmetrical pairs. For the 8-faced forms there are two pairs of faces above and two pairs below in alternating positions. For the 12-faced forms there are three pairs of faces above and three pairs below in alternating positions. In perfectly developed crystals, each face is a scalene triangle.

Trapezohedron. 6-, 8-, or 12-faced forms with 3, 4, or 6 faces above offset from 3, 4, or 6 faces below (Figs. 35–37). In addition there is an isometric trapezohedron, a 24-faced form. In well-developed trapezohedrons each face is a trapezium.

Dipyramid. 6-, 8-, 12-, 16-, or 24-faced closed forms (Figs. 38–42). The dipyramids can be considered as formed from pyramids by reflection across a horizontal symmetry plane.

Rhombohedron. A closed form composed of six faces, the inter-section edges of which are not at right angles. Rhombohedrons are found only on crystals of the rhombohedral division of the hexagonal system.

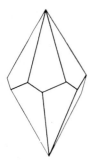

Fig. 37. Hexag-onal Trapezo-hedron.

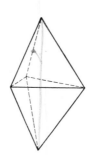

Fig. 38. Trigo-nal Dipyramid.

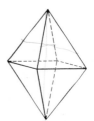

Fig. 39. Tetragonal Dipyramid.

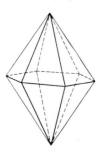

Fig. 40. Hexagonal Dipyramid.

Fig. 41. Ditetragonal Dipyramid.

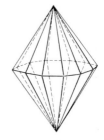

Fig. 42. Dihexagonal Dipyramid.

In crystal drawings it is found convenient to indicate the faces of a form by the same letter. The choice of which letter shall be assigned to a given form rests largely with the person who first describes the crystal. However, there are certain simple forms that, owing to con-vention, usually receive the same letter. Thus the three pinacoids that cut the a, b, and c axes are lettered respectively a, b, and c (Fig. 43). The letter m is usually given to {110}, and p to {111} (Fig. 44).

Zones. One of the conspicuous features on many crystals is the arrangement of a group of faces in such a manner that their intersec-tion edges are mutually parallel. Considered collectively, these faces form a *zone*. A line through the center of the crystal that parallels the

lines of face intersections is called the *zone axis*. In Fig. 45 the faces
m′, *a*, *m*, and *b* are in one zone, and *b*, *r*, *c*, and *r′* in another. The
lines given as [001] and [100] are the zone axes.

A zone can be indicated by a symbol similar to that for Miller
indices of faces, the generalized expression of which is [*uvw*]. Any
two nonparallel faces determine a zone, and the zone symbol for two

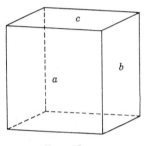 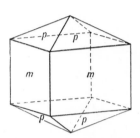

Fig. 43.   Fig. 44.

Conventional Lettering on Crystal Drawings.

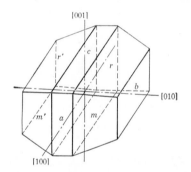

Fig. 45.   Crystal Zones and Zone Axes.

such faces, (*hkl*) and (*pqr*), is: [*kr* − *lq*, *lp* − *hr*, *hq* − *kp*]. For
example, assume that face *m*, Fig. 45, is (*hkl*) with the index (110)
and that face *b* is (*pqr*) with index (010). The zone symbol is thus
written as [1·0 − 0·1, 0·0 − 1·0, 1·1 − 1·0] or [001]. If face *c* is (001)
and *r* is (011), Fig. 45, the zone symbol can be determined as [100].
It should be noted that the zone symbols are inclosed in brackets,
as [*uvw*], to distinguish them from face and form symbols.

Crystal habit. By crystal habit is meant the common and characteristic form or combination of forms in which a mineral crystallizes.
It also includes the general shape and irregularities of crystal growth
if such irregularities are of common occurrence. Galena, for example,
has a cubic habit, magnetite octahedral, and malachite fibrous. This

means that, although these minerals are found in crystals that show other forms, such occurrences are comparatively rare, and their "habit" is to crystallize as indicated. Little is known regarding the factors that determine habit; but the kind of solution, the rate of crystal growth, temperature, and pressure are all thought to play a part.

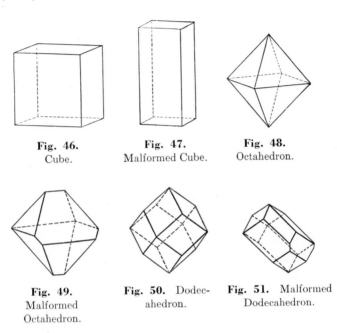

Fig. 46.
Cube.

Fig. 47.
Malformed Cube.

Fig. 48.
Octahedron.

Fig. 49.
Malformed
Octahedron.

Fig. 50. Dodec-
ahedron.

Fig. 51. Malformed
Dodecahedron.

Crystals may grow more rapidly in one direction than in another; other surrounding crystals may interfere, and in various ways symmetrical growth may be prevented. Such crystals are said to be malformed. Ordinarily the amount of malformation is not so great as to prevent one from readily imagining what the ideally developed crystal would be like and so determining its symmetry. It is to be noted that the real symmetry of a crystal does not depend upon the symmetrical shape and size of its faces but rather on the physical appearance of the faces and the symmetrical arrangement of the interfacial angles. In Figs. 46 to 51 are given various crystal forms, first ideally developed and then malformed.

D. CRYSTAL PROJECTIONS

Introduction. A crystal projection is a means of representing the three-dimensional crystal on a two-dimensional plane surface. Different projections are used for different purposes, but each is made according to some definite rule so that the projection bears a known and reproducible relationship to the crystal. The crystal drawings in this book are known as *clinographic projections* and are a type of perspective drawing which yields a portraitlike picture of the crystal in two dimensions. This is the best means of conveying the appearance of a crystal and generally serves much better for the purpose than a photograph.

Since the actual size and shape of the different faces on a crystal are chiefly the result of accidents of growth, we wish to minimize this aspect of crystals in projecting. At the same time it is important to emphasize the angular relation of the faces to each other, for, as Steno's law points out, there is a constancy of interfacial angles on all crystals of a given mineral species.

Spherical projection. In order to plot the faces strictly according to their angular relations and without regard for shape or size, we may use the *spherical projection*. We can envisage the construction of such a projection in the following way. Imagine a hollow model of a crystal containing a bright point source of light. Now let us place this model within a large hollow sphere of translucent material in such a way that the light source is at the center of the sphere. If now we make a pinhole in each of the faces so that the ray of light emerging from the hole is perpendicular to the face, these rays of light will fall on the inner surface of the sphere and make bright spots. The whole situation much resembles a planetarium in which the crystal model with its internal light source and pinholes is the projector and the translucent sphere is the dome. If we now mark on the sphere the position of each spot of light, we may remove the model and have a permanent record of its faces. Each of the crystal faces is represented on the sphere by a point called the face *pole*. This is the spherical projection.

The position of each pole and thus its angular relationship to other poles can be fixed by *angular coordinates* on the sphere. This is done in a manner similar to the location of points on the earth's surface by means of longitude and latitude. For example, the angular coordinates 74° 00′ west longitude, 40° 45′ north latitude, locate a point in New York City. This means that the angle, measured at the center of the earth, between the plane of the equator and a line from the center of the earth through that point in New York is exactly 40° 45′; and the angle between the Greenwich meridian and the meridian passing through the point in New York, measured west in the plane of the equator, is exactly 74° 00′. These relations are shown in Fig. 52.

A similar system may be used to locate the poles of faces on the spherical projection of a crystal. There is one major difference between locating points on a spherical projection and locating points on the earth's surface. On the earth, the latitude is measured in degrees north or south from the equator, whereas the angle used in the spherical projection is the colatitude, or *polar angle*, which is measured in degrees from the north pole. The north pole of a crystal

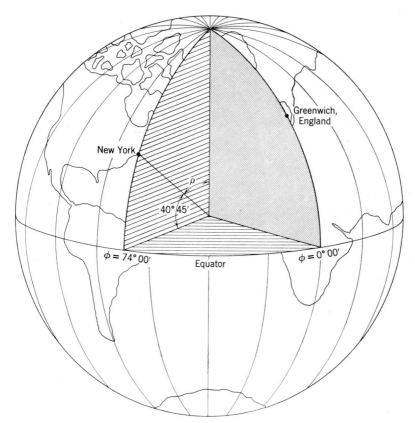

Fig. 52. Latitude and Longitude of New York City.

projection is thus at a colatitude of 0°, the equator at 90°. The colatitude of New York City is 49° 15′. This angle is designated in crystallography by the Greek letter ρ (rho).

The "crystal longitude" of the pole of a face on the spherical projection is measured, just as are longitudes on earth, in degrees up to 180°, clockwise and counterclockwise from a starting meridian analogous to the Greenwich meridian of geography. To locate this starting meridian, the crystal is oriented in conventional manner with the (010) face to the right of the crystal. The meridian passing through the pole of this face is taken as zero. Thus, to determine the crystal longitude of any crystal face, a meridian is passed through the pole of that face, and the angle between it and the zero meridian is measured in the plane of the equator. This angle is designated by the Greek letter ϕ (phi).

If any plane is passed through a sphere, it will intersect the surface of the sphere in a circle. The circles of maximum diameter are those formed by planes passing through the center and having a diameter equal to the diameter of the sphere. These are called *great circles*. All other circles formed by passing planes through the sphere are *small circles*. The meridians on the earth are great circles, as is the equator, whereas the parallels of latitude are small circles.

The spherical projection of a crystal brings out interesting zonal relationships, for the poles of all the faces in a zone lie along a great circle of the projection. In Fig. 53 (spherical projection) faces (001), (101), (100), (10$\bar{1}$), and (00$\bar{1}$) lie in a zone with the zone axis [010]. Since the great circle along which the poles of these faces lie passes through the north and south poles of the projection, it is called a *vertical great circle*. The zone axis is always perpendicular to the plane containing the face poles and thus all vertical circles have horizontal zone axes.

Stereographic projection. The spherical projection is analogous to a terrestrial globe, that is, a map of the earth on the surface of a sphere. The process, then, of reduction of the spherical projection to a two-dimensional projection is analogous to the process by which the cartographer reduces the surface of the substantially spherical earth to a flat map. The mapmaker is concerned with the preservation of shapes and areas as well as maintaining reproducible relations between separated points. His choice of projection is at best a compromise, for the sphere cannot be represented on a sheet of paper without some distortion. Fortunately in mapping the faces of crystals, we are not concerned with shape or area. We wish to represent only the angular positions of the faces in such a way that an idealized version of the crystal revealing its true symmetry can be pictured. We wish also to be able to make calculations from the projection, to recover from it the angular data that went into making it, and on occasion to make perspective drawings of the crystal from it. For these purposes, two projections are most useful: (1) The *stereographic projection* is best for determining symmetry, is the most compact and the easiest to construct, and hence is the only one that will be considered here.

(2) The *gnomonic projection* is superior for making crystal drawings (clinographic projections) and graphical determinations of axial ratios and for correlating and indexing crystal faces with data derived from x-ray diffraction measurements.

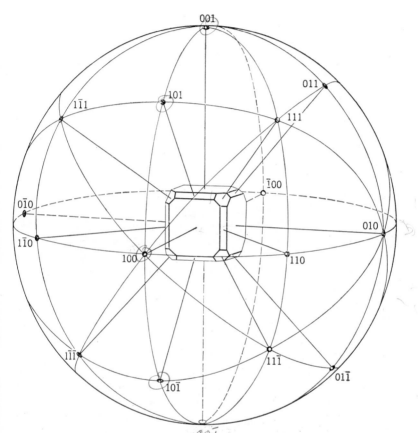

Fig. 53. Spherical Projection of Isometric Forms.

The stereographic projection is a representation in a plane of half of the spherical projection, usually the northern hemisphere. The plane of the projection is the equatorial plane of the sphere, and the *primitive* circle (the circle outlining the projection) is the equator itself. If one were to view the poles of crystal faces located in the northern hemisphere of the spherical projection with the eye at the south pole, the intersection of the lines of sight with the equatorial plane would be the corresponding poles on the stereographic projection. We can thus construct a stereographic projection by drawing lines from the south pole to the face poles in the northern hemisphere. The corresponding poles on the stereographic projection are located where these lines intersect the equatorial plane. The relationship of the two projections is brought out in Fig. 54.

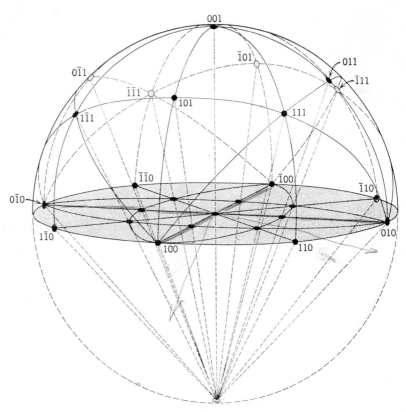

Fig. 54. Relation of Spherical and Stereographic Projections. After E. E. Wahlstrom, *Optical Crystallography,* John Wiley and Sons, New York, 1951.

Since in practice one plots poles directly on the stereographic projection, it is necessary to determine stereographic distances in relation to angles of the spherical projection. Figure 55 shows a vertical section through the spherical projection of a crystal in the plane of the "zero meridian," that is, the plane containing the pole of (010). The ϕ angle of any face which lies in this section is 0° if to the right of the center, and 180° if to the left of center. N and S are respectively the north and south poles of the sphere of projection, O is the center of the projected crystal. Consider the face (011). OD is the perpendicular to the face (011), and D is the pole of this face on the spherical projection. The line from the south pole, SD, intersects the trace of the plane of the equator, FG, in the point D', the stereographic pole of (011). The angle NOD will be recognized as the angle ρ (rho). In order to plot D' directly on the stereographic projection, it is necessary to determine the distance OD' in terms of angle ρ. Since $\triangle SOD$ is isosceles, $\angle ODS = \angle OSD$. $\angle ODS + \angle OSD = \angle NOD = \rho$.

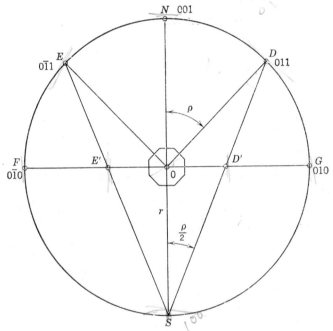

Fig. 55. Section through Sphere of Projection showing Relation of Spherical to Stereographic Poles.

Therefore, $\angle OSD = \rho/2$. $OS = r$, the radius of the primitive of the projection.

$$\tan \rho/2 = OD'/r, \text{ or } OD' = r \tan \rho/2.$$

To sum up, in order to find the stereographically projected distance from the center of the projection of the pole of any face, find the natural tangent of one-half of ρ of that face and multiply by the radius of the projection. The distance so obtained will be in whatever units are used to measure the radius of the primitive of the projection.

In addition to determining the distance a pole should lie from the center of the projection, it is also necessary to determine its "longitude" or ϕ (phi) angle. Since the angle is measured in the plane of the equator, which is also the plane of the stereographic projection, it may be laid off directly on the primitive by means of a circular protractor. It is first necessary to fix the "zero meridian" by making a point on the primitive circle to represent the pole of (010). A straight line drawn through this point and the center of the projection is the zero meridian. With the protractor edge along this line and center point at the center of the projection, the ϕ angle can be marked off. On a construction line from the center of the projection through

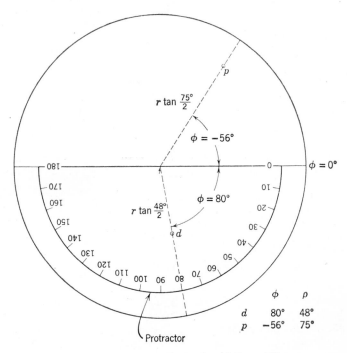

Fig. 56. Stereographic Projection of Crystal Faces.

this point lie all possible face poles having the specified ϕ angle. Positive ϕ angles are laid off clockwise from (010); negative ϕ angles are laid off counterclockwise, as shown in Fig. 56.

In order to plot the pole of the face having this given ϕ value, it is necessary to find the natural tangent of one-half of ρ, to multiply by the radius of the projection, and to lay off the resulting distance along the ϕ line. Although any projection radius may be chosen, one of 10 centimeters is usually used. This is large enough to give accuracy, but not be unwieldly, and at the same time simplifies the calculation. With a 10-centimeter radius, it is only necessary to look up the natural tangent, move the decimal point one place to the right, and plot the result as centimeters from the center of the projection.

When the poles of crystal faces are plotted stereographically as explained above, their symmetry of arrangement should be apparent. (See Fig. 57.) We have seen (page 36) that a great circle in the

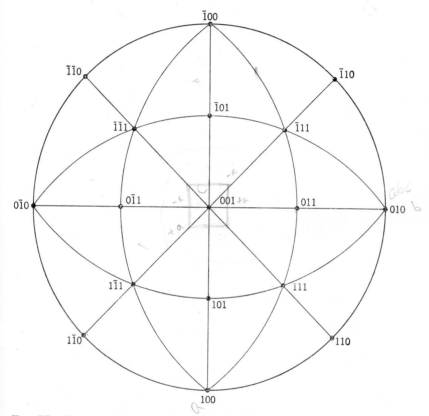

Fig. 57. Stereographic Projection of Isometric Faces. After E. E. Wahlstrom, *Optical Crystallography,* John Wiley and Sons, New York, 1951.

spherical projection is the locus of poles of faces lying in a crystal zone. When projected stereographically, vertical great circles become diameters of the projection; all other great circles project as circular arcs which subtend a diameter. The limiting case of such great circles is the primitive of the projection which is itself a great circle common to both the spherical and stereographic projections. The poles of vertical crystal faces lie on the primitive and thus are projected without distortion.

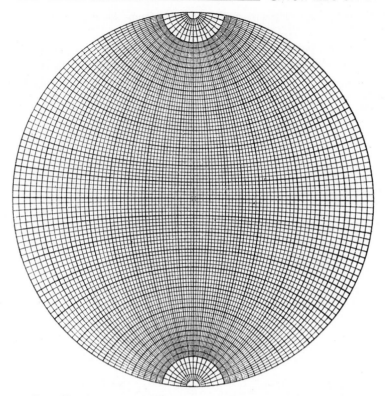

Fig. 58. Stereographic (Wulff) net. Radius equals 5 centimeters.

Stereographic net. Both the measurement and plotting of angles on the stereographic projection are greatly facilitated by means of the stereographic net.[1] (Fig. 58.) Both great and small circles are drawn on the net at intervals of 1° or 2°. In Fig. 58 the intervals are 2°. A projection made on tracing paper may be placed over the net and the angles read directly. The ϕ angles are determined where a straight line from the center of the projection through the face pole intersects the primitive. To determine the ρ angle, the projection must be rotated about the center until the face pole lies on one of the vertical great circles. The angle can then be read directly from the net.

If the ϕ and ρ angles are known, the stereogram can be constructed by reversing the process. First, one should make a mark on the primitive at $\phi = 0°$ so that it is always possible to return the projection to its initial setting. The pole of a face is located as follows: (1) Mark

---

[1] The stereographic net is also called the Wulff net, named after G. V. Wulff, Russian crystallographer (1863–1925).

See inside back cover for stereographic net of 10 centimeter radius.

a point on the primitive at the ϕ angle. (2) Rotate the projection until this point is at the end of a vertical great circle. (3) Mark off the ρ angle along this line at the proper distance from the center. This is the face pole.

Instead of measuring ϕ and ρ angles the elementary student usually measures interfacial angles which can be plotted easily with the help of the stereographic net. As an example consider Fig. 59, a crystal drawing of the orthorhombic mineral, anglesite. The starting point,

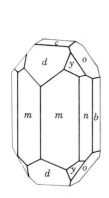

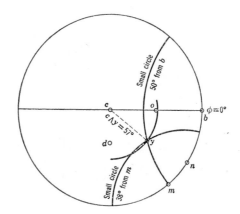

Fig. 59. Anglesite. **Fig. 60.** Location of Poles using Stereo-graphic Net.

as in all projections, is the side pinacoid, (010), face b. (Fig. 60.) The pole of this face should be placed on the primitive at 0°. The interfacial angles $b \wedge n = 32\frac{1}{2}°$, and $b \wedge m = 52°$ can be measured and plotted as ϕ angles on the primitive. Face c is the basal pinacoid, (001); it makes an angle of 90° with b and its pole should be placed at the center of the projection. Face o is in zone with c and b and thus has a ϕ angle of 0°. Its ρ angle, $c \wedge o = 52°$, can be measured directly and plotted along the vertical great circle. Face d lies in a vertical zone at 90° to the zone c, o, b. It thus has $\phi = 90°$ and $c \wedge d = 39\frac{1}{2}°$ which can be plotted along the vertical great circle of the net. The pole of face y cannot be plotted directly, but the angles $b \wedge y = 50°$ and $c \wedge y = 57°$ can be measured. To locate this pole, the projection is rotated 90° so that b lies along the radii of the small circles of the net, and a tracing of the 50° circle is made. This small circle is the locus of all poles 50° from b. The projection is again rotated until this tracing of the circle intersects a vertical great circle at 57° $(c \wedge y)$. This is the pole of y.

To check this position, measure the angle $m \wedge y = 38°$. Now with pole m placed along the radii of the small circles, trace the 38° small circle. It should also intersect at the common point. Having located pole y, its ϕ ($32\frac{1}{2}°$) and ρ (57°) angles can be read directly from the stereographic net.

E.   MEASUREMENT OF CRYSTAL ANGLES

In the preceding section on crystal projection, it was pointed out how to record graphically the angles between crystal faces.   The meas-

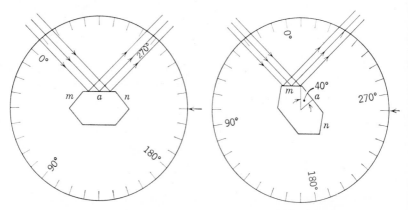

Fig. 61.   Angular Measurement by Reflecting Goniometer.

urement of these angles is accomplished by instruments known as goniometers.   For accurate work, particularly with small crystals, a

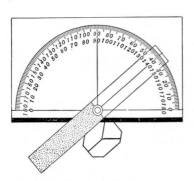

Fig. 62.   Contact Goniometer.

type known as a reflecting goniometer is used.   This is an instrument upon which the crystal to be measured is mounted so as to rotate about a zone axis and to reflect beams of light from its faces through a telescope to the eye.   The angle through which a crystal must be turned in order to throw successive beams of light from two adjacent faces into the telescope determines the angle between the faces.

It will be seen from Fig. 61 that the angle between m and a can be determined by recording the reflection positions first from face a and then from face m and noting the angular difference. The angle thus determined is the *internal* angle. These internal angles, supplements of the external interfacial angles, are the ones given in crystallographic data.

A simpler instrument used for approximate work and with larger crystals is known as a *contact goniometer*. Its appearance and use are illustrated in Fig. 62. In using the contact goniometer, it is imperative that the plane determined by the two arms of the goniometer be exactly at right angles to the edge between the measured faces. It must also be remembered that it is the internal angle that is recorded. Thus in Fig. 62, the angle should be read as 40°, not as 140°.

F. THE THIRTY-TWO CRYSTAL CLASSES

In the following section the thirty-two crystal classes, listed on page 21, are described under the crystal systems in which they are grouped. The symmetry of each class is given in terms of planes and axes, but it is also shown by means of stereograms, giving projections of all the faces of the general forms. These are the forms from which the classes derive their names. In the stereograms it is necessary to show faces in the southern as well as in the northern hemisphere in order to give completely the symmetry of the class. This is done by superimposing stereographic projections of the two hemispheres with the poles in the northern hemisphere represented by solid points and those in the southern hemisphere by circles. Thus if two poles lie directly one above the other on the sphere, they will be represented by a solid point surrounded by a circle. A vertical face is represented by a single point on the primitive, for, although such a pole would appear on projections of both top and bottom of the crystal, it would represent but one face.

Figure 63 is a drawing of a crystal with a horizontal symmetry plane.[1] The stereogram of this crystal, Fig. 64, consequently, has for all faces solid points circled to indicate corresponding faces at the top and bottom of the crystal. Figure 65 is a drawing of a crystal lacking a horizontal symmetry plane. Its stereogram, Fig. 66, has twelve

---

[1] A solid primitive circle of the projection indicates a horizontal plane of symmetry; a broken primitive circle indicates the lack of a horizontal symmetry plane. A solid line drawn as a great circle (vertical or otherwise) indicates a plane of symmetry. Broken straight lines indicate the positions of crystal axes or symmetry axes; crystal axes are labeled *a, b,* or *c,* whereas symmetry axes are so indicated by symbols at the ends of these lines. Symmetry axes of rotation are denoted with solid symbols as follows: ◖ 2-fold axis, ▲ 3-fold axis, ■ 4-fold axis, ⬣ 6-fold axis. Axes of rotary inversion are denoted with open symbols as: △ 3-fold, ☐ 4-fold, ○ 6-fold.

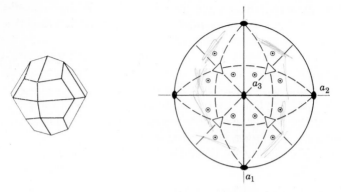

Fig. 63.   **Fig. 64.**

Crystal with symmetry $2/m\,\overline{3}$.   The stereogram shows a symmetry plane at right angles to each of the 2-fold rotation axes, and four 3-fold axes of rotary inversion. The solid primitive circle denotes a horizontal symmetry plane which indicates faces at the bottom of the crystal directly below those at the top.

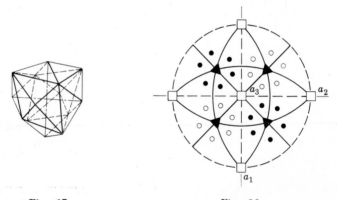

Fig. 65.   **Fig. 66.**

Crystal with symmetry $\overline{4}3m$.   Stereogram shows three 4-fold axes of rotary inversion, six symmetry planes, and four 3-fold rotation axes. The broken primitive circle indicates lack of a horizontal symmetry plane and faces at the top of the crystal do not lie above those at the bottom.

solid points as poles of faces in the northern hemisphere and twelve circles as poles of faces in the southern hemisphere.

ISOMETRIC SYSTEM

Crystallographic axes.   The crystal forms of all the classes of the isometric system are referred to three axes of equal length that make right angles with each other. Since the axes are identical, they are interchangeable, and all are designated by the letter a. When properly oriented, one axis, a_1, is horizontal and oriented front to back, a_2 is horizontal and right to left, and a_3 is vertical (see Fig. 67).

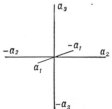

Fig. 67. Isometric Crystal Axes.

Form symbols. Although the symbol of any face of a crystal form might be used as the form symbol, it is conventional, when possible, to use one in which h, k, and l are all positive. In forms that have two or more faces with h, k, and l positive, the above statement is ambiguous. In such cases the rule followed is to take the form symbol with $h < k < l$. For example, the form with a face symbol (123) also has faces with symbols (132), (213), (231), (312), and (321). Following the rule, {123} would be taken as the form symbol, for here $h < k < l$.

In giving the angular coordinates of a form, it is customary to give those for only one face; the others can be determined knowing the symmetry. The face for which these coordinates are given is the one with the least ϕ and ρ values. This is the face of the form in which $h < k < l$.

Hexoctahedral Class—$4/m\bar{3}2/m$

Symmetry—C, $3A_4$, $4A_3$, $6A_2$, $9P$. There is a center of symmetry. The three crystallographic axes are axes of 4-fold symmetry (see Fig. 68). There are also four diagonal axes of 3-fold symmetry. These axes

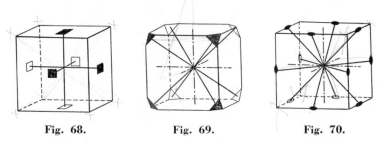

| **Fig. 68.** | **Fig. 69.** | **Fig. 70.** |

Isometric Symmetry Axes, Hexoctahedral Class.

emerge in the middle of each of the octants formed by the intersection of the crystallographic axes (Fig. 69). Further, there are six diagonal axes of 2-fold symmetry, each of which bisects one of the angles between two of the crystallographic axes, as illustrated in Fig. 70.

This class has nine planes of symmetry: three of them are known as the axial planes, since each includes two crystallographic axes (Fig. 71); and six are called diagonal planes, since each bisects the angle between two of the axial planes (Fig. 72).

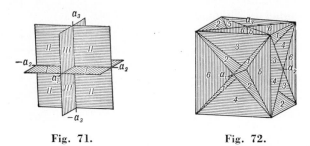

Fig. 71.   Fig. 72.

Isometric Symmetry Planes, Hexoctahedral Class.

This symmetry, the highest possible in crystals, defines the hexoctahedral class of the isometric system. Every crystal form and every combination of forms that belong to this class must show its complete symmetry. It is important to remember that in this class

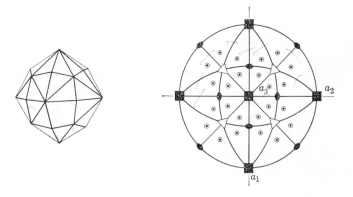

Fig. 73. Hexoctahedron.   Fig. 74. Stereogram of Hexoctahedron.

the three crystallographic axes are axes of 4-fold symmetry. Thus one can easily locate the crystallographic axes and properly orient the crystal.

The hexoctahedron, the general form from which the class derives its name, is shown in Fig. 73. Figure 74 is a stereogram showing the symmetry of the class by giving the face poles of the hexoctahedron. Once the student understands the use of the stereogram, it becomes apparent how elegantly the symmetry can be conveyed by its use, for in one diagram is shown the same symmetry as in the five diagrams of Figs. 68–72.

Forms. 1. *Cube* or *Hexahedron* {001}. The cube is a form composed of six square faces that make 90° angles with each other.[1] Each

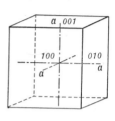

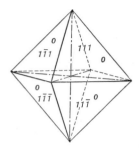

Fig. 75. Cube.   **Fig. 76.** Octahedron.

face intersects one of the crystallographic axes and is parallel to the other two. Figure 75 represents a simple cube.

2. *Octahedron* {111}. The octahedron is a form composed of eight equilateral triangular faces, each of which intersects all three of the crystallographic axes equally. Figure 76 represents a simple octa-

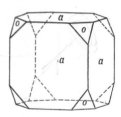

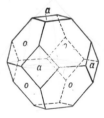

Fig. 77.   **Fig. 78.**

Cube and Octahedron.

hedron, and Figs. 77 and 78 show combinations of a cube and an octahedron. When in combination the octahedron can be recognized by its eight similar faces, each of which is equally inclined to the three crystallographic axes. It is to be noted that the faces of an octahedron truncate symmetrically the corners of a cube.

[1] In the description of forms on the following pages the geometrically perfect model of the unmodified form is considered in each case. It should be kept in mind that in nature this ideal is rarely obtained, and that crystals not only are frequently malformed but also are usually bounded by a combination of forms.

3. *Dodecahedron* or *Rhombic Dodecahedron* {011}. The dodecahedron is a form composed of twelve rhomb-shaped faces. Each face intersects two of the crystallographic axes equally and is parallel to the third. Figure 79 shows a simple dodecahedron; Fig. 80 shows a com-

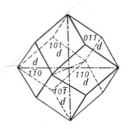

Fig. 79. Dodec-
ahedron.

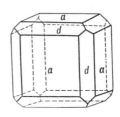

Fig. 80. Cube and
Dodecahedron.

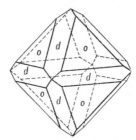

Fig. 81. Octahedron
and Dodecahedron.

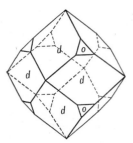

Fig. 82. Dodecahedron
and Octahedron.

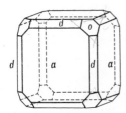

Fig. 83. Cube, Octahedron,
and Dodecahedron.

bination of dodecahedron and cube; Figs. 81 and 82, combinations of dodecahedron and octahedron; and Fig. 83, a combination of cube, octahedron, and dodecahedron. It is to be noted that the faces of a dodecahedron truncate the edges of both the cube and the octahedron. The dodecahedron is sometimes called the rhombic dodecahedron to distinguish it from the pentagonal dodecahedron and the regular geometrical dodecahedron.

4. *Tetrahexahedron* {0kl}. The tetrahexahedron is a form composed of twenty-four isosceles triangular faces, each of which intersects one axis at unity and the second at some multiple and is parallel to the third. There are a number of tetrahexahedrons which differ from each other in respect to the inclination of their faces. The commonest has the parameter relations $\infty a_1, 2a_2, 1a_3$, the symbol of which would be {012}. The indices of other forms are {013}, {014}, {023}, etc., or, in general, {0kl}. It is helpful to note that the tetrahexahedron, as its name indi-

cates, is like a cube the faces of which have been replaced by four others. Figure 84 shows a simple tetrahexahedron, and Fig. 85 a cube with its edges beveled by the faces of a tetrahexahedron.

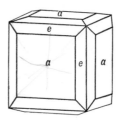

Fig. 84. Tetrahexahedron.　　**Fig. 85.** Cube and Tetrahexahedron.

5. *Trapezohedron* or *Tetragonal Trisoctahedron* {*hhl*}. The trapezohedron is a form composed of twenty-four trapezium-shaped faces each of which intersects one of the crystallographic axes at unity and the other two at equal multiples. There are various trapezohedrons with their faces having different angles of inclination. A common trapezohedron has for its parameters $2a_1$, $2a_2$, $1a_3$, the symbol for which would be {112}. The indices for other trapezohedrons are {113}, {114}, {223}, etc., or, in general, {*hhl*}. It will be noted that a trapezohedron is an octahedral-like form and may be conceived as an octahedron each of the planes of which has been replaced by three faces. Consequently, it is sometimes called a tetragonal trisoctahedron. The qualifying word tetragonal is used to indicate that each of its faces has four edges and to distinguish it from the other trisoctahedral form, the description of which follows. Trapezohedron, however, is the name most commonly used.

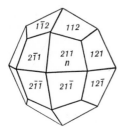

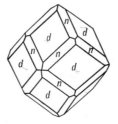

Fig. 86. Trapezohedron.　　**Fig. 87.** Dodecahedron and Trapezohedron.

The following are aids to the recognition of the form when it occurs in combinations: the three similar faces to be found in each octant; the relations of each face to the axes; and the fact that the middle edges between the three faces in any one octant go toward points which are equidistant from the ends of the two adjacent crystallographic axes. Figure 86 shows a simple trapezohedron, and Figs. 87 and 88 each show a trapezohedron in combination with a dodecahedron. It is to be noted that the faces of the common trapezohedron n {112} (Fig. 87) truncate the edges of the dodecahedron. Figure 89 shows a combination of cube and trapezohedron.

6. *Trisoctahedron* or *Trigonal Trisoctahedron* {*hll*}. The trisoctahedron is a form composed of twenty-four isosceles triangular faces each of which intersects two of the crystallographic axes at unity and the third axis at some multiple. There are various trisoctahedrons, the faces of which have different inclinations. A common trisoctahedron has for its parameters $2a_1$, $1a_2$, $1a_3$, its symbol being {122}. Other trisoctahedrons have the indices {133}, {144}, {233}, etc., or, in general, {*hll*}. It is to be noted that the trisoctahedron, like the trapezohedron, is a form that may be conceived as an octahedron each face of which has been replaced by three others. Frequently it is spoken of as the

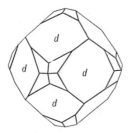

Fig. 88. Dodecahedron
and Trapezohedron.

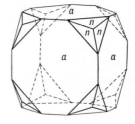

Fig. 89. Cube and
Trapezohedron.

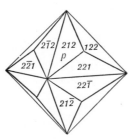

Fig. 90. Trisoctahedron.

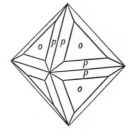

Fig. 91. Octahedron
and Trisoctahedron.

trigonal trisoctahedron, the modifying word indicating that its faces have each three edges and so differ from those of the trapezohedron. But when the word *trisoctahedron* is used alone it refers to this form.

The following points will aid in its identification when found in combinations: the three similar faces in each octant; their relations to the axes; and the fact that the middle edges between them go towards the ends of the crystallographic axes. Figure 90 shows the simple trisoctahedron, and Fig. 91 a combination of a trisoctahedron and an octahedron. It will be noted that the faces of the trisoctahedron bevel the edges of the octahedron.

7. *Hexoctahedron* {*hkl*}. The hexoctahedron is a form composed of forty-eight triangular faces each of which cuts differently all three crystallographic axes. There are several hexoctahedrons, which have varying ratios of intersection with the axes. A common hexoctahedron has for its parameter relations $6a_1$, $3a_2$, $2a_3$, with indices {123}. Other hexoctahedrons have indices {124}, {135}, etc., or, in general, {*hkl*}. It is to be noted that the hexoctahedron is a form that may be considered as an octahedron each face of which has been replaced by six others. It can be recognized when in combination by the facts that there are six similar faces in each octant and that each face intercepts

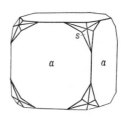

Fig. 92. Hexoctahedron.   Fig. 93. Cube and Hexoctahedron.

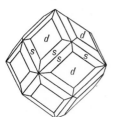

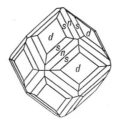

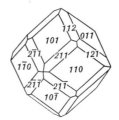

Fig. 94. Dodecahedron and Hexoctahedron.   Fig. 95. Dodecahedron, Trapezohedron, and Hexoctahedron.   Fig. 96. Dodecahedron and Trapezohedron.

the three axes differently. Figure 92 shows a simple hexoctahedron; Fig. 93, a combination of cube and hexoctahedron; Fig. 94, a combination of dodecahedron and hexoctahedron; and Fig. 95, a combination of dodecahedron, trapezohedron, and hexoctahedron.

Determination of indices of isometric forms. In determining the forms present on any isometric crystal of the hexoctahedral class, it is first necessary to locate the crystallographic axes (axes of 4-fold symmetry). Once the crystal has been oriented by these axes, the faces of the cube, dodecahedron, and octahedron are easily recognized, since they intersect respectively one, two, and three axes at unit distances. The indices can be quickly obtained for faces of other forms which truncate symmetrically the edges between known faces. The algebraic sums of the h, k, and l indices of two faces give the indices of the face symmetrically truncating the edge between them. Thus in Fig. 96 the algebraic sum of the two dodecahedron faces (101) and (011) is (112), or the indices of a face of a trapezohedron.

Occurrence of isometric forms of the hexoctahedral class. The cube, octahedron, and dodecahedron are the most common of the isometric forms. The trapezohedron is also frequently observed as the only form on a few minerals. The other forms, the tetrahexahedron, trisoctahedron, and hexoctahedron, are rare and are ordinarily observed only as small truncations in combinations.

A large group of minerals crystallize in the hexoctahedral class. Some of the most common are:

analcime	galena	leucite
cerargyrite	garnet	silver
copper	gold	spinel group
cuprite	halite	sylvite
fluorite	lazurite	uraninite

Gyroidal Class—432

Symmetry—$3A_4$, $4A_3$, $6A_2$. The symmetry axes are identical with those of the hexoctahedral class as shown in Figs. 54–56. However, there are no symmetry planes nor center. The drawing Fig. 97 represents the gyroid, and Fig. 98 its stereogram shows the symmetry of the class.

Forms. The *gyroid* $\{hkl\}$ right, $\{khl\}$ left. These forms each have twenty-four faces and are *enantiomorphic*. That is, they have the relation to one another as a right hand and a left hand; the reflection of one form yields the other. All the forms of the hexoctahedral class with the exception of the hexoctahedron can be present in the gyroidal class.

For many years cuprite was considered gyroidal, but more recent studies have shown that it is probably hexoctahedral. With the elimination of cuprite, no known mineral crystallizes in the gyroidal class.

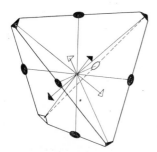

Fig. 97. Gyroid.

Fig. 98. Stereogram of Gyroid.

Hextetrahedral Class—$\bar{4}3m$

Symmetry—$3A_2$, $4A_3$, $6P$. The three crystallographic axes are axes of apparent 2-fold symmetry; actually they are 4-fold axes of rotary inversion. The four diagonal axes are axes of 3-fold symmetry (Fig. 99).

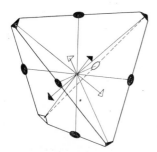

Fig. 99. Symmetry Axes.

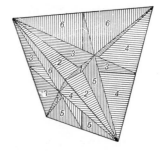

Fig. 100. Symmetry Planes.

Symmetry of Hextetrahedral Class.

There are six diagonal planes of symmetry (Fig. 100), the same planes shown in Fig. 72 for the hexoctahedral class. The general form, the hextetrahedron, is illustrated in Fig. 101, and a stereogram of this form is given in Fig. 102.

Forms. 1. *Tetrahedron* $\{111\}$ *positive*, $\{1\bar{1}1\}$ *negative*. The tetrahedron is a form composed of four equilateral triangular faces, each of which intersects all the crystallographic axes at equal lengths. It can be considered as derived from the octahedron of the hexoctahedral class by the omission of the alternate faces and the extension of the others, as shown in Fig. 103. This form, shown also in Fig. 104, is known as the positive tetrahedron {111}. If the other four faces of the octahedron had been extended, the tetrahedron resulting would have had a different orientation, as shown in Fig. 105. This is known

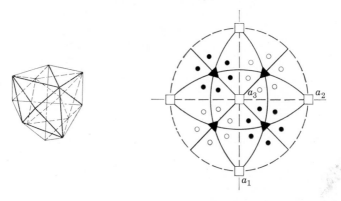

Fig. 101. Hextetrahedron.

Fig. 102. Stereogram of Hextetrahedron.

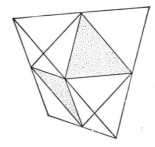

Fig. 103. Relation between the Octahedron and Tetrahedrons.

as the negative tetrahedron {1Ī1}. The positive and negative tetrahedrons when occurring alone are geometrically identical, and the only reason for recognizing the possibility of the existence of two different orientations is that they may occur truncating each other, as shown in Fig. 106. If a positive and negative tetrahedron occurred together with equal development, the resulting crystal could not be distinguished from an octahedron unless, as often happens, the faces of the two forms showed different lusters, etchings, or striations that would serve to differentiate them.

2. *Tristetrahedron* {hhl} *positive*, {hh̄l} *negative*. These forms have twelve faces which correspond to one-half of the faces of a trapezo- hedron (Fig. 107) taken in alternating groups of three above and three

below. The positive form may be made negative by a rotation of 90°
about the vertical axis.

3. *Deltoid dodecahedron* $\{hll\}$ *positive,* $\{h\bar{l}l\}$ *negative.* This is a twelve-
faced form in which the faces correspond to one-half of those of the

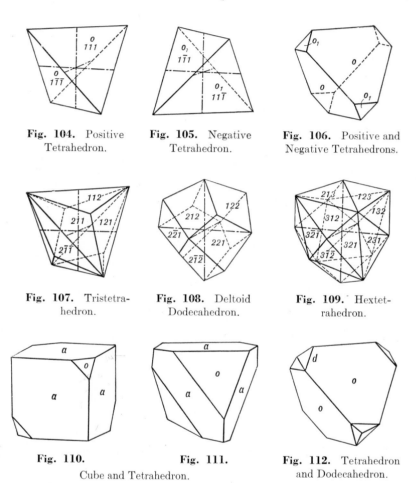

Fig. 104. Positive
Tetrahedron.

Fig. 105. Negative
Tetrahedron.

Fig. 106. Positive and
Negative Tetrahedrons.

Fig. 107. Tristetra-
hedron.

Fig. 108. Deltoid
Dodecahedron.

Fig. 109. Hextet-
rahedron.

Fig. 110.

Fig. 111.

Cube and Tetrahedron.

Fig. 112. Tetrahedron
and Dodecahedron.

trisoctahedron taken in alternate groups of three above and three
below (Fig. 108).

4. *Hextetrahedron* $\{hkl\}$ *positive,* $\{h\bar{k}l\}$ *negative.* The hextetrahedron
(Fig. 109) has twenty-four faces which correspond to one-half of the
faces of the hexoctahedron taken in groups of six above and six below.

The cube, dodecahedron, and tetrahexahedron are also present on
crystals of the hextetrahedral class. Figures 110 and 111 show com-

binations of cube and tetrahedron. It will be noted that the tetrahedron faces truncate the alternate corners of the cube or that the
cube faces truncate the edges of a tetrahedron. Figure 112 shows the

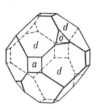

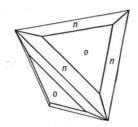

Fig. 113. Dodecahedron,
Cube, and Tetrahedron.

Fig. 114. Tetrahedron and
Tristetrahedron.

combination of tetrahedron and dodecahedron. Figure 113 represents
a combination of cube, dodecahedron, and tetrahedron. Figure 114
shows a combination of tetrahedron and tristetrahedron.

Tetrahedrite and related tennantite are the only common minerals
that ordinarily show distinct hextetrahedral forms. Sphalerite occasionally exhibits them, but commonly its crystals are complex and malformed. Diamond is believed to be hextetrahedral, but from the usual
form development one would place it in the hexoctahedral class.

Diploidal Class—$2/m\bar{3}$

Symmetry—C, $3A_2$, $4A_3$, $3P$. The three crystallographic axes are
axes of 2-fold symmetry; the four diagonal axes, each of which emerges
in the middle of an octant, are axes of 3-fold symmetry; the three

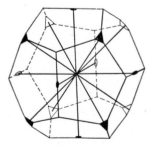

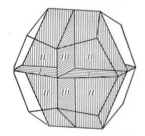

Fig. 115. Symmetry Axes.

Fig. 116. Symmetry Planes.

Symmetry of Diploidal Class.

axial planes are planes of symmetry (Figs. 115 and 116). Figure 117
illustrates a positive diploid, and Fig. 118 a stereogram showing its
symmetry.

Forms. 1. *Pyritohedron* or *Pentagonal Dodecahedron* {*h0l*} *positive*, {*0kl*} *negative*. This form consists of twelve pentagonal-shaped faces, each of which intersects one crystallographic axis at unity, intersects the second axis at some multiple of unity, and is parallel to the third.

Fig. 117. Diploid.   **Fig. 118.** Stereogram of Diploid.

There are a number of pyritohedrons which differ from each other in respect to the inclination of their faces. The most common positive pyritohedron has the parameter relations $2a_1$, ∞a_2, $1a_3$, the indices of which are {102} (Fig. 119). Figure 120 shows the corresponding

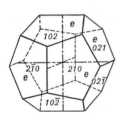

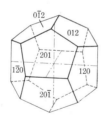

Fig. 119. Positive Pyritohedron.   **Fig. 120.** Negative Pyritohedron.   **Fig. 121.** Relation between Pyritohedron and Tetrahexahedron.

negative pyritohedron. It will be noted that the general symbol {0*kl*} for the negative pyritohedron is the same as that for the tetrahexahedron. A pyritohedron may be considered as derived from a corresponding tetrahexahedron by the omission of alternate faces and the extension of those remaining. Figure 121 shows the relations of the two forms, the shaded faces of the tetrahexahedron being those which when extended would form the faces of the pyritohedron.

2. *Diploid* {*khl*} *positive*, {*hkl*} *negative.* The diploid is a rare form composed of twenty-four faces which correspond to one-half of the faces of a hexoctahedron. The diploid may be pictured as having two faces built up on each face of the pyritohedron (Fig. 118). As in

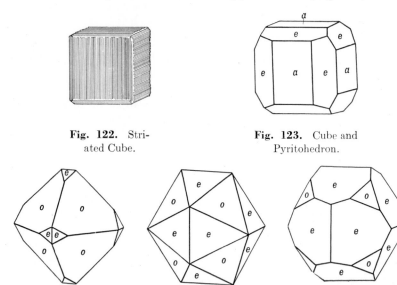

Fig. 122. Striated Cube.

Fig. 123. Cube and Pyritohedron.

Fig. 124.

Fig. 125.

Fig. 126.

Pyritohedron and Octahedron.

the case of the pyritohedron, a rotation of 90° about one of the crystallographic axes brings the positive diploid into the negative position.

In addition to the pyritohedron and the diploid, there may be present the cube, dodecahedron, octahedron, trapezohedron, and trisoctahedron. On some crystals these forms may appear alone and so perfectly developed that they cannot be told from the forms of the hexoctahedral class. This is often true of octahedrons of pyrite. Usually, however, they will show by the presence of striation lines or etching figures that they do not possess the high symmetry of the hexoctahedral class but conform rather to the symmetry of the diploidal class. This is shown in Fig. 122, which represents a cube of pyrite with characteristic striations, which are so disposed that the crystal shows the lower symmetry. Figure 123 represents a combination of cube and pyritohedron, in which it will be noted that the faces of the pyritohedron truncate asymmetrically the edges of the cube. Figures 124, 125, and 126 represent combinations of pyritohedron and octahedron with various developments. Figure 127 shows a cube truncated by the pyritohedron and octahedron. Figure 128 represents a combination of cube and diploid {124}. These figures should be studied to impress upon one the characteristic symmetry of the class.

The chief mineral of the diploidal class is pyrite; other rarer minerals of this class are skutterudite, chloanthite, gersdorffite, and sperrylite.

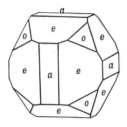

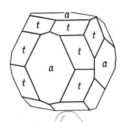

Fig. 127. Pyritohedron, Cube, and Octahedron.

Fig. 128. Diploid and Cube

Tetartoidal Class—23

Symmetry—$3A_2$, $4A_3$. The three crystallographic axes are axes of 2-fold symmetry, and the four diagonal axes are axes of 3-fold symmetry. The symmetry axes are the same as those of the diploid class

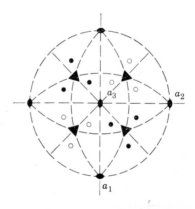

Fig. 129. Tetartoid. **Fig. 130.** Stereogram of Tetartoid.

(Fig. 115), but there are no symmetry planes and no center. Figure 129 is a drawing of the positive right tetartoid, and Fig. 130 its stereogram.

Forms. There are four separate forms of the tetartoid. These are: positive right {hkl}, positive left {khl}, negative right {khl}, negative left {hk̄l}. They comprise two enantiomorphic pairs, positive right and left, and negative right and left. Other forms that may be present are the cube, dodecahedron, pyritohedrons, tetrahedrons, and deltoid dodecahedrons.

Cobaltite and ullmanite, NiSbS, are the most common mineral representatives crystallizing in the tetartoidal class.

Characteristics of Isometric Crystals

The striking characteristics of isometric crystals which aid in their recognition may be summarized as follows:

Undistorted crystals are equidimensional in three directions at right angles to each other. These three directions are those of the crystallographic axes. Four 3-fold symmetry axes are common to all the classes of the isometric system. The crystals commonly show faces that are squares or equilateral triangles or these figures with truncated corners. They are characterized by the large number of similar faces; the smallest number on any form of the hexoctahedral class is six. Every form by itself would make a solid and is, thus, a *closed form*. The same indices are used for forms in the different classes, and, therefore, in referring to a form by its indices, it is necessary to give the class.

Some important *interfacial angles* of the isometric system which may aid in the recognition of the commoner forms are as follows:

Cube (100) $\wedge$ cube (010) = 90° 00′
Octahedron (111) $\wedge$ octahedron ($\bar{1}$11) = 70° 32′
Dodecahedron (011) $\wedge$ dodecahedron (101) = 60° 00′
Cube (100) $\wedge$ octahedron (111) = 54° 44′
Cube (100) $\wedge$ dodecahedron (110) = 45° 00′
Octahedron (111) $\wedge$ dodecahedron (110) = 35° 16′

HEXAGONAL SYSTEM

There are twelve crystal classes in the hexagonal system which are divided into two groups—the *hexagonal division* and the *rhombohedral division*. The crystal classes in the hexagonal division have a 6-fold symmetry axis of either rotation or rotary inversion, whereas the crystal classes in the rhombohedral division have a 3-fold axis of either rotation or rotary inversion. However, even on well-formed crystals, it may be difficult to determine the crystal class from morphology alone. Rhombohedral crystals may appear hexagonal because of the presence of dominant hexagonal forms; and hexagonal crystals may appear rhombohedral, for a 6-fold axis of rotary inversion ($\bar{6}$) is equivalent to a 3-fold axis with a plane at right angles ($3/m$).

Crystallographic axes. The forms of both the hexagonal and rhombohedral divisions are referred to four crystallographic axes as proposed by Bravais. Three of these, the a axes, lie in the horizontal plane and are of equal length with angles of 120° between the positive ends; the fourth axis c is vertical. The length of the horizontal axes is taken as unity; and the vertical axis, which is of different length in each hexagonal mineral, is expressed in terms of it. Thus, for beryl, the vertical axis, designated as c, has a length that in relation to the length of the horizontal axes can be expressed as $c = 0.499$.

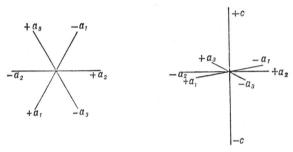

Fig. 131.   Fig. 132.

Hexagonal Crystal Axes.

When properly oriented, one of the horizontal crystallographic axes is left to right, and the other two make 30° angles on either side of a line perpendicular to it. Figure 131 shows the proper position of the horizontal axes when viewed in the direction of the vertical axis. As the three horizontal axes are interchangeable with each other, they are usually designated a_1, a_2, a_3. Note that the positive end of a_1 is to the front and left, the positive end of a_2 is to the right, and the positive end of a_3 is to the back and left. Figure 132 shows the four axes in clinographic projection. In stating the indices for any face of a hexagonal crystal, four numbers (the Bravais symbol) must be given, since there are four axes. The numbers expressing the reciprocals of the intercepts of a face on the three horizontal axes are given in the order a_1, a_2, a_3, and the number expressing the reciprocal of the intercept on the vertical axis is given last. The general Bravais form symbol is $\{hkil\}$ with $h > k$. The third digit of the index is always equal to the sum of the first two times -1; or, stated another way, $h + k + i = 0$.

HEXAGONAL DIVISION

Dihexagonal-Dipyramidal Class—$6/m\,2/m\,2/m$

Symmetry—C, $1A_6$, $6A_2$, $7P$. The vertical axis is an axis of 6-fold symmetry. There are six horizontal axes of 2-fold symmetry, three of them coincident with the crystallographic axes and the other three lying midway between them (Fig. 133). There are six vertical planes of symmetry perpendicular to the 2-fold axes and one horizontal plane

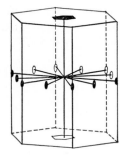

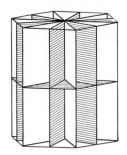

Fig. 133. Symmetry Axes.   **Fig. 134.** Symmetry Planes.

Symmetry of Dihexagonal-Dipyramidal Class.

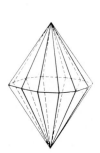

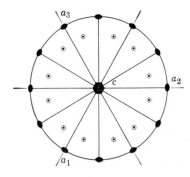

Fig. 135. Dihexago-   **Fig. 136.** Stereogram of
nal Dipyramid.   Dihexagonal Dipyramid.

of symmetry (Fig. 134). Figure 135 is an illustration of a dihexagonal dipyramid, and Fig. 136 is its stereogram showing the symmetry of the class.

Forms. 1. *Basal Pinacoid* $\{0001\}$. The basal pinacoid is a form composed of two horizontal faces. It is shown in combination with different prisms in Figs. 137, 138, and 139.

2. *Prism of First Order* $\{10\bar{1}0\}$. This is a form consisting of six vertical faces, each of which intersects two of the horizontal crystallographic axes equally and is parallel to the third. Figure 137 shows the prism of the first order.

3. *Prism of Second Order* $\{11\bar{2}0\}$. This is a form consisting of six vertical faces, each of which intersects two of the horizontal axes

equally and the intermediate horizontal axis at one-half this distance. Figure 138 shows the prism of the second order. The prisms of the first and second order are geometrically identical forms; the distinction between them is only in their orientation.

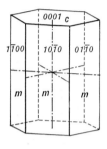 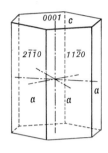 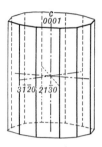

Fig. 137. First-Order Prism.   **Fig. 138.** Second-Order Prism.   **Fig. 139.** Dihexagonal Prism.

Hexagonal Prisms.

4. *Dihexagonal Prism* $\{hk\bar{i}0\}$. The dihexagonal prism has twelve vertical faces, each of which intersects all three of the horizontal crystallographic axes at different lengths. There are various dihexagonal prisms, depending upon their different relations to the horizontal axes. A common dihexagonal prism with indices $\{21\bar{3}0\}$ is shown in Fig. 139.

5. *Dipyramid of First Order* $\{h0\bar{h}l\}$. This form consists of twelve isosceles triangular faces, each of which intersects two of the horizontal crystallographic axes equally, is parallel to the third horizontal axis, and intersects the vertical axis (see Fig. 140). Various dipyramids of the first order are possible, depending upon the inclination of the faces to the c axis. The unit form has the indices $\{10\bar{1}1\}$.

6. *Dipyramid of Second Order* $\{hh\overline{2h}l\}$. This is a form composed of twelve isosceles triangular faces, each of which intersects two of the horizontal axes equally and the third and intermediate horizontal axis at one-half this distance, and also intersects the vertical axis (see Fig. 141). Various dipyramids of the second order are possible, depending upon the inclination of the faces to c. A common form (Fig. 141) has the indices $\{11\overline{2}2\}$. The relations between the dipyramids of the first and second order are the same as between the corresponding prisms.

If only one dipyramid is present on a crystal, it is usually set up as of the first order. If dipyramids of both orders are present, the dominant one, in the absence of other evidence, is considered the first order. If a dipyramid is combined with prismatic forms, the orientation of the crystal is usually determined by the dipyramid.

7. *Dihexagonal Dipyramid* {*hkīl*}. The dihexagonal dipyramid is a form composed of twenty-four triangular faces. Each face is a scalene triangle which intersects all three of the horizontal axes differently and also intersects the vertical axis. A common form, {$21\bar{3}1$}, is shown in Fig. 142.

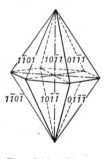

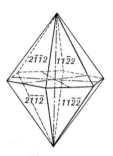

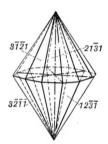

Fig. 140. First-Order Dipyramid.

Fig. 141. Second-Order Dipyramid.

Fig. 142. Dihexagonal-Dipyramid.

Hexagonal Dipyramids.

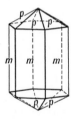

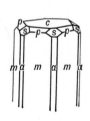

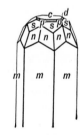

Fig. 143.

Fig. 144.

Fig. 145.

Combinations of Hexagonal Forms.

Figures 143–145 show combinations of the forms of this class.

Beryl affords the best example of a mineral representative in this class. Other minerals are molybdenite, pyrrhotite, and niccolite.

Hexagonal-Trapezohedral Class—622

Symmetry—$1A_6$, $6A_2$. The vertical axis is a 6-fold symmetry axis of rotation, and six 2-fold symmetry axes lie in a plane at right angles to it. The symmetry axes are the same as those in the dihexagonal-dipyramidal class (Fig. 133), but there are no symmetry planes nor symmetry center. Figure 146 shows a hexagonal trapezohedron and Fig. 147 a stereogram of this form.

Forms. The *hexagonal trapezohedron* {*hkil*} *right* and {*ihkl*} *left* are enantiomorphic forms, each with six trapezium-shaped faces. Other forms that may be present are the pinacoid, first- and second-order hexagonal prisms and dipyramids, and dihexagonal prisms.

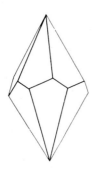

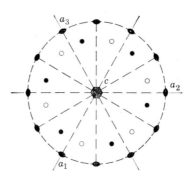

Fig. 146. Hexagonal Trapezohedron.

Fig. 147. Stereogram of Hexagonal Trapezohedron.

High quartz and kalsilite, $KAlSiO_4$, are the only mineral representatives in this class.

Dihexagonal-Pyramidal Class—6mm

Symmetry—$1A_6$, $6P$. There is a vertical axis of 6-fold symmetry and six vertical symmetry planes intersecting in this axis. Figure 148

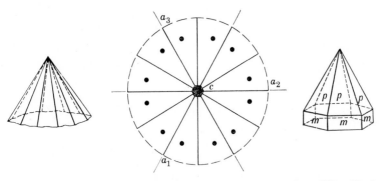

Fig. 148. Dihexagonal Pyramid.

Fig. 149. Stereogram of Dihexagonal Pyramid.

Fig. 150. Zincite.

is a dihexagonal pyramid and Fig. 149 is a stereogram of this form showing the symmetry of the class.

Forms. The forms of the dihexagonal-pyramidal class are similar to those of the dihexagonal-dipyramidal class, but, inasmuch as a horizontal plane of symmetry is lacking, different forms appear at the top and bottom of the crystal. The *dihexagonal pyramid* is thus two forms: $\{hk\bar{\imath}l\}$ upper and $\{hk\bar{\imath}\bar{l}\}$ lower. The hexagonal-pyramidal forms are: $\{h0\bar{h}l\}$ upper and $\{h0\bar{h}\bar{l}\}$ lower; and $\{hh\overline{2h}l\}$ upper and $\{hh\overline{2h}\bar{l}\}$ lower. The pinacoid cannot exist here, but instead there are two pedions $\{0001\}$ and $\{000\bar{1}\}$. The first- and second-order hexagonal prisms and the dihexagonal prism may be present.

Wurtzite, greenockite, and zincite are the commonest mineral representatives in this class. Figure 150 represents a zincite crystal with a hexagonal prism terminated above by a hexagonal pyramid and below by a pedion.

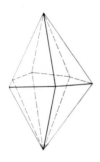

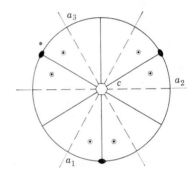

Fig. 151. Ditrigonal Dipyramid.

Fig. 152. Stereogram of Ditrigonal Dipyramid.

Ditrigonal-Dipyramidal Class—$\bar{6}m2$

Symmetry—$1A_3$, $3A_2$, $4P$. The vertical axis is a 6-fold axis of inversion which is equivalent to a 3-fold axis of rotation with a horizontal symmetry plane. There are three additional symmetry planes intersecting in the vertical axis. Three horizontal 2-fold axes lie in the vertical symmetry planes. Figure 151 represents the ditrigonal dipyramid, and Fig. 152 is its stereogram.

Forms. The ditrigonal dipyramid $\{hkil\}$ is a twelve-faced form with six faces at the top of the crystal and six at the bottom. Additional forms that may be present are: pinacoid, trigonal prisms (see page 77), second-order hexagonal prism, ditrigonal prisms, trigonal dipyramids, and second-order hexagonal dipyramids.

Benitoite is the only mineral that has been described as definitely crystallizing in this class.

Hexagonal-Dipyramidal Class—$6/m$

Symmetry—C, $1A_6$, $1P$. There is a vertical axis of 6-fold symmetry, a horizontal plane of symmetry, and a symmetry center. Figure 153 is a drawing of the hexagonal dipyramid, and Fig. 154 is its stereogram.

Forms. The general forms of this class are the dipyramids, $\{hk\bar{\imath}l\}$ *positive*, $\{hk\bar{\imath}\bar{l}\}$ *negative*. These forms consist of twelve faces, six above and six below, which correspond in position to one-half the faces of

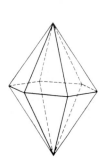

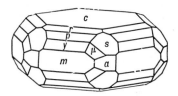

| **Fig. 153.** Hexagonal Dipyramid. | **Fig. 154.** Stereogram of Hexagonal Dipyramid. |

a dihexagonal dipyramid. Other forms that may be present are: pinacoid and hexagonal prisms $\{hki0\}$.

The hexagonal-dipyramidal class has as its chief mineral representatives the minerals of the apatite group. The dipyramid revealing the symmetry of the class is rarely seen but is illustrated as face μ Fig. 155.

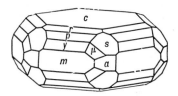

Fig. 155. Apatite.

Hexagonal-Pyramidal Class—6

Symmetry—$1A_6$. A vertical 6-fold rotation axis is the only symmetry of this class. The stereogram Fig. 157 shows the poles of the general form, the hexagonal pyramid (Fig. 156).

Forms. There are four hexagonal pyramids $\{hkil\}$, two at the top and two at the bottom of the crystal, each of which corresponds to six faces of the dihexagonal dipyramid. Other forms that may be present are pedions and hexagonal prisms $\{hki0\}$.

The form development of crystals is rarely sufficient to enable one without other evidence to place unequivocally a crystal in this class. The mineral nepheline is the chief mineral representative.

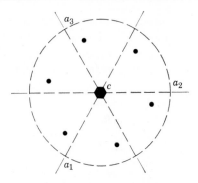

Fig. 156. Hexagonal Pyramid.

Fig. 157. Stereogram of Hexagonal Pyramid.

Trigonal-Dipyramidal Class—$\bar{6}$

Symmetry—$1A_3$, $1P$. The vertical axis is a 6-fold axis of rotary inversion ($\bar{6}$) which is equivalent to a 3-fold axis of rotation with a symmetry plane at right angles to it ($3/m$). The trigonal dipyramid is shown in Fig. 158 and its stereogram in Fig. 159.

Forms. There are four trigonal dipyramids $\{hkil\}$, each with six faces corresponding to six faces of the dihexagonal dipyramid. Other forms that may be present are the pinacoid and trigonal prisms $\{hki0\}$.

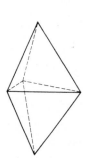

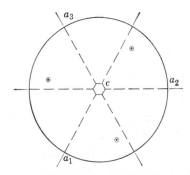

Fig. 158. Trigonal Dipyramid.

Fig. 159. Stereogram of Trigonal Dipyramid.

The symmetry does not permit hexagonal prisms, but instead there are two trigonal prisms. For example, the first-order hexagonal prism $\{10\bar{1}0\}$ becomes the two trigonal prisms $\{10\bar{1}0\}$ and $\{01\bar{1}0\}$.

There is no example of an authenticated mineral or other crystalline substance belonging to this crystal class.

RHOMBOHEDRAL DIVISION

The forms of the crystal classes of the rhombohedral division of the hexagonal system are referred to the same crystallographic axes as the forms in the classes of the hexagonal division. However, some workers use three axes parallel to the three culminating edges of the unit rhombohedron to describe the forms. All the classes are characterized by a 3-fold axis of either rotation or rotary inversion. The crystals usually show a lower symmetry than those of the hexagonal division, which is generally recognized by a 3-fold distribution of faces at the ends of the principal axis. In the section on descriptive mineralogy the crystal system of minerals crystallizing in the rhombohedral division is designated as *Hexagonal–R*.

Hexagonal-Scalenohedral Class—$\bar{3}\,2/m$

Symmetry—C, $1A_3$, $3A_2$, $3P$. The vertical crystallographic axis is one of 3-fold symmetry, and the three horizontal crystallographic axes are axes of 2-fold symmetry (see Fig. 160). There are three vertical

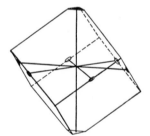   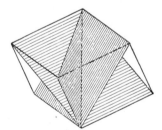

Fig. 160. Symmetry Axes.   **Fig. 161.** Symmetry Planes.

Symmetry of Hexagonal-Scalenohedral Class.

planes of symmetry bisecting the angles between the horizontal axes (see Fig. 161). Figure 162 is the hexagonal scalenohedron and Fig. 163 the stereogram of this form showing the symmetry of the class.

Forms. 1. *Rhombohedron* $\{h0\bar{h}l\}$ *positive*, $\{0h\bar{h}l\}$ *negative*. The rhombohedron is a form consisting of six rhomb-shaped faces, which correspond in their position to the alternate faces of a hexagonal dipyramid of the first order. The relation of these two forms to each other is shown in Fig. 164. The rhombohedron may also be thought of as a cube deformed in the direction of one of the axes of 3-fold symmetry. The deformation may appear either as an elongation along the symmetry axis producing an acute solid angle, or compression along the symmetry axis producing an obtuse solid angle. Depending on the angle, the rhombohedron is known as acute or obtuse.

There are two different orientations of the rhombohedron. A *positive* rhombohedron is shown in Fig. 165 and a *negative* rhombohedron in Fig. 166. It is to be noted that when properly oriented the positive rhombohedron has one of its faces, and the negative rhombohedron

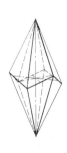

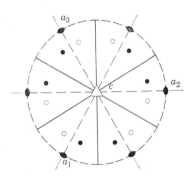

Fig. 162. Hexagonal Scalenohedron.

Fig. 163. Stereogram of Hexagonal Scalenohedron.

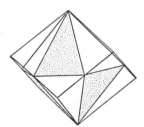

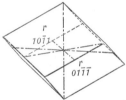

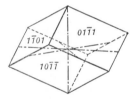

Fig. 164. Relation between First-Order Hexagonal Dipyramid and Rhombohedron.

Fig. 165. Positive Rhombohedron.

Fig. 166. Negative Rhombohedron.

one of its edges, toward the observer. There are various rhombohedrons, which differ from each other in the inclination of their faces to the c axis. The index symbol of the unit positive rhombohedron is $\{10\bar{1}1\}$ and of the unit negative rhombohedron $\{01\bar{1}1\}$. Characteristic combinations of positive and negative rhombohedrons with each other and with other hexagonal forms are shown in Figs. 167–175. As in the tetrahedrons of the isometric system, the distinction between the positive and negative rhombohedrons is only one of orientation.

The rhombohedron is such an important form in the hexagonal system that it need not appear externally on a crystal to determine the

orientation. The orientation of calcite is determined by the rhombohedral cleavage, and the orientation of corundum is determined by
rhombohedral parting (see page 151). Thus in calcite the only external

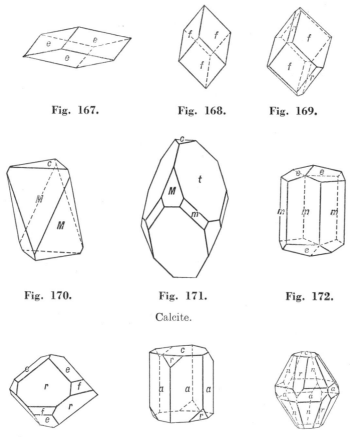

Fig. 167.   Fig. 168.   Fig. 169.

Fig. 170.   Fig. 171.   Fig. 172.

Calcite.

Fig. 173. Chabazite.   Fig. 174. Corundum.   Fig. 175. Corundum.

rhombohedral form may be negative, and in corundum the rhombohedral parting invariably necessitates orienting the crystal so that
the prism is of the second order. However, if but one rhombohedron
is present on a crystal, it is oriented, in the absence of other determining
properties, in the positive position (Fig. 174).

2. *Scalenohedron* $\{hk\bar{\imath}l\}$ *positive,* $\{kh\bar{\imath}l\}$ *negative.* This form consists
of twelve scalene triangular faces. These faces correspond in position
to the alternate *pairs* of faces of a dihexagonal dipyramid as shown in
Fig. 176. The striking characteristics of the scalenohedron are the

zigzag appearance of the middle edges, which differentiates it from the dipyramid, and the alternately more and less obtuse angles over the edges that meet at the vertices of the form. The scalenohedron is in the positive position when an edge with the greater angle is toward the observer and in the negative position when an edge with the lesser angle is toward the observer (see Figs. 177 and 178).

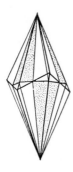

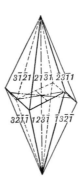

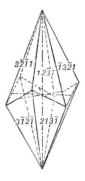

Fig. 176. Relation between Dihexagonal Dipyramid and Scalenohedron.

Fig. 177. Positive Scalenohedron.

Fig. 178. Negative Scalenohedron.

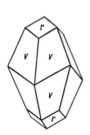

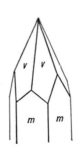

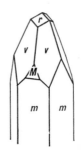

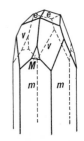

Fig. 179. Positive Scalenohedron and Positive Rhombohedron.

Fig. 180. Positive Scalenohedron, First-Order Prism.

Fig. 181. Prism, Positive Scalenohedron, and Two Positive Rhombohedrons.

Fig. 182. Prism, Positive Scalenohedron, Positive Rhombohedron, Negative Rhombohedron.

There are many different possible scalenohedrons, depending on the varying slope of the faces. A common form in calcite is the scalenohedron {21$\bar{3}$1} shown in Fig. 177.

The rhombohedron and scalenohedron of the hexagonal-scalenohedral class may combine with forms found in classes of higher hexagonal

symmetry. Thus the first- and second-order hexagonal prisms, dihexagonal prisms, the second-order dipyramid, and the basal pinacoid are
found in combination with the rhombohedron and scalenohedron (Figs.
170–175 and 180–182).
Several common minerals crystallize in this class. Chief among
them is calcite and the other members of the calcite group. Other
minerals are corundum, hematite, brucite, soda niter, arsenic, millerite,
antimony, and bismuth.

Trigonal-Trapezohedral Class—32

Symmetry—$1A_3$, $3A_2$. The vertical crystallographic axis is an
axis of 3-fold symmetry, and the three horizontal crystallographic
axes are axes of 2-fold symmetry. The symmetry axes are the same
as in the scalenohedral class, but planes of symmetry are lacking.
The stereogram Fig. 184 is a projection of the positive right trigonal
trapezohedron of Fig. 183.

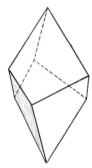

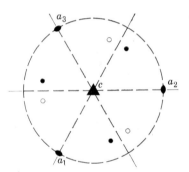

Fig. 183. Trigonal Trapezo-   **Fig. 184.** Stereogram of Trig-
hedron.   onal Trapezohedron.

Forms. There are four trigonal trapezohedrons, each made up of
six trapezium-shaped faces. These faces correspond in position to one-
quarter of the faces of a dihexagonal dipyramid and thus have similar
symbols, as follows: positive right $\{hk\bar{\imath}l\}$, positive left $\{i\bar{k}\bar{h}l\}$, negative
left $\{kh\bar{\imath}l\}$, negative right $\{\bar{k}i\bar{h}l\}$. These forms can be grouped into
two enantiomorphic pairs each with a *right* and *left* form. Other forms
that may be present are: pinacoid, first-order hexagonal prism, ditrigonal
prisms, and rhombohedrons. The second-order hexagonal prism is not
present, but instead there are two trigonal prisms $\{11\bar{2}0\}$ and $\{2\bar{1}\bar{1}0\}$.
Likewise the second-order hexagonal dipyramid becomes two trigonal
dipyramids $\{hh\,\bar{2}\bar{h}l\}$ and $\{2h\bar{h}\bar{h}\,l\}$.
Low-temperature quartz is the most common mineral crystallizing

in this class, but only rarely can faces of the trigonal trapezohedron' be observed. When this form is present, the crystals can be distinguished as right-handed (Fig. 185) or left-handed (Fig. 186), depending on whether, with a prism face fronting the observer, the trigonal trapezo-

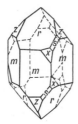

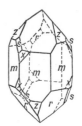

Fig. 185.   Right-Hand Quartz.   **Fig. 186.**   Left-Hand Quartz.

hedral faces, x, truncate the edges between prism and the top rhombohedron faces at the right or at the left. The faces marked s are trigonal dipyramids.

Cinnabar and the rare mineral berlinite, $AlPO_4$, also crystallize in the trigonal trapezohedral class.

Ditrigonal-Pyramidal Class—$3m$

Symmetry—$1A_3$, $3P$. The vertical axis is a 3-fold symmetry axis, and there are three symmetry planes that intersect in this axis. Figure 187 represents the ditrigonal pyramid, and Fig. 188 is its stereogram.

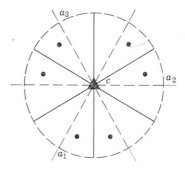

Fig. 187.   Ditrigonal   **Fig. 188.**   Stereogram of Ditrigonal
Pyramid.   Pyramid.

Forms. The forms are similar to those of the hexagonal scalenohedral class but with only half the number of faces. Because of the lack of 2-fold symmetry axes, the faces at the top of the crystals belong to different forms than those at the bottom. There are four ditrigonal pyramids. Each of these forms corresponds to half the faces of either the positive or negative scalenohedron with indices: $\{hk\bar{i}l\}$, $\{kh\bar{i}l\}$, $\{hk\bar{i}\bar{l}\}$, $\{kh\bar{i}\bar{l}\}$. Other forms that may be present are pedions, second-order hexagonal prism and pyramids, trigonal pyramids, trigonal prisms, and ditrigonal prisms. There are four trigonal pyramids; two of these are at the top of the crystal, one corresponding to the top three faces of the positive rhombohedron, the other corresponding to

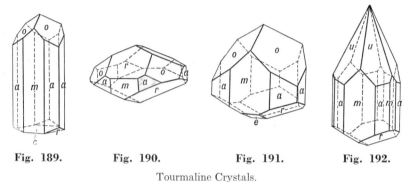

Fig. 189.   **Fig. 190.**   **Fig. 191.**   **Fig. 192.**

Tourmaline Crystals.

the top three faces of the negative rhombohedron. Their respective indices are $\{h0\bar{h}l\}$ and $\{0h\bar{h}l\}$. The two trigonal pyramids at the bottom of the crystal correspond to the bottom faces of the rhombohedron with indices $\{0h\bar{h}\bar{l}\}$ and $\{h0\bar{h}\bar{l}\}$. The trigonal prisms $\{10\bar{1}0\}$ and $\{01\bar{1}0\}$ each corresponds to three faces of the first-order hexagonal prism. There are two ditrigonal prisms, $\{hk\bar{i}0\}$ and $\{kh\bar{i}0\}$, each corresponding to half the faces of a dihexagonal prism.

Tourmaline is the most common mineral crystallizing in this class, but in addition there are pyrargyrite, proustite, and alunite. Figures 189–192 represent characteristic tourmaline crystals showing the symmetry of the ditrigonal-pyramidal class.

Rhombohedral Class—$\bar{3}$

Symmetry—C, $1A_3$. There is one 3-fold axis of inversion. This is equivalent to a 3-fold rotation axis and a center as shown by the stereogram, Fig. 194, of the rhombohedron, Fig. 193.

Forms. The rhombohedron, which is here the general form $\{hk\bar{i}l\}$, is described on page 71 as a special form of the hexagonal-scalenohedral class. If it were to appear alone on a crystal, it would have the morphological symmetry of that class $(\bar{3}2/m)$. It is only in combination with other forms that its true symmetry becomes apparent. In addition to the rhombohedron there may be the pinacoid and various hexagonal prisms, {$hki0$}.

Dolomite is the most common mineral crystallizing in this class; other representatives are ilmenite, willemite, and phenacite.

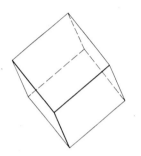

Fig. 193. Rhombohedron.

Fig. 194. Stereogram of Rhombohedron.

Trigonal-Pyramidal Class—3

Symmetry—$1A_3$. One 3-fold rotation axis is the only symmetry. The trigonal pyramid is shown in Fig. 195, and its stereogram in Fig. 196.

Forms. The trigonal pyramid, {$hkil$}, is the general form. In combination with the pedion it appears to have the symmetry of the ditrigonal-pyramidal class ($3m$) with three vertical symmetry planes

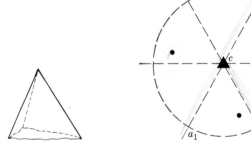

Fig. 195. Trigonal Pyramid.

Fig. 196. Stereogram of Trigonal Pyramid.

(Fig. 187). It is only when certain trigonal pyramids are in combination with one another that the true symmetry is revealed. The forms, in addition to trigonal pyramids, that may be present are pedions and trigonal prisms,

Possibly the mineral gratonite, $Pb_9As_4S_{15}$ belongs in this class; there are no other mineral representatives.

TETRAGONAL SYSTEM

Crystallographic axes. The forms of the tetragonal system are referred to three crystallographic axes that make right angles with each other. The two horizontal axes, a, are equal in length and interchange-

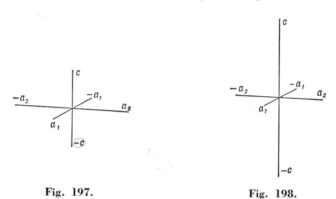

Fig. 197.   **Fig. 198.**

Tetragonal Crystal Axes.

able, but the vertical axis, c, is of a different length, characteristic for each tetragonal mineral. Figure 197 represents the crystallographic axes for the tetragonal mineral zircon where c is less than a. Figure 198 represents the crystallographic axes of the mineral octahedrite where c is greater than a. The length of the horizontal axes is taken as unity, and the relative length of the vertical axis is expressed in terms of the horizontal. This length must be determined for each tetragonal mineral by measuring the interfacial angles on a crystal and making the proper calculations (see page 123). For zircon the length of the vertical axis is expressed as $c = 0.901$, for octahedrite as $c = 1.777$. The proper orientation of the crystallographic axes and the method of their notation are similar to those of the isometric system and are shown in Figs. 197 and 198.

Ditetragonal-Dipyramidal Class—$4/m\,2/m\,2/m$

Symmetry—C, $1A_4$, $4A_2$, $5P$. The vertical crystallographic axis is an axis of 4-fold symmetry. There are four horizontal axes of 2-fold symmetry, two of which are coincident with the crystallographic axes, whereas the other two bisect the angles between them. Figure 199 shows the axes of symmetry. There are five planes of symmetry, one horizontal and four vertical. One of the horizontal axes of symmetry lies in each of the vertical symmetry planes. The position of the planes of symmetry is shown in Fig. 200. Figure 201 is a ditetragonal dipyramid and Fig. 202 a stereogram of this form.

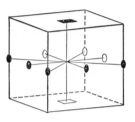

Fig. 199. Symmetry Axes.   **Fig. 200.** Symmetry Planes.

Symmetry of Ditetragonal-Dipyramidal Class.

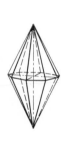
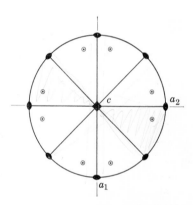

Fig. 201. Ditetragonal   **Fig. 202.** Stereogram of Ditetragonal
Dipyramid.   Dipyramid.

Forms. The forms of the ditetragonal-dipyramidal class are listed below. When the general form symbols are used, $h < k$.

1. *Basal Pinacoid* {001}. The basal pinacoid, basal plane, or base, as it is variously called, is a form composed of two horizontal faces. It is shown in combination with different prisms in Figs. 203, 204, and 205.

2. *Prism of First Order* {110}. The prism of the first order consists of four rectangular vertical faces, each of which intersects the two horizontal crystallographic axes equally. The form is represented in Fig. 203.

3. *Prism of Second Order* {010}. The prism of the second order consists of four rectangular vertical faces, each of which intersects one

horizontal crystallographic axis and is parallel to the other two axes. The form is represented in Fig. 204. The prisms of the first and second orders are identical forms, except for their orientation. They can be converted into each other by a revolution of 45° about the vertical axis. Since both may occur together upon the same crystal, it is necessary to recognize the two forms.

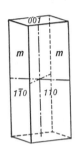

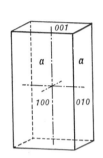

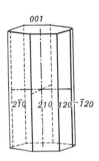

Fig. 203. First-Order Prism.

Fig. 204. Second-Order Prism.

Fig. 205. Ditetragonal Prism.

Tetragonal Prisms.

4. *Ditetragonal Prism* {hk0}. The ditetragonal prism is a form consisting of eight rectangular vertical faces, each of which intersects the two horizontal crystallographic axes unequally. There are various ditetragonal prisms, depending upon their differing relations to the horizontal axes. A common form, represented in Fig. 205, has indices {120}.

5. *Dipyramid of First Order* {hhl}. The dipyramid of the first order is a form consisting of eight isosceles triangular faces, each of which intersects all three crystallographic axes, with equal intercepts upon the two horizontal axes. There are various dipyramids of the first order, depending upon the inclination of their faces to c. The unit dipyramid {111}, which intersects all the axes at their unit lengths, is the most common. Indices of other dipyramids of the first order are {221}, {331}, {112}, {113}, etc., or, in general, {hhl}. Figure 206 represents the unit dipyramid of zircon.

6. *Dipyramid of Second Order* {0kl}. The dipyramid of the second order is a form composed of eight isosceles triangular faces, each of which intersects one horizontal axis and the vertical axis and is parallel to the second horizontal axis. There are various dipyramids of the second order, with different intersections upon the vertical axis. The most common form is the unit dipyramid {011}. Other dipyramids of the second order have indices {021}, {031}, {012}, {013}, or, in gen-

eral {0kl}. Figure 207 represents the dipyramid {011} on zircon. The relationship between the dipyramids of the first and second order is similar to that between the prisms of the first and second order. As a general rule in the absence of other evidence, if one dipyramid is present on a crystal, it is set up as the first order. If two dipyramids of different orders are present, the dominant one is usually set up as the first order. In the orientation of a crystal, the prisms are subordinate to the dipyramids. Thus, an important prism may be relegated to second order by the presence of a small dipyramid.

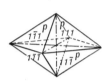
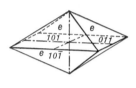
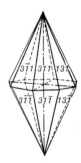

Fig. 206. First-Order Dipyramid.   **Fig. 207.** Second-Order Dipyramid.   **Fig. 208.** Ditetragonal Dipyramid.

7. *Ditetragonal Dipyramid* {hkl}. The ditetragonal dipyramid is a form composed of sixteen triangular faces, each of which intersects all three of the crystallographic axes, cutting the two horizontal axes at different lengths. There are various ditetragonal dipyramids, depending upon the different intersections on the crystallographic axes. One of the most common is the dipyramid {131} shown in Fig. 208.

Several common minerals crystallize in the ditetragonal-dipyramidal class. Major representatives are rutile, anatase, cassiterite, apophyllite zircon, and idocrase.

Tetragonal combinations. Characteristic combinations of ditetragonal-dipyramidal forms as found on crystals of different minerals are represented in Figs. 209–218.

Tetragonal-Trapezohedral Class—422

Symmetry—$1A_4$, $4A_2$. The vertical axis is one of **4**-fold symmetry, and there are four 2-fold axes at right angles to it. The symmetry axes are the same as those in the ditetragonal-dipyramidal class (Fig. 199), but symmetry planes and center are lacking. Figure 219 is a tetragonal trapezohedron and its stereogram, Fig. 220, shows the symmetry.

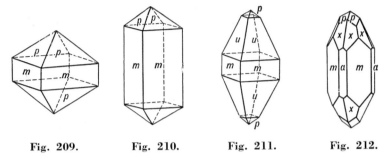

Fig. 209.   Fig. 210.   Fig. 211.   Fig. 212.

Combinations of Tetragonal Forms Shown on Zircon Crystals.

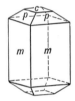

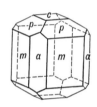

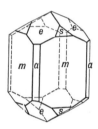

Fig. 213. Idocrase with First-Order Prism, First-Order Dipyramid, Basal Pinacoid.

Fig. 214. Idocrase with First- and Second-Order Prisms, First-Order Dipyramid, Basal Pinacoid.

Fig. 215. Rutile with First- and Second-Order Prisms, First- and Second-Order Dipyramids.

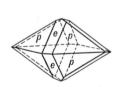

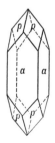

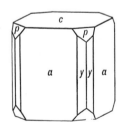

Fig. 216. Cassiterite with First- and Second-Order Dipyramids.

Fig. 217. Apophyllite with First-Order Dipyramid and Second-Order Prism.

Fig. 218. Apophyllite with First-Order Dipyramid, Second-Order Prism, Ditetragonal Prism, Basal Pinacoid.

Forms. The tetragonal trapezohedron has eight faces, corresponding to half the faces of the ditetragonal dipyramid. There are two enantiomorphic forms, right $\{hkl\}$ (Fig. 219) and left $\{h\bar{k}l\}$. Other

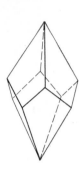

Fig. 219. Tetragonal
Trapezohedron.

Fig. 220. Stereogram of Tetragonal
Trapezohedron.

forms that may be present are: pinacoid, first- and second-order tetragonal prisms, ditetragonal prism, and first- and second-order tetragonal dipyramids.

Phosgenite, $Pb_2CO_3Cl_2$, is the only mineral representative in this class.

Ditetragonal-Pyramidal Class—4mm

Symmetry—$1A_4$, $4P$. The vertical axis is a 4-fold symmetry axis, and four planes of symmetry intersect in this axis. Figure 221 is a ditetragonal pyramid and Fig. 222 its stereogram.

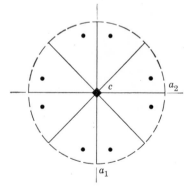

Fig. 221. Ditetragonal
Pyramid.

Fig. 222. Stereogram of Ditetragonal
Pyramid.

Forms. The lack of a horizontal symmetry plane gives rise to different forms at the top and bottom of crystals of this class. These are pedions {001} and {00$\bar{1}$}. The first-order {hhl} and second-order {$h0l$} tetragonal pyramids have corresponding lower forms, {$hh\bar{l}$} and {$h0\bar{l}$}. The ditetragonal pyramid {hkl} is an upper form, whereas {$hk\bar{l}$} is the lower form. The first- and second-order tetragonal prisms as well as ditetragonal prism may be present.

The rather rare mineral diaboleite, $Pb_2Cu(OH)_4Cl_2$, is the only mineral representative in this crystal class.

Tetragonal-Scalenohedral Class—$\bar{4}2m$

Symmetry—$3A_2$, $2P$. The vertical crystallographic axis is a 4-fold axis of rotary inversion that appears morphologically as a 2-fold rotation axis. The a crystallographic axes are axes of 2-fold symmetry. At right angles to these axes are two vertical symmetry planes intersecting in the vertical axis. (See Figs. 223 and 224.) Figure 225 represents the tetragonal scalenohedron, and Fig. 226 is its stereogram.

 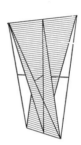

Fig. 223. Symmetry Axes.   **Fig. 224.** Symmetry Planes.

Symmetry of Scalenohedral Class, Tetragonal System.

 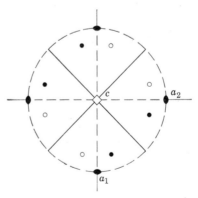

Fig. 225. Tetragonal   **Fig. 226.** Stereogram of Tetragonal
Scalenohedron.   Scalenohedron.

Forms. 1. *Disphenoid* {hhl} *positive*, {$h\bar{h}l$} *negative* are the only important forms in this class. They consist of four isosceles triangular faces which intersect all three of the crystallographic axes, with equal intercepts on the two horizontal axes. The faces correspond in their position to the alternating faces of the tetragonal dipyramid of the first order. There may be different disphenoids, depending upon their varying intersections with the vertical axis. Two different disphenoids are shown in Figs. 227 and 228. There may also be a combination of a positive and a negative disphenoid as represented in Fig. 229.

Fig. 227.   **Fig. 228.**   **Fig. 229.** Positive and

Positive Disphenoids.   Negative Disphenoids.

The disphenoid differs from the tetrahedron in the fact that its vertical crystallographic axis is not the same length as the horizontal axes. The only common mineral in the tetragonal-scalenohedral class is chalcopyrite, crystals of which ordinarily show only the disphenoid {112}. This disphenoid closely resembles a tetrahedron, and it requires accurate measurements to prove its tetragonal character.

2. *Tetragonal scalenohedron* {hkl}. This form, Fig. 225, if it were to occur by itself, is bounded by eight similar scalene triangles, which correspond in their position to alternate *pairs* of faces of the ditetragonal dipyramid. It is a rare form and observed only in combination with others. Other forms that may be present are: pinacoid, first- and second-order tetragonal prisms, ditetragonal prisms, and second-order tetragonal dipyramids.

Chalcopyrite and stannite are the only common minerals that crystallize in this class.

Tetragonal-Dipyramidal Class—4/m

Symmetry—*C*, 1*A*₄, 1*P*. There is a vertical 4-fold symmetry axis with a symmetry plane at right angles. The symmetry is shown by the stereogram Fig. 231 of the tetragonal dipyramid of Fig. 230.

Forms. The tetragonal dipyramid, {hkl}, is an eight-faced form having four upper faces directly above four lower faces. This form by itself appears to have higher symmetry, and it must be in combination with other forms to reveal the absence of vertical symmetry planes. The basal pinacoid and tetragonal prisms {hk0} may be present. The tetragonal prism $\{hk0\}$ is equivalent to four alternate faces of the ditetragonal prism and is present in those classes which have no vertical symmetry planes or 2-fold horizontal symmetry axes.

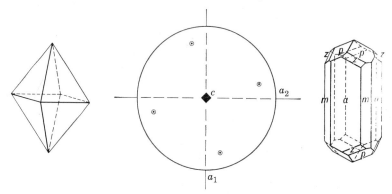

Fig. 230. Tetragonal Dipyramid. **Fig. 231.** Stereogram of Tetragonal Dipyramid. **Fig. 232.** Scapolite.

Mineral representatives in this class are: fergusonite, scheelite, powellite, and scapolite. Figure 232 illustrates a crystal of scapolite showing the true symmetry of this class.

Tetragonal-Pyramidal Class—4

Symmetry—$1A_4$. The vertical axis is one of 4-fold symmetry. There are no symmetry planes or center. The tetragonal pyramid is shown in Fig. 233 and its stereogram in Fig. 234.

Fig. 233. Tetragonal Pyramid.

Fig. 235. Wulfenite.

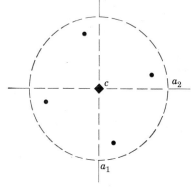

Fig. 234. Stereogram of Tetragonal Pyramid.

Forms. The tetragonal pyramid is a four-faced form. The upper form $\{hkl\}$ is different from the lower form $\{hk\bar{l}\}$, and each has a right- and left-hand variation. There are thus two enantiomorphic pairs of tetragonal pyramids. Pedions and the tetragonal prism may also be present.

As in some other classes, the true symmetry is not shown morphologically unless the general form is in combination with other forms. Figure 235, is a drawing of wulfenite. Other mineral representatives are unknown.

Tetragonal-Disphenoidal Class—$\bar{4}$

Symmetry—$1A^4_P$. The vertical axis is a 4-fold axis of rotary inversion. There is no other symmetry. The tetragonal disphenoid is shown in Fig. 236 and its stereogram in Fig. 237.

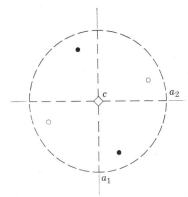

Fig. 236. Tetragonal Disphenoid.

Fig. 237. Stereogram of Tetragonal Disphenoid.

Forms. The tetragonal disphenoid $\{hkl\}$ is a closed form composed of four wedge-shaped faces. In the absence of other modifying faces, the form appears to have two vertical symmetry planes giving it the symmetry $\bar{4}2m$. The true symmetry is shown only in combination with other forms. The pinacoid and tetragonal prisms may be present.

The only mineral representative in this class is the rare mineral, cahnite, $CaB(OH)_4AsO_4$.

Characteristics of Tetragonal Crystals

The striking characteristics of tetragonal crystals may be summarized as follows: one and only one axis of 4-fold symmetry; the length of the crystal parallel to this axis is usually greater or less than its other dimensions; the cross section of a well-formed crystal when viewed in the direction of the axis of tetragonal symmetry is a square or a truncated square. Chalcopyrite is the only common tetragonal mineral to which the above does not apply, but it can be easily recognized by its disphenoidal crystals and physical properties.

ORTHORHOMBIC SYSTEM

Crystallographic axes. The forms of the crystal classes in the orthorhombic system are referred to three crystallographic axes of unequal length that make angles of 90° with each other. The relative lengths of the axes, or the axial ratios, must be determined for each orthorhombic mineral. In orienting an orthorhombic crystal the convention has been adopted by crystallographers to set the crystal so that $c < a < b$. In the past, however, this convention has not necessarily been observed, and it is customary to conform to the orientation given in the literature. One finds, therefore, that any one of the three axes may have been chosen as the vertical or c axis. The longer of the other two is then taken as the b axis and the shorter as the a axis.

The decision in the past as to which of the three axes should be chosen as the vertical or c axis rested largely upon the crystal habit of the mineral. If its crystals commonly showed an elongation in one direction, this direction was conventionally chosen as the c axis (see Figs. 251–253, page 92). If on the other hand the crystals showed a prominent pinacoid and therefore were tabular in habit, this pinacoid was usually taken as the horizontal (basal) pinacoid with the c axis normal to it (see Figs. 256–258, page 92). Cleavage also aided in orienting orthorhombic crystals. If, as in topaz, there was one pinacoidal cleavage, it was taken as basal cleavage. If, as in barite, there were two equivalent cleavage directions, they were set vertical and their intersection edges determined the c axis. After the orientation has been determined, the length of the axis chosen as b is taken as unity, and the relative lengths of the a and c axes are given in terms of it. Figure 238 represents the crystallographic axes for the orthorhombic mineral sulfur, whose axial ratios are $a:b:c = 0.813:1:1.903$.

Rhombic-Dipyramidal Class—$2/m\,2/m\,2/m$

Symmetry—C, $3A_2$, $3P$. The three crystallographic axes are axes of 2-fold symmetry (Fig. 239), and perpendicular to each of them there is a plane of symmetry (Fig. 240). From this combination of symmetry planes and axes, it follows that there is also a symmetry center. Figure 241 is a drawing of the rhombic dipyramid, the general form, and Fig. 242 is its stereogram, showing the symmetry of the class.

Forms. There are three types of forms in the rhombic-dipyramidal class—pinacoids, prisms, and dipyramids. They are as follows:

1. *Front or* a *Pinacoid* {100}. The front pinacoid has two parallel faces, each of which intersects the a axis and is parallel to the b and c

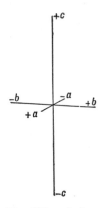

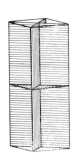

Fig. 238. Ortho-
rhombic Crystal
Axes.

Fig. 239. Symmetry
Axes.

Fig. 240. Symmetry
Planes.

Symmetry of Orthorhombic-Dipyramidal Class.

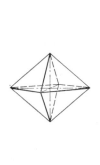

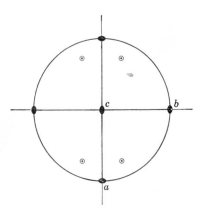

Fig. 241. Rhombic
Dipyramid.

Fig. 242. Stereogram of Rhombic
Dipyramid.

axes. It is represented in Fig. 243 in combination with the basal and side pinacoids.

2. *Side or* b *Pinacoid* {010}. The side pinacoid is a form consisting of two parallel faces, each of which intersects the b axis and is parallel to the a and c axes (Figs. 243 and 245).

3. *Basal or c Pinacoid* {001}. The basal pinacoid is a form consisting of two parallel faces, each of which intersects the *c* axis and is parallel to the *a* and *b* axes (Figs. 243 and 246).

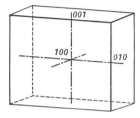

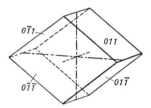

Fig. 243. Orthorhom-
bic Pinacoids.

Fig. 244. Unit First-Order
Prism and Front Pinacoid.

4. *Prism of First Order* {0*kl*}. The prism of the first order consists of four faces which are parallel to the *a* or *first* axis and intersect the *b* and *c* axes. There are various first-order prisms with different axial intercepts. The unit form {011} is illustrated in Fig. 244 in combination with the front pinacoid.

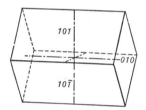

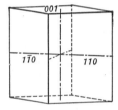

Fig. 245. Unit Second-Order
Prism and Side Pinacoid.

Fig. 246. Unit Third-
Order Prism and
Basal Pinacoid.

5. *Prism of Second Order* {*h0l*}. The prism of the second order is a form consisting of four faces, each of which intersects the *a* and *c* axes and is parallel to the *b* or *second* axis. There are various second-order prisms with different axial intercepts. The unit form {101} is illustrated in Fig. 245 in combination with the side pinacoid.

6. *Prism of the Third Order* {*hk0*}. The prism of the third order has four vertical faces that are parallel to the *c* or *third* axis and intersect the two horizontal axes. There are various third-order prisms with different axial intercepts giving various values for *h* and *k*. The unit prism {110} intersects the two horizontal axes at unit lengths (Fig. 246).

Since each of the prisms intersects two axes and is parallel to the

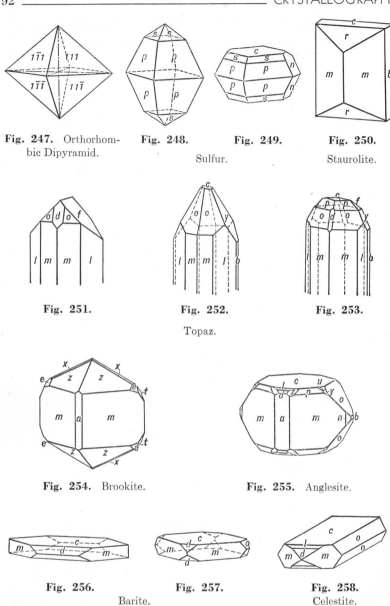

Fig. 247. Orthorhombic Dipyramid.

Fig. 248. Sulfur.

Fig. 249.

Fig. 250. Staurolite.

Fig. 251.

Fig. 252. Topaz.

Fig. 253.

Fig. 254. Brookite.

Fig. 255. Anglesite.

Fig. 256. Barite.

Fig. 257.

Fig. 258. Celestite.

third, one prism will be transformed into another by a different orientation of axes.

7. *Dipyramid* {*hkl*}. An orthorhombic dipyramid has eight triangular faces, each of which intersects all three of the crystallographic

axes. It is the general form from which the orthorhombic-dipyramidal class receives its name. Figure 247 represents the unit dipyramid {111}.

Combinations. Practically all orthorhombic crystals consist of combinations of two or more forms. Characteristic combinations of the various forms are given in Figs. 248–258.

There are many mineral representatives in this class. Among the more common are the following:

andalusite	columbite	marcasite
anthophyllite	cordierite	olivine
aragonite (group)	danburite	sillimanite
barite (group)	enstatite	stibnite
brookite	goethite	sulfur
chrysoberyl	lawsonite	topaz

Rhombic-Disphenoidal Class—222

Symmetry—$3A_2$. There are three axes of 2-fold symmetry coincident with the crystallographic axes (Fig. 239). There are no planes and no center of symmetry. Figure 259 illustrates a disphenoid, and Fig. 260 is its stereogram.

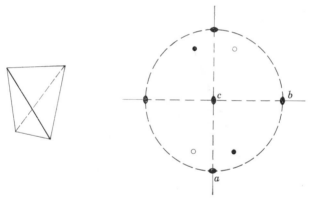

Fig. 259. Rhombic Disphenoid.   **Fig. 260.** Stereogram of Rhombic Disphenoid.

Forms. The rhombic disphenoid is a form composed of four faces, two in the upper hemisphere and two in the lower. It resembles the tetragonal disphenoid, but each face is a scalene triangle; whereas in the tetragonal disphenoid each face is an isosceles triangle. There are two disphenoids. The right {hkl} and left {h̄kl} are enantiomorphic forms.

The three pinacoids and the three prisms may be present in this class. Although there are several representative minerals crystallizing in this class, they are all comparatively rare. The most common are epsomite and olivenite.

Rhombic-Pyramidal Class—mm2

Symmetry—$1A_2$, $2P$. The c crystallographic axis is an axis of 2-fold symmetry. Two planes of symmetry at right angles to each

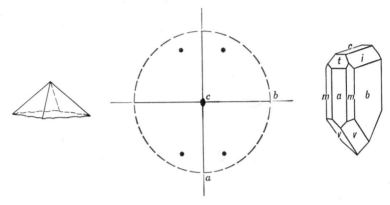

Fig. 261. Rhombic Pyramid. **Fig. 262.** Stereogram of Rhombic Pyramid. **Fig. 263.** Hemimorphite.

other intersect in this axis. Figure 261 is a drawing of the rhombic pyramid, and Fig. 262 is its stereogram.

Forms. Because of the absence of a horizontal symmetry plane, the forms at the top of the crystal are different from those at the bottom. The rhombic dipyramid thus becomes two rhombic pyramids, $\{hkl\}$ at the top and $\{hk\bar{l}\}$ at the bottom. Likewise the first-order and second-order prisms do not exist. In the place of each there are two domes (two-faced forms). $\{0kl\}$ and $\{0k\bar{l}\}$ are the first-order domes, and $\{h0l\}$ and $\{h0\bar{l}\}$ are second-order domes. In addition to these forms there are also pedions, $\{001\}$ and $\{00\bar{1}\}$, and third-order prisms.

Only a few minerals crystallize in this class; the most common representatives are hemimorphite, Fig. 263, and bertrandite.

MONOCLINIC SYSTEM

Crystallographic axes. In the monoclinic system the crystal forms are referred to three crystallographic axes of unequal lengths. The axes a and b, and b and c, make 90° angles with each other, but a and c make some oblique angle with each other. The relative lengths of the axes and the angle between the a and c axes vary for each monoclinic mineral and must be determined from appropriate measurements. When properly oriented, the b axis is horizontal and placed in a left-to-right position; the a axis is inclined downward toward the front; and c is vertical. The length of the b axis is taken as unity, and the lengths of the a and c axes are expressed in terms of it. The larger of the two supplementary angles that a and c make with each other is designated as β. Figure 264 represents the crystallographic axes of the monoclinic mineral orthoclase, the axial constants of which are expressed as $a:b:c = 0.658:1:0.555; \beta = 116° 03'$.

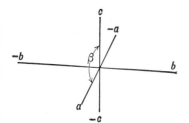
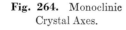
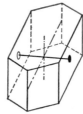

Fig. 264. Monoclinic   Fig. 265. Symmetry Fig. 266. Symmetry
Crystal Axes.   Axis.   Plane.

Symmetry of Monoclinic System.

In any monoclinic crystal the positions of the b axis and of the plane in which the a and c axes lie are fixed by the symmetry (see Figs. 265 and 266). The directions which shall serve as the a and c axes, however, are matters of choice and depend upon the crystal habit and the cleavage. If the crystals of the substance show an elongated development (prismatic habit) parallel to some direction in the a–c plane, that direction often serves as the c axis (see Figs. 278–280, page 99). Further, if there is a prominent sloping plane or planes, such as planes c in Figs. 283–285, or planes r in Figs. 280 and 281, the a axis may be taken as parallel to these. It is quite possible that there may be two, or even more, different choices that are equally good as to the directions of the a and c axes in a monoclinic crystal. Once established, the orientation of the crystals of a given substance is usually followed in subsequent descriptions.

Cleavage is also an important factor in orienting a monoclinic crystal. If there is a good pinacoidal cleavage parallel to the b axis, as in orthoclase, Fig. 283, it is usually taken as the basal cleavage. If there are two equivalent cleavage directions, as in the amphiboles and pyroxenes, they are usually taken to be vertical prismatic cleavages.

Prismatic Class—2/m

Symmetry—C, $1A_2$, $1P$. The b crystallographic axis is an axis of 2-fold symmetry, and the a–c plane of the crystallographic axes is a symmetry plane. Thus with a 2-fold axis at right angles to a symmetry plane, there must also be a center of symmetry. The stereogram Fig. 268 shows the symmetry of the prism (fourth order) in Fig. 267. Since the a axis slopes down and to the front, it does not lie in the equatorial plane, and the positive end intersects the sphere of projection in the southern hemisphere.

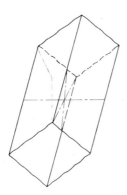
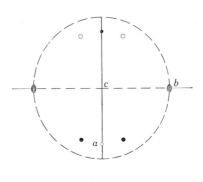

Fig. 267. Monoclinic Prism.   **Fig. 268.** Stereogram of Monoclinic Prism.

Forms. There are but two general types of forms in the prismatic class of the monoclinic system—pinacoids and prisms. They are as follows:

1. *Front or* a *Pinacoid* {100}. The front pinacoid (see Fig. 269) has two parallel faces, each of which intersects the a axis and is parallel to the b and c axes. Figure 269 shows {100} in combination with {010} and {001}.

2. *Side or* b *Pinacoid* {010}. The side pinacoid (see Figs. 269 and 272) consists of two parallel faces, each of which intersects the b axis and is parallel to the a and c axes.

3. *Basal or* c *Pinacoid* {001}. The basal pinacoid (see Figs. 269 and 270) consists of two parallel faces, each of which intersects the c axis and is parallel to the a and b axes. Unlike the basal pinacoid of the orthorhombic system, it is not perpendicular to the c axis.

4. *Second-Order Pinacoids* {$h0l$} *positive*, {$\bar{h}0l$} *negative*. These forms are each composed of two parallel faces and, like the basal pinacoid and front pinacoid, are parallel to the b axis. However, they lie in a

position intermediate to the other pinacoids and thus intersect both the *a* and *c* axes. There are various second-order pinacoids with different axial intercepts. Since the opposite ends of the *a* axis in the monoclinic system are not interchangeable, there are two distinct types of second-order pinacoids, depending on whether the face at the upper end of the

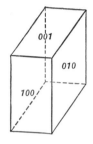

Fig. 269. Front, Side, and Basal Pinacoids.

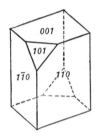

Fig. 270. Positive Second - Order Pinacoid and Basal Pinacoid.

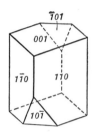

Fig. 271. Negative Second-Order Pinacoid and Basal Pinacoid.

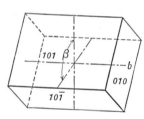

Fig. 272. Positive and Negative Second-Order Pinacoids and Side Pinacoid.

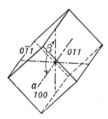

Fig. 273. First-Order Prism and Front Pinacoid.

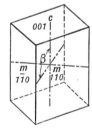

Fig. 274. Third-Order Prism and Basal Pinacoid.

crystal intersects the positive or negative end of the *a* axis. If such a face intersects the positive end of the *a* axis, the form is designated as a *positive second-order pinacoid*; if it intersects the negative end of the *a* axis, the form is designated as a *negative second-order pinacoid*. It should be emphasized that these two forms are entirely independent of each other, and the presence of one in no way necessitates the presence of the other. The unit positive second-order pinacoid {101} and the unit negative second-order pinacoid {Ī01} are illustrated respectively in Figs. 270 and 271 in combination with the vertical prism and the basal pinacoid. The two forms are illustrated together in Fig. 275 in combination with the vertical prism and basal pinacoid.

5. *Prisms of the First Order* {0*kl*}. The first-order prism is a form having four faces, each of which intersects the *b* and *c* axes and is parallel to the inclined *a* axis. There are various first-order prisms with differing axial intercepts; the unit form {011} is represented in Fig. 273.

6. *Vertical Prisms or Prisms of the Third Order* {*hk*0}. The monoclinic third-order prism has four vertical faces, each of which intersects the *a* and *b* axes and is parallel to the *c* axis. There are various vertical prisms with different axial intercepts; the unit form {110} is represented in Figs. 274–277.

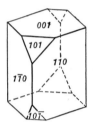 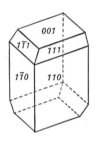 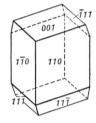

Fig. 275. Positive and Negative Second-Order Pinacoids, Basal Pinacoid, and Vertical Prism.

Fig. 276. Positive Fourth-Order Prism, Basal Pinacoid, and Vertical Prism.

Fig. 277. Negative Fourth-Order Prism, Basal Pinacoid, and Vertical Prism.

7. *Prisms of the Fourth Order* {*hkl*} *positive*, {*h̄kl*} *negative*. These forms are each composed of four faces and lie between the {0*kl*} and {*hk*0} prisms; they thus intersect all three axes. There are different fourth-order prisms, depending on the axial intercepts. Two independent forms exist and are differentiated by determining whether the two faces on the upper half of the crystal intersect the positive or negative end of the *a* axis. If two such faces of a form intersect the positive end of the *a* axis, the form is known as a *positive fourth-order prism*; if they intersect the negative end of the *a* axis, the form is known as a *negative fourth-order prism*. It should be emphasized that these two forms are entirely independent of each other and one of them can exist without the presence of the other. The unit positive fourth-order prism represented in Fig. 276 and the unit negative fourth-order prism represented in Fig. 277 are shown in combination with the vertical prism and basal pinacoid.

It should be noted that the only monoclinic form that is absolutely fixed in its designation is the side pinacoid. The other forms may vary with a variation in the choice of the directions of the *a* and *c* axes. For instance, the front pinacoid, basal pinacoid, and second-order pinacoid may be converted into each other by a rotation about the b axis. In the same manner the three prisms can be changed from one position to another.

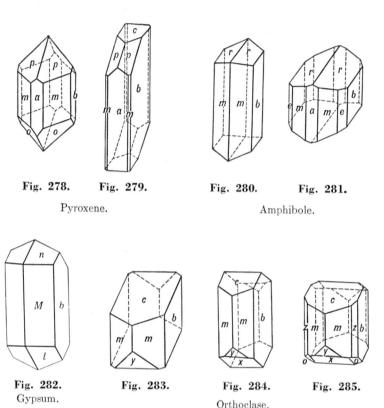

Fig. 278.   Fig. 279.   Fig. 280.   Fig. 281.

Pyroxene.   Amphibole.

Fig. 282.   Fig. 283.   Fig. 284.   Fig. 285.
Gypsum.   Orthoclase.

Combinations.   Characteristic combinations of the forms described above are given in Figs. 278–285.

Many minerals crystallize in the monoclinic, prismatic class; some of the most common are:

azurite	gypsum	orthoclase
borax	heulandite	realgar
calaverite	kaolinite	sphene
chlorite	malachite	spodumene
colemanite	monazite	talc
datolite	muscovite (and	tremolite (and
diopside (and	other micas)	other amphiboles)
other pyroxenes)	orpiment	wolframite
epidote		

Sphenoidal Class—2

Symmetry—$1A_2$. The b crystallographic axis is an axis of 2-fold symmetry. The sphenoid is illustrated in Fig. 286 and its stereogram in Fig. 287.

Forms. With the absence of the a–c symmetry plane the b axis is polar, and different forms are present at the opposite ends. The {010} pinacoid in class $2/m$ becomes two *pedions*, {010} and {0$\bar{1}$0}. Likewise the prisms—first, third, and fourth order—each degenerate

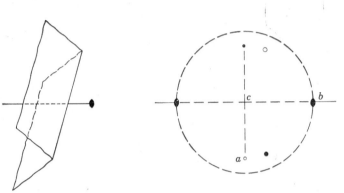

Fig. 286. Sphenoid.   **Fig. 287.** Stereogram of Sphenoid.

into a pair of enantiomorphic sphenoids. A *sphenoid* is a two-faced form with symmetry about an axis, b, in contrast to a *dome* with symmetry across a plane. The general form is thus the sphenoid {hkl} with its enantiomorphic equivalent {$h\bar{k}l$}. The other special prismatic forms of class $2/m$ become sphenoids {$0kl$}, {$0\bar{k}l$}, and {$hk0$}, {$h\bar{k}0$}. The pinacoids {100}, {001}, and {$h0l$} may be present.

Natrolite crystallizes in the sphenoidal class. Other representatives are rare, but chief among these are the members of the halotrichite isostructural group, of which pickeringite, $MgAl_2(SO_4)_4 \cdot 22H_2O$, is the most common member.

Domatic Class—m

Symmetry—$1P$. There is one vertical symmetry plane (010) that includes the a and c crystallographic axes. Figure 289 is the stereogram of the dome shown in Fig. 288.

Forms. The *dome* is a two-faced form symmetrical across a plane of symmetry in contrast to a sphenoid (Fig. 286) which is symmetrical about a 2-fold symmetry axis. The general forms {hkl} and {$\bar{h}kl$} each correspond to two of the faces of the fourth-order prism of the prismatic class. The special prisms {0*kl*} and {*hk*0} of class 2/*m* also become domes, {0*kl*}, {0*kl̄*}, and {*hk*0}, {*h̄k*0}. The form {010} is a pinacoid,

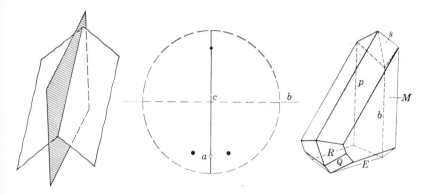

Fig. 288. Dome. **Fig. 289.** Stereogram of Dome. **Fig. 290.** Hilgardite.

but all faces lying across the symmetry plane as {100}, {1̄00}, {001}, {001̄}, and {*h0l*}, {*h̄0l*} are pedions.

The rare minerals hilgardite, $Ca_8B_{18}O_{33}Cl_4 \cdot 4H_2O$ (Fig. 290), and clinohedrite, $H_2CaZnSiO_5$, crystallize in this class.

Characteristics of Monoclinic Crystals

Most monoclinic crystals have been oriented with the *c* crystallographic axis the axis of elongation, but a few, as orthoclase feldspar, are elongated in the direction of the *a* axis. Some minerals, as epidote, are elongated parallel to the *b* axis. Monoclinic crystals are to be distinguished chiefly by their low symmetry. The fact that they possess but one plane of symmetry or one axis of 2-fold symmetry or a combination of a plane and axis at right angles serves to distinguish them from crystals of all other systems. Usually the inclination of the crystal faces that are parallel to the *a* axis is marked, and only in rare instances does the angle between the *a* and *c* axes closely approach 90°.

TRICLINIC SYSTEM

Crystallographic axes. In the triclinic system the crystal forms are referred to three crystallographic axes of unequal lengths that make oblique angles with each other (Fig. 291). The three rules that the elementary student should follow in orienting a triclinic crystal and thus in determining the position of the crystallographic axes are: (1) The most pronounced zone should be set vertical. The axis of this zone then becomes the *c* axis. (2) The basal pinacoid should slope forward and to the right. (3) Two forms in the vertical zone should be selected: one as the front pinacoid, the other as the side pinacoid. The directions of the a and b axes are determined respectively by the intersections of the side and front pinacoids with the basal pinacoid. The b axis should be longer than the a axis. In reporting on the crystallography of a new triclinic mineral or one that has not been recorded in the literature, the convention should be followed that $c < a < b$. The relative lengths of the three axes and the angles between them can be established only with difficulty and must be calculated for each mineral from appropriate measurements. The angles between the positive ends of b and c, c and a, and a and b are designated respectively as α, β, and γ (see Fig. 291). For example, the crystal constants of the triclinic mineral axinite are as follows $a:b:c = 0.492:1:0.480$; $\alpha = 82° 54'$, $\beta = 91° 52'$, $\gamma = 131° 32'$.

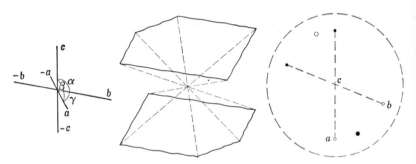

Fig. 291. Triclinic **Fig. 292.** Pinacoid. **Fig. 293.** Stereogram of
Crystal Axes. Pinacoid.

Pinacoidal Class—$\bar{1}$

Symmetry—C. The symmetry consists of a 1-fold axis of rotary inversion which is equivalent to a symmetry center. The general form, a pinacoid is shown in Fig. 292, and Fig. 293 is its stereogram.

Forms. All the forms of the pinacoidal class are pinacoids and thus consist of two similar and parallel faces. Once a crystal is oriented, the Miller indices of a crystal face establish its position. However names are given to the various pinacoids which, in a general way, designate their relation to the crystallographic axes. In addition to the front, side, and basal pinacoids, there are first-, second-, third-, and fourth-order pinacoids.

1. *Front, Side, and Basal Pinacoids.* Each of these pinacoids intersects one crystallographic axis and is parallel to the other two. The front or a pinacoid, {100}, intersects the a axis and is parallel to the other two; the side or b pinacoid, {010}, intersects the b axis; the basal

or c pinacoid, {001}, intersects the c axis. These three pinacoids are shown in combination in Fig. 294.

2. *Pinacoids of the First Order* {0kl} *positive,* {0k̄l} *negative.* These forms are parallel to the a or first axis and intersect the other two, as in Fig. 295. The positive forms intersect the ($+$) end of the b axis, the negative forms intersect the ($-$) end.

3. *Pinacoids of the Second Order* {h0l} *positive,* {h̄0l} *negative.* These forms intersect the a and c axes and are parallel to the b or second axis. (See Fig. 296.) Positive forms intersect the ($+$) end of the a axis; negative forms intersect the ($-$) end.

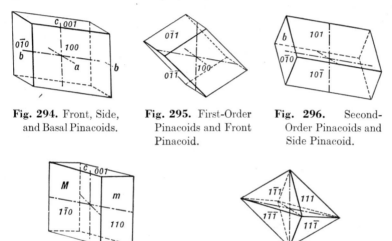

Fig. 294. Front, Side, and Basal Pinacoids.　　Fig. 295. First-Order Pinacoids and Front Pinacoid.　　Fig. 296. Second-Order Pinacoids and Side Pinacoid.

Fig. 297. Third-Order Pinacoids and Basal Pinacoid.　　Fig. 298. Fourth-Order Pinacoids.

4. *Pinacoids of the Third Order* {hk0} *positive,* {hk̄0} *negative.* The faces of these forms are parallel to the c or third axis and are vertical. They intersect the a and b axes. Positive forms intersect the ($+$) end of the b axis; negative forms intersect the ($-$) end. Figure 297 shows the basal pinacoid in combination with the third-order pinacoids {110} and {1̄10}.

There are various first-, second-, and third-order pinacoids with different axial intercepts. The presence of a positive pinacoid in no way indicates that the corresponding negative form will be present.

5. *Fourth-Order Pinacoids* {hkl} *positive right,* {hk̄l} *positive left,* {h̄kl} *negative right,* {h̄k̄l} *negative left.* Each of these is a two-faced form and can exist independently of the others. Various fourth-order pinacoids are possible, depending on the axial intercepts. Figure 298 shows a combination of the four unit fourth-order pinacoids.

Among the minerals that crystallize in the pinacoidal class are:

amblygonite	polyhalite
chalcanthite	rhodonite
microcline	turquoise
pectolite	ulexite
plagioclase feldspars	wollastonite

Pedial Class—1

Symmetry. There is merely a 1-fold rotation axis, which is equivalent to no symmetry. The stereogram, Fig. 300, thus shows only one pole, that of the pedion, Fig. 299.

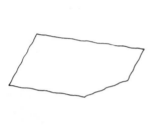

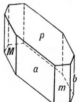

Fig. 299. Pedion.   Fig. 300. Stereogram of Pedion.

Forms. The general form {hkl} as well as all other forms are pedions and thus each face stands by itself. Each pinacoidal form of class ($\bar{1}$) becomes two pedions.

Axinite is the only common mineral that crystallizes in the pedial class.

Fig. 301. Rhodonite.   Fig. 302. Chalcanthite.

Characteristics of Triclinic Crystals

With the exception of the plagioclase feldspars, there are few common triclinic minerals, and they rarely form distinct and well-developed crystals. When such crystals do occur, they are usually recognized by the fact that they have no plane or rotation axis of symmetry. Figures 301 and 302 represent characteristic triclinic crystals.

G. TWIN CRYSTALS AND CRYSTALLINE AGGREGATES

In the foregoing discussion of the various crystal systems, the character of ideally developed individual crystals has been considered. Such crystals are the exception, and minerals are more frequently found in crystals not showing ideal symmetry or intergrown with one another. An intergrowth may result in a parallel, subparallel, or haphazard grouping of the crystalline units. More rarely two or more crystals are observed intergrown according to a definite law and are called twin crystals.

Twin Crystals

When two or more crystals are intergrown according to some deducible law so that certain directions of the lattices are parallel whereas other directions are in reverse position, the group is said to be a *twin crystal*. The component parts of a twin crystal are related to each other in the following ways: (1) The relation may be as if one part were derived from the other by reflection over a plane common to both. This plane, about which the two parts of the twin are symmetrically disposed, is called the *twin plane*. (2) One part of the twin may appear to have been derived from the other by a revolution about some crystal direction common to both. Although there are some exceptions, the angular revolution is usually 180° and the line about which it may be considered to take place is called the *twin axis*. (3) The two individuals may be symmetrical about a point. In this case the twin is said to have a *twin center*. Twinning is defined by a *twin law*, which states whether there is a center of twinning, an axis of twinning, or a plane of twinning, and gives the crystallographic orientation for the axis or plane.

The surface on which two individuals are united is known as the *composition surface*. If this surface is a plane, it is called the *composition plane*. The composition plane is commonly, but not invariably, the twin plane. However, if the twin law can be defined only by a twin plane, the twin plane is always parallel to a possible crystal face but never parallel to a plane of symmetry. The twin axis is a zone axis or a direction perpendicular to a possible crystal face; but it can never be an axis of even symmetry (2-, 4-, 6-fold) if the rotation involved is 180°. A 90° rotation about a 2-fold axis can be considered a twin operation.

Twin crystals are usually designated as either *contact twins* or *penetration twins*. Contact twins have a definite composition surface separating the two individuals, and the twin law is defined by a twin plane (Fig. 308). Penetration twins are made up of interpenetrating individuals having an irregular composition surface, and the twin law is defined by a twin axis. (See Fig. 309.)

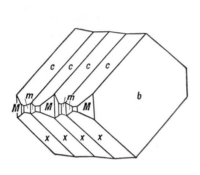

Fig. 303. Albite Twins.

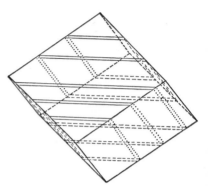

Fig. 304. Calcite Twinned on Negative Rhombohedron.

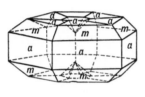

Fig. 305. Rutile.

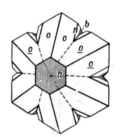

Fig. 306. Chrysoberyl.

Cyclic Twinning.

Repeated or multiple twins are made up of three or more parts all twinned according to the same law. If all the successive composition surfaces are parallel, the resulting group is called a *polysynthetic twin*. If the successive composition planes are not parallel, a *cyclic twin* results. Common examples of polysynthetic twinning are albite twinning in plagioclase feldspar (Fig. 303) and twinning on the negative rhombohedron $\{01\bar{1}2\}$ in calcite (Fig. 304). When a large number of individuals in a polysynthetic twin are closely spaced, crystal faces or cleavages crossing the composition planes show striations owing to the reversed positions of adjacent individuals. Figures 305 and 306 of rutile and chrysoberyl illustrate cyclic twinning.

Twinning in the lower symmetry groups generally produces a resulting aggregate symmetry higher than that of each individual because the twin plane is an added symmetry plane.

Common twin laws. *Isometric System.* In the hexoctahedral class of the isometric system the twin axis, with a few rare exceptions, is a 3-fold symmetry axis, and the twin plane is thus parallel to a face of the octahedron. Figure 307 shows an octahedron with

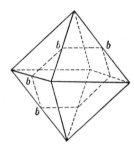

Fig. 307. Octahedron Showing Orientation of Twin Plane.

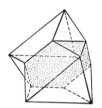

Fig. 308. Spinel Twin.

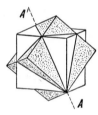

Fig. 309. Fluorite Penetration Twin.

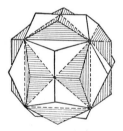

Fig. 310. Pyrite Iron Cross.

plane *bb* a possible twin plane, and Fig. 308 shows an octahedron twinned according to this law, forming a contact twin. This type of twin is especially common in gem spinel and hence is called a *spinel twin*. Figure 309 shows two cubes forming a penetration twin with the 3-fold symmetry axis the twin axis.

In the diploidal class of the isometric system penetration twins of two pyritohedrons, as shown in Fig. 310, are common. Here the twin axis is normal to a face of the rhombic dodecahedron. A 90° rotation about the 2-fold axis would produce the same result. This twin is known as the *iron cross*.

Hexagonal System. In the hexagonal division of this system twins are rare and unimportant, but in the rhombohedral division twins are common. The rhombohedral carbonates, especially calcite, serve as excellent illustrations of three of the twinning laws. The twin plane may be parallel to the basal pinacoid, with the *c* axis as the twin axis, as shown in Figs. 311 and 312. A plane parallel to a face of the negative rhombohedron $\{01\bar{1}2\}$ commonly serves as the twin plane (Fig. 313).

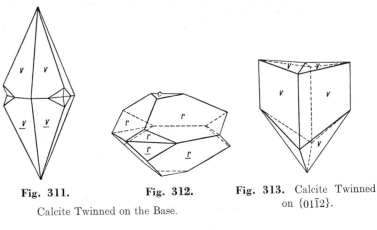

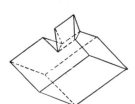

Fig. 311.   **Fig. 312.**   **Fig. 313.** Calcite Twinned

Calcite Twinned on the Base.   on $\{01\bar{1}2\}$.

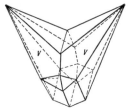

Fig. 314. Artificial Twinning   **Fig. 315.** Calcite Twinned

in Calcite.   on $\{10\bar{1}1\}$.

Polysynthetic twinning frequently takes place according to this law, and may form as the result of pressure (Fig. 304). A cleavage fragment of Iceland spar may be twinned artificially by the pressure of a knife blade according to the same law, as shown in Fig. 314. In Fig. 315 a plane parallel to a face of the positive rhombohedron $\{10\bar{1}1\}$ serves as a twin plane.

In the trigonal trapezohedral class the mineral quartz shows several types of twinning. In Fig. 316 the *Brazil law* is illustrated with the twin plane perpendicular to one of the *a* crystallographic axes. Here, right- and left-hand individuals have formed a penetration twin. In Fig. 317 a Dauphiné twin is shown. This is a penetration twin with the *c* axis the twin axis. Such twins are composed either of two right- or two left-hand individuals. In Fig. 318 is illustrated the *Japanese law* with the twin plane parallel to a rhombohedron, $\{11\bar{2}2\}$. The re-entrant angles usually present on twinned crystals do not show on either Brazil or Dauphiné twins.

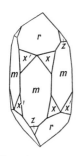

Fig. 316. Brazil
Twin.

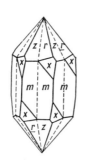

Fig. 317. Dauphiné
Twin.

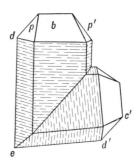

Fig. 318. Japanese
Twin.

Twinning in Quartz.

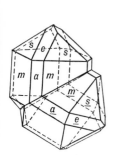

Fig. 319.
Cassiterite.

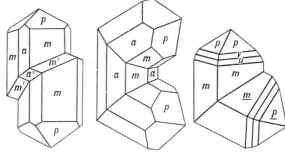

Fig. 320. Rutile. **Fig. 321.** Rutile. **Fig. 322.** Zircon.

Tetragonal System. The most common type of twin in the tetragonal system has a plane parallel to a face of the dipyramid of the second order $\{011\}$ as the twin plane. Figures **319–322** represent crystals of cassiterite, rutile, and zircon twinned according to this law.

Orthorhombic System. In the orthorhombic system a plane parallel to a prism face most frequently serves as the twin plane. Figure **323** represents a contact twin of aragonite and Fig. **324** a cross section of a cyclic twin of the same mineral formed in this manner. Figure **325** shows a similar cyclic twin of cerussite. The pseudohexagonal appearance of Figs. **324** and **325** results from the fact that the prism angles are nearly 60°. Two types of twinning are common in the mineral staurolite, as shown in Fig. **326**, where a plane parallel to a face of the first-order prism {032} is the twin plane; and in Fig. 327, where a plane parallel to a face of the dipyramid {232} is the twin plane.

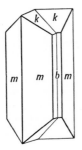

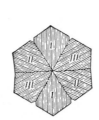

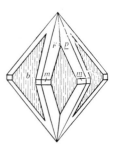

Fig. 323. Aragonite.   **Fig. 324.** Cross Section of Cyclic Aragonite Twin.   **Fig. 325.** Cerussite.

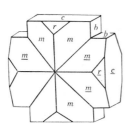

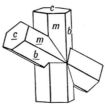

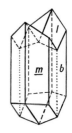

Fig. 326.   **Fig. 327.**   **Fig. 328.**
Staurolite Twins.   Gypsum.

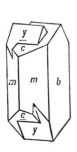

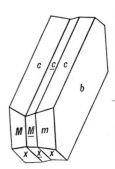

Fig. 329.   **Fig. 330.**   **Fig. 331.**   **Fig. 332.** Albite
Carlsbad   Manebach   Baveno Twin.   Twinning.
Twin.   Twin.

Monoclinic System. In the monoclinic system twinning on pinacoids, {100} or {001}, is most common. Figure 328 of gypsum illustrates twinning with the front pinacoid {100} the twin plane. Figure 330 is of a *Manebach twin* of orthoclase in which the basal pinacoid {001} is the twin plane. Orthoclase also forms penetration twins according to the *Carlsbad law,* in which the *c* crystallographic axis is the twin axis, and the individuals are united on an irregular surface roughly parallel to {010} (Fig. 329). The *Baveno twin* is also found in orthoclase. Here a plane parallel to a face of the first-order prism {021} is the twin plane (Fig. 331).

Triclinic System. The feldspars illustrate best the twinning of the triclinic system. They are almost universally twinned according to the *albite law,* with the side pinacoid {010} the twin plane, as shown in Fig. 332. Another important type in feldspar is twinning according to the *pericline law,* with the crystallographic *b* axis the twin axis.

Crystal Habit and Crystalline Aggregates

Certain terms used to express the appearance or habit of individual crystals, or of aggregates of crystals, are given below:

1. When a mineral consists of isolated and distinct crystals, the following terms may be used:
   a. Acicular. In slender needlelike crystals.
   b. Capillary and filiform. In hairlike or threadlike crystals.
   c. Bladed. Elongated crystals flattened like a knife blade.

2. When a mineral consists of a group of distinct crystals the following terms are used:
   a. Dendritic. Arborescent, in slender divergent branches, somewhat plant-like, made up of more or less distinct crystals.
   b. Reticulated. Latticelike groups of slender crystals.
   c. Divergent or *radiated.* Radiating crystals groups.
   d. Drusy. A surface is drusy when covered with a layer of small crystals.

3. When a mineral consists of parallel or radiating groups of individuals, the following terms are used:
   a. Columnar. In stout columnlike individuals.
   b. Bladed. An aggregate of many flattened blades.
   c. Fibrous. In slender fibrous aggregates.
   d. Stellated. Radiating individuals forming starlike or circular groups.
   e. Globular. Radiating individuals forming spherical or hemispherical groups.
   f. Botryoidal. When the globular forms are in groups. The word is derived from the Greek for a "bunch of grapes."
   g. Reniform. Radiating individuals terminating in rounded masses resembling a kidney in shape. (Fig. 333.)
   h. Mammillary. Large rounded masses resembling mammae, formed by radiating individuals.
   i. Colloform. It is frequently difficult to distinguish between aggregates represented by the last three terms, and as a result the term colloform has been proposed to include all the more or less spherical forms.

Fig. 333. Reniform Hematite, Cumberland, England.

4. When a mineral consists of scales or lamellae, the following terms are used:

  a. *Foliated.* When a mineral separates easily into plates or leaves.
  b. *Micaceous.* Similar to foliated, but the mineral can be split into exceedingly thin sheets, as in the micas.
  c. *Lamellar* or *tabular.* When a mineral consists of flat platelike individuals superimposed upon and adhering to each other.
  d. *Plumose.* Consisting of fine scales with divergent or featherlike structure.

5. When a mineral consists of grains.

  Granular. When a mineral consists of an aggregate of large or small grains.

6. Miscellaneous.

  a. *Stalactitic.* When a mineral occurs in pendent cylinders or cones. Stalactites form by deposition from mineral-bearing waters dripping from the roof of some cavity.
  b. *Concentric.* Consisting of more or less circular layers superimposed upon one another about a common center.
  c. *Pisolitic.* A mineral consisting of rounded masses about the size of peas.
  d. *Oölitic.* A mineral aggregate formed of small spheres resembling fish roe.
  e. *Banded.* When a mineral occurs in narrow bands of different color or texture.
  f. *Massive.* A mineral composed of compact material with an irregular form, without any peculiar appearance like those described above.
  g. *Amygdaloidal.* When a rock such as basalt contains almond-shaped nodules.

h. Geodes. When a cavity has been lined by the deposition of mineral material but not wholly filled, the more or less spherical mineral shell is called a geode. The mineral is often banded, owing to successive depositions of the material, and the inner surface is frequently covered with projecting crystals.

i. Concretions. Roughly spherical masses formed by deposition of material on a nucleus.

H. RULES FOR CRYSTAL ORIENTATION

In general the process of orientation is one of correlating the visible morphological features of the crystal with the crystallographic co-ordinate axes. The student must keep in mind a clear-cut distinction between the crystallographic axes, which are a purely synthetic device, and the axes and planes of symmetry, which are as real a feature of the crystal as are the faces, edges, and solid angles that indicate their presence. When we orient a crystal, we are endeavoring to bring the regular array of atoms that make it up into a standard position for study, using the morphology and apparent symmetry as a guide.

It is possible on crystals of any symmetry class to distinguish three principal zones in which lie the faces of all forms, with the exception of the general form. In the orthorhombic, monoclinic, and triclinic systems these three principal zones are defined by the pinacoids {100}, {010}, and {001} and have as their zone axes the three crystallographic axes a, b, and c. We may designate these zones by Roman numerals, as follows:

Zone	Determined by	Zone Axis
I	basal (001) and side (010) pinacoid	a
II	basal (001) and front (100) pinacoid	b
III	front (100) and side (010) pinacoid	c

The stereograms Fig. 334 show the relationships between these three principal zones in the orthorhombic, monoclinic, and triclinic systems.

In order to name the forms on any crystal of these three systems and assign them Miller indices, orient the crystal according to the customary rules for the crystal system to which it belongs. Then rotate the crystal in turn about each of the three principal zone axes.

1. Any face lying on the intersection of two principal zones is a principal pinacoid. (See table above.)

2. Any face in a zone with two principal pinacoids is of the order given by the number of the zone. All faces in Zone I belong to *first-order* forms, all faces in Zone II to *second-order* forms, and all faces in Zone III to *third-order* forms.

3. Any face not lying in a principal zone belongs to a general form whose name is given to the class.

Zone	Orthorhombic	Monoclinic	Triclinic
I	1st-order prism $(0kl)$	1st-order prism $(0kl)$	±1st-order pinacoid $(0kl)$ $(0\bar{k}l)$
II	2nd-order prism $(h0l)$	±2nd-order pinacoid $(h0l)$ $(\bar{h}0l)$	±2nd-order pinacoid $(h0l)$ $(\bar{h}0l)$
III	3rd-order prism $(hk0)$	3rd-order prism $(hk0)$	±3rd-order pinacoid $(hk0)$ $(h\bar{k}0)$
...	rhombic dipyramid (hkl)	±4th-order prism (hkl) $(h\bar{k}l)$	±R ±L 4th-order pinacoid (hkl) $(h\bar{k}l)$ $(\bar{h}kl)$ $(\bar{h}\bar{k}l)$

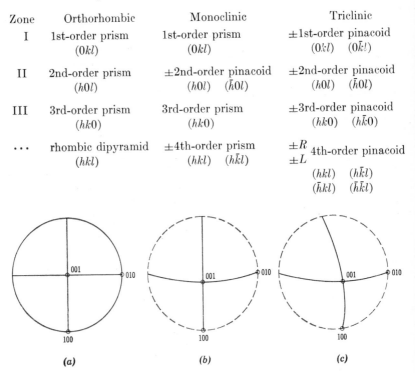

Fig. 334. (a) Orthorhombic, (b) Monoclinic, (c) Triclinic stereograms showing the relationships between the three principal zones.

Rules for orientation. In the orientation of crystals of the orthorhombic, monoclinic, and triclinic systems it is conventional to choose the crystallographic axes such that $c < a < b$ if the cell dimensions are known, or if the axial ratios have been established, and if symmetry permits. If, as is commonly the case, the cell dimensions and axial ratios are not known, the crystal must be oriented on the basis of its morphological development.

In the inclined crystal systems there are a few general rules or principles which will assist in making the proper choice of orientation on the basis of crystal habit.

1. An orientation that yields simple indices is generally preferable to one which yields more complex indices. Thus, an orientation that assigns the faces present to first-, second-, or third-order forms is preferable to one which assigns the same faces to dipyramids or fourth-

order forms. The list of forms whose indices yield the lowest numerical total is the most likely to correspond with the conventional setting based on the internal structure. The physical basis for this rule is the generally greater stability and abundance of faces having a high density of lattice points.

2. Where there is a choice between positive and negative forms, settings that yield positive indices for the prominent forms are preferable.

3. Settings that yield interaxial angles close to 90° are to be sought. Such orientations yield crystallographic axes that are as nearly orthogonal as possible, stressing the morphological resemblances to higher symmetry systems.

Orthorhombic. The three 2-fold symmetry elements characterizing the orthorhombic system are made to coincide with the three crystallographic axes. In the classes $2/m\,2/m\,2/m$ and 222 the three 2-fold symmetry axes are set as the crystallographic axes and become the zone axes of the three principal zones. In the class $mm2$ the unique 2-fold axis is chosen as c. Pinacoids are perpendicular to the symmetry axes and hence are easily recognized. Prisms lie in the principal zones, and dipyramids lie between principal zones.

If the convention of $c < a < b$ is disregarded, there are three possible ways to orient an orthorhombic crystal. In the past, orthorhombic crystals usually have been oriented with c parallel to the longest dimension or perpendicular to the shortest dimension. This has been done without regard to the convention of $c < a < b$, and no attempt has been made to reorient these crystals. However, once these crystals have the c axis fixed, the shorter of the other two orthogonal directions is usually taken as a and the longer as b.

Monoclinic. The 2-fold symmetry axis is set as the b crystallographic axis in classes $2/m$ and 2; the symmetry plane in class m is made to coincide with the plane of the a and c axes. There is no exception to this rule. A prominent face in the zone whose zone axis is b is generally chosen as a basal pinacoid so as to make the a axis slope gently down toward the observer. If no suitable face is developed, an effort is made to select a first-order prism whose edge of intersection defines the a axis. Note that only the side pinacoid is perpendicular to the axis it cuts.

Triclinic. Maximum latitude in choice of setting is afforded by crystals of this system, and as a result there is wide diversity of opinion as to proper interpretation of morphology. All forms are pinacoids in the class $\bar{1}$, pedions in the class 1, and the naming depends entirely on orientation. It is customary to choose the most prominent zone on such crystals as parallel to the *c* crystallographic axis. In this zone, prominent faces are chosen as the front and side pinacoid in such a way as to make the crystallographic angle γ (gamma) as near 90° as possible. A prominent face is then chosen as the basal pinacoid so as to make the crystallographic angles β (beta) and α (alpha) obtuse and as near 90° as possible. In the absence of suitable faces to select as principal pinacoids, first-, second-, and third-order pinacoids should be chosen so as to define as nearly orthogonal a set of axes as is consistent with the other rules for orientation. Note that none of the principal pinacoids or pedions is perpendicular to a crystallographic axis.

Hexagonal. In all classes there is a unique 6- or 3-fold axis of symmetry which is set as the *c* crystallographic axis. Where there are three horizontal 2-fold symmetry axes they are made to coincide with the *a* crystallographic axes. In the absence of horizontal symmetry axes, or where there are six such axes, there exists an ambiguity of orientation that leads to two possible settings. In these cases, it is customary to place the dominant forms, whether inclined or vertical, in such a position that a face is toward the observer.

Tetragonal. The unique 4-fold symmetry axis, whether a rotational axis or one of inversion, is set as the *c* crystallographic axis in all classes. In classes with four horizontal 2-fold symmetry axes, the crystallographic axes are set to coincide with two of these. There exist two possible orientations. The one preferred is to make the dominant forms first order, that is, orientated in such a way as to intersect both horizontal crystallographic axes.

I. AXIAL RATIOS—CALCULATIONS

We have seen that crystals are described with reference to coordinate axes whose interaxial angles are the same as those of the unit cell or of the space lattice upon which the crystal is built. For crystals in the triclinic system it is necessary to specify all the three interaxial angles, α, β, and γ, since they are all unequal. In the monoclinic system α = γ = 90° is understood, and it is necessary to give only β (≠90°). The axial directions in the orthorhombic, tetragonal, and isometric systems are said to be *orthogonal* since they are all at right angles. Although crystals built on hexagonal and rhombohedral lattices may be described with reference to three axes, most crystallographers have adopted Bravais' four-axis scheme. There the interaxial angles between the three horizontal a axes are all $120°$, and the angle between the c axis and an a axis is $90°$.

Since the size of the unit cell differs from one crystal to another, even when both have the same symmetry, it is not feasible to lay off coordinate axes according to an absolute linear scale, such as angstrom units or millimeters. This would result in highly irrational intercepts and would make the cutting parameters for a given face depend on the size of the crystal and the distance of the face from the origin. Hence, the axes are conceived of as being proportional to the lengths of the unit-cell edges, and "unity" on an axis depends on the identity period within the crystal in that direction.

If these identity periods are measured by x-ray diffraction methods, they are denoted by the letter of the axis parallel to which the unit translation is measured, a, b, or c, with a subscript zero. Hence, in the triclinic, monoclinic, and orthorhombic systems, in which all three unit-cell edges or identity periods are different, the cell dimensions are given as a_0, b_0, and c_0, generally in angstrom units.[1]

In the tetragonal and hexagonal systems the equal, interchangeable cell edges are denoted by a_0, and the unique cell edge by c_0. In the isometric system the edges of the unit cell are identical and interchangeable, and only one cell dimension is given, a_0.

In this way, any unit cell may be fully described by giving the interaxial angles and cell edges, or unit translations.

These actual lengths are not important in determining the geometry of arrangement of the external faces on the crystal. It is only the *ratios* of the lengths of the edges of the unit cell that determine the slopes of the faces, since these faces may be of any size and at any distance from the origin of the coordinate system. It is axiomatic that any crystal face may be considered as moved parallel to itself without affecting the symmetry of the crystal or its Miller indices. The size and shape of the faces on a crystal are accidents of growth and have no significance in the interpretation of the external form in terms of the internal structure. For this reason, in morphological description it is customary to replace the cell dimensions with *axial ratios*, even in those cases where the internal structure is completely known. The axial ratios are expressed as ratios between the lengths of the unit cell along the three axes, in terms of one of them which is taken as unity. It is conventional to take the b axis as unity in those systems in which a, b, and c are of different lengths (see page 23) and to take the a axis as unity in those systems in which the a axes are equal and interchangeable. Thus, in the orthorhombic, mono-

[1] In some books data are given in kX units. One angstrom = 1.00202 kX units.

clinic, and triclinic systems the structural axial ratios are equal to

$$a_0:b_0:c_0 = \frac{a_0}{b_0} : \frac{b_0}{b_0} : \frac{c_0}{b_0}$$

Thus, for the mineral *aragonite*, symmetry $2/m\ 2/m\ 2/m$, the unit cell dimensions are given in Dana's *System of Mineralogy*, 7th edition, as $a_0 = 4.94\ kX$, $b_0 = 7.94\ kX$, $c_0 = 5.72\ kX$. From these cell dimensions the axial ratios may be calculated as: $a_0 : b_0 : c_0 = 0.622 : 1 : 0.720$. Note that the axial ratios are dimensionless numbers.

Now, since the relative dimensions, and hence the shape, of the unit building blocks of aragonite are known, simple trigonometry permits us to calculate the slopes and angular relations of the external faces. We can imagine the face (021) as a sloping surface (like one of the faces of the Pyramids of Gizeh) underlain by the building

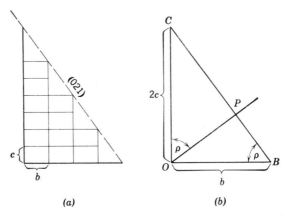

Fig. 335. A sloping surface resulting from the regular stacking of rectangular units.

blocks of the crystal and made up like a flight of stairs of treads one unit cell wide in the b dimension and risers two unit cells high in the c direction. This relationship is shown in Fig. 335. If we imagine that the number of steps becomes almost infinite, the flight of steps becomes, for all practical purposes, identical with the plane parallel to the slope. This is the case in crystals. Note that the *intercepts* on the axes $1b$ and $2c$ must be used in determining the relative height of the risers as compared with the treads. The indices (021) lead to the intercepts or parameters $\propto a$, $1b$, $2c$ by inverting and clearing of fractions—the reverse of the process by which indices are obtained from intercepts.

In Fig. 335b, the trigonometrical relations between the face (021), the face normal (OP), the crystallographic axes b and c, and the crystallographic angle ρ (rho) are shown. The angle POC, the angle between the c axis and the face normal, is the angle ρ and is equal to the angle CBO. From these relations we see that:

$$\tan CBO = \tan \rho = 2c/b$$

Thus for aragonite, since b is always taken as 1, the tangent of $\rho = 2c = 2 \times 0.720$. If we look up $2 \times 0.720 = 1.440$ in a table of natural tangents, we find $\rho = 55° \ 14'$. (021) is in the zone whose zone axis is a, as indicated by the zero for the first index, so ϕ must $= 0° \ 00'$. Hence we may now write in the form of an angle table:

Form	ϕ	ρ
021	0° 00'	55° 14'

Actual measurement of a crystal of aragonite reveals a face at $\phi = 0° \ 00'$, $\rho = 55° \ 14\frac{1}{2}'$. We may confidently identify this face as (021).

The geometry becomes a bit more complex when a general form, that is, one which cuts all three axes at different intercepts, is taken. Consider the simplest example of such a general face, (132), as shown in Fig. 336. OP is the face normal, and OD is normal to AB. The angle DOB is the crystallographic angle ϕ, and in the triangle DOB, angle OBD is $90° - \phi$. Then in the triangle AOB, the angle OAB must also be ϕ.

Reducing the indices (132) to intercepts we find the edge $AO = 6a$, $OC = 3c$ and the edge $OB = 2b = 2$, since $b = 1$. Hence we may find the ϕ of face (132) by either of the following:

$$\tan OAB = \tan \phi = \frac{2}{6a} \quad \text{or} \quad \cot \phi = \frac{6a}{2}$$

The latter expression is usually easier to calculate. Substituting the a value for aragonite, $\cot \phi = 1.866$ and $\phi = 28° \ 11'$.

In order to find the ρ angle of such a face, it is necessary first to have calculated ϕ, as we have done above. Now, in the triangle COD, $\tan \rho = 3c/OD$. In the triangle BOD, $\cos \phi = OD/2$. Setting both of these expressions equal to OD:

$$OD = \frac{3c}{\tan \rho} \qquad OD = 2 \cos \phi$$

Eliminating OD between these equations:

$$\frac{3c}{\tan \rho} = 2 \cos \phi \qquad \tan \rho = \frac{3c}{2 \cos \phi}$$

Substituting the values for aragonite, $\tan \rho = 1.2253$ and $\rho = 50°\ 48'$. Hence the face (132) of aragonite has the angular coordinates: $\phi = 28°\ 11'$, $\rho = 50°\ 48'$.

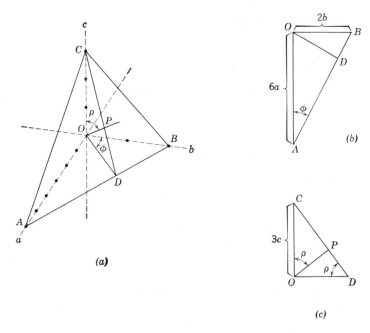

Fig. 336. Intercepts of Face (132).

Much more commonly, x-ray data are not available, and the crystallographer is faced with the problem of determining the axial ratios from morphological measurements made with a goniometer. Prior to the development of x-ray diffraction techniques, all axial ratios were determined in this way. Even today such measurements are used to improve the precision of determination of axial ratios. Hence we must consider how axial ratios may be calculated from angular data.

With the contact goniometer the angles measured on a crystal are usually interfacial angles, which must be transformed into the standard crystallographic angles, ϕ and ρ. (See pages 34–43.) These are tabulated in the form of an *angle table* as follows:

Angle Table*

ARAGONITE   CaCO$_3$—$2/m$ $2/m$ $2/m$ ORTHORHOMBIC; DIPYRAMIDAL
$a:b:c = 0.6223:1:0.7206$

Form	ϕ	ρ	Form	ϕ	ρ
c 001	$\cdots$	0° 00′	i 021	0° 00′	55° 14½′
b 010	0° 00′	90 00	u 101	90 00	49 11
m 110	58 06	90 00	p 111	58 06	53 45
x 012	0 00	19 49	E 132	28 10½	50 48
k 011	0 00	35 46½			

*The angles in the table, taken from Dana's *System of Mineralogy,* were obtained using a reflecting goniometer. They are thus of higher precision than those obtained with a contact goniometer.

The letters prefixed to the indices of the forms above are arbitrarily assigned. Angles are given to the nearest one-half minute in most tables, as this is generally the limiting precision of the method of measurement. For stereographic plotting and for many crystallographic calculations, a much lower precision is satisfactory.

Crystallographic calculations generally involve three variables: (1) *the axial ratios,* (2) *the indices,* and (3) *the angles ϕ and ρ.* When two of these variables are known the third may be calculated. These calculations are simple and straightforward for the orthogonal crystal systems but become involved and tedious in the inclined systems. Since no new principles are gained by making calculations in the inclined systems and the labor is greatly increased, examples in this book will be confined to the orthogonal systems.

We have seen in the example above that there are simple trigonometric relations among the angles ϕ and ρ, the indices of the face $\{hkl\}$, and the axial ratios. Transforming those relationships so that they may be solved for the axial ratios, we have

$$c = \frac{l \tan \rho \cos \phi}{k} \qquad a = \frac{h \cot \phi}{k}$$

where a and c are the relative axial lengths with b taken as 1; h, k, and l are the Miller indices. Let us try these relations for the mineral aragonite, using the face E (132). (See angle table above.)

$$b = 1 \qquad a = \frac{1 \times \cot 28° \, 10\frac{1}{2}′}{3} \qquad a = 0.6223$$

$$c = \frac{2 \times \tan 50° \, 48′ \times \cos 28° \, 10\frac{1}{2}′}{3} \qquad c = 0.7206$$

Hence, $a:b:c = 0.6223:1:0.7206$.

This result is in agreement to the fourth significant figure with the published axial ratios for aragonite. We may consider this computation to be an example of a problem of the first type: *Given* the indices of a face of a general form and its angular coordinates ϕ and ρ; *to determine* the axial ratios. Note that, in the example above, the *indices* are used rather than the intercepts, and hence the values of h, k, and l bear an inverse relationship to the actual lengths cut off on the axes.

Solution of a problem of the first type is possible by the use of faces of forms that cut only two axes, but in this case two faces must be used; one cutting a and b, and the other cutting either b and c or a and c. The formula $a = (h \cot \phi)/k$ does not contain l and hence may be used with a face that does not cut c. The formula $c = (l \tan \rho \cos \phi)/k$ does not contain h and hence may be used with a face that does not cut a. Faces that do not cut a lie in the zone whose zone axis is a and have $\phi = 0° \ 00'$. Since the $\cos 0° \ 00' = 1$, the formula reduces to $c = (l \tan \rho)/k$ for faces in that zone. We may take as an example the faces m (110) and i (021). To obtain a from the face m (110)

$$a = \cot \phi_{110} = 0.6224$$

Now, from the angles for the face i (021)

$$c = \frac{\tan \rho_{021}}{2} = 0.7206$$

It is left as a problem for the student to find the axial ratio c from the face u (101). Note that the axial ratio values obtained from all faces must agree. Lack of agreement indicates poor quality of measurements, inaccuracy of calculation, or a mistake in assignment of indices. The last case is usually easily detectable by the fact that the incorrect axial ratio is a simple multiple or fraction of the value obtained from the other faces on the crystal.

A problem of the second type may be stated: *Given* the axial ratios and the measured angles for a face; *to find* its indices.

An example is a crystal of aragonite on which a face has been measured as $\phi = 38° \ 46\frac{1}{2}'$, $\rho = 61° \ 35\frac{1}{2}'$. The axial ratios are known. (See angle table.) Find the indices of the face. This type of problem arises very frequently in the description of crystals of known species containing unfamiliar forms, as from a new locality.

First, by inspection we see that the face belongs to a form that cuts all three axes. If this were not so, either ϕ or ρ would be $0° \ 00'$ or $90° \ 00'$. We may therefore set up the general equations in such a way as to permit solving for the *ratios* of the indices $h:k$, and $k:l$, as follows:

$$\frac{h}{k} = \frac{a}{\cot \phi} \qquad \frac{k}{l} = \frac{\tan \rho \cos \phi}{c}$$

Substituting:

$$\frac{h}{k} = \frac{0.6223}{1.2452} = \frac{1}{2} \qquad \frac{k}{l} = \frac{1.8488 \times 0.7796}{0.7206} = \frac{2}{1}$$

Hence, $h:k:l = 1:2:1$, and the indices are (121).

A problem of the third type may be stated: *Given* the axial ratios and the Miller indices; *to find* the angles ϕ and ρ. This type of problem arises when it is desirable to calculate the angular coordinates when observed values are obviously inaccurate; also in technologic crystallography where it is desired to find the attitude of a plane in a crystal so that the crystal may be sawed along that plane, or otherwise treated.

Let us suppose that we wish to cut an oriented crystal of aragonite parallel to the plane (122), the axial ratios being known. First, we may transpose the formulas into a convenient form.

$$\cot \phi = \frac{ka}{h} \qquad \tan \rho = \frac{kc}{l \cos \phi}$$

Substituting:

$$\cot \phi_{122} = 2 \times 0.6224 = 1.2448 \qquad \phi = 38° \, 46\tfrac{1}{2}'$$

$$\tan \rho_{122} = \frac{2 \times 0.7206}{2 \times 0.7796} \qquad \rho = 42° \, 45'$$

All three types of problems may be solved for faces that cut only two axes simply by use of the functions of $0° \, 00'$ and $90° \, 00'$ where appropriate, remembering that division by zero is impossible.

Calculations in the Tetragonal System

Axial-ratio calculations in the tetragonal system make use of the same formal geometrical relations as in the orthorhombic system, allowing the a_2 axis to substitute for the b axis, and the a_1 axis for the a axis. The axial ratios are $a_1:a_2:c = 1:1:c$ and hence may be stated simply $a:c = 1:?$, or even more briefly Axis $c = ?$.

Solution of all three types of problems using a general form (hkl) is performed in the same way as in the orthorhombic system, using the formula

$$c = \frac{l \tan \rho \cos \phi}{k}$$

If a dipyramid of the first order in which $\phi = 45° \ 00'$ is used, $\cos \phi$ is equal to 0.70711; whereas, with a dipyramid of the second order where $\phi = 0° \ 00'$, $\cos \phi$ becomes 1, and the formula becomes $c = (l \tan \rho)/k$.

For example, the face (231) on the common mineral *rutile*, which is ditetragonal dipyramidal, $4/m \ 2/m \ 2/m$, has the angles $\phi = 33° \ 41\frac{1}{2}'$, $\rho = 66° \ 42\frac{1}{2}'$. The axial ratio $a:c$ may be found as follows:

$$c = \frac{\tan 66° \ 42\frac{1}{2}' \cos 33° \ 41\frac{1}{2}'}{3} = \frac{2.3229 \times 0.8320}{3} = 0.6442$$

Hence, $a:c = 1:0.6442$.

The problem—what is the ρ of face (221) on rutile?—is simplified by the fact that the indices $\{hhl\}$ show the form to be a first-order dipyramid, hence $\phi = 45°$, with the relation

$$\tan \rho_{hhl} = \frac{kc}{0.7071 \times l}$$

Substituting:

$$\tan \rho_{221} = \frac{2 \times 0.6442}{0.7071} = 1.8220$$

$$\rho_{221} = 61° \ 14\frac{1}{2}'$$

Calculations in the Hexagonal System

The axial ratio in the hexagonal system is expressed as $a:c = 1:?$ or Axis $c = ?$, as in the tetragonal system, since the three a axes are equal and interchangeable and are all taken as unity. The chief pitfall for the student in making calculations in this system is the convention that the negative end of the a_3 axis is taken as $\phi = 0° \ 00'$. The convention in all the other systems would lead one to expect that the positive end of the a_2 axis should be chosen. According to this convention, the ϕ of the second-order forms is $0° \ 00'$, whereas the ϕ of the first-order forms is $30° \ 00'$. This apparent inconsistency has definite advantages; for, in working with crystals in the rhombohedral division, it gives all positive forms positive values of ϕ and all negative forms negative values of ϕ. (See Fig. 337.) The ϕ of the type face of the general positive form will lie between $0°$ and $30°$ as limits. Calculation of the c axis from the ϕ and ρ angles for a face of a general form will utilize essentially the same formula that has been used for the general forms of the orthorhombic and tetragonal systems. The only difference is that c must be expressed in terms of the a_3 axis taken as unity since this axis is at the position of $\phi = 0°$.

The reciprocal of the intercept on this axis is $i = h + k \times (-1)$. The formula for determining c from the angles of the general form is thus:

$$c = \frac{l \tan \rho_{hk\bar{\imath}l} \cos \phi}{h + k}$$

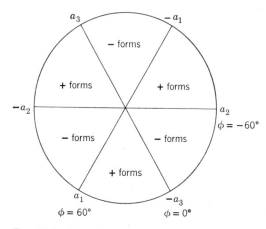

Fig. 337. Distribution of Rhombohedral Forms.

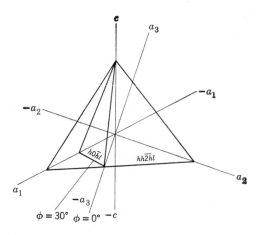

Fig. 338. First-Order and Second-Order Hexagonal Forms.

If a second-order form is used, $\phi = 0°$, and $\cos \phi = 1$; hence the term $\cos \phi$ disappears from the equation, leaving

$$c = \frac{l \tan \rho_{hh\bar{2}hl}}{h + k}$$

If a first-order form is used, $\phi = 30° 00'$, $\cos \phi = 0.8660$, and the equation becomes

$$c = \frac{l \tan \rho_{h0\bar{h}l} \times 0.8660}{h + k}$$

Some examples based on an angle table for the mineral *hematite* may be considered.

Angle Table

HEMATITE   HEXAGONAL-R; HEXAGONAL-SCALENOHEDRAL $\bar{3}\,2/m$

$$a:c = 1:1.3652$$

Form	ϕ	ρ	Form	ϕ	ρ
c 0001	. . .	0° 00′	p 11$\bar{2}$3	0° 00′	42° 18$\frac{1}{2}$′
m 10$\bar{1}$0	30° 00′	90 00	r 10$\bar{1}$1	30 00	57 36$\frac{1}{2}$
a 11$\bar{2}$0	0 00	90 00	i 42$\bar{6}$5	10 53$\frac{1}{2}$	59 03$\frac{1}{2}$
u ?	30 00	21 30$\frac{1}{2}$	x 12$\bar{3}$2	−10 53$\frac{1}{2}$	64 23

Calculating the axial ratio from the general form x ($12\bar{3}2$):

$$c = \frac{l \tan \rho_{12\bar{3}2} \cos \phi}{h + k} \qquad c = \frac{2 \times 2.0865 \times 0.98201}{3} = 1.3659$$

Repeating the calculation with the data for the face i ($42\bar{6}5$)

$$c = \frac{5 \times 1.6692 \times 0.98201}{6} = 1.3659$$

Good agreement indicates that the indices chosen for these faces are mutually consistent. We may test the axial ratio by means of a second-order dipyramid ($11\bar{2}3$).

$$c = \frac{3 \times 0.9102}{2} = 1.3653$$

We may now calculate the indices of the unknown form u. The $\phi = 30°$ indicates a first-order dipyramid with indices of the type ($h0\bar{h}l$). Hence we must find the ratio of $h:l$.

$$\frac{h}{l} = \frac{\tan \rho \times 0.866}{c} = \frac{0.3941 \times 0.866}{1.365} = \frac{1}{4}$$

Hence, the indices of the face u must be 10$\bar{1}$4.

J. X-RAY CRYSTALLOGRAPHY

The application of x-rays to the study of crystals was the greatest single impetus ever given to crystallography. Prior to 1912, crystallographers had correctly deduced from cleavage, optical properties, and the regularity of external form that crystals had an orderly structure; but their thinking concerning the geometry of crystal lattices had only the force of a hypothesis. Since the use of x-rays, it has been possible not only to measure the distance between successive atomic planes but also to tell the positions of the various atoms within the crystal.

X-rays were discovered accidentally by Wilhelm Conrad Roentgen in 1895 while experimenting with the production of cathode rays in sealed discharge tubes wrapped in black paper. The electron stream in the discharge tube, striking the glass of the tube, produced low-intensity x-radiation which caused some fluorescent material nearby to glow in the dark. Röentgen correctly inferred that a new type of penetrating electromagnetic radiation was being produced, fittingly called "x-radiation" because of the many mysteries connected with it. Röentgen was unsuccessful in his efforts to measure the wave length of x-rays, and it was this unsolved problem that led to the discovery of the diffraction of x-rays by crystals.

The fact that most substances are more or less transparent to x-rays brought about their almost immediate use in hospitals for medical purposes in the location of fractures, foreign bodies, and diseased tissue in much the same manner in which they are used today. The production of shadow pictures by means of x-rays is called *radiography* and is widely used, not only for medical purposes but also for industrial inspection and process control.

It was not until 1912, seventeen years after the discovery of x-radiation, that, at the suggestion of Max von Laue, x-rays were used to study crystals. The original experiments were carried out at the University of Munich where von Laue was a lecturer in Professor Sommerfeld's department. Sommerfeld was interested in the nature and excitation of x-rays and Laue in interference phenomena. Also at the University of Munich was Paul Heinrich Groth, a leading crystallographer. With the gathering together of such a group of distinguished scientists having these special interests, the stage was set for the momentous discovery.

In 1912, Paul Ewald was working under Sommerfeld's direction on a doctor's dissertation involving the scattering of light waves on passing through a crystal. In thinking about this problem, von Laue raised the question: what would be the effect if it were possible to use electromagnetic waves having essentially the same wave length as the interatomic distances in crystals? Would a crystal act as a three-dimensional diffraction grating forming spectra that could be recorded? If so, it would be possible to measure precisely the wave length of the x-rays employed, assuming interatomic spacing of the crystal; or assuming a wave length for the x-rays, measure the interplanar spacing of the crystal. Methods for making such an experiment were discussed, and Friedrich and Knipping, two research students, agreed to carry them out. Several experiments in which copper sulfate was used as the object crystal were unsuccessful. Finally they passed a narrow beam of x-rays through a cleavage plate of sphalerite, ZnS, allowing the beam to fall on a photographic plate. The developed plate showed a large number of small spots arranged in geometrical pattern around the large spot produced by the direct x-ray beam. This pattern was shown to be identical with that predictable from the diffraction of x-rays by a regular arrangement of scattering points within the crystal. Thus, a single experiment demonstrated the regular, orderly arrangement of atomic particles within crystals and the agreement as to order of magnitude of the wave length of x-rays with the interplanar spacing of crystals. Although largely replaced by more powerful means of x-ray investigation, this technique, the *Laue method*, is still in use.

Within the next few years, great strides were made as a result of the work of the English physicists, William Henry Bragg and William Lawrence Bragg, father and son. In 1914 the structure of the first compound, halite, NaCl, was worked out by the Braggs; and in the years following many more structures were solved by them. The Braggs also greatly simplified von Laue's mathematical generalizations as to the geometry of x-ray diffraction and popularized the results of their research through their well-written books on the subject.[1]

Electromagnetic waves form a continuous series varying in wavelength from long radio waves of wave lengths of the order of thousands of meters to cosmic radiation whose wave lengths are of the order of 10^{-12} meters (a millionth of a millionth of a meter!). All forms of electromagnetic radiation have certain properties in common such as propagation along straight lines at a speed of 300,000 meters per second in vacuum, reflection, refraction according to Snell's law, diffraction at edges and by slits or gratings, and a relation between

[1] W. H. Bragg and W. L. Bragg, *X-rays and Crystal Structures*, G. Bell and Sons, Ltd., London, 1924.

W. H. Bragg and W. L. Bragg, *The Crystalline State*, The Macmillan Company, New York, 1934.

W. H. Bragg, *An Introduction to Crystal Analysis*, G. Bell and Sons, Ltd., London, 1928.

W. L. Bragg, *Atomic Structure of Minerals*, Cornell University Press, Ithaca, New York, 1937.

energy and wave length given by Planck's law: $e = h\nu = hc/\lambda$, where e is energy, ν frequency, c velocity of propagation, λ wave length, and h Planck's constant. Thus, the shorter the wave the greater the energy involved in its production and the greater its powers of penetration. X-rays occupy only a small portion of the spectrum, with wave

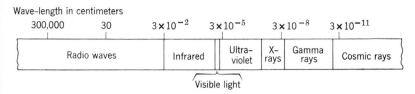

Wave-length in centimeters

Fig. 339. The Electromagnetic Spectrum.

lengths varying between slightly more than 100 Å and 0.02 Å. (See Fig. 339.) X-rays used in investigation of crystals have wave lengths of the order of 1 Å. Visible light has wave lengths between 7200 and 4000 Å, more than 1000 times as great, and hence is less penetrating and energetic than x-radiation.

When electrons moving at a high velocity strike the atoms of any element, x-rays are produced. Orbital electrons of the K, L, and M shells, deep within the extranuclear structure of the element being bombarded, are raised briefly to excited states by the energy contribution of the bombarding electrons. From these excited states the orbital electrons fall back to their ground, or stable, state, emitting quanta of energetic radiation in the process. This is x-radiation.

Early x-ray tubes were not much different from cathode-ray or discharge tubes and were essentially glass tubes fitted with opposing metal electrodes across which a high direct-current potential could be applied. In operation, the tube is evacuated until the pressure drops to about 0.01 millimeter of mercury. When the high voltage is applied, ionization of the remaining gas produces positive ions which are drawn to the cathode and bombard it, releasing electrons. These electrons are then accelerated by the high voltage to very high speeds and produce x-rays upon striking the anode, or target. In such tubes, called *gas tubes*, there is an interdependence between pressure, voltage, and current. Since the gas pressure drops as the tube operates, causing the character of the emitted x-rays to change, such tubes require considerable attention.

Because of these inherent disadvantages, the gas tube has been largely replaced by the Coolidge, or high-vacuum, tube. This tube is evacuated as completely as possible. The cathode is a tungsten filament which, upon being heated by passage of a current, evolves thermal electrons. Application of a high direct-current voltage accelerates these electrons, and the impact of the electrons on the positive anode, or target, generates the x-radiation. In these tubes, current and voltage are essentially independent, and the constant character of the x-rays may be maintained.

The nature of the x-rays depends on the metal of the target and the applied voltage. No x-rays are produced until the voltage reaches a certain minimum value dependent on the target material. At that point a continuous x-ray spectrum is generated. On increasing potential, the intensity of all wave lengths increases, and the value of the minimum wave length becomes progressively less (Fig. 340a). This continuous spectrum containing all wave lengths within a given range is analogous to white light in the visible spectrum and is called *white radiation*.

As the voltage across the tube is increased there becomes superimposed on the white radiation a *line spectrum* or *characteristic radiation* peculiar to the target material. This characteristic radiation, many times more intense than the white radiation, consists of several isolated wave lengths from which a single wave length may be selected by filtering. (Fig. 340b.) It is thus analogous to monochromatic light in the visible spectrum and is called *monochromatic x-radiation*.[1]

Following the original successful experiment with x-rays at Munich, von Laue worked out three equations (the Laue equations) to explain the observed diffraction phenomena. He showed that to produce a spot on a photographic plate three conditions must be simultaneously satisfied. Shortly thereafter, W. L. Bragg, working on x-ray diffraction in England, pointed out that, although x-rays are indeed diffracted by crystals, they act as though they were reflected from planes within the crystal. However, unlike the reflection of light, x-rays are not "reflected" continuously from a given crystal plane. Using a given wave length, λ, Bragg showed that a "reflection" took place from a given family of parallel planes only under certain conditions. These conditions must satisfy the equation: $n\lambda = 2d \sin \theta$ where n is an integer $(1, 2, 3, \cdots, n)$, λ the wave length, d the distance between successive parallel planes, and θ the angle of incidence and reflection

---

[1] The wave lengths of the characteristic x-radiation emitted by the various metals have been accurately determined. The $K\alpha$ wavelengths of those most commonly used are:

Molybdenum	0.7091 Å	Cobalt	1.7889
Copper	1.5405	Iron	1.9360
Nickel	1.6578	Chromium	2.2896

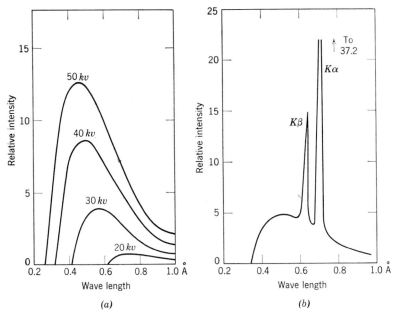

Fig. 340. X-ray Spectrum. (*a*) Distribution of intensity with wave length in the continuous x-ray spectrum of tungsten at various voltages. (*b*) Intensity curve showing characteristic wave length superimposed on the continuous x-ray spectrum of molybdenum. (After Ulrey, *Phys. Rev.*, **11**, 401.)

of the x-ray beam from the given atomic plane. This equation, known as the *Bragg law*, expresses in a simpler manner the simultaneous fulfillment of the three Laue equations.

DERIVATION OF THE BRAGG EQUATION

We have seen on page **7** that crystals are made up of atoms or groups of atoms having a periodic repetition at lattice points, and the faces most likely to appear on crystals are those parallel to atomic planes having the greatest density of these lattice points. Parallel to each is a family of equispaced identical planes. When an x-ray beam strikes a crystal it penetrates it, and the resulting "reflection" is not from a single plane but from an almost infinite number of parallel planes, each plane contributing a small bit to the total "reflection." In order that the "reflection" be of sufficient intensity to be recorded, the individual reflections must be in phase with one another. The following conditions necessary for reinforcement were demonstrated by W. L. Bragg.

In Fig. 341 the lines p, p_1, and p_2 represent the trace of a family of atomic planes with spacing d. X-rays striking any of these planes by itself would be reflected at the incident angle θ, whatever the value of θ. However, to reinforce one another in order to give a reflection that can be recorded, these reflected rays must be in phase. The path of the waves along DEF reflected at E is longer than the path of the wave along ABC reflected at B. If the two sets of waves are to be in phase, the path difference of ABC and DEF must be a whole number of wave

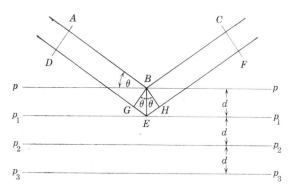

Fig. 341. Geometry of X-Ray Reflection.

lengths ($n\lambda$). In Fig. 341 BG and BH are drawn perpendicular to AB and BC respectively so that $AB = DG$ and $BC = HF$. To satisfy the condition that the two waves be in phase $GE + EH$ must be equal to an integral number of wave lengths. BE is perpendicular to the lines p and p_1 and is equal to the interplanar spacing d. In $\triangle GBE$, $d \sin \theta = GE$; and, in $\triangle HBE$, $d \sin \theta = EH$. Thus for in-phase reflection $GE + EH = 2d \sin \theta = n\lambda$.

This is the Bragg equation. For a given d spacing and given λ, reflections can take place only at those angles of θ which satisfy the equation. Suppose for example, a monochromatic x-ray beam is parallel to a cleavage plate of halite and the plate is supported in such a way that it can be rotated about an axis at right angles to the x-ray beam. As the halite is slowly rotated there is no reflection until the incident beam makes an angle θ which satisfies the Bragg equation, with $n = 1$. On continued rotation there are further reflections only when the equation is satisfied at certain θ angles with $n = 2, 3, 4, 5$, etc. These are known as the first-order, second-order, third-order, etc., reflections.

LAUE METHOD

In the Laue method a single crystal which remains stationary is used. A photographic plate or flat film, enclosed in a light-tight envelope is placed a known distance, usually 5 centimeters, from the crystal. A beam of white x-radiation is passed through the crystal at right angles to the photographic plate. The direct beam causes a darkening at the center of the photograph so that a small disc of lead is usually placed in front of the film to intercept and absorb it. The angle of incidence, θ, between the x-ray beam and the various atomic planes with their given d spacings within the crystal is fixed. How-

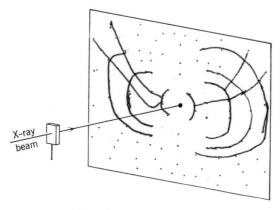

X-ray beam

Fig. 342. Laue Photograph.

ever, since x-rays of all wave lengths are present, the Bragg law, $n\lambda = 2d \sin \theta$, can be satisfied by each family of atomic planes provided $(2d \sin \theta)/n$ is within the range of wave lengths furnished by the tube. Around the central point of a Laue photograph are arranged diffraction spots, each one resulting from reflection of x-rays from a certain given series of atomic planes (Fig. 342).

The Laue method, although of great historical interest, has largely been replaced by other more powerful methods of x-ray crystal analysis. Its use today is primarily for determining symmetry. If a crystal is so oriented that the x-ray beam is parallel to a symmetry element, the arrangement of spots on the photograph reveals this symmetry. A Laue photograph of a mineral taken with the x-ray beam parallel to the 2-fold axis of a monoclinic crystal will show a 2-fold arrangement of spots; if the beam is parallel to the symmetry plane, the photograph shows a line of symmetry. A photograph of an orthorhombic crystal with the beam parallel to a crystallographic axis shows a 2-fold arrangement as well as two lines of symmetry. Figure 343 shows a 6-fold arrangement of spots as given by beryl with the x-ray beam parallel to the 6-fold symmetry axis.

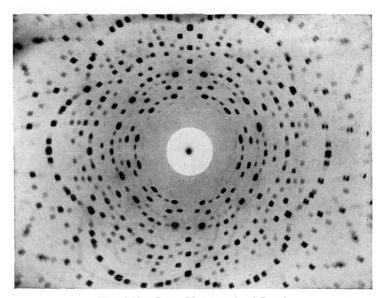

Fig. 343. Laue Photograph of Beryl.

ROTATION METHOD

In the rotation method and all refinements of it, a single crystal is used. The crystal must be oriented in such a fashion that it can be rotated around one of the principal crystallographic axes. If crystal faces are present orientation is effected most easily by means of an optical goniometer; without crystal faces orientation is possible but laborious. The camera is a cylinder of known diameter, coaxial with the axis of rotation of the crystal, and a photographic film, protected from the light by an envelope, is wrapped around the inside of the cylindrical camera. A beam of monochromatic x-rays enters the camera through a slit and strikes the crystal.

Under these conditions, with a stationary crystal, any reflection that occurs would be fortuitous. However, as the crystal is slowly rotated, various families of atomic planes will be brought into position, so that for them θ has a value that will, with known wave length, λ, satisfy $n\lambda = 2d \sin \theta$. A given family of planes gives rise to separate reflections when $n = 1, 2, 3, 4$, etc.

When a rotation photograph is developed (Fig. 344) and the film laid flat, there are found to be spots arranged in parallel rows, known as *layer lines*, at right angles to the axis of rotation of the crystal. Each spot is the result of reflection from a series of atomic planes, but, since the orientation of the crystal is not completely known, there is no easy way to identify the planes that gave rise to a particular spot.

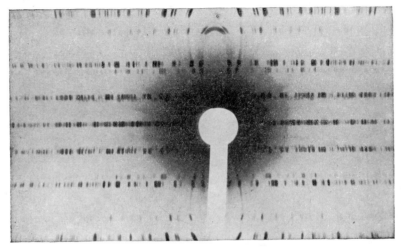

Fig. 344. Rotation Photograph of Scolecite.

Identification of the planes giving rise to reflections on an x-ray photograph is called *indexing*, because the planes are identified by Miller indices. Several modifications of the rotation method have been devised to permit complete indexing of the reflections. The methods most commonly used are the *oscillation* method, in which the range of rotation is limited so that the number of planes producing spots is sharply circumscribed; the *Weissenberg* method, in which the camera is translated to and fro during rotation so as to spread out the layer lines; and the *precession* method in which a flat film and the crystal both move in a complex gyratory motion to separate individual reflections for indexing. Consideration of these methods is beyond the scope of this discussion. However, valuable information can be obtained from a rotation photograph without identifying individual reflections.

We have learned that a crystal is built about a three-dimensional lattice with a characteristic periodicity or *identity period* along each of the crystallographic axes. We have also seen that this lattice acts as a three-dimensional grating in scattering x-rays. The scattering may be pictured as taking place independently along each of the principal rows of atoms parallel to the crystallographic axes, but, for a diffracted beam to be recorded on the photographic film, the scattering from rows in all three dimensions must be in phase.

Consider a single row of scattering points of periodicity c. (Fig. 345.) The scattered rays will reinforce each other when they are in phase, that is, when they have a path difference of an integral number of wave lengths. Thus, the in-phase scattering makes definite angles with the row of atoms dependent on the periodicity along the row and the wave length of x-rays.

In Fig. 346 rays 1 and 2 will be in phase only when $n\lambda = c \cos \phi$. For any value of $n\lambda$, ϕ is constant, and the diffracted rays form a cone with the row of points as axis. Since the scattered rays will be in phase for the same angle ϕ on the other side of the incident beam, there will be another similar but inverted cone on that side (Fig. 347). When $n = 0$, the cone is a plane which includes the incident beam. The greater the value of n the larger the value of ϕ, and hence the narrower the cones. All have the same axis however, and all have their vertices at the same point, the intersection of the incident beam and the row of atoms.

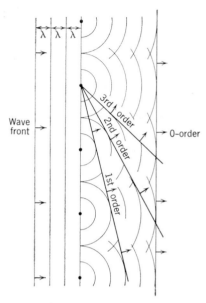

Fig. 345. Scattering of X-Rays by a Row of Atoms.

In a three-dimensional lattice there are two other axial directions, each with its characteristic periodicity of scattering points and each capable of generating its own series of nested cones with characteristic apical angles. Diffraction cones from the three rows of scattering atoms intersect each other, but only when all three intersect in a common line is there a diffracted beam (Fig. 348). This line of intersection is the direction of the beam which is recorded on the film. For all other possible directions, destructive interference takes place. When the three cones intersect in a common line, the Bragg law, $n\lambda = 2d \sin \theta$ is also satisfied.

In taking a rotation photograph, the crystal is rotated about one of the principal lattice rows, usually a crystallographic axis. This lattice row is at right angles to the incident x-ray beam. Consequently, whatever diffracted beams arise must lie along cones having axes in

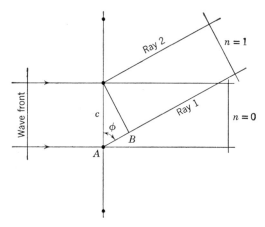

Fig. 346. Conditions for X-Ray Diffraction from a Row of Atoms.

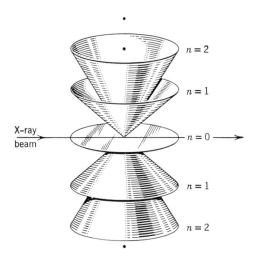

Fig. 347. Diffraction Cones from Row of Atoms.

common with the axis of rotation of the crystal. This axis is also the axis of the cylindrical film, and therefore the cones intersect the film in a series of circles (Fig. 349). When the film is laid flat the circles appear as straight parallel lines. Each of these is a *layer line*, which

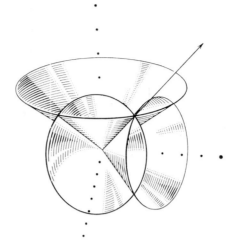

Fig. 348. Diffraction Cones from Three Rows of Scattering Atoms, Intersecting in a Common Line.

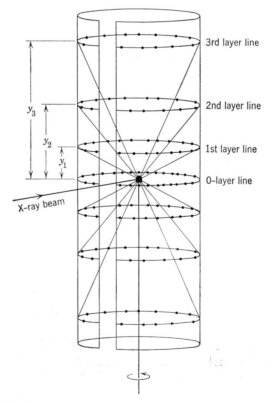

Fig. 349. Intersection of Diffraction Cones with Cylindrical Film.

corresponds to a cone of diffracted rays for which n has some integral value. Thus, the layer line including the incident beam is called the 0-layer, the first layer line is that for which $n = 1$, the next $n = 2$, and so on. The layer lines are not continuous since diffraction spots appear only where all three cones intersect.

The separation of the layer lines is determined by the cone angles, which are in turn dependent on the spacing in the lattice row about which the crystal was rotated. Therefore, if we know: (1) the diameter of the cylindrical film ($2r$), (2) the wave length of the x-rays

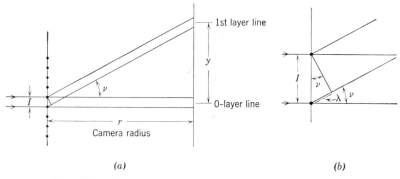

(a)   (b)

Fig. 350. Geometry for Calculation of Identity Period, I.

(λ), (3) the distance from the 0-layer to the nth layer on the film (y_n), it is possible to determine the spacing, or *identity period* (I), along the rotation axis of the crystal from the following relations:

$$\frac{y_n}{r} = \tan \nu \text{ (Fig. 350a)} \qquad I = \frac{n\lambda}{\sin \nu} \text{ (Fig. 350b)}$$

If rotation photographs are taken with the crystal rotating about each of the three crystallographic axes, it is possible to determine the unit-cell dimensions. The identity periods determined by rotating the crystal successively about the a, b, and c crystallographic axes are the edges of the unit cell, a_0, b_0, and c_0 respectively. This is true for a crystal of any symmetry. However, in the isometric system one photograph to determine a_0 suffices; in the tetragonal and hexagonal, two photographs are necessary, one about the c axis and one about an a axis.

POWDER METHOD

The relative rarity of well-formed crystals and the difficulty of making the precise orientation required by the Laue and rotating crystal methods led to the discovery of the *powder method* of x-ray investigation. For the powder method, the specimen is ground as finely as possible and bonded together by an amorphous material, such as flexible collodion, into a needlelike spindle 0.2 to 0.3 millimeter in diameter. This spindle, the *powder mount*, consists ideally of crystalline particles in completely random orientation. To insure randomness of orientation of these tiny particles with respect to the impinging x-ray beam, the mount is generally rotated in the path of the beam during the exposure.

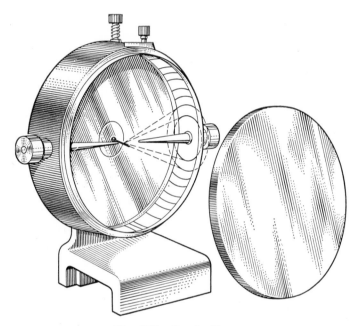

Fig. 351. Powder Camera.

The powder camera is a flat, disc-shaped box like a round biscuit tin with an adjustable pin at the center for attachment of the mount. The cylindrical wall of the camera is pierced diametrically for a demountable slit system and opposing beam catcher. The light-tight lid may be removed to insert and remove the film, which, for the most popular type of camera, is a narrow strip about 14 inches long and 1 inch wide. Two holes are punched in the film and so located that, when the film is fitted snugly to the inner curve of the camera, the slit tube and beam catcher pass through the holes. This type of mounting is called the Straumanis method (Fig. 351).

A narrow beam of monochromatic x-rays is allowed to pass through the collimating slit and fall on the spindle-shaped mount, which is carefully centered on the short axis of the camera so that the mount remains in the x-ray beam as it rotates during the exposure. The undeviated beam passes through and around the mount and enters the lead-lined beam catcher, through which it leaves the camera.

When the beam of monochromatic x-rays strikes the mount, all possible diffractions take place simultaneously. If the orientation of the crystalline particles in the mount is truly random, for each family

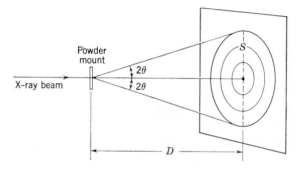

Fig. 352. X-Ray Diffraction from Powder Mount Recorded on a Flat Plate.

of atomic planes with its characteristic d spacing, there are many particles whose orientation is such that they make the proper θ angle with the incident beam to satisfy the Bragg law, $n\lambda = 2d \sin \theta$. The reflections from a given set of planes form cones with the incident beam as axis and the internal angle 4θ. Any set of atomic planes yields a series of nested cones corresponding to reflections of the first, second, third and higher orders ($n = 1, 2, 3 \ldots$). Different families of planes with different d spacings will satisfy the Bragg law at appropriate values of θ for different integral values of n, thus giving rise to separate sets of nested cones of reflected rays.

If the rays forming these cones are permitted to fall on a flat photographic plate at right angles to the incident beam, a series of concentric circles will result (Fig. 352). However, only reflections with small values of the angle 2θ can be recorded in this manner.

In order to record reflections of 2θ up to $180°$, the film is fitted snugly into a cylindrical camera at the axis of which the specimen is mounted in the path of the x-ray beam. Under these conditions, the film intercepts the cones of reflected rays along curved lines (Fig. 353). Since the axes of the cones coincide with the x-ray beam, for each cone there will be two curved lines on the film symmetrically disposed on each side of the slit through which the x-rays leave the camera. The angular distance between these two arcs is 4θ.

When the film is developed and laid flat, the arcs are seen to have their centers at the two holes in the film. Reflections of low θ have their center at the exit hole through which the beam catcher passes through the film. Going out from this point, the arcs are of increasing radius until at $2\theta = 90°$ they are straight lines. Lines made by reflections with $2\theta > 90°$ curve in the opposite direction and are concentric about the hole through which the x-rays enter the camera. These are known as *back reflections*.

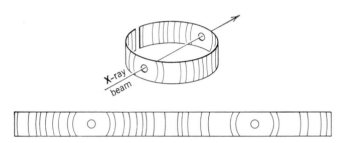

Fig. 353. X-Ray Diffraction from Powder Mount Recorded on Cylindrical Film.

If a flat film is used and the distance D from the specimen to the film is known, it is possible to calculate θ by measuring S, the diameter of the rings. It may be seen in Fig. 352 that $\tan 2\theta = S/2D$. When a cylindrical camera is used, the distance S is measured with the film laid flat. Under these conditions, $S = R \times 4\theta$ in radians[1] or $\theta = S/4R$ in radians where R is the radius of the camera and S is measured in the same units as R. Most powder cameras are constructed with a radius such that S, measured in millimeters on the flat film can be converted easily to θ. For example, when the radius of the camera is 57.3 millimeters, the circumference is 360 millimeters. Using such a camera, each millimeter measured along the film is equal to $1°$. Hence, a distance S of 60 millimeters measured on the film is equal to $60° = 4\theta$, and θ is accordingly equal to $15°$.

It is not possible to measure the symmetrical distance S for values of θ much in excess of $40°$ ($S = 160$ millimeters) on two-hole films of the Straumanis type. In order to obtain θ for lines of θ higher than about $40°$, the center about which the low θ lines are concentric must first be found by measurement of a number of such lines. Then the distance $S/2$ may be measured. It must be borne in mind that, if

[1] One radian $= 57.3°$.

the camera radius is not 57.3 degrees, a correction factor must be applied. Thus, if a camera having a radius of 28.65 millimeters is used, the correction factor is $57.3/28.65 = 2$, and all S values measured must be divided by 2 to obtain θ in degrees.

The Straumanis method, the type of mounting described with two holes in the film, is now widely used. In older type powder cameras the x-ray beam entered between the ends of the cylindrical film and left through a centered hole. The Straumanis camera has the advantage that the effective diameter of the film can be calculated from film measurements. During the process of developing, the film usually shrinks and thus for accurate work the diameter of the camera is disregarded and the effective diameter of the film is used in making calculations.

When the reflecting angle θ corresponding to a given line on a powder photograph has been determined, it is possible to calculate the interplanar spacing of the family of atomic planes that gave rise to the reflection by use of the Bragg equation $n\lambda = 2d \sin \theta$, or $d = n\lambda/(2 \sin \theta)$. Since it is usually impossible to tell the order of a given reflection, n in the formula above is generally given the value 1, and d is determined in every case as though the line was produced by a first-order reflection. For substances crystallizing in the isometric, tetragonal, hexagonal, and orthorhombic systems, it is possible to index the lines of a powder photograph and thus determine cell dimensions and axial ratios. This method is little used except for crystals of the isometric system and is impossible for crystals of the monoclinic and triclinic systems.

The powder method finds its chief use in mineralogy as a determinative tool. One can use it for this purpose without knowing anything of the crystal structure or symmetry. Every crystalline substance produces its own powder pattern, which, since it is dependent on the internal structure, is characteristic for that substance. The powder photograph is often spoken of as the "fingerprint" of a mineral, since it differs from the powder pattern of every other mineral. Thus, if an unknown mineral is suspected of being the same as a known mineral, powder photographs of both are taken. If the photographs correspond exactly line for line, the two minerals are identical. Many organizations maintain extensive files of standard photographs of known minerals, and by comparison, an unknown mineral may be identified readily if there is some indication as to its probable nature.

However, one is frequently completely at a loss as to the identity of the unknown mineral, and a systematic comparison with the thousands of photographs in the reference file would be too time consuming. When this happens, the investigator turns to the card file of x-ray diffraction data prepared by the American Society for Testing Materials (ASTM). (Fig. 354.) On these cards there are recorded the d spacings for thousands of crystalline substances, just as the fingerprints of known criminals are kept in the fingerprint files of law-enforcement agencies. In order to use the cards, the investigator must calculate the d spacings for the most prominent lines in the powder pattern of his unknown substance and estimate the relative intensity of the lines on a scale where the strongest line is taken as 100. Then he may seek a corresponding series of d's in the ASTM file cards,

d	3.35	4.26	1.37	4.26	α-SiO$_2$		α-SiO$_2$
I/I_1	100	80	80	80	Silicon dioxide, alpha		α-Quartz

Left data column			dÅ	I/I_1	hkl	dÅ	I/I_1	hkl
Rad. λ 1.5405 Filter			4.26	80		1.26	40	
Dia. Cut off Coll.			3.72B	30		1.23	20	
I/I_1 B d corr. abs.?			3.35	100		1.20	40	
Ref.			2.46	60		1.18	50	
J. Ch. L. Favejee, Z. Krist. 100, 430 (1939)			2.28	60		1.15	30	
Sys. Hex. (Rhomb. Div.) S.G. D$_6^4$,C3$_1$2; D$_3^6$,C3$_2$2			2.24	30		1.08	40	
a_0 4.903 b_0 c_0 5.393 A C 1.100			2.13	50		1.05	30	
α β γ Z 3			1.98	40		1.04	30	
Ref. B			1.82	70+		1.02	30	
J. Ch. L. Favejee, Z. Krist. 100, 430 (1939)			1.67	50		0.988	40	
8α nωβ* 1.5448 γ 1.55337 Sign +			1.54	70				
2V D 2.653 mp Color Various			1.45	20				
Ref. C.C. 2.654 Colorless in section			1.42	10				
Wn			1.37	80				
No calculations			1.29	30				
Transition to β at 573°								
*Sodium light								

Fig. 354. ASTM Card for Quartz. At the top of the card the three strongest lines and their relative intensities are given. The fourth d is of the greatest spacing.

which are arranged in order of d of the most intense line. Since many substances have intense lines corresponding to the same d value and since many factors may operate to change the relative intensity of the lines in a powder pattern, all substances are cross-indexed for their second and third most intense lines. After the most likely "suspects" have been selected from the file, comparison of the weaker reflections, which are also listed on the ASTM card, will speedily identify the substance in most cases. In this way a completely unknown substance may generally be identified in a short time, by means of a nondestructive test on a very small volume of sample.

The powder method is of wider usefulness, however, and there are several other applications in which it is of great value. Variations in chemical composition of a known substance involve the substitution of atoms, generally of a somewhat different size, for atoms properly occurring in certain sites in the lattice. As a result of this substitution the cell dimensions and hence the interplanar spacings are slightly changed, and the positions of the lines on the powder photograph corresponding to these interplanar spacings are accordingly shifted. By measuring these small shifts in position of the lines in powder patterns of substances of known structure, changes in chemical composition may often be accurately detected.

Further, the relative proportions of two or more known minerals in a mixture may be often determined conveniently by the comparison of the intensities of the lines in the mixture with the intensities of the same lines in photographs of prepared controls of known composition.

X-RAY DIFFRACTOMETER

In recent years the usefulness of the powder method has been greatly increased and its field of application extended by the introduction of the *x-ray diffractometer*. This powerful research tool uses monochromatic x-radiation and a finely powdered sample, as does the powder-film method, but records the information as to the reflections present as an inked trace on a printed strip chart. The equipment supplied by one manufacturer is shown in Fig. 355.

The sample is prepared for diffractometer analysis by grinding to a fine powder, which powder is then spread uniformly over the surface of a glass slide, using a small amount of adhesive binder. The instrument is so constructed that this slide, when clamped in place, rotates in the path of a collimated x-ray beam while a Geiger tube, mounted on an arm, rotates about it to pick up the reflected x-ray beams.

When the instrument is set at the zero position, the x-ray beam is parallel to the slide and passes directly into the Geiger tube. The slide mount and Geiger tube are driven by a motor through separate gear trains so that, while the slide and specimen rotate through the angle θ, the Geiger tube rotates through 2θ. The purpose of this arrangement is to maintain such a relation among x-ray source, sample, and Geiger tube that no reflections are cut off by the glass slide.

If the specimen has been properly prepared, there will be thousands of tiny crystalline particles on the slide in random orientation. As in powder photography, all possible reflections from atomic planes take place simultaneously. However, instead of recording all of them on a film at one time, the Geiger tube receives each reflection separately.

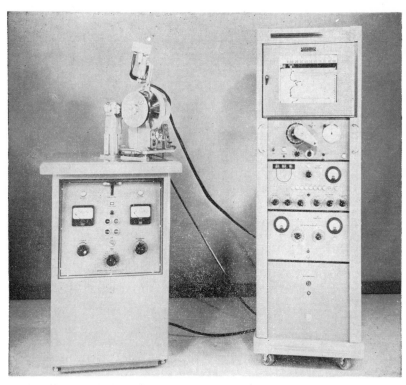

Fig. 355. X-ray Diffractometer. Courtesy of Philips Electronics Co., Inc., Mt. Vernon, N. Y.

In operation, the sample, the Geiger tube, and the paper drive of the strip chart recorder are all set in motion simultaneously. If an atomic plane has a d spacing such that a reflection occurs at $\theta = 20°$, there is no evidence of this reflection until the Geiger tube has been rotated through 2θ, or $40°$. At this point the reflected beam enters the tube causing it to conduct. The current pulse thus generated is amplified and causes a deflection on the recording strip chart. Thus, as the Geiger tube scans, the strip chart records as peaks the reflections from the specimen. The angle 2θ at which the reflection occurred may be read directly from the position of the peak on the strip chart. The heights of the peaks are directly proportional to the intensities of the reflections causing them.

The chart on which the record is drawn is divided in tenths of inches and moves at a constant speed, generally 0.5 inch per minute. At this chart speed and a scanning speed of the Geiger tube of 1° per minute, 0.5 inch on the chart is equivalent to a 2θ of 1°. The positions

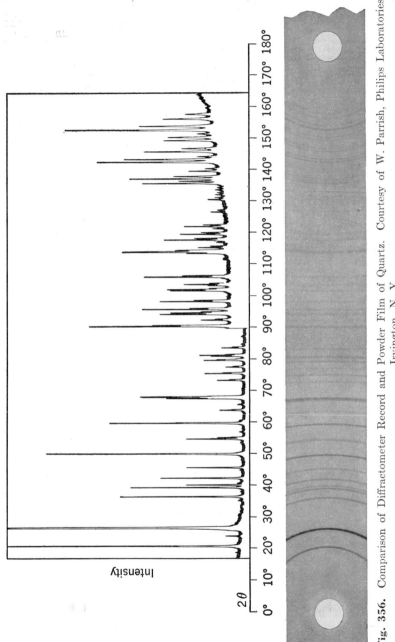

Fig. 356. Comparison of Diffractometer Record and Powder Film of Quartz. Courtesy of W. Parrish, Philips Laboratories, Irvington, N. Y.

of the peaks on the chart can be read easily to a 2θ of $0.05°$, and d spacings of the atomic planes giving rise to them can be determined by use of the equation $n\lambda = 2d \sin \theta$. As in powder photography, the reflections are all considered as first order, unless the record is to be indexed with a view to determining the cell constants.

Although the diffractometer yields data similar to those derived from a powder photograph, it has definite advantages. The powder method requires several hours of exposure plus the time necessary for developing, fixing, washing, and drying the film; a diffractometer run can be made in 1 hour. It is frequently difficult to estimate the intensity of the lines on a powder photograph, whereas the height of peaks on a diffractometer chart can be determined graphically with good precision. The powder photograph must be carefully measured to obtain 2θ values, whereas 2θ can be read directly from the diffractometer strip chart. Figure 356 compares a diffractometer strip chart with a powder photograph of the same mineral and indicates how the data may be used to enter the ASTM card file.

REFERENCES

Geometrical Crystallography

F. C. Phillips, *An introduction to crystallography.* Longmans, Green and Co., New York, 1956.

M. J. Buerger, *Elementary crystallography.* John Wiley and Sons, New York, 1956. A rigorous treatment of geometrical crystallography from the standpoint of symmetry.

C. W. Wolfe, *Manual for geometrical crystallography.* Edwards Brothers, Ann Arbor, 1953.

G. Tunnell and J. Murdoch, *Laboratory manual of crystallography for students of mineralogy and geology.* Wm. C. Brown Co., Dubuque, 1957.

X-ray Crystallography

H. P. Klug and L. E. Alexander, *X-ray diffraction procedures for polycrystalline and amorphous material.* John Wiley and Sons, New York, 1954, Chapter 5. A discussion of the use of the diffractometer.

L. V. Azaroff and M. J. Buerger, *The powder method in x-ray crystallography.* McGraw-Hill Book Co., New York, 1958. An exhaustive treatment of the powder method.

K. Lonsdale, *Crystals and x-rays.* G. Bell and Sons, London, 1948. A readable account of the various x-ray methods.

C. W. Bunn, *Chemical crystallography.* Clarendon Press, Oxford, 1946. Chapters 5 and 6 deal with the powder and rotation methods.

W. H. Bragg and W. L. Bragg, *X-ray and crystal structure.* G. Bell and Sons, London, 1924, pp. 103–188.

3

PHYSICAL MINERALOGY

The physical properties are highly important in the rapid determination of minerals, since most of them can be recognized at sight or determined by simple tests.

A. CLEAVAGE, PARTING, AND FRACTURE

1. **Cleavage.** If a mineral, when the proper force is applied, breaks so that it yields definite plane surfaces, it is said to possess a *cleavage*. Cleavage may be perfect as in the micas, more or less obscure as in beryl and apatite or, as in some minerals, lacking altogether.

Cleavage is dependent on the crystal structure and takes place only parallel to atomic planes. If a family of parallel atomic planes has a weak binding force between them, cleavage is likely to take place along these planes. This weakness may be due to a weaker type of bond, to a greater lattice spacing in the crystal at right angles to the cleavage, or frequently to a combination of the two. Graphite has a platy cleavage. Within the plates there is a strong bond, but across the plates there is a weak bond giving rise to the cleavage. A weak bond is usually accompanied by a large lattice spacing since the attractive force can not hold the planes closely together. Diamond

Fig. 357. Cleavage. (*a*) Galena {001}; (*b*) Fluorite {111}; (*c*) Sphalerite {011}; (*d*) Calcite {10$\bar{1}$1}; (*e*) Barite {001}, {110}; (*f*) Topaz {001}; (*g*) Feldspar {001}, {010}; (*h*) Scapolite {110} and minor {010}.

has but one bond type, and its excellent cleavage takes place along those lattice planes having the largest spacing. (See Fig. 398.)

Because cleavage is the breaking of a crystal between atomic planes, it is a directional property, and any parallel plane through the crystal is a potential cleavage plane. Moreover, it is always parallel to crystal faces or possible crystal faces (usually those with simplest indices), since both faces and cleavage reflect the same crystal structure.

In describing a cleavage its quality, ease of production, and crystallographic direction should all be given. The quality is expressed as perfect, good, fair, etc. The direction is expressed by the name or indices of the form which the cleavage parallels, as cubic {001} (Fig. 357), octahedral {111}, rhombohedral {10$\bar{1}$1}, prismatic {110}, pinacoidal {001}, etc. Cleavage is always consistent with the symmetry; thus, if one octahedral cleavage direction is developed, it implies that there must be three other directions similar to it. If one dodecahedral cleavage direction is present, it likewise implies five other, similar directions. Not all minerals show cleavage, and only a comparatively few show it in an eminent degree, but in these it serves as an outstanding diagnostic criterion.

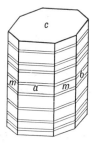

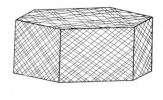

Fig. 358. Basal Parting of Pyroxene.

Fig. 359. Rhombohedral Parting of Corundum.

2. Parting. Certain minerals when subjected to stress or pressure develop planes of structural weakness along which they may subsequently be broken. Twin crystals, especially polysynthetic twins, may separate easily along the composition planes. When plane surfaces are produced on a mineral by its breaking along some such predetermined plane, it is said to have a *parting*. This phenomenon resembles cleavage but is to be distinguished from it by the fact that not every specimen of a certain mineral will exhibit it, but only those specimens which are twinned or have been subjected to the proper pressure. Even in these specimens there are only a certain number of planes in a given direction along which the mineral will break. If a mineral possesses cleavage, every specimen will, in general, show it, and it can be produced in a given direction in all parts of a crystal. Familiar examples of parting are found in the octahedral parting of magnetite, the basal parting of pyroxene, and the rhombohedral parting of corundum (see Figs. 358 and 359).

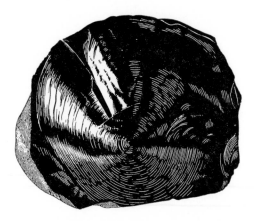

Fig. 360. Conchoidal Fracture in Obsidian.

3. Fracture. By the fracture of a mineral is meant the way in which it breaks when it does not yield along cleavage or parting surfaces.

The following terms are commonly used to designate different kinds of fracture:

a. Conchoidal. When the fracture has smooth, curved surfaces like the interior surface of a shell (see Fig. 360). This is most commonly observed in such substances as glass and quartz.

b. Fibrous or Splintery. When the mineral breaks showing splinters or fibers.

c. Hackly. When the mineral breaks with a jagged, irregular surface with sharp edges.

d. Uneven or Irregular. When the mineral breaks into rough and irregular surfaces.

B. HARDNESS

The resistance that a smooth surface of a mineral offers to scratching is its *hardness* (designated by **H**). Like the other physical properties of minerals, hardness is dependent on the crystal structure. The stronger the binding forces between the atoms, the harder the mineral. The degree of hardness is determined by observing the comparative ease or difficulty with which one mineral is scratched by another, or by a file or knife. The hardness of a mineral might then be said to be its "scratchability." A series of ten common minerals has been chosen as a scale, by comparison with which the relative hardness of any mineral can be told. The following minerals arranged in order of increasing hardness comprise what is known as the *Mohs scale of hardness:*

Scale of Hardness

1. Talc	6. Orthoclase
2. Gypsum	7. Quartz
3. Calcite	8. Topaz
4. Fluorite	9. Corundum
5. Apatite	10. Diamond

Talc, number 1 in the scale, has a structure made up of plates so weakly bound to one another that the pressure of the fingers is sufficient to slide one plate over the other. At the other end of the scale is diamond with its constituent carbon atoms so firmly bound to each other that no other mineral can force them apart to cause a scratch.

In order to determine the relative hardness of any mineral in terms of this scale, it is necessary to find which of these minerals it can and which it cannot scratch. In making the determination, the following should be observed: Sometimes when one mineral is softer than another, portions of the first will leave a mark on the second which may be mistaken for a scratch. It can be rubbed off, however, whereas a true scratch will be permanent. Some minerals are frequently altered on the surface to material which is much softer than the original mineral. A fresh surface of the specimen to be tested should therefore be used. The physical nature of a mineral may prevent a correct determination of its hardness. For instance, if a mineral is pulverulent, granular, or splintery, it may be broken down and apparently scratched by a mineral much softer than itself. It is always advisable when making the hardness test to confirm it by reversing the order of procedure; that is, do not always try to scratch mineral *A* by mineral *B*, but also try to scratch *B* by *A*.

The following materials may serve in addition to the above scale: the hardness of the finger nail is a little over 2, a copper coin about 3, the steel of a pocket knife a little over 5, window glass $5\frac{1}{2}$, and the steel of a file $6\frac{1}{2}$. With a little practice, the hardness of minerals

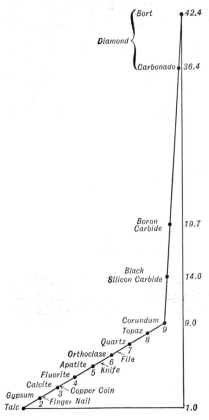

Fig. 361. Relative Hardness of Minerals in the Scale of Hardness (after Wooddell).

under 5 can be quickly estimated by the ease with which they can be scratched with a pocket knife.

Hardness, we have seen, is dependent on the structure of the mineral. Since the strength of the forces holding the atoms together differs in different directions, hardness is a vectorial property. Thus crystals may show varying degrees of hardness depending on the directions in which they are scratched. The directional hardness differences in most common minerals are so slight that, if they can be detected at all, it is only through the use of delicate instruments. Two exceptions are kyanite and calcite. In kyanite $\mathbf{H} = 5$ parallel to the length, but $\mathbf{H} = 7$ across the length. The hardness of calcite is 3 on all surfaces except {0001}. On this form, however, it can be scratched by the fingernail and has a hardness of 2.

It can be seen that only within relatively wide limits can one be quantitative in the determination of hardness. Moreover, the interval of hardness between different pairs of minerals in the scale varies. For instance, the hardness difference between corundum and diamond is many times greater than that between topaz and corundum. Figure 361 is based on quantitative data obtained by one investigator, who determined that, if quartz is 7 and corundum is 9 in hardness on an absolute scale, diamond would be 42.4.

C. TENACITY

The resistance that a mineral offers to breaking, crushing, bending, or tearing—in short, its cohesiveness—is known as tenacity. The following terms are used to describe various kinds of tenacity in minerals:

1. *Brittle.* A mineral that breaks or powders easily.
2. *Malleable.* A mineral that can be hammered out into thin sheets.
3. *Sectile.* A mineral that can be cut into thin shavings with a knife.
4. *Ductile.* A mineral that can be drawn into wire.
5. *Flexible.* A mineral that bends but does not resume its original shape when the pressure is released.
6. *Elastic.* A mineral that after being bent, will resume its original position upon the release of the pressure.

D. SPECIFIC GRAVITY

The *specific gravity* (**G**) or relative density[1] of a mineral is a number that expresses the ratio between its weight and the weight of an equal volume of water at $4°$ C. If a mineral has a specific gravity of 2, it means that a given specimen of that mineral weighs twice as much as the same volume of water. The specific gravity of a mineral of fixed composition is frequently an important aid in its identification, particularly in working with fine crystals or gemstones, when other tests would injure the specimens.

The specific gravity of a crystalline substance is dependent on two factors: (1) the kind of atoms of which it is composed, and (2) the manner in which the atoms are packed together. In isostructural compounds (see page 199), in which the packing is constant, those with elements of higher atomic weight will usually have the higher specific gravity. This is well shown by the orthorhombic carbonates listed below in which the chief difference lies in the cations.

Specific Gravity Change with Change in Cation

Mineral	Composition	At. Wt. of Cation	Specific Gravity
Aragonite	$CaCO_3$	40.08	2.95
Strontianite	$SrCO_3$	87.63	3.7
Witherite	$BaCO_3$	137.36	4.3
Cerussite	$PbCO_3$	207.21	6.55

Many pairs of isostructural minerals form solid-solution series (see page 204) in which the composition may vary continuously. In

[1] *Density* and specific gravity are sometimes used interchangeably. However, *density* requires the citation of units, for example, grams per cubic centimeter or pounds per cubic foot.

such series there is a continuous change in specific gravity. For example, the mineral olivine is a solid-solution series between forsterite, Mg_2SiO_4 (**G** 3.2), and fayalite, Fe_2SiO_4 (**G** 4.4). Thus from determination of specific gravity one can obtain a close approximation of the chemical composition.

The influence of the packing of atoms on specific gravity is well illustrated in polymorphous compounds (see page 174). In these compounds the composition remains constant, but the packing of the atoms varies. The most dramatic example is given by diamond and graphite, both elemental carbon. Diamond with specific gravity 3.5 has a closely packed structure, giving a high density of atoms per unit volume; whereas in graphite, specific gravity 2.2, the carbon atoms are loosely packed.

Average specific gravity. Most people in handling objects of everyday experience acquire a sense of relative weight. With but little experience a similar sense is developed in regard to minerals. For example, ulexite (**G** 1.96) seems light, whereas barite (**G** 4.5) seems heavy for nonmetallic minerals. This means that one has developed an idea of an average specific gravity or a feeling of what a nonmetallic mineral of a given size should weigh. This average specific gravity can be considered to be between 2.65 and 2.75. The reason for this is that quartz (**G** 2.65), feldspar (**G** 2.60–2.75), and calcite (**G** 2.71), the most common and abundant nonmetallic minerals, fall mostly within this range. The same sense may be developed in regard to metallic minerals. Graphite (**G** 2.2) seems light, while silver (**G** 10.5) seems heavy. The average specific gravity for metallic minerals can be considered about 5.0, that of pyrite. Thus, with a little practice, one can become expert enough to distinguish from each other minerals that have comparatively small differences in specific gravity, by merely lifting a specimen.

In order to determine accurately the specific gravity of a mineral several conditions must be observed. The mineral must be pure, a requirement frequently difficult to fulfill. It must also be compact with no cracks or cavities within which bubbles or films of air could be imprisoned. For normal mineralogical work, the specimen should have a volume of about one-eighth of a cubic inch; this would be a cube one-half an inch on a side. If these conditions cannot be met, a specific-gravity determination by any rapid and simple method means little.

The necessary steps in making an ordinary specific-gravity determination are briefly as follows: The mineral is first weighed in air. Let this weight be represented by W_a. It is then immersed in water and weighed again. Under these conditions it weighs less, since any object immersed in water is buoyed up by a force equivalent to the weight of the water displaced. Let the weight in water be represented by W_w. Then $W_a - W_w$ equals the loss of weight caused by immersion in water, or the weight of an equal volume of water. The expression $W_a/(W_a - W_w)$ will therefore yield a number which is the specific gravity of the mineral. Since specific gravity is merely a ratio, it is not necessary to determine the absolute weight of the specimen but merely some value that is proportional to the weight.

Jolly balance. One of the best methods of obtaining the specific gravity of a mineral is by means of a *Jolly balance*, Fig. 362, in which the data for making the calculations are obtained by measuring the stretching of a spiral spring. From the spring are suspended two small pans, c and d, one above the other. The apparatus is so arranged that the lower pan, d, is always immersed in a beaker of water which, resting upon the adjustable platform B, can be placed at the required height. In all types of Jolly balances it is necessary to adjust the apparatus so that the index on the spring is at zero with the lower pan immersed in water. The mineral is then placed in the upper pan, and the stretching of the spring, W_a, necessary to bring the indicator to zero again, is determined by means of an affixed scale. The specimen is then placed in the lower pan, another adjustment is made, and W_w reading taken. The specific gravity is then calculated by:

$$\mathbf{G} = \frac{W_a}{W_a - W_w}$$

Figure 363 represents an improved type of Jolly balance devised by Kraus. The description of it by its manufacturer[1] is as follows:

The balance consists of an upright tube to which the inner, fixed vernier and the movable, double graduated scale are attached. This tube contains a round tube which can be moved by a large milled head. To this second tube, the outer, movable vernier is fastened. A movement of the round tube upward carries the second vernier and the graduated scale with it. Within the round tube there is a rod of adjustable length, which carries the spiral spring, index, and scale pans. With this form of balance only two readings and a simple division are necessary to determine the specific gravity.

In using the balance it is necessary that the graduated scale, the two verniers, and the index, which is attached to the spiral spring, all be at zero, the lower scale pan being immersed in water. This is accomplished by adjusting approximately by hand the length of the rod carrying the spring and then introducing the necessary correction by means of the micrometer screw. A fragment is then placed on the upper scale pan, and by the turning of the large milled head, the round tube, graduated scale, and outer vernier are all

[1] Manufactured by Eberbach and Son, Ann Arbor, Michigan.

driven upward until the index on the spring is again at zero. The fixed inner vernier, W, now records the elongation of the spring due to the weight of the fragment in the air. The scale is then clamped by means of the screw at the lower end of it. The fragment is now transferred to the lower scale pan and immersed in water, and the round tube is lowered by the large milled head

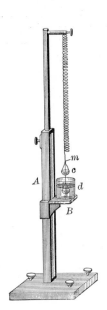

Fig. 362. Jolly Balance.

Fig. 363. Improved Jolly Balance.

until the index again reads at zero. During this operation the outer vernier moves downward on the graduated scale and its position may now be indicated by L. This is obviously the decrease in the elongation of spring due to the immersion of the fragment in water. The readings at W and L are all the data necessary for the calculation of the specific gravity.

$$\text{Specific gravity} = \frac{\text{Weight in air}}{\text{Loss of weight in water}} = \frac{L}{W}$$

It is also obvious that these readings are recorded so that they may be checked, if necessary, after the operation and calculation are completed.

A delicate torsion balance has been adapted by H. Berman for taking specific gravities of small single particles weighing less than 25 milligrams (Fig. 364).[1] To the advanced worker in mineralogy interested in accurate determination of specific gravity this balance is particu-

[1] This balance is distributed through Bethlehem Instrument Company, Bethlehem, Pennsylvania.

larly helpful, since frequently it is possible to obtain only a tiny mineral fragment free from impurities. In using it, however, one must make correction for temperature and use a liquid with a low surface tension.

Fig. 364. Berman Balance.

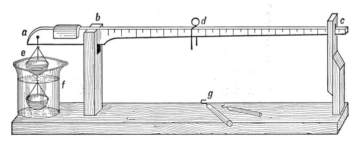

Fig. 365. Beam Balance.

Beam balance. The beam balance is a very convenient and accurate instrument for determining specific gravity. Moreover, owing to its simplicity, it can be easily and inexpensively constructed at home. The balance illustrated in Fig. 365 was devised by S. L. Penfield, whose description of its operation, slightly modified, is as follows:

The beam made of wood or brass is supported at b on a fine wire or needle, which permits it to swing freely. The long arm bc is divided into a decimal scale; the short arm carries a double arrangement of pans so suspended that one of them is in air and the other in water. A piece of lead on the short arm serves to almost counterbalance the long arm. When the pans are empty, the beam is brought to a horizontal position, marked upon the upright near c, by means of a rider d. A number of counterpoises are needed; but, since it is their position on the beam and not their actual weight that is recorded, they need not be of any specific denomination. After the beam is adjusted by means of the rider d, a mineral fragment is placed in the upper pan and a counterpoise is chosen which, when placed near the end of the long arm, will bring it into a horizontal position. A value, W_a, proportional to the weight of the mineral in air, is given by the position of the counterpoise on the scale. The mineral is next transferred to the lower pan, and the same counterpoise is brought nearer the fulcrum b until the beam becomes horizontal again. The position of the counterpoise now gives a value, W_w, proportional to the weight of the mineral in water. The specific gravity can then be determined as follows:

$$G = \frac{W_a}{W_a - W_w}$$

Pycnometer. When a mineral cannot be obtained in a homogeneous mass large enough to permit use of one of the balance methods, the

specific gravity of a powder or an aggregate of mineral fragments can be accurately obtained by means of the *pycnometer*. The pycnometer is a small bottle (Fig. 366) fitted with a ground-glass stopper through which a capillary opening has been drilled.

In making a specific-gravity determination, the dry bottle with stopper is first weighed empty (P). The mineral fragments are then introduced into the bottle and a second weighing (M) is made. The bottle is partially filled with distilled water and boiled for a few minutes to drive off any air bubbles. After cooling, the pycnometer is filled with distilled water and weighed (S), care being taken that the water rises to the top of the capillary opening but that no excess water is present. The last weighing (W) is made after emptying the bottle and refilling with distilled water alone. The specific gravity can thus be determined:

Fig. 366.
Pycnometer.

$$G = \frac{M - P}{W + M - P - S}$$

Heavy liquids. Several liquids with relatively high specific gravities are sometimes used in the determination of the specific gravity of minerals. The two liquids most easily used are bromoform (**G** 2.89) and methylene iodide (**G** 3.33). These liquids are miscible with one another and also with acetone (**G** 0.79), and thus, by mixing, a solution of any intermediate specific gravity may be obtained. A mineral grain is introduced into the heavy liquid, and the solution is diluted with a liquid of lesser specific gravity until the mineral neither rises nor sinks. The specific gravity of the liquid and the mineral are then the same, and that of the liquid may be quickly determined by means of a Westphal balance.

Heavy liquids are frequently used in the separation of mineral grains from mixtures composed of several constituents.

Calculation of specific gravity. If one knows the number of the various kinds of atoms in the unit cell and the volume of the unit cell, the specific gravity can be calculated. The chemical formula of the mineral gives the proportions of the different atoms but not necessarily the exact number, for some minerals have several formula weights per cell. The number, usually small, is indicated by $-Z$. For example, in aragonite, $CaCO_3$, the ratios of the atoms is $1Ca : 1C : 3O$, but there are four formula weights per cell or 4Ca, 4C, 12O. The molecular weight, M, of $CaCO_3$ is 100.09; the molecular weight of the contents of the unit cell ($Z = 4$) is $4 \times 100.09 = 400.36$.

The volume of the unit cell, V, in the orthogonal crystal systems is found by multiplying the cell dimensions, as $a_o \times b_o \times c_o = V$. In the inclined systems the angles between cell edges must also be considered in obtaining the volume. Aragonite is orthorhombic with cell dimensions: $a_o = 4.95$ Å, $b_o = 7.96$, $c_o = 5.73$. Therefore $V = 225.76$ Å^3.

Converting Å^3 to cm^3, we divide by $(10^8)^3 = 10^{24}$ or $V = 225.76 \times 10^{-24}$ cm^3. Knowing the values M and V, the density, D, can be calculated using the formula:

$$D = \frac{Z \times M}{N \times V}$$

where N is Avogadro's number 6.02338×10^{23}. Substituting values for aragonite,

$$D = \frac{4 \times 100.09}{6.02338 \times 10^{23} \times 225.76 \times 10^{-24}} = 2.945 \text{ gr/cm}^3$$

This value, 2.945, for the calculated specific gravity of aragonite is in excellent agreement with the best measured values which are 2.947 ± 0.002.

In the study of new minerals the numerical value of Z is commonly not known. Hence it is necessary to make successive trials of the calculations given above, using different values of Z until the best possible agreement with the measured specific gravity is secured. Z is always an integer and generally small.

E. PROPERTIES DEPENDING UPON LIGHT

Luster. The general appearance of the surface of a mineral in reflected light is called *luster*. The luster of minerals can be divided into two types, *metallic* and *nonmetallic*. There is no sharp line dividing these two groups, and those minerals lying between are sometimes said to be *submetallic*.

A mineral having the brilliant appearance of a metal has a metallic luster. Moreover, such minerals are quite opaque to light and, as a result, give a black or very dark streak (see page 163). Galena, pyrite, and chalcopyrite are common minerals with metallic luster.

All minerals without a metallic appearance have, as the term implies, a nonmetallic luster. They are, in general, light colored and will transmit light through thin edges. The streak of a nonmetallic mineral is either colorless or very light in color. The following terms are used to describe further the appearance of nonmetallic minerals:

Vitreous. Having the luster of glass. Example, quartz.

Resinous. Having the appearance of resin. Example, sphalerite.

Pearly. Having the iridescent appearance of a pearl. This is usually observed in minerals on surfaces that are parallel to cleavage planes. Example, basal plane on apophyllite.

Greasy. Looking as if covered with a thin layer of oil. Examples, nepheline and some specimens of sphalerite and massive quartz.

Silky. Like silk. It is the result of a fine fibrous parallel aggregate. Examples, fibrous gypsum, malachite, and serpentine.

Adamantine. Having a hard, brilliant luster like that of a diamond. It is due to the mineral's high index of refraction (see page 166). The transparent lead minerals, like cerussite and anglesite, show it.

Color. The color of minerals is one of their most important physical properties. For many minerals, especially those showing a metallic luster, color is a definite and constant property and will serve as an important means of identification. The brass yellow of chalcopyrite, the lead-gray of galena, the black of magnetite, and the green of malachite are examples in which color is a striking property of the mineral. It is to be noted, however, that surface alterations may change the color even in minerals whose color is otherwise constant. This is shown in the yellow tarnish frequently observed on pyrite and marcasite, the purple tarnish on bornite, etc. In noting the color of **a**

mineral, therefore, a fresh surface should be examined. Many minerals, however, do not show a constant color in their different specimens. This variation in color in the same species may be due to different causes. A change in color is often produced by a change in composition. The progressive replacement of zinc by iron in sphalerite (see page 204) will change its color from white through yellow and brown to black. The minerals of the *amphibole group* show a similar variation in color. The amphibole tremolite, which is a silicate with only calcium and magnesium as bases, is very light in color; actinolite and hornblende, which are amphiboles that contain increasing amounts of iron, range in color between green and black. Again, a mineral may show a wide range of color without any apparent change in composition. Fluorite is a striking example of this, for it is found in crystals that are colorless, white, pink, yellow, blue, green, and violet. Such wide variations in color are rare, however. Minerals are also frequently colored by various impurities. The red cryptocrystalline variety of quartz, known as jasper, is colored by small amounts of hematite. From the above it is seen that, though the color of a mineral is one of its important physical properties, it is not always constant and must, therefore, be used with caution in the identification of some species.

Streak. The color of the fine powder of a mineral is known as its *streak*. The streak is frequently used in the identification of minerals, for, although the color of a mineral may vary between wide limits, the streak is usually constant. This property can be conveniently determined in the laboratory by rubbing the mineral on a piece of unglazed porcelain, known as a *streak plate*. The streak plate has a hardness of about 7, and thus it cannot be used with minerals of a greater hardness.

Play of colors. A mineral is said to show a *play of colors* when on turning it several spectral colors are seen in rapid succession. This is seen especially well in diamond and precious opal. A mineral is said to show a *change of color* when on turning it the colors change slowly with position. This is observed in some labradorite.

Iridescence. A mineral is *iridescent* when it shows a series of spectral colors in its interior or on its surface. An internal iridescence is usually caused by the presence of small fractures or cleavage planes, whereas an external iridescence is caused by the presence of a thin surface film or coating.

Opalescence. A milky or pearly reflection from the interior of a specimen is known as *opalescence*. It is observed in some opal, moonstone, and cat's-eye.

Tarnish. A mineral is said to show a *tarnish* when the color of the surface differs from that of the interior. Tarnish is frequently shown by the copper minerals, chalcocite, bornite, and chalcopyrite, after fresh surfaces have been exposed to the air.

Chatoyancy. Some minerals have in reflected light a silky appearance which results from the presence of many inclusions arranged parallel to a crystallographic direction. When a cabochon gem stone is cut from such a mineral, it is crossed by a beam of light at right angles to the direction of the inclusions. This property, known as *chatoyancy*, is shown by *cat's eye*, a gem variety of chrysoberyl.

Asterism. Some crystals, especially those of the hexagonal system, when viewed in the direction of the vertical axis, show starlike rays of light. This phenomenon arises from peculiarities of structure along the axial directions or from inclusions arranged at right angles to these directions. The outstanding example is the star sapphire.

Pleochroism. Some minerals possess a selective absorption of light in different crystallographic directions and may thus appear variously colored when viewed in different directions in transmitted light. This property is known as *pleochroism*. If a mineral has only two such absorption directions, the property is called *dichroism*. This property is shown by transparent varieties of tourmaline, cordierite and spodumene.

Luminescence. Any emission of light by a mineral that is not the direct result of incandescence is known as *luminescence*. The phenomenon may be brought about in several ways, apparently quite independent of one another. Most luminescence is faint and can be observed only in the dark.

Triboluminescence is a property possessed by some minerals of becoming luminous on being crushed, scratched, or rubbed. Most minerals showing this property are nonmetallic and anhydrous and possess a good cleavage. Fluorite, sphalerite, and lepidolite may be triboluminescent and, less commonly, pectolite, amblygonite, feldspar, and calcite.

Thermoluminescence is the property possessed by some minerals of emitting visible light when heated to a temperature below that of red heat. Like triboluminescence, this phenomenon is best shown in non-metallic, anhydrous minerals. When a thermoluminescent mineral is heated, the initial visible light, usually faint, is given off at a temperature between 50° and 100° C, and light usually ceases to be emitted at temperatures higher than 475° C. Fluorite for a long time has been known to possess this property; the variety *chlorophane* was named because of the green light emitted. Other minerals which are commonly thermoluminescent are calcite, apatite, scapolite, lepidolite, and feldspar.

Fluorescence and Phosphorescence. Minerals that become luminescent during exposure to ultraviolet light, x-rays, or cathode rays are *fluorescent.* If the luminescence continues after the exciting rays are shut off, the mineral is said to be *phosphorescent.* Phosphorescence was early observed on some minerals that, after exposure to the sun, would glow on removal to a dark room. There is no sharp distinction between fluorescence and phosphorescence, for some minerals that appear only to fluoresce can be shown by refined methods to continue to glow for a small fraction of a second after the removal of the exciting rays. Consequently, the phenomena are considered by some to be the same.

More minerals show fluorescence than other types of luminescence, and, since it is easier to produce, much work has been done on it. Fluorescence is shown by some fluorite, the mineral from which the property receives its name. Other minerals that frequently, but by no means invariably, fluoresce are willemite, scheelite, calcite, scapolite, diamond, hyalite, and autunite. Fluorescence is a property that cannot be predicted, for some specimens of a given mineral will show it, whereas other, apparently similar, specimens will not. Not only do the fluorescent colors of different minerals and different specimens of the same mineral vary greatly, but also they bear no relation to the natural color of the minerals. A well-arranged display of fluorescent minerals makes a beautiful and striking exhibit. (See frontispiece.)

Fluorescence is most commonly produced by excitation with ultraviolet light, and each year sees improvements in the methods of producing such light. It is best to have a source of ultraviolet light with a minimum of accompanying visible light so that the fluorescent effects will not be lessened by reflection. The iron spark, the mercury-vapor lamp, and the argon tube, or some variation of these, are most commonly used. The wave length or color of the light emitted during fluorescence varies considerably with the wave length or source of the ultraviolet light.

Fluorescence is having an increasing commercial and industrial significance, and much work is being done on synthetic material. In connection with minerals, the property has a practical use at Franklin, New Jersey, where ultraviolet light is used to determine the amount of willemite that goes into the tailings. Also, since most scheelite fluoresces, prospecting for that mineral is frequently carried out at night with the aid of ultraviolet light.

Apparently no simple relation exists between luminescence of various kinds, for any kind may exist alone or with any of the others. Moreover, the color of the different types of luminescence may vary in the same specimen. Luminescence is rarely shown by pure compounds, and therefore one factor that may be common to all minerals showing luminescence is a small amount of impurity.

Diaphaneity. The property possessed by some minerals to transmit light is known as *diaphaneity*. The following terms are used to express varying degrees of this property:

Transparent. A mineral is transparent if the outline of an object viewed through it is perfectly distinct.

Translucent. A mineral is translucent if it will transmit light but if objects cannot be seen through it.

Opaque. A mineral is opaque if, even on its thinnest edges, it will transmit no light.

Refraction of light. When light comes into contact with a non-opaque mineral, part of it is reflected from the surface and part enters the mineral. The light that enters the mineral is in general refracted. When light passes from a rarer into a denser medium, as in passing from air into a mineral, its velocity is retarded. This change in velocity is accompanied by a corresponding change in the direction in which the light travels, and it is this change in direction of propagation that is known as refraction of light. The amount of refraction of a given light ray is directly proportional to the ratio existing between the velocity of light in air and that in the mineral. The ratio between these two velocities is known as n, the index of refraction. The ratio is equal to V/v, where V represents the velocity of light in air and v the velocity of light in the mineral. The velocity of light in air may be considered equal to 1, and therefore $n = 1/v$, or the index of refraction is equal to the reciprocal of the light velocity. Thus, if the index of refraction of a mineral is 2.0, light will travel in the mineral with one-half the velocity it has in air.

In Fig. 367 let M–M represent the surface of a crystal of fluorite. Let N–O be normal to that surface. Let A–O be one of a number of parallel light rays striking the surface M–M in such a way as to make the angle i (angle of incidence) with the normal N–O. Let O–P be at right angles to the rays and represent the wave front of the light in air. Since the crystal is the denser medium, the light will travel in it more slowly. Therefore, as each ray in turn strikes the surface M–M, it will be retarded and the direction of its path will be changed proportionately. In going from a rarer into a denser medium, the ray will be bent toward the normal N–O. To find the direction of the rays and line of wave front in the crystal, proceed as follows: Since the index

of refraction of fluorite is 1.43, ray A will travel in the crystal, in the
time it takes ray C to travel from P to R, $1/1.43$ of that distance, or
to some point on the circular arc, the length of whose radius OA' is
$1/1.43$ of the distance P-R. Similarly, ray B will travel in the mineral,
during the period of time in which ray C travels from S to R, a distance
equal to $1/1.43$ of the distance S-R, or the radius TB'. The same
reasoning will hold true for all other rays. The wave front in the
crystal can then be determined by drawing a tangent—the line $A'B'R$
—to these various circular arcs; and lines perpendicular to this wave

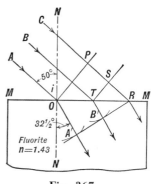

Fig. 367.   Fig. 368.

Refraction of Light.

front will represent the direction in which the light travels in the
mineral, and the angle NOA' or r will be the angle of refraction.
Figure 368 shows the same construction as that of Fig. 367, but the
mineral in question is here assumed to be diamond. Since the index
of refraction of diamond ($n = 2.42$) is much greater than that of
fluorite, light will travel in it with a still lower velocity. Consequently,
in diamond, refraction will be greater. This is shown in the two figures,
in both of which the angle of incidence is the same.

The refractive power toward light that a mineral possesses often has
a distinct effect upon the appearance of the mineral. For example, a
mass of cryolite may almost always be identified at sight by its
peculiar appearance, somewhat like that of wet snow, and quite
different from that of ordinary white substances; this is due to the
fact that the index of refraction of cryolite is unusually low for a
mineral. An instructive experiment may be tried by finely pulveriz-
ing some pure white cryolite and throwing the powder into water,
where it will apparently disappear, as if it had instantly gone into
solution. The powder, however, is insoluble, and may be seen indis-

tinctly as it settles to the bottom of the vessel. The reason for this disappearance of the cryolite is that its index of refraction (about 1.34) is near that of water (1.335); hence the light travels almost as readily through the mineral as through water, and consequently it undergoes little reflection or refraction.

Substances with an unusually high index of refraction have an appearance that it is hard to define and that is generally spoken of as adamantine luster. This kind of luster may be comprehended best by examining specimens of diamond ($n = 2.419$) or of cerussite ($n =$ about 2.1). They have a flash and quality, some diamonds almost a steel-like appearance, which is not possessed by minerals of low index of refraction; compare, for example, cerussite and fluorite ($n = 1.434$). It is their high index of refraction that gives to many gem minerals their great brilliancy and charm.

Many nonopaque minerals have a refractive index not far from 1.5, which gives to the minerals the luster of glass, designated as vitreous. Quartz and feldspar are good examples.

Double refraction. All crystalline minerals except those belonging to the isometric system show, in general, a double refraction of light. That is, when a ray of light enters such a mineral it is broken up into two rays, each of which travels through the mineral with a characteristic velocity and has its own refractive index. Thus, the angle of refraction will be different for the two rays, and they will diverge. In other words, the light undergoes double refraction. In the majority of minerals, the amount of this double refraction is small, and the fact that it exists can be demonstrated only by special instruments. Calcite, however, shows such a strong double refraction that it can be easily observed. This is shown in Fig. 369 where a double image may be seen through a block of clear calcite (Iceland spar).

The divergence of the two rays in a given mineral depends, first, on its birefringence (the difference between the greatest and least refractive index); second, on the thickness of the mineral block; and, last, on the crystallographic direction in which the light is traveling. In tetragonal and hexagonal minerals, there is one direction (that of the vertical crystallographic axis) in which no double refraction takes place (Fig. 370). As soon as a ray of light in the mineral deviates from this direction it is doubly refracted, and the amount of double refraction increases as the path of the light becomes more oblique and attains its maximum when it is at right angles to the vertical axis. Such minerals belong to the optical class known as uniaxial. In orthorhombic, monoclinic, and triclinic minerals, there are two directions similar to the one described above, in which no double refraction

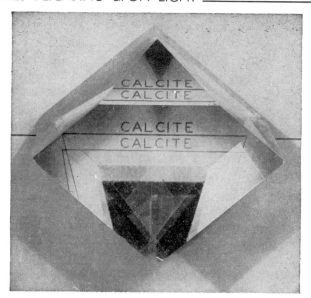

Fig. 369. Calcite, Viewed Normal to the Rhombohedron Face Showing Double Refraction. The double repetition of "calcite" at the top of the photograph is seen through a face cut on the specimen parallel to the base.

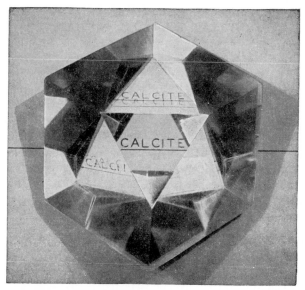

Fig. 370. Calcite Showing No Double Refraction. Viewed parallel to the *c* axis.

takes place, and the minerals of these systems are therefore spoken of as optically biaxial.

The optical properties of minerals comprise an important branch of mineralogy but are beyond the scope of this book. For an adequate consideration of optical properties the reader is referred to books of a more specialized nature.

F.   ELECTRICAL AND MAGNETIC PROPERTIES

Piezoelectricity. If an electric charge is developed on the surface of a crystal by exerting pressure at the ends of a crystal axis, the crystal is said to show piezoelectricity. Only those minerals crystallizing in symmetry classes that lack a symmetry center and thus have polar axes can show this property. By reference to the table on page 21 it will be seen that there are twenty-one such classes. Quartz is probably the most important piezoelectric mineral, for an extremely slight pressure parallel to an "electric axis" (any of the three a axes) can be detected by the electric charge set up. Because of this property, quartz is used extensively in carefully oriented plates to control radio frequency. Tourmaline has also been used to a limited extent in a similar manner, but it is more important in the construction of pressure gauges. Today several synthetic crystalline substances that have strong piezoelectric response are manufactured.

Pyroelectricity. The simultaneous development of positive and negative charges of electricity at opposite ends of a crystal axis under the proper conditions of temperature change is called *pyroelectricity*. Only those crystals that belong to the ten crystal classes having a unique polar axis are considered to show "true" or *primary* pyroelectricity. For example, tourmaline has a single polar axis, c, and falls within this group, whereas quartz with its three polar a axes does not. However, a temperature gradient in all other crystals lacking a symmetry center, such as quartz, will produce a pyroelectric effect. In such crystals the polarization is the result of the deformation resulting from unequal thermal expansion that produces piezoelectric effects. If quartz is heated to about 100° C, it will develop on cooling positive charges at three alternate prismatic edges and negative charges at the three remaining edges. These charges have been called *secondary* pyroelectric polarization.

Magnetism. Those minerals that, in their natural state, will be attracted to an iron magnet are said to be magnetic. Magnetite, Fe_3O_4, and pyrrhotite $Fe_{(1-x)}S$, are the only two common magnetic minerals.

Lodestone, a variety of magnetite, itself has the attracting power and polarity of a true magnet.

In the magnetic field of a powerful electromagnet many other minerals, especially those containing iron, are drawn to the magnet. Because of this, the electromagnet is an important means of separating mixtures of mineral grains having different magnetic susceptibilities.

4

CHEMICAL MINERALOGY

A. INTRODUCTION

The chemical composition of a mineral is of fundamental importance, for all other properties are in great measure dependent upon it. However, these properties depend not only on the chemical composition but also upon the geometry of arrangement of the constituent atoms and the nature of the electrical forces which bind them together.

For more than a century, the classification of minerals has been firmly placed on a chemical basis. Consequently, the final proof of identity of a mineral has been chemical composition. The present-day classification of minerals, however, considers structure as well as gross chemical composition and takes cognizance of the wide latitude in chemical content permitted by the substitution of atoms of one element for those of another in a given structural framework. Considerable clarification of the relationships among minerals results from the introduction of structural concepts into mineral classification, and may have economic significance.

For example, the value of many ore minerals arises from their content of a metal which is a vicarious, rather than an essential, constituent. This is true of thorium in monazite, silver in tetrahedrite, and in general of gallium, germanium, indium, and many other

172

elements. In these cases, a knowledge of the mechanism by which the vicarious constituents come to be present may be of great economic significance.

In this section on chemical mineralogy the general principles relating the chemistry of minerals to their crystallography and physical properties is discussed under the heading of *crystal chemistry*. This is followed by a brief description of the methods of testing for different elements found in minerals. Because of the scope and size of this book, it is necessary to assume that the reader is familiar with at least the essentials of chemical fact and nomenclature.

B. CRYSTAL CHEMISTRY

That a relation exists between chemical composition and crystal morphology was recognized in the eighteenth century. The ability to determine crystal structure by x-ray diffraction methods added a new dimension to this relationship and aroused interest among both chemists and crystallographers. In recent years a new science, *crystal chemistry*, has come into being. The goal of this science is the elucidation of the relationships between chemical composition, internal structure, and physical properties in crystalline matter, and the corollary goal, the synthesis of crystalline materials having any desired combination of properties.

Many of the concepts of crystal chemistry are directly applicable to mineralogy and their introduction has resulted in considerable simplification and clarification of mineralogical thought. The function of crystal chemistry in mineralogy is to serve as a unifying thread upon which the often apparently unrelated facts of descriptive mineralogy may be strung.

RELATION OF CHEMISTRY TO MINERAL CLASSIFICATION

Chemical composition is the basis for the modern classification of minerals. According to this scheme, minerals are divided into classes depending on the dominant anion or anionic group. (See page 222.) There are a number of reasons why this criterion suggested itself to mineralogists as a valid basis for the broad framework of mineral classification. First, minerals having the same anion or anionic group dominant in their composition have unmistakable family resemblances, in general stronger and more clearly marked than those shared by minerals containing the same dominant cation. Thus the carbonates resemble each other more closely than do the minerals of copper.

Second, minerals related by dominance of the same anion tend to occur together or in the same or similar geologic environment. Thus the sulfides occur in close mutual association in deposits of vein or replacement type, whereas the silicates make up the great bulk of the rocks of the earth's crust. Third, such a scheme of mineral classification agrees well with the current chemical practice in the naming and classification of inorganic compounds.

It is apparent, however, that so one-sided a view of the nature of minerals leaves many troublesome questions unanswered. Why do minerals deviate so widely from the properties expected on the basis of chemical composition alone? Why do the anionic groups influence the properties of most compounds more than the cations? What uniformity connect those substances of similar crystallography and properties but diverse chemical composition? We shall have to deal with these questions and many more before we can hope to reach an adequate understanding of the nature of mineral substances.

Ordinarily the first task of a student in a course in general chemistry is the discrimination of physical properties and physical change as opposed to chemical properties and chemical change. The most cursory examination reveals that both chemical and physical properties depend to some extent on composition. Lead is heavy, and compounds that contain it generally have notably high specific gravities reflecting the influence of component elements on the physical properties. Likewise, radicals that are groups or combinations of elements, although they cannot exist in the free state like an element, have characteristic properties which they confer on all compounds containing them. Thus the carbonate radical characteristically reacts with acids to yield carbon dioxide, which is liberated from the scene of the reaction as bubbles of gas.

We may therefore specify the chemical properties of the compound lead carbonate, the mineral cerussite, in part by listing those characteristic reactions or tests for the elements contained in it. Such a specification of tests for the elements enables us to place cerussite unambiguously in the scheme of classification of minerals according to chemical composition. We may make the chemical definition of the mineral cerussite more rigorous by specifying not only that it must yield qualitative tests for lead and carbonate but also that *quantitative* chemical analysis must yield proportions by weight of lead and carbonate of 83.5 per cent PbO and 16.5 per cent CO_2.

Polymorphism. From these considerations it seems as though quantitative chemical composition should serve admirably as an exact and rigorous basis of classification. However, if we examine compounds of calcium and carbonate ion, we speedily find that the quantitative chemical classification is not unambiguous. In nature *two* stable compounds of calcium and carbonate exist, having precisely the same percentage content of calcium and carbonate. These compounds, the minerals calcite and aragonite, are indistinguishable by chemical means, yet they differ in almost every other property. Calcite is hexagonal scalenohedral; aragonite is orthorhombic. Calcite has a perfect rhombohedral cleavage; aragonite has prismatic and pinacoidal cleavage. The minerals differ slightly in specific gravity and hardness and, what is more devastating to any notion of their identity, show totally unlike x-ray diffraction patterns.

Further examples of this ambiguity are: pyrite and marcasite, which share the composition FeS_2; graphite and diamond, both elemental carbon; and the silica system, which includes no less than eight physically distinct substances of diverse crystallography all having the composition SiO_2.

Comparison of Dimorphous Minerals

Chemical Substance	Mineral	Crystal System	Hardness	Specific Gravity
C	Diamond	Isometric	10	3.5
	Graphite	Hexagonal	1	2.2
FeS_2	Pyrite	Isometric	6	5.0
	Marcasite	Orthorhombic	6	4.85
$CaCO_3$	Calcite	Rhombohedral	3	2.71
	Aragonite	Orthorhombic	$3\frac{1}{2}$	2.95

This phenomenon, in which the same chemical substance exists in two or more physically distinct forms, is termed *polymorphism* or *allotropy*. Compounds are said to be *dimorphous* if they exist in two modifications, *trimorphous* if they exist in three modifications.

The introduction into our thinking of this factor of structure resolves the problem posed by polymorphous forms. Diamond is harder and denser than graphite simply because its component particles of carbon are more closely packed and more tightly bonded together. Not only does the concept of the importance of structure account for every case of polymorphism, but also it resolves the difficulty presented by the apparently anomalous variation in physical properties of other compounds from those predictable on the basis of chemical composition alone. Thus, on the basis of composition, it is predictable that all

Periodic Table of the Chemical Elements with Atomic and Ionic Radii

(Radii of the positive ions according to Ahrens 1952, of the negative ions according to Goldschmidt 1926.)

Period	I	II	III	IV	V	VI	VII	VIIIa	VIIIb
1	1 H 0.46							2 He 1.78	
2	3 Li 1.52 / Li^+ 0.68	4 Be 1.12 / Be^{2+} 0.35	5 B 0.97 / B^{3+} 0.23	6 C 0.77 / C^{4+} 0.16	7 N 0.71 / N^{3+} 0.16 / N^{5+} 0.13	8 O^{2-} 1.32 / O 0.60 / O^{6+} 0.10	9 F^- 1.33 / F^{7+} 0.08	10 Ne 1.60	
3	11 Na 1.86 / Na^+ 0.97	12 Mg 1.60 / Mg^{2+} 0.66	13 Al 1.43 / Al^{3+} 0.51	14 Si^{4-} 1.98 / Si 1.17 / Si^{4+} 0.42	15 P / P^{3+} 0.44 / P^{5+} 0.35	16 S^{2-} 1.74 / S 1.04 / S^{4+} 0.37 / S^{6+} 0.30	17 Cl^- 1.81 / Cl 1.07 / Cl^{5+} 0.34 / Cl^{7+} 0.27	18 Ar 1.91	
4 (a)	19 K 2.31 / K^+ 1.33	20 Ca 1.96 / Ca^{2+} 0.99	21 Sc 1.51 / Sc^{3+} 0.81	22 Ti 1.46 / Ti^{3+} 0.76 / Ti^{4+} 0.68	23 V 1.30 / V^{2+} 0.88 / V^{3+} 0.74 / V^{4+} 0.63 / V^{5+} 0.59	24 Cr 1.25 / Cr^{3+} 0.63 / Cr^{6+} 0.52	25 Mn 1.18 / Mn^{2+} 0.80 / Mn^{3+} 0.66 / Mn^{4+} 0.60 / Mn^{7+} 0.46		26 Fe 1.24 / Fe^{2+} 0.74 / Fe^{3+} 0.64 · 27 Co 1.25 / Co^{2+} 0.72 / Co^{3+} 0.63 · 28 Ni 1.24 / Ni^{2+} 0.69
4 (b)	29 Cu 1.28 / Cu^+ 0.96 / Cu^{2+} 0.72	30 Zn 1.33 / Zn^{2+} 0.74	31 Ga 1.22 / Ga^{3+} 0.62	32 Ge 1.22 / Ge^{2+} 0.73 / Ge^{4+} 0.53	33 As 1.25 / As^{3+} 0.58 / As^{5+} 0.46	34 Se^{2-} 1.91 / Se 1.16 / Se^{4+} 0.50 / Se^{6+} 0.42	35 Br^- 1.96 / Br 1.19 / Br^{5+} 0.47 / Br^{7+} 0.39	36 Kr 2.01	
5 (a)	37 Rb 2.43 / Rb^+ 1.47	38 Sr 2.15 / Sr^{2+} 1.12	39 Y 1.81 / Y^{3+} 0.92	40 Zr 1.56 / Zr^{4+} 0.79	41 Nb 1.43 / Nb^{4+} 0.74 / Nb^{5+} 0.69	42 Mo 1.36 / Mo^{4+} 0.70 / Mo^{6+} 0.62	43 Tc / Tc^{7+} 0.56		44 Ru 1.33 / Ru^{4+} 0.67 · 45 Rh 1.34 / Rh^{3+} 0.68 · 46 Pd 1.37 / Pd^{2+} 0.80 / Pd^{4+} 0.65
5 (b)	47 Ag 1.44 / Ag^+ 1.26 / Ag^{2+} 0.89	48 Cd 1.49 / Cd^{2+} 0.97	49 In 1.62 / In^{3+} 0.81	50 Sn^{4-} 2.15 / Sn 1.40 / Sn^{2+} 0.93 / Sn^{4+} 0.71	51 Sb 1.45 / Sb^{3+} 0.76 / Sb^{5+} 0.62	52 Te^{2-} 2.11 / Te 1.43 / Te^{4+} 0.70 / Te^{6+} 0.56	53 I^- 2.20 / I 1.36 / I^{5+} 0.62 / I^{7+} 0.50	54 X 2.20	
6 (a)	55 Cs 2.62 / Cs^+ 1.67	56 Ba 2.17 / Ba^{2+} 1.34	57 La* 1.86 / La^{3+} 1.14	72 Hf 1.58 / Hf^{4+} 0.78	73 Ta 1.58 / Ta^{5+} 0.68	74 W 1.43 / W^{4+} 0.70 / W^{6+} 0.62	75 Re 1.36 / Re^{4+} 0.72 / Re^{7+} 0.56		76 Os 1.35 / Os^{6+} 0.69 · 77 Ir 1.35 / Ir^{4+} 0.68 · 78 Pt 1.38 / Pt^{2+} 0.80 / Pt^{4+} 0.65
6 (b)	79 Au 1.44 / Au^+ 1.37 / Au^{3+} 0.85	80 Hg 1.50 / Hg^{2+} 1.10	81 Tl 1.70 / Tl^+ 1.47 / Tl^{3+} 0.95	82 Pb 1.75 / Pb^{2+} 1.20 / Pb^{4+} 0.84	83 Bi 1.55 / Bi^{3+} 0.96 / Bi^{5+} 0.74	84 Po 1.55 / Po^{6+} 0.67	85 At / At^{7+} 0.62	86 Rn	
7	87 Fr / Fr^{1+} 1.80	88 Ra / Ra^{2+} 1.43	89 Ac† / Ac^{3+} 1.18	104 —	105 —	106 —	107 —	108 —	109 — · 110 —

* See footnote, page 177.   † See footnote, page 177.

compounds of lead will have high densities. This is true, but in fact the compounds of lead do not show a simple proportional relation between density and percentage of lead. In terms of structure, these departures may easily be explained on the basis of differences in packing. A similar consideration accounts for the otherwise baffling fact that corundum, Al_2O_3, entirely made up of light elements, is nearly as dense as chalcopyrite, $CuFeS_2$, a compound largely made up of much heavier elements.

ATOMS, IONS, AND THE PERIODIC TABLE

It may be well to review briefly the nature of the units of which all matter is composed. As nearly everyone is aware in this atomic age, these units are atoms or ions. A recent survey reveals thirty-four different kinds of subatomic particles, either surely known or fairly safely inferred. Fortunately for students of mineralogy, it is necessary to consider only three of these—the proton, the neutron, and the electron—in order to have a satisfactory understanding of the role of atoms in the structure of crystals.

An atom may be thought of as the smallest subdivision of matter that retains the characteristics of the element, and it may be regarded as consisting of a very small, massive nucleus composed of protons and neutrons surrounded by a much larger region thinly populated by electrons. Atoms are so small that it is impossible to see them even with the highest magnification of the electron microscope (100,000 diameters), although at this magnification the largest molecules appear as separate units. Nevertheless, the sizes of atoms have been measured and are generally expressed as atomic radii in angstrom units. For example, the smallest atom, hydrogen, has a radius of only 0.46 Å, whereas the largest, cesium, has a radius of 2.62 Å. (See table page 176.)

It is to the Danish physicist Niels Bohr that we are indebted for the most widely accepted picture of the atom. As a result of his investigations of the relation between electrons and nucleus, he developed in 1912 the concept of the "planetary" atom in which the electrons are visualized as circling the nucleus in "orbits" or energy levels at dis-

---

*Lanthanides: **58**Ce 1.82 Ce^{3+} 1.07 Ce^{4+} 0.94 **59**Pr 1.81 Pr^{3+} 1.06 Pr^{4+} 0.92 **60**Nd 1.80 Nd^{3+} 1.04 **61**Pm **62**Sm^{3+} 1.00 **63**Eu^{3+} 0.98 **64**Gd^{3+} 0.97 **65**Tb^{3+} 0.93 Tb^{4+} 0.81 **66**Dy^{3+} 0.92 **67**Ho^{3+} 0.91 **68**Er 1.86 Er^{3+} 0.89 **69**Tm^{3+} 0.87 **70**Yb^{3+} 0.86 **71**Lu^{3+} 0.85.

†Actinides: **90**Th 1.80 Th^{4+} 1.02 **91**Pa^{3+} 1.13 Pa^{4+} 0.98 Pa^{5+} 0.89 **92**U 1.38 U^{4+} 0.97 U^{6+} 0.80 **93**Np^{3+} 1.10 Np^{4+} 0.95 Np^{7+} 0.71 **94**Pu^{3+} 1.08 Pu^{4+} 0.93 **95**Am^{3+} 1.07 Am^{4+} 0.92.

tances from the nucleus depending on the energies of the electrons. According to this mechanical model, the atom can be considered as a minute solar system. At the center, corresponding to the sun, is the *nucleus* which, except in the hydrogen atom, is made up of *protons* and *neutrons*. The hydrogen *nucleus* is made up of a single proton. Each proton carries a unit charge of positive electricity; the neutron, as the name implies, is electrically neutral. Each electron, which, like a planet of the solar system, moves in an orbit around the nucleus, carries a charge of negative electricity. Since the atom as a whole is electrically neutral, there must be as many electrons as protons. The weight of the atom is concentrated in the nucleus, for the mass of an electron is only 1/1850 that of the lightest nucleus. Although the

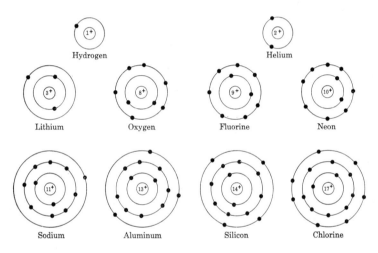

Fig. 371. Schematic Diagram of Atoms.

electrons and nuclei are both extremely small, the electrons move so rapidly about the nuclei that they give to the atoms relatively large effective diameters—ten to twenty thousand times the diameter of the nucleus.

The simplest atom is that of hydrogen, in which the nucleus has one electron moving around it, as is shown diagrammatically in Fig. 371. Atoms of the other natural elements have from two electrons (helium) to ninety-two electrons (uranium) moving in orbits about their nuclei.

The fundamental difference between atoms of the different elements lies in the electrical charge of the nucleus. This positive charge is the same as the number of protons, and this number, equal to the number of electrons, is called the *atomic number*. The *atomic weight* of an element is a number expressing its relative weight in terms of the weight of the element oxygen, which is taken as 16.0000. Thus hydrogen has an atomic weight of 1.0080 and titanium an atomic weight of 47.9. This means that a hydrogen atom has about one-sixteenth the mass of an oxygen atom, whereas a titanium atom has about four times the mass of an oxygen atom. The atomic number and atomic weights of the elements are listed with the symbols for the elements on page 180.

Up to the present time the occurrence of one hundred and three different elements has been established. This number includes the eleven transuranium elements recently manufactured, all of which were unknown before 1940. With the exception of the gases in the atmosphere all the natural elements are found in minerals.

The chemical attributes of the elements, with which the mineralogist is concerned, depend upon the configuration of the electronic superstructure of their atoms. The electrons, whose number depends upon the charge of the nucleus, are considered to be arranged about the nucleus in energy levels, or shells, formerly called the K, L, M, N, O, P, and Q shells but more commonly alluded to today by the numbers 1, 2, 3, 4, 5, 6, and 7. Each shell contains a number of subshells, each capable of containing two electrons whose "spin" is such that their magnetic moments cancel out. These subshells are designated by the letters s, p, d, and f. The s subshell may contain but one electron pair, the p three electron pairs, the d five, and the f subshell seven pairs. The 1-shell contains only two electrons, both in the 1-s subshell. The 2-shell can contain a maximum of eight electrons, two in the 2-s and six in the 2-p subshell. The 3-shell can contain a total of eighteen electrons, two in the 3-s, six in the 3-p, and ten in the 3-d subshell. In all the higher numbered shells, the f subshell may be occupied by a maximum of fourteen electrons. In the heaviest and most complex atoms, the 7-s subshell is fully occupied, and some electrons occur in all lower numbered subshells except the 6-f.

In the lighter elements between hydrogen and argon (atomic numbers 1 to 18) electrons are added in regular succession to the 1-shell, the 2-shell, and the 3-shell until all subshells including the 3-p are filled, yielding a total of eighteen electrons.

There is a close relationship between the electronic superstructure of the atom, the chemical properties of the element, and the place in the periodic table. The elements between hydrogen and argon constitute the first three "short" periods of the periodic table. In the first period, hydrogen, having a nucleus containing but a single proton and hence having a positive charge of one, has but a single planetary

INTERNATIONAL ATOMIC WEIGHTS
1956

Element	Symbol	Atomic Number	Atomic Weight	Element	Symbol	Atomic Number	Atomic Weight
Actinium	Ac	89	227	Mercury	Hg	80	200.61
Aluminum	Al	13	26.98	Molybdenum	Mo	42	95.95
Americium	Am	95	[243]	Neodymium	Nd	60	144.27
Antimony	Sb	51	121.76	Neon	Ne	10	20.183
Argon	Ar	18	39.944	Neptunium	Np	93	[237]
Arsenic	As	33	74.91	Nickel	Ni	28	58.71
Astatine	At	85	[210]	Niobium	Nb	41	92.91
Barium	Ba	56	137.36	Nitrogen	N	7	14.008
Berkelium	Bk	97	[249]	Osmium	Os	76	190.2
Beryllium	Be	4	9.013	Oxygen	O	8	16
Bismuth	Bi	83	209.00	Palladium	Pd	46	106.4
Boron	B	5	10.82	Phosphorus	P	15	30.975
Bromine	Br	35	79.916	Platinum	Pt	78	195.09
Cadmium	Cd	48	112.41	Plutonium	Pu	94	[242]
Calcium	Ca	20	40.08	Polonium	Po	84	210
Californium	Cf	98	[249]	Potassium	K	19	39.100
Carbon	C	6	12.011	Praseodymium	Pr	59	140.92
Cerium	Ce	58	140.13	Promethium	Pm	61	[145]
Cesium	Cs	55	132.91	Protactinium	Pa	91	231
Chlorine	Cl	17	35.457	Radium	Ra	88	226.05
Chromium	Cr	24	52.01	Radon	Rn	86	222
Cobalt	Co	27	58.94	Rhenium	Re	75	186.22
Columbium (see				Rhodium	Rh	45	102.91
Niobium)				Rubidium	Rb	37	85.48
Copper	Cu	29	63.54	Ruthenium	Ru	44	101.1
Curium	Cm	96	[245]	Samarium	Sm	62	150.35
Dysprosium	Dy	66	162.46	Scandium	Sc	21	44.96
Erbium	Er	68	167.2	Selenium	Se	34	78.96
Europium	Eu	63	152.0	Silicon	Si	14	28.09
Fluorine	F	9	19.00	Silver	Ag	47	107.880
Francium	Fr	87	[223]	Sodium	Na	11	22.991
Gadolinium	Gd	64	157.26	Strontium	Sr	38	87.63
Gallium	Ga	31	69.72	Sulfur	S	16	32.066
Germanium	Ge	32	72.60	Tantalum	Ta	73	180.95
Gold	Au	79	197.0	Technetium	Tc	43	[99]
Hafnium	Hf	72	178.50	Tellurium	Te	52	127.61
Helium	He	2	4.003	Terbium	Tb	65	158.93
Holmium	Ho	67	164.94	Thallium	Tl	81	204.39
Hydrogen	H	1	1.0080	Thorium	Th	90	232.05
Indium	In	49	114.82	Thulium	Tm	69	168.94
Iodine	I	53	126.91	Tin	Sn	50	118.70
Iridium	Ir	77	192.2	Titanium	Ti	22	47.90
Iron	Fe	26	55.85	Tungsten	W	74	183.86
Krypton	Kr	36	83.80	Uranium	U	92	238.07
Lanthanum	La	57	138.92	Vanadium	V	23	50.95
Lead	Pb	82	207.21	Xenon	Xe	54	131.30
Lithium	Li	3	6.940	Ytterbium	Yb	70	173.04
Lutetium	Lu	71	174.99	Yttrium	Y	39	88.92
Magnesium	Mg	12	24.32	Zinc	Zn	30	65.38
Manganese	Mn	25	54.94	Zirconium	Zr	40	91.22
Mendelevium	Mv	101	[256]				

A value given in brackets denotes the mass number of the most stable known isotope.

electron which occupies the 1-s subshell. Helium has 2 protons and hence a nuclear charge of 2 and has 2 electrons which completely fill the 1-s subshell. Atoms having completely filled outer electron shells are extremely stable and nonreactive and form a group of elements called the noble gases, of which helium is the lightest. A third proton, giving a nuclear charge of three, requires three orbital electrons, two, of which fill the 1-shell, while the third normally occupies the 2-s shell. This third electron is relatively weakly bound and may be readily lost, forming a positively charged ion with high chemical activity. This is the element lithium, the lightest of the alkali-metal group. Addition of another proton produces a nucleus with a charge of four, and, hence, there are four orbital electrons, two in the 1-s subshell and two in the 2-s subshell. Although the 2-s subshell is filled, the 2-shell is not, and we have the chemically reactive metal beryllium, capable of losing its two outermost electrons to form divalent positive ions.

In like manner, we may construct the pattern of the outer electron shell of boron, in which the fifth electron enters the 2-p subshell. There is little energy difference between 2-s and 2-p electrons, so boron usually loses all three of its 2-shell electrons to form trivalent ions. Carbon similarly forms tetravalent positive ions. The seven, eight, and nine electrons characteristic, respectively, of nitrogen, oxygen, and fluorine similarly fill the 1-s and 2-s subshells and enter the 2-p. The energy requirements of the 2-p make it possible for these atoms to pick up electrons from their environment to form negative ions— trivalent for nitrogen, divalent for oxygen, and monovalent for fluorine. A further increase in the charge of the nucleus requires a total of ten electrons, completely filling the 2-shell. This is another inert gas, neon, heavier but essentially the same in its chemical properties as the first of the group, helium.

The building of the elements of the third period, between sodium and argon, follows exactly the same pattern. The 1- and 2-shells remain filled, while the 3-shell is progressively filled, one electron at a time, forming a series of elements between sodium and chlorine, which closely resemble the corresponding elements of the second period. The series closes with a third inert gas, argon. The chemical similarities joining lithium and sodium; beryllium and magnesium; boron and aluminum; silicon and carbon; nitrogen and phosphorus; oxygen and sulfur; fluorine and chlorine; and helium, neon, and argon have their origin in the similar configuration of the *outer* electrons of the similar elements. In most chemical reactions and in most natural environments only the outermost electrons participate in the change atoms undergo, and hence these electrons are the ones that determine chemical behavior and periodic relationships.

Addition of one more electron to the argon superstructure results in an atom (potassium) chemically like sodium; addition of two, an atom (calcium) chemically resembling magnesium. These two electrons, however, enter the 4-s subshell, not the 3-d, which remains vacant. More electrons cannot further fill the 4-s, and hence they enter the 3-d. A sequence of ten elements thus intervenes before the 3-d is filled and further addition to the 4-shell may continue. These ten elements, scandium through copper, are transition metals and do not resemble the elements of the short periods. In general, they behave as metals and form positive ions. With zinc, electrons again enter the 4-shell, forming a sequence of elements from gallium through bromine which resemble the elements of the three short periods. The fourth period, the first "long" period, ends with a noble gas, krypton.

The fifth period of the periodic table is analogous to the fourth, starting with an alkali metal (rubidium), and an alkali earth (strontium), and containing a sequence of transition metals from yttrium through palladium. This is followed by a sequence resembling the short periods, from silver to iodine, and closing with another noble gas, xenon. Those of the transition metals, in which a single unpaired electron enters a sublevel, may, because the magnetic moment of that electron is uncompensated, display magnetic properties. Iron, cobalt, and nickel are examples.

The sixth period is like the fifth but is complicated by the long rare-earth sequence from cerium to lutecium. In this sequence, the 5-s, 5-p, and 6-s subshells are filled while addition of extra electrons takes place in the 4-f subshell. The 4-f is so effectively masked by the overlying higher energy subshells that additions of electrons have little effect on the properties of the elements. Hence, all rare earths have similar properties and tend to occur together in nature.

Because there is little change in the over-all architecture of the electronic superstructure throughout the entire sixth "long" period, the atoms with which the sixth period ends are about the same size as those with which it begins. This anomaly in the sizes of atoms, which results in gold (at. wt. 197) having the same atomic radius as silver (at. wt. 108), is called the *lanthanide contraction* and is of considerable significance in determining ability of elements to substitute for one another.

ABUNDANCE OF THE ELEMENTS

In the universe, insofar as we have knowledge of it, hydrogen and helium, the lightest elements, are by far the most abundant. The abundance of the remaining elements is roughly in inverse proportion to their atomic numbers, with cyclic peaks of unusual abundance, as at iron. The lightest elements are, however, not abundant in the earth

Abundance of the Chemical Elements*

(In weight per cent for all elements more abundant than 0.01% by weight.)

In the Cosmos		In Igneous Rocks		In Sandstones		In Shales		In Limestones		In the Ocean	
H	63.70	O	46.60	O	~51.	O	~49.	O	~49.	Cl	1.898
He	34.90	Si	27.72	Si	36.75	Si	27.28	Ca	30.45	Na	1.056
Ne	2.13	Al	8.13	Al	2.53	Al	8.19	C	11.35	Mg	0.127
O	0.41	Fe	5.00	Ca	3.95	Fe	4.73	Mg	4.77	S	0.084
N	0.21	Ca	3.63	C	1.38	K	2.70	Si	2.42	Ca	0.040
C	0.084	Na	2.83	K	1.10	Ca	2.23	Al	0.43	K	0.038
Fe	0.064	K	2.70	Fe	0.99	Mg	1.48	Fe	0.40	CO_2	(gas)
Si	0.048	Mg	2.09	Mg	0.71	C	1.53	P	0.11		
Mg	0.036	Ti	0.44	Na	0.33	Na	0.97	S	0.11		
A	0.017	P	0.12	S	0.28	Ti	0.43	Sr	0.049		
		Mn	0.10	Ti	0.096	S	0.26	Mn	0.039		
		F	0.070	P	0.035	P	0.074	Na	0.037		
		S	0.075	Rb	0.027	Cr	0.068	F	0.027		
		Rb	0.035	Cr	0.020	Mn	0.062	Cl	0.020		
		C	0.032	Ba	0.017	F	0.051	K	0.015		
		Cl	0.031			Ba	0.046	Ba	0.012		
		Sr	0.030			B	0.031				
		Ba	0.025			Rb	0.028				
		Zr	0.022			Cu	0.019				
		Cr	0.020			Sr	0.017				
		V	0.015			Zr	0.112				
						V	0.112				

* Jack Green, Geochemical Table of the Elements for 1953, *Bulletin Geological Society of America*, 64, 1953.

because the earth's gravity is insufficient to retain them. Segregation and concentration of the remaining elements has been made on the earth by the operation of various processes of geologic differentiation, such as gravitational separation of minerals from magmas and chemical differentiation of rocks by weathering at the surface. The life processes of plants and animals, the separation of different minerals from sea water, and the sorting action of sedimentary processes are all partly responsible for the differentiation of the chemical elements. The abundance of the chemical elements in different environments (see table, page 183) shows the results of these processes. It is to be noted that, although the percentages in all the tables total over 99 per cent, such important elements as zinc, lead, silver, gold, tin, mercury, nickel, arsenic, and antimony do not appear in any list. In all rocks, oxygen is by far the most abundant element and, because it is a relatively light element, occupies an even more important place in the earth's crust from a volumetric standpoint.

BONDING FORCES IN CRYSTALS

The forces that bind together the particles composing crystalline solids are electrical in nature. The kind and intensity of these forces are of great importance in determining the physical and chemical properties of minerals. Hardness, cleavage, fusibility, electrical and thermal conductivity, and the coefficient of thermal expansion are directly related to the kind and strength of the electrical binding forces. In general, the stronger the bond the harder the crystal, the higher its melting point, and the smaller its coefficient of thermal expansion. Thus we attribute the great hardness of diamond to the very strong electrical forces linking its constituent carbon atoms. The structural patterns of the minerals periclase, MgO, and halite, NaCl, are similar, yet periclase melts at 2800° C, whereas halite melts at 801° C. The greater amount of heat energy required to separate the atoms in periclase indicates the existence in that mineral of a stronger electrical bond than in halite.

These electrical forces are *chemical bonds* and are described as belonging to one or the other of four principal *bond types*; ionic, covalent, metallic, and van der Waals'. It should be clearly understood that this classification is one of expediency and that transitions may exist between all types. Each crystal structure represents a unique solution of the problem of the geometric marshaling of structural units in space consistent with electrical neutrality and minimum lattice energy. The electrical interaction among the ions or atoms constituting the structural units determines the properties of the resulting crystal. It is the resemblance in properties among crystals having similar types of electrical interaction that justifies the use of the classification of bonding mechanisms. Thus, the bonding forces linking the atoms of silicon and oxygen in quartz display in almost equal amount the characteristics of the ionic and the covalent bond.

Likewise, the mineral galena, PbS, displays some of the characteristics of the metallic bond, such as good electrical conductivity, and some of the ionic bond, such as excellent cleavage and brittleness. Furthermore, many crystals such as mica contain two or more bond types of different character and strength. Such crystals are called *heterodesmic* in contrast with crystals like diamond, quartz, and halite in which all bonds are of the same kind—*homodesmic.*

The Ionic Bond

A comparison of the chemical activity of elements with the configuration of their outer, or valence, electron shells leads to the conclusion that all atoms have a strong tendency to achieve a stable configuration of the outer shell in which all possible electron sites are filled. In the noble gases, helium, neon, argon, krypton, and xenon, which are almost completely inert, this condition is met. We have seen that sodium, for example, has a single valence electron in the 3-s shell, which it loses readily, leaving the atom with an unbalanced positive charge. Such a charged atom is called an *ion.* Positively charged atoms are called *cations,* and an atom bearing a single positive charge, such as sodium, is a *monovalent cation* and is represented by the symbol Na'. In similar fashion, we will speak of divalent, trivalent, tetravalent, and pentavalent cations (Ca'', Fe''', Ti^{+4} and P^{+5}). On the other hand chlorine and the other elements of the seventh group of the periodic table most easily attain the stable configuration by capturing an electron to fill the single vacancy in their outer valence shells. This produces *monovalent anions* (Cl$^-$, Br$^-$, F$^-$, I$^-$) with a net unbalanced negative charge. Oxygen, sulfur, and elements of the sixth group form divalent anions (O$^=$, S$^=$, Se$^=$, Te$^=$).

A solution of sodium chloride is thought of as containing free ions of sodium carrying unit positive electrical charges and negatively charged ions of chlorine. The incessant colliding of molecules of the solvent with the ions keeps them dissociated as long as the free energy of the particles in the solution is kept high. If, however, the temperature is reduced, or the volume of the solution decreased below a certain critical value, the mutual attraction of the opposing electrical charges of the sodium and chlorine ions exceeds the disruptive forces of collision, and the ions lock together to form the nucleus of a crystal. When a sufficient number of ions have attached themselves to the growing nucleus, it settles out of solution.

A crystal of sodium chloride removed from the solution in which it crystallized has definite and characteristic properties by which it may be recognized. The cubic crystal habit, cleavage, specific gravity, index of refraction, etc., are subject to little variation. These properties in no way resemble those of the shining metal or the greenish, acrid gas which are the elemental constituents of the substance. Touching the crystal to the tongue yields the taste of the solution.

The properties conveyed into the crystal by its constituent particles are the properties of the ions, not of the elements. We may correctly infer that the crystal is made up of ions which require only the presence of a suitable solvent to dissociate into free charged particles. These ions are joined together in the crystal structure by the attraction of their unlike electrostatic charges, and hence such a bonding mechanism is referred to as *ionic* or *electrostatic bond*.

As we have seen in the example of sodium chloride, the ionic bond confers on crystals in which it is dominant the important property of dissolving in polar solvents such as water to yield conducting solutions containing free ions.

Physically, ionic-bonded crystals are generally of moderate hardness and specific gravity, have fairly high melting and boiling points, and are very poor conductors of electricity and heat. Because the electrostatic charge constituting the ionic bond is spread over the whole surface of the atom, this bond type is not highly directional and the symmetry of the resultant crystal is generally high.

Ionic radius. Atoms and ions do not possess definite surfaces and must be thought of as tiny, very dense, and highly charged nuclei surrounded by space which is sparsely inhabited by clouds of electrons whose density varies with distance from the nucleus, falling finally to zero. Hence, the radius of an ion cannot be defined precisely except in terms of its interaction with other ions.

Between any pair of oppositely charged ions there exists an attractive electrostatic force directly proportional to the product of their charges and inversely proportional to the square of the distance between their centers (Coulomb's law). When ions approach each other under the influence of these forces, repulsive forces are set up. These repulsive forces arise from the interaction of the negatively charged electron clouds and from the opposition of the positively charged nuclei and increase rapidly with diminishing internuclear distance. The distance at which these repulsive forces balance the attractive forces is the characteristic interionic spacing for this pair of ions. In the simplest case, when both cations and anions are fairly large and feebly charged and both have numerous symmetrically disposed neighbors of opposite sign, ions may be regarded as spheres in contact. Sodium chloride, in which both cation and anion are monovalent, fairly large, and surrounded by six neighbors of opposite polarity, is a good example. In such crystals, the interionic distance may be regarded as the sum of the radii of the two ions in contact.

The interionic distance may be measured as an interplanar spacing from x-ray diffraction data (see page 134). Thus, if we assume the radius of one of the ions, the radius of the other may be found. It was in this way that the ionic radii of the periodic table (page 176) were obtained. The values shown are based in part on a radius of 1.32 Å for the oxygen ion but contain numerous correction factors. These ionic radii apply only to ionic bonded crystals and strictly only to those in which both cations and anions have six closest neighbors. Atoms and ions are not rigid bodies but respond to external electrical forces by dilatation and deformation. A larger number of neighboring ions tends to distend the central ion; a smaller number allows it to collapse a little. Some distortion of shape may accompany the distension of ions. These effects are collectively called *polarization* and are of great importance in crystal structures.

If the bond is not predominantly ionic, the interionic spacing will not agree with the sum of the radii as taken from the table, even after applying correction for polarization. Thus, the length of the silicon-oxygen bond in silicates is characteristically about 1.6 Å, much less than the sum of the radii taken from the table (1.75 Å). The large discrepancy in the case of the silicon-oxygen bond, which is regarded as about 50 per cent ionic and 50 per cent covalent, may be contrasted with the good agreement of the sum of the tabulated radii with the measured interionic spacing in halite. (Sum of the radii from table = 2.78 Å; measured interionic spacing from x-ray data is 2.81 Å.)

In summation, the size of ions in the same family in the periodic table increases with increasing atomic number up to element 57, lanthanum. Above 57 the size of ions of given charge diminishes in the rare-earth sequence, giving rise to the *lanthanide contraction*, after which the size again increases. For any atomic number, the size of the ion depends on the state of ionization. Cations are in general smaller, more rigid, and less extensible than anions, and for a given element the positive ionization states are always markedly smaller than the negative. Thus, sulfur forms both divalent negative ions and tetra- and hexavalent positive ions. The contrast between the ionic radii characterizing the different valence states is typical.

$S^=$	S^0	S^{4+}	S^{6+}
1.85	1.04	0.37	0.30

Anions are generally larger, more easily polarized, and less sensitive to variation in size with change in valence than cations.

Bond strength and physical properties. The strength of the ionic bond, that is, the amount of energy required to break it, depends on two factors: the center-to-center spacing between the two ions and their total charge. In a crystal with a "pure" ionic-bonding mechanism, such as sodium chloride, this law holds rigorously.

The effect of increased interionic distance on the strength of the ionic bond is readily seen in the halides of sodium. The table below shows the melting points and interionic distances for these compounds. It is apparent that the strength of the bond, as measured by the melting temperature, is inversely proportional to the length of the bond. The melting temperatures of the fluorides of the alkali metals illustrate that it does not matter whether it is the size of the anion or cation that is varied; bond strength varies in inverse proportion to bond length. LiF offers an intriguing exception to this generalization, explained by anion-anion repulsion in a structure having a very small cation.

Melting Point vs. Interionic Distance in Ionic-Bonded Compounds*

Compound	Interionic Distance (Å)	M.P. (°C)	Compound	Interionic Distance (Å)	M.P. (°C)
NaF	2.31	980–997	SrO	2.55	2430
NaCl	2.81	801	BaO	2.75	1923
NaBr	2.97	755			
NaI	3.23	651	LiF	2.01	870
			NaF	2.31	980–997
MgO	2.10	2800	KF	2.67	880
CaO	2.40	2580	RbF	2.82	760

*Data from *Handbook of Chem. and Phys.*, 37th ed., Chem. Rubber Publishing Co.

Hardness vs. Interionic Distance in Ionic-Bonded Compounds*

Compound	Interionic Distance (Å)	Hardness (Mohs)	Compound	Interionic Distance (Å)	Hardness (Mohs)
BeO	1.65	9.0	Na^+F^-	2.31	3.2
MgO	2.10	6.5	$Mg^{2+}O^{-2}$	2.10	6.5
CaO	2.40	4.5	$Sc^{3+}N^{-3}$	2.23	7–8
SrO	2.57	3.5	$Ti^{4+}C^{-4}$	2.23	8–9
BaO	2.77	3.3			

*Data from *Crystal Chemistry*, R. C. Evans, Cambridge University Press, 1952.

The charge on the coordinated ions has an even more powerful effect on the strength of the bond. Comparison of the absolute values of melting temperature for the alkali-earth oxides, which are divalent compounds, with the absolute values for the monovalent alkali fluorides, in which the interionic spacings are closely comparable, reveals the magnitude of this effect. Although the interionic distance, or bond length, is almost the same for corresponding oxides and fluorides, the bonds uniting the more highly charged ions are obviously much stronger. The table shows the effect of interionic spacing and charge on the hardness for a number of substances. All substances cited as examples in the table have the same structure and may be regarded as ionic bonded.

Covalent Bond

We have seen that ions of chlorine may enter into ionic-bonded crystals as stable units of structure because, by taking a free electron from the environment, they achieve a filled outer valence shell. A single atom of chlorine, with a void in its valence shell, is not stable and is in a very highly reactive condition. Such *monatomic* chlorine is highly reactive in a chemical sense and seizes upon and combines with almost anything in its neighborhood. Generally, the nearest neighbor of such a single chlorine atom is another chlorine atom, and the two promptly unite in such a way that one electron does double duty in the outer valence shells of both atoms, and both thus achieve the stable inert-gas configuration. As a result of this sharing of an electron the two atoms of chlorine are bound together in an extremely tight, intimate relation.

This electron-sharing or *covalent* bond is the strongest of the chemical bonds. Minerals so bonded are characterized by general insolubility, great stability, and very high melting and boiling points. They do not yield ions to such solutions as they form and hence are non-conductors of electricity both in the solid state and in solution. Because the electrical forces constituting the bond are sharply localized in the vicinity of the shared electron, the bond is highly directional and the symmetry of the resulting crystals is likely to be lower than where ionic bonding occurs. In chlorine, the bonding energy of the atom is entirely consumed in linking to one neighbor, and stable Cl_2 molecules result, which show little tendency to link together. Certain other elements—in general, those near the middle of the periodic table, such as carbon, silicon, aluminum, and sulfur—have two, three, and four vacant spaces in the outer electron shell, and hence not all the bonding energy is consumed in linking to one neighboring atom. Such elements tend, therefore, to unite in covalent bonding with a number of adjacent atoms, forming very stable groups of atoms of rigidly fixed shape and dimensions, which may then link together to form aggregates or groups.

Carbon is an outstanding example of such an atom. Carbon atoms have four vacancies in their valence shells which they may fill by electron sharing with four other carbon atoms, forming a very stable, firmly bonded configuration having the shape of a tetrahedron with carbon atoms at the four apices. Every carbon atom is linked in this way to four others to form a continuous network. The energy of the bond is strongly localized in the vicinity of the shared electrons, producing a very rigid and highly polarized structure—that of diamond, the hardest natural substance.

Covalent atomic radii. In covalent bonded structures, the interatomic distance is generally equal to the arithmetic mean of the interatomic distances in crystals of the elemental substances. Thus, in diamond, the C–C spacing is 1.54 Å; in metallic silicon the Si–Si distance is 2.34 Å. We may therefore suppose that if these atoms unite to form a compound, SiC, the silicon-carbon distance will be near 1.94 Å, the arithmetic mean of the elemental spacings. X-ray measurement determines this spacing in the familiar synthetic abrasive, silicon carbide, as 1.93 Å.

Estimation of the character of the bonding mechanism. It is now generally recognized that there is some electron sharing in most ionic-bonded crystals, whereas atoms in covalent-bonded substances often display some electrostatic charges. Assessment of the relative proportions of ionic to covalent character is based in part on the polarizing power and polarizability of the ions involved. Compounds of a highly polarizing ion with an easily polarized ion, such as AgI, may show strongly covalent character. In contrast, AgF, because of the lower polarizability of the smaller fluorine ion, is a dominantly ionic-bonded compound. In general, the presence of ions of small size and high charge tends to favor electron sharing as a bonding mechanism.

Bonds between elements of the first and seventh groups of the periodic table and between the second and the sixth groups are dominantly ionic. Examples are the alkali halides and the alkali-earth oxides. Bonds between like atoms or atoms close together in the periodic table will be covalent. The silicon-oxygen bond is 50 per cent ionic, the aluminum-oxygen bond 63 per cent, but the boron-oxygen bond only 44 per cent ionic. Pauling has generalized this concept and rendered it quantitative by assigning to each element a numerical value of *electronegativity*. The greater the difference in electro-negativity between any two elements, the more ionic the bond between them. (See table below and Fig. 372.)

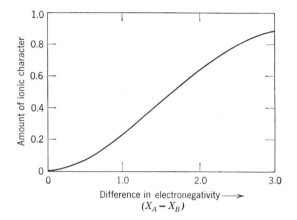

Fig. 372. Curve Relating the Amount of Ionic Character of a Bond A—B to the Difference in Electronegavity X_A—X_B of the Atoms. (After Linus Pauling, *The Nature of the Chemical Bond,* Cornell University Press, Ithaca, 1948.)

Electronegativity of Elements*

Li	Be	B	C		N	O	F
1.0	1.5	2.0	2.5		3.0	3.5	4.0
Na	Mg	Al	Si		P	S	Cl
0.9	1.2	1.5	1.8		2.1	2.5	3.0
K	Ca	Sc	Ti	Ge	As	Se	Br
0.8	1.0	1.3	1.6	1.8	2.0	2.4	2.8
Rb	Sr	Y	Zr	Sn	Sb	Te	I
0.8	1.0	1.3	1.6	1.7	1.8	2.1	2.5
Cs	Ba						
0.7	0.9						

* Linus Pauling, *The Nature of the Chemical Bond,* Cornell University Press, Ithaca, 1948.

Van der Waals' Bond

Returning to the chlorine molecules, if we take energy from these Cl_2 molecules by cooling the gas, the molecules will ultimately collapse into the close-packed, chaotic liquid state. If still more heat energy is taken away, the amplitude of vibration of the Cl_2 molecules is further reduced, and ultimately the minute, stray electrical fields existing about the essentially electrically neutral atoms will serve to lock the sluggishly moving molecules into the orderly structure of the solid state. This phenomenon of the solidification of chlorine takes place at very low temperatures, and warming above $-102°$ C will permit the molecules to break the very weak bonds and return to the disordered state of a liquid. This weak bond which ties neutral molecules and essentially uncharged structure units into a lattice by virtue of the small residual charges on their surfaces is called the *van der Waals'* or stray-field bond and is the weakest of the chemical bonds. Common only in organic compounds and solidified gases, it is not often encountered in minerals, but, when it is, it generally defines a zone of ready cleavage and low hardness. An example is the mineral graphite, which consists of covalent bonded sheets of carbon atoms linked only by van der Waals' bonds.

Metallic Bond

Elemental sodium metal is soft, lustrous, opaque, and sectile and conducts heat and electric current well. X-ray diffraction analysis reveals that the structural units are marshaled, like those of sodium chloride or solid chlorine, into the regular repetitive pattern of a true crystalline solid. The properties of the metal differ so from those of its salts and solidified gases that we are led to suspect a different mechanism of bonding. Sodium, like all true metals, conducts electricity, which means that electrons are free to move readily through the structure. So prodigal with their electrons are sodium and its close relatives, cesium, rubidium, and potassium, that the impact of the radiant energy of light knocks a considerable number entirely free of the structure. This photoelectric effect, on which such instruments as exposure meters depend, shows that the electrons are very weakly tied into the metal structure. We may thus postulate that the structural units of true metals are really the atomic nuclei bound together by the aggregate electric charge of a cloud of electrons that surrounds the nuclei. An electron owes no allegiance to any particular nucleus and is free to drift through the structure or even out of it entirely without disrupting the bonding mechanism. This type of bond is fittingly called the *metallic bond.* To it metals owe their high plasticity, tenacity, ductility, and conductivity, as well as their generally low hardness, melting point, and boiling point. Among minerals, only the native metals display pure metallic bonding.

Crystals with More Than One Bond Type

Among naturally occurring substances, with their tremendous diversity and complexity, the presence of only one type of bonding is rare, and two or more bond types coexist in most minerals. Where this is so, the crystal shares in the properties of the different bond types represented, and often strongly directional properties result. Thus, in the mineral graphite, the cohesion of the thin sheets in which the mineral generally occurs is the result of the strong covalent bonding in the plane of the sheets, whereas the excellent cleavage, one of the best among minerals, reflects the weak van der Waals' bond joining the sheets together. The micas, which consist of sheets of strongly bonded silica tetrahedra (see page 455), with the relatively weak ionic bond joining the sheets together through the cations, similarly reflect in their remarkable cleavage the difference in strength of the two bond types. The prismatic habit and cleavage of the pyroxenes and amphiboles, and the chunky, blocky habit and cleavage of the feldspars, we shall see, may likewise be traced to the influence of relatively weak bonds joining together more strongly bonded structure units having a chain, band, or block shape.

THE COORDINATION PRINCIPLE

When oppositely charged ions unite to form a crystal structure in which the binding forces are dominantly electrostatic, each ion tends to gather to itself, or to *coordinate*, as many ions of opposite sign as size permits. When the atoms are linked by simple electrostatic bonds, they may be regarded as spheres in contact, and the geometry is simple. The coordinated ions always cluster about the central coordinating ion in such a way that their centers lie at the apices of a regular polyhedron. Thus, in a stable crystal structure, each cation lies at the center of a *coordination polyhedron* of anions. The number of anions in the polyhedron is the coordination number (**C.N.**) of the cation with respect to the given anion, and is determined by their relative sizes. Thus, in NaCl each Na has six closest Cl neighbors and is said to be in 6-fold coordination with Cl (**C.N. 6**). In fluorite, CaF_2, each calcium ion is at the center of a coordination polyhedron consisting of eight fluorine ions and hence is in 8-fold coordination with respect to fluorine (**C.N. 8**).

Anions may also be regarded as occupying the centers of coordination polyhedra formed of cations. In NaCl each chloride ion has six sodium neighbors and hence is in 6-fold coordination with respect to sodium.

Since both sodium and chlorine are in 6-fold coordination, there must be equal numbers of both, in agreement with the formula, NaCl. On the other hand, examination of the fluorite structure (see Fig. 467) reveals that each fluorine ion has four closest calcium neighbors and hence is in 4-fold coordination with respect to calcium (**C.N. 4**). Although these four calcium ions do not touch each other, they form a definite coordination polyhedron about the central fluorine ion in such a way that the calcium ions lie at the apices of a regular tetrahedron. Since each calcium ion has eight fluorine neighbors, while each fluorine ion has only four calcium neighbors, it is obvious that there are twice as many fluorine as calcium ions in the structure. This accords with the formula CaF_2, and with the usual valences for calcium and fluorine.

It is easily seen that the relative sizes of the calcium and fluorine ions would permit a structure containing equal numbers of each with both ions in 8-fold coordination. The fact that in fluorite only half the possible calcium sites are filled calls attention to an important restriction on crystal structures; viz., *the total numbers of ions of all kinds in any stable crystal structure must be such that the crystal as a whole is electrically neutral.* That is, the total number of positive charges must equal the total number of negative charges; hence, in fluorite there may be only half as many divalent positive calcium ions as there are monovalent negative fluorine ions.

RADIUS RATIO

Although each ion in a crystal affects every other ion to some extent, the strongest forces exist between ions which are nearest neighbors. These are said to constitute the *first coordination shell*. The geometry of arrangement of this shell and hence the coordination number are dependent on the relative sizes of the coordinated ions. The relative size of ions is generally expressed as a *radius ratio*, $R_A : R_X$, where R_A is the radius of the cation and R_X the radius of the anion in angstrom units. The radius ratio of sodium and chlorine in halite, NaCl, is therefore

$$R_{Na} = 0.97 \text{ Å} \qquad R_{Cl} = 1.81 \text{ Å}$$

$$R_{Na} : R_{Cl} = 0.97/1.81 = 0.54$$

The radius ratio of calcium and fluorine in fluorite, CaF_2, is

$$R_{Ca} = 0.99 \text{ Å} \qquad R_F = 1.36 \text{ Å}$$

$$R_{Ca} : R_F = 0.99/1.36 = 0.73$$

When two or more cations are present in a structure, coordinated with the same anion, separate radius ratios may be computed for each. Thus, in spinel, $MgAl_2O_4$, both magnesium and aluminum coordinate oxygen anions. Hence,

$$R_{Mg} = 0.66 \text{ Å} \qquad R_{Al} = 0.51 \text{ Å} \qquad R_O = 1.32 \text{ Å}$$

$$R_{Mg} : R_O = 0.66/1.32 = 0.50 \qquad R_{Al} : R_O = 0.51/1.32 = 0.39$$

When coordinating and coordinated ions are of the same size, the radius ratio is 1. Trial with a tray of identical spheres, such as pingpong balls, reveals that identical spherical units may be packed stably together in either of two equally economical ways, called hexagonal closest packing (as in brucite, see Fig. 585) and cubic closest packing (as in copper, see Fig. 389). Either way each sphere has its twelve closest neighbors all mutually in contact (**C.N.** 12). Twelve-fold coordination is rare in minerals, occurring in the native metals of the gold group, which are not, however, ionic bonded, and in micas where the alkali-metal cation has **C.N.** = 12 with respect to oxygen.

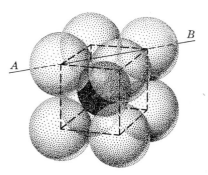

Fig. 373. Cubic or 8-Fold Coordination of X Ions about an A Ion. $R_A : R_X > 0.732$.

When the coordinating cation is slightly smaller than the anions, 8-fold coordination is stable. This is also called *cubic coordination*

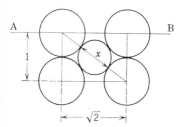

$$(1 + x)^2 = (1)^2 + (\sqrt{2})^2$$
$$1 + x = \sqrt{1 + 2} = 1.732$$
$$x = 0.732$$

Fig. 374. Limiting Condition for Cubic Coordination.

for the centers of the anions lie at the eight corners of a cube (Fig. 373). If we consider a cubic coordination polyhedron in which the anions touch each other as well as the central cation, we may compute the limiting value of radius ratio for **C.N.** = 8. Allowing the radius of the anion to equal unity, the radius of the cation for this limiting condition must be 0.732 (Fig. 374). Hence, cubic coordination has maximum stability for radius ratios between 0.732 and 1.000.

For values of radius ratio less than 0.732, 8-fold coordination is not as stable as 6-fold, in which the centers of the coordinated ions lie at the apices of a regular octahedron. Six-fold coordination is accordingly called *octahedral coordination* (Fig. 375). We may, as before, calculate the limiting value of radius ratio for the condition in which the six coordinated anions touch each other and the central cation. The lower limit of radius ratio for stable 6-fold coordination is found to be 0.414 (Fig. 376). Hence, we may expect six to be the common coordination number when the radius ratio lies between 0.732 and 0.414. Na and Cl in halite, Ca and CO_3 in calcite, the B-type cations in spinel and the Y-type ions in silicates are examples of 6-fold coordination.

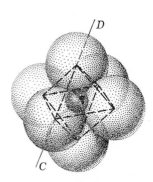

Fig. 375. Octahedral or 6-Fold Coordination of X Ions about an A Ion. $R_A : R_X = 0.732 - 0.414$.

Figure 377 illustrates the change from 6-fold to 8-fold coordination in the alkali chlorides with increasing ionic radius of the cation. It is interesting to note that rubidium may be in both 6- and 8-fold coordination and thus rubidium chloride is polymorphic.

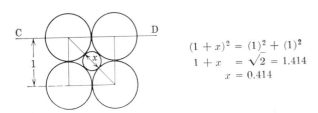

$$(1 + x)^2 = (1)^2 + (1)^2$$
$$1 + x = \sqrt{2} = 1.414$$
$$x = 0.414$$

Fig. 376. Limiting Condition for Octahedral Coordination.

It may be proved in similar fashion that 4-fold or *tetrahedral* coordination, in which the centers of the coordinated ions lie at the apices of a regular tetrahedron, has maximum stability between radius ratio limits of 0.414 and 0.225. Tetrahedral coordination is typified by the SiO_4 group in silicates, by the A-type ion in spinel, and by the ZnS structure (Fig. 378).

Threefold, or *triangular*, coordination is stable between limits of 0.225 and 0.155 and is common in nature in the CO_3, NO_3, and BO_3 ionic groups (Fig. 379).

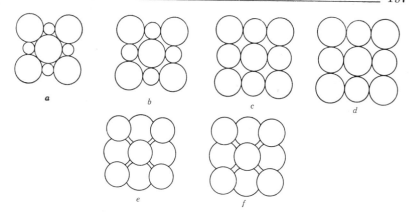

Fig. 377. Packing of Ions.

a. Lithium Chloride
b. Sodium Chloride
c. Potassium Chloride

d. Rubidium Chloride
e. Rubidium Chloride
f. Cesium Chloride

a, b, c, and d have sodium chloride structure with 6-fold coordination; e and f have cesium chloride structure with 8-fold coordination. In each figure the larger circles represent anions, the smaller circles cations.

Twofold coordination is very rare in ionic-bonded crystals. Examples are the uranyl group $(UO_2)''$, the nitrite group $(NO_2)^=$, and copper with respect to oxygen in cuprite, Cu_2O (Fig. 380).

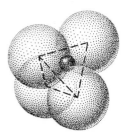

Fig. 378. Tetrahedral or 4-Fold Coordination of X Ions about an A Ion.
$R_A : R_X = 0.414 - 0.225.$

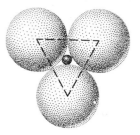

Fig. 379. Triangular Coordination of X Ions about an A Ion.
$R_A : R_X = 0.225 - 0.155.$

Although rare, examples of 5-, 7-, 9-, and 10-fold coordination are known. Such coordination numbers are possible only in complex structures and result from the filling of interstices between other coordination polyhedra.

If the bonding mechanism is not purely ionic, radius-ratio considerations may not be safely used to determine the coordination number.
The smaller and more strongly polarizing the coordinating cation, or
the larger and more polarizable the anion,
the wider the expectable departure from the
theoretical radius-ratio limits.

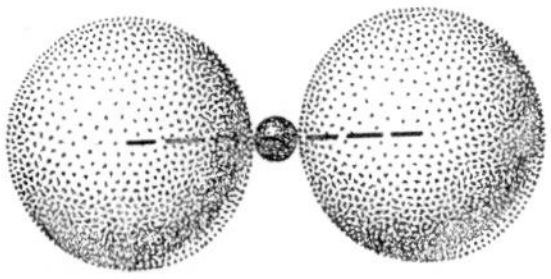

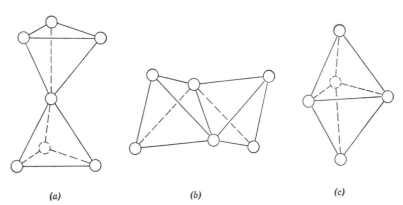

Obviously, every ion in a crystal structure has some effect on every other ion—
attractive if the charges are opposite, repulsive if the same. Hence, ions tend to group
themselves in space to form crystal lattices
in such a way that cations are as far apart
as possible yet consistent with the coordina-
tion of the anions that will result in electrical neutrality. Thus, when
cations share anions between them, they do so in such a way as to
place themselves as far apart as possible. Hence, the coordination
polyhedra formed around each are linked more commonly through
corners than through edges or faces (Fig. 381). Cations tend to share
as small a number of anions as possible, and sharing of as many as
three or four anions is rare.

Fig. 380. Linear or 2-Fold
Coordination of X Ions
about an A Ion.
$R_A : R_X < 0.155$.

(a)   *(b)*   *(c)*

Fig. 381. Tetrahedra Sharing Corners, Edges, and Faces.

Pauling's rules. Every stable crystal, in its ordered internal
architecture, bears witness to the operation of certain universal principles which determine the structure of solid matter. These principles
were enunciated in 1929 by Pauling in the form of the following
five rules:

Rule 1. A coordinated polyhedron of anions is formed about each cation, the cation-anion distance being determined by the radius sum and the coordination number of the cation by the radius ratio.

Rule 2. *The electrostatic valency principle.* In a stable coordination structure the total strength of the valency bonds which reach an anion from all the neighboring cations is equal to the charge of the anion.

Rule 3. The existence of edges, and particularly of faces, common to two anion polyhedra in a coordinated structure decreases its stability; this effect is large for cations with high valency and small coordination number and is especially large when the radius ratio approaches the lower limit of stability of the polyhedron.

Rule 4. In a crystal containing different cations, those of high valency and small coordination number tend not to share polyhedron elements with each other.

Rule 5. *The principle of parsimony.* The number of essentially different kinds of constituents in a crystal tends to be small.

These rules constitute a formal statement of principles that have been discussed elsewhere. Rule 5, the principle of parsimony, refers not to chemically different kinds of constituents but to structurally distinct types of atomic sites. Thus, in crystals of very complex composition, a number of different ions may occupy the same structural position. These ions must be considered as a single "constituent" in the sense of rule 5.

STRUCTURE TYPE

Although there seems to be little in common between uraninite, UO_2, and fluorite, CaF_2, their x-ray powder patterns show analogous lines, although different in spacing and intensity. Structure analysis reveals that the uranium atoms in uraninite are in 4-fold coordination with respect to oxygen, whereas eight oxygens are grouped about each uranium. In fluorite, four calcium ions are grouped about each fluorine, and eight fluorines are packed about each calcium. Uraninite and fluorite have structures that are analogous in every respect, although the cell dimensions are different and the properties are, of course, utterly unlike. These two substances are said to be *isostructural*, or *isotypous*, and belong to the same *structure type*. All crystals in which the centers of the constituent atoms occupy geometrically similar positions, regardless of the size of the atoms or the absolute dimensions of the structure, are said to belong to the same structure type. For example, all crystals in which there are equal numbers of cations and anions in 6-fold coordination belong to the

NaCl structure type. A large number of minerals of diverse composition belong to this structure type, including KCl, sylvite; MgO, periclase; NiO, bunsenite; PbS, galena; MnS, alabandite; AgCl, cerargyrite; TiN, osbornite; and many others.

Of great importance in mineralogy is the concept of the *isostructural group:* a group of minerals related to each other by analogous structures, generally having a common anion, and frequently displaying extensive ionic substitution. Many groups of minerals are isostructural, of which the barite group of sulfates, the calcite group of carbonates, and the aragonite group of carbonates are perhaps the best examples. The extremely close relationship that exists among the members of many groups is illustrated by the aragonite group listed herewith.

Aragonite Group

Mineral	Chemical Composition	Axial Ratios $a:b:c$	110 $\wedge$ 1$\bar{1}$0	Cleavage	
Aragonite	$CaCO_3$	0.622:1:0.721	63° 48′	{110}	{010}
Witherite	$BaCO_3$	0.603:1:0.730	62° 12′	{110}	{010}
Strontianite	$SrCO_3$	0.609:1:0.724	62° 41′	{110}	
Cerussite	$PbCO_3$	0.610:1:0.723	62° 46′	{110}	{021}

ELECTROSTATIC VALENCY

A fundamental principle of organization of ionic-bonded crystals is that the sum of the strength of all bonds reaching an ion must equal the valence of that ion. Therefore, we may compute the relative strength of any bond in a crystal structure by dividing the total charge on the coordinating ion by the number of nearest neighbors to which it is linked. The resulting number, called the *electrostatic valency* (e.v.) is a measure of the strength of any of the bonds reaching the coordinating ion from its nearest neighbors. For instance, in sodium chloride, each sodium ion has a single positive charge and has six nearest neighbors; hence the electrostatic valency equals 1/6. This number is a measure of the strength of the bond reaching any sodium ion from any neighboring chlorine ion. The chlorine ions have also a single charge and are in 6-fold coordination with respect to sodium, hence the e.v. for chlorine is also 1/6. Crystals in which all bonds are of equal strength are called *isodesmic.* This generalization is so simple that it seems trivial, but in some cases unexpected results emerge from calculation of electrostatic valencies. For example, minerals of the spinel group have formulas of the type AB_2O_4, where A is a divalent cation such as magnesium or ferrous iron and B is a trivalent cation such as aluminum or ferric iron. Such compounds have often been called aluminates and ferrates, by analogy with such compounds as borates and oxalates. This nomenclature suggests that ionic clusters or radicals are present in the structure. X-ray data reveal that the A ions are in 4-fold coordination whereas the B ions are in 6-fold. Hence, for the A ions, e.v. $= 2/4 = 1/2$; and, for B ions, e.v. $= 3/6 = 1/2$. In spite of the appearance of the formula, all bonds are the same strength. Such crystals are isodesmic and are multiple oxides, not oxysalts.

When small, highly charged cations coordinate larger and less strongly charged anions, compact, firmly bonded groups result, as the carbonates and nitrates. If the strength of the bonds within such groupings is computed the numerical value of the e.v. is always greater than one-half the total charge on the anion. This means that in such groups, the anions are more strongly bonded to the central coordinating cation than they can possibly be bonded to any other ion. For example, in the carbonate group, tetravalent carbon (Ion. rad. 0.16 Å) coordinates divalent oxygen (Ion. rad. 1.32 Å). The radius ratio of 0.121 indicates that 3-fold coordination will be stable, and hence we may compute the e.v. $= 4/3 = 1\frac{1}{3}$. This is greater than one-half the charge on the oxygen ion, and hence a functional group, or radical, exists. This is the carbonate triangle, the basic structural unit of carbonate minerals. Another example is the sulfate group. Hexavalent positive sulfur (Ion. rad. 0.30 Å) coordinates oxygen. The radius ratio of 0.234 indicates that 4-fold coordination will be stable; hence the e.v. $= 6/4 = 1\frac{1}{2}$. Since this is greater than one-half the charge on the oxygen ion, the sulfate radical forms a tightly knit group, and oxygen is bonded to sulfur more strongly than it can be bound to any other ion in the structure. This is the tetrahedral unit that is the fundamental basis of the structure of all sulfates. Such compounds as sulfates and carbonates are said to be *anisodesmic*.

Of course, it must be understood that, if the radicals are regarded as single structural units, then in a compound such as $CaCO_3$, calcite, all calcium-carbonate bonds are of equal strength and resemble those of an isodesmic crystal. Likewise, in simple sulfates like barite, all barium-sulfate bonds may be equal in strength. The crystals are, however, called anisodesmic because the presence of the strong carbon-oxygen and sulfur-oxygen bonds in addition to the weaker calcium-carbonate and barium-sulfate bonds.

Logic requires a third case: that in which the strength of bonds joining the central coordinating cation to its coordinated anions equals exactly half the bonding energy of the anion. In this case each anion may be bonded to some other unit in the structure just as strongly as it is to the coordinating cation. The other unit may be an identical cation, and the anion shared between two cations may enter into the coordination polyhedra of both. Let us consider the case of boron-oxygen groupings. Boron is trivalent with ionic radius 0.23. Hence the radius ratio with oxygen is 0.173, indicating triangular coordination, and the e.v. will hence be $3/3 = 1$. This is half the bonding strength of the oxygen ion. Consequently, a BO_3 triangle may link to some other ion just as strongly as to the central B ion. If this ion is another B''', two triangles may result, linked through a common oxygen to form a single $B_2O_5{}^{-4}$ group. In similar fashion, BO_3 triangles may join, or *polymerize*, to form chains, sheets, or boxworks by sharing oxygen ions. Such crystals are called *mesodesmic*, and the most important example is the silicates.

All ionic crystals may now be classified on the basis of the relative strength of their bonds into isodesmic, mesodesmic, and anisodesmic crystals.

COMPOSITIONAL VARIATION IN MINERALS

Minerals in nature crystallize from solutions of complex composition, and hence ample opportunity is afforded for the substitution of one ion for another. As a result, practically all minerals display variation in their chemical composition between localities and even between one specimen and another from the same locality.

Compositional variation in minerals takes place by substitution, in a given structure, of an ion or ionic group for another ion or ionic group. We may call this relationship *ionic substitution*. There are several factors that determine the extent to which it may take place. The most important is the size of the ion. Ions of two elements can readily substitute for each other only if their ionic radii are similar and differ by less than 15 per cent. If the radii of two ions differ by 15 to 30 per cent substitution is limited and rare; if they differ by more than 30 per cent, little substitution is likely. These limits are only approximate but are based on empirical data derived from study of a number of mineral systems displaying ionic substitution. Another factor of great importance is the temperature at which the crystal is grown. The higher the temperature, the greater the amount of thermal disorder, and the less stringent the space requirements of the lattice. Hence, crystals grown at high temperatures may display extensive ionic substitution that would not have taken place at lower temperatures. An example is the high-temperature potassium feldspar sanidine, which contains much larger amounts of sodium than could be accommodated stably in crystals grown at lower temperatures.

In some cases, the extent of ionic substitution is definitely limited. Thus, divalent iron may enter the lattice of sphalerite, ZnS, in amounts up to about 36 per cent. Iron cannot, however, completely replace zinc in sphalerite, for FeS, troilite, is hexagonal, whereas sphalerite is isometric. Although the ionic radii would indicate possible extensive replacement of zinc by ferrous ion, this replacement is severely curtailed. Recent investigations have shown that temperature of crystallization, rather than ionic radius, is the chief factor determining the extent to which iron may replace zinc in sphalerite. The relation between iron content and temperature of crystallization is shown graphically in Fig. 382.

COUPLED IONIC SUBSTITUTION

It may seem that, for one ion to substitute for another, the two must have the same charge. This is not necessarily so, for frequently an ion may substitute for another of different charge. Electrical neutrality of the crystal is maintained by the simultaneous substitution elsewhere in the lattice of another ion whose charge balances out the deficit or excess caused by the first substitution. Thus, Ca″ may

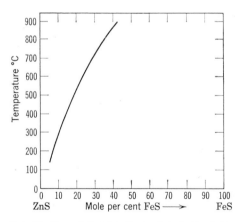

Fig. 382. Substitution of Fe″ for Zn in Sphalerite (after Kullerud).

readily substitute for Na′ because the ions are almost identical in size. The deficit of one electron caused by the substitution of Ca″

for Na′ may be balanced by the simultaneous substitution, in another type of ionic site of Al‴ for Si^{+4}. Thus, $Ca″ + Al‴ = Na′ + Si^{+4}$, and the growing crystal retains its electrical neutrality. This is the mechanism of compositional variation in the soda-lime feldspars and is called *coupled substitution*. Coupling may involve two cations as in the example cited; a cation and an anion, two anions, or even the substitution of a neutral atom or a lattice vacancy for a cation or an anion in order to achieve electrical neutrality. Neutral atoms in lattice vacancies introduced in this way may have important effects on the electrical and optical properties of the crystal.

Fig. 383. Random Substitution of Anions in Sodium Chloride Structure. Cations — small dark; anions — large white and black.

SOLID SOLUTION OR ISOMORPHISM

Numerous examples of complete ionic substitution are offered by isostructural mineral groups. In the calcite group ferrous iron may enter the lattice of magnesite, $MgCO_3$, in any proportion, and magnesium is likewise capable of entering the lattice of siderite, $FeCO_3$, in all proportions. It is apparent that the magnesite and siderite lattices are sufficiently close in their space requirements so that either ion may fill those requirements with equal ease. (Since the charge of both ions is the same, the substitution is simple. In such a case, the relation between siderite and magnesite may be pictured as being one of *solid solution,* and the minerals of intermediate composition regarded as though they were homogeneous solutions of $MgCO_3$ in $FeCO_3$ or vice versa. Of course, it is clearly understood that there are no actual molecules of either of these pure compounds and that ionic substitution is completely random within the framework of the lattice (see Fig. 383). (However, the idea of the solid solution is useful and may be used to express the relationships in any mineral series in which the compositions lie between two pure compounds, called *end members,* as limits. (Examples of such solid-solution series are the plagioclase feldspars, in which the end members are albite, $NaAlSi_3O_8$ and anorthite, $CaAl_2Si_2O_8$, and the garnets in which complete solid-solution relations exist between most of the named varieties.)

The term *isomorphism,* originally proposed in 1819 to describe crystals which had the same outward form, is used today by many mineralogists synonymously with *solid solution.* It is felt wiser to restore the term isomorphism to its original meaning and to use solid solution for those cases of complete ionic substitution within the framework of an isostructural group.)

EXSOLUTION

Another aspect of crystal growth to which radius ratio and geometry of packing afford a clear approach is that of disordered, nonequilibrium crystals. What happens to a rapidly grown alkali halide crystal growing from a solution containing all the alkali metals and all the halogens? If crystallization is at a sufficiently high temperature and growth is sufficiently rapid, there is a good deal of "play" in the structure, organization is loose, and ions whose sizes do not meet the equilibrium requirements for radius ratio may be incorporated in the structure, as, for example, Rb' and Cs' in the NaCl structure. When such a crystal is cooled, large stresses which tend to force them from the lattice exist as a result of the poor fit of the outsize ions. If sufficient time is allowed, these misfit ions migrate through the lattice and tend to group locally. Such concentrations of alien ions then arrange themselves into coordinations better suited to their size and form nuclei of a different structure which grow in the solid body of the host crystal.

This process of segregation and growth of rejected ions into crystal domains in the solid state from a disordered crystal is called *exsolution.* It is important in the interpretation of many natural mineral intergrowths. Thus, thin lamellae of sodium feldspar in potassium feldspar are interpreted as the result of exsolution of excess sodium from the potassium feldspar after crystallization. These intergrowths, called *perthite,* are very common in rocks, and this crystal chemical explanation of their formation aids materially in interpreting the history of the rock. Similarly, lenticular bodies of ilmenite in magnetite are interpreted as exsolved crystals.

Homeomorphism. Although similarities in crystals of different minerals usually result from chemically identical or similar ions in the structure, some minerals closely resemble others in crystal habit although they are quite unlike chemically. If the geometry of the arrangement of dissimilar ions is the same, similar-appearing crystals may result, as, for example, rutile, TiO_2, and zircon, $ZrSiO_4$. Both these minerals are tetragonal with similar crystal forms and axial ratios in spite of their unlike chemical compositions. Such minerals are called *homeomorphs.*

PSEUDOMORPHS

If a crystal of a mineral is altered so that the internal structure is changed but the external form is preserved, it is called a *pseudomorph,* or *false form.* The chemical composition and structure of a pseudomorph belong to one mineral species, whereas the crystal outline corresponds to another. For example, pyrite may change to limonite but preserve all the external features of the pyrite. Such a crystal is described as a pseudomorph of *limonite after pyrite.* Pseudomorphs are usually further defined according to the manner in which they were formed, as by:

1. *Substitution.* In this type of pseudomorph there is a gradual removal of the original material and a corresponding and simultaneous replacement of it by another with no chemical reaction between the two. A common example of this is the substitution of silica for the wood fiber to form petrified wood. Another example is quartz, SiO_2, after fluorite, CaF_2.

2. *Incrustation.* In the formation of this type of pseudomorph a crust of one mineral is deposited over crystals of another. A common example is quartz incrusting cubes of fluorite. The fluorite may later be entirely carried away by solution, but its former presence is indicated by the casts left in the quartz.

3. *Alteration.* In this type of pseudomorph there has been only a partial addition of new material, or a partial removal of the original material. The change of anhydrite, $CaSO_4$, to gypsum, $CaSO_4 \cdot 2H_2O$, and the change of

galena, PbS, to anglesite, $PbSO_4$, are examples of alteration pseudomorphs. A core of the unaltered mineral may be found in such pseudomorphs.

4. *Paramorphism.* The name paramorph is given to a crystal whose internal structure has changed to that of a polymorphous form without producing any change in external form. Thus aragonite frequently goes over to calcite, and rutile changes to brookite.

MINERALOIDS

There are a number of mineral substances whose analyses do not yield definite chemical formulas and which further show no sign of crystallinity. They have been called *gel minerals* or *mineraloids*. A mineral may exist in a crystalline phase with a definite composition and crystal structure, or, formed under different conditions, practically the same substance may occur as a mineraloid. The mineraloids are formed under conditions of low pressure and temperature and are commonly substances originating during the process of weathering of the materials of the earth's crust. They characteristically occur in mammillary, botryoidal, stalactitic, and similar-shaped masses. The power of these minerals to absorb other substances to a considerable extent accounts for their often wide variations in chemical composition. Limonite and opal are familiar examples of gel minerals.

REFERENCES

Crystal Chemistry

R. C. Evans, *An introduction to crystal chemistry.* Cambridge University Press, Cambridge, England, 1952. A discussion of the general principles of crystal chemistry.

W. L. Bragg, *Atomic structure of minerals.* Cornell University Press, Ithaca, 1937. A presentation of the crystal structure of selected minerals and a discussion of the general principles regarding mineral structures.

L. Pauling, *The nature of the chemical bond.* Cornell University Press, Ithaca, 1948. A treatment of the various bonding mechanisms and their effect on the physical and chemical properties of crystal structures.

Brian Mason, *Principles of Geochemistry,* 2nd ed. John Wiley and Sons, New York, 1958. Chapters 1–4. A brief treatment of structure and composition of the earth, the abundance of elements, and some of the thermodynamic principles of crystal chemistry.

Paul Niggli (translated by R. L. Parker), *Rock and mineral deposits.* W. H. Freeman, San Francisco, 1954. Chapters 2–4 deal with the structures of the principal minerals.

A. N. Winchell and Horace Winchell, *Elements of optical mineralogy,* Part II, 4th ed. John Wiley and Sons, New York, 1951. Contains a wealth of information regarding variation of properties of minerals with chemical composition.

C. DERIVATION OF A CHEMICAL FORMULA FROM THE ANALYSIS OF A MINERAL

All the chemical formulas that are assigned to minerals have been calculated from chemical analyses. An analysis gives the percentage composition of a mineral, or, in other words, the parts by weight in 100 parts of the different elements or radicals present. Consider the following analysis of chalcopyrite:

1 Percentages	2 Atomic Weights	3 Atomic Proportions	4 Atomic Ratio	
Cu = 34.30	63.54	= 0.5398	= 1	
Fe = 30.59	55.85	= 0.5477	= 1	approx.
S = 34.82	32.07	= 1.0857	= 2	

In the first column the numbers given indicate the weight percentages of the different elements in the mineral; but, as these elements have different atomic weights, the numbers do not represent the ratios of the different atoms to each other in the chemical compound. In order to derive the relative proportions of the atoms of the different elements to each other, the percentages as given are divided in each case by the atomic weight of the element. This gives a series of numbers which represents the atomic proportions in the compound and from which the atomic ratios can be quickly derived. In the analysis of chalcopyrite, these ratios become $S:Cu:Fe = 2:1:1$. Consequently, $CuFeS_2$ will constitute the chemical formula for the mineral.

If the mineral is an oxygen compound, the results of the analysis are given by convention as percentages of the oxides present. By a calculation similar to that outlined above, the ratios of these oxides to each other in the compound is determined, the only difference in the process being that in this case the percentage numbers are divided by the sum of the atomic weights of the elements present in the different oxides. As an example consider the following analysis of gypsum:

1 Percentages	2 Molecular Weights	3 Molecular Proportions	4 Molecular Ratio	
CaO = 32.44	56.1	= 0.578	= 1	
SO_3 = 46.61	80.06	= 0.582	= 1	approx.
H_2O = 20.74	18.0	= 1.152	= 2	
99.79				

From this it is seen that the ratios of the oxides to each other in the compound are $SO_3 : CaO : H_2O = 1 : 1 : 2$, and consequently the composition of gypsum can be represented by $CaO \cdot SO_3 \cdot 2H_2O$ or $CaSO_4 \cdot 2H_2O$.

It is frequently desirable to determine the theoretical composition of a mineral from its chemical formula as a check on the validity of the formula. The process of calculation is the reverse of that described in the preceding division. Take, for example, the mineral chalcopyrite, $CuFeS_2$; what are the proportions by weight of the different elements in 100 parts of the mineral? The process consists in first adding up the atomic weights of the different elements present and so obtaining the molecular weight of the compound, as follows:

$$\begin{array}{rcl}
 & \text{Atomic Weights} & \\
\text{Cu} & = & 63.54 \\
\text{Fe} & = & 55.85 \\
S_2 = 32.07 \times 2 & = & \underline{64.14} \\
\text{Molecular weight } CuFeS_2 & = & 183.53
\end{array}$$

It is obvious from the above that in 183.53 parts by weight of chalcopyrite there are 63.6 parts of copper, etc. In order to find the parts of copper in 100 parts of the mineral, or, in other words, the percentage, the following proportion is made:

$$183.53 : 63.54 = 100 : x$$

When this equation is solved, x becomes 34.62, or the theoretical percentage of copper in chalcopyrite. The percentages of the iron and sulfur are obtained in a similar manner.

D. INSTRUMENTS AND METHODS OF TESTING

On the following pages are described a series of tests, collectively called "blowpipe tests," that have been standard mineralogical procedure since the middle of the nineteenth century. The *Manual of Determinative Mineralogy* (1874) by George J. Brush popularized the tests and the sixteenth edition (1926) revised by Samuel L. Penfield[1] has been a standard reference.

During the twentieth century, with the increasing use of new methods of mineralogical study, blowpipe tests have fallen into disuse by some teachers of mineralogy. However, the author is convinced that

[1] George J. Brush and Samuel L. Penfield, *The Manual of Determinative Mineralogy with an Introduction on Blowpipe Analysis,* 16th ed., John Wiley and Sons, New York, 1926.

the blowpipe has its place in modern mineralogy, particularly in the beginning course. Minerals are chemical elements or compounds and their chemistry is their most important property. Aside from being excellent determinative procedures, the blowpipe tests keep the chemistry of minerals constantly before the student.

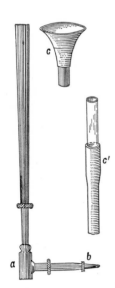

Fig. 384. Common Blowpipe.

The blowpipe and its uses. Many chemical tests made on minerals are quickly and easily performed by means of a blowpipe. The ordinary blowpipe consists essentially of a tapering tube ending in a small opening through which air can be forced in a thin stream under high pressure. When this current of air is directed into a luminous flame, combustion takes place more rapidly and completely, producing a very hot flame.

Figure 384 represents a common type of blowpipe. The mouthpiece, either c or c', is fitted into the upper end of the tube, and air from the lungs forced into it issues from the small opening at the other end. The tip of the blowpipe, b, is placed just within a flame rich in carbon (Fig. 385). The resulting blowpipe flame should be nonluminous, narrow, sharp-pointed, and clean-cut. If illuminating gas is not available, a candle can be used.

Figure 386 illustrates a more elaborate blowpipe. It resembles the blowpipe described above but is constructed with a gas fitting, c (Fig.

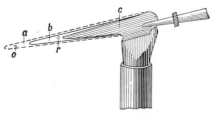

Fig. 385. Blowpipe Flame. a—oxidizing flame, b—reducing flame, c—unburned gas. o and r indicate positions of assay in oxidizing and reducing flames respectively.

386), in such a way that air, forced into the tube through the mouthpiece a, and gas admitted through tube d, issue together from the opening e.

The art of blowpiping. It usually requires some practice before one can produce a steady and continuous blowpipe flame. Some blowpipe tests can be completed before it is necessary to replenish the supply of air in the lungs. Frequently, however, an operation takes a longer time than this permits, and an interruption in order to fill the lungs afresh materially interferes with the success of the experiment. Consequently, it often becomes important to be able to maintain a steady stream of air from the blowpipe for a considerable time. This is accomplished by distending the cheeks so as to form a reservoir of air in the mouth. When the supply of air in the lungs is exhausted, the passage from the mouth into the throat is closed by lifting the root

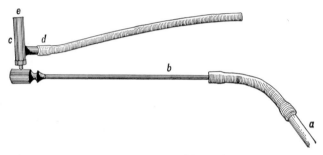

Fig. 386. Improved Blowpipe.

of the tongue and, while a new supply is being obtained by breathing in through the nose, a steady stream of air is also being forced out of the reservoir in the mouth. In this way a constant flame may be obtained.

Fusion by means of the blowpipe flame. A good blowpipe flame may reach a temperature as high as 1500° C, but the temperature varies somewhat, depending on the type of gas used and the mixture of gas and air. The determination of the degree of fusibility of a mineral is an important aid to its identification. It should be emphasized that, although the temperature of the blowpipe flame is high, the amount of heat is small. Thus for best results small fragments of uniform size should be used. The small mineral fragment on which a blowpipe test is made is known as the *assay*.

In making the fusion test the assay, if possible a sharply pointed fragment of the mineral, should be inserted into the blowpipe flame just beyond the tip of the inner cone, where the combustion is most rapid and the temperature the highest. If it melts and rounds over, losing its sharp outline, it is said to be fusible in the blowpipe flame.

Minerals can therefore be divided into two classes, those fusible and those infusible in this flame. The minerals which are fusible can be further classified according to the ease with which they fuse. To assist in this classification, a series of six minerals which show different degrees of fusibility has been chosen as a scale to which all fusible minerals may be referred. For instance, when a mineral is said to have a fusibility of 3, it means that it will fuse as easily as the mineral listed as 3 in the scale. In making such comparative tests, it is necessary to use fragments of the same size and to have the conditions of the experiments uniform. In the table below the minerals of the scale of fusibility are given with the approximate temperature at which each fuses.

Scale of Fusibility

Number	Mineral	Approximate Fusing Point	Remarks
1	Stibnite	525° C	Very easily fusible in the candle flame
2	Chalcopyrite	800°	A small fragment will fuse easily in the Bunsen burner flame
3	Garnet (Almandite)	1,050°	Infusible in the Bunsen burner flame but fuses easily in the blowpipe flame
4	Actinolite	1,200°	A sharp-pointed splinter fuses with little difficulty in the blowpipe flame
5	Orthoclase	1,300°	The edges of fragments are rounded with difficulty in the blowpipe flame
6	Bronzite	1,400°	Practically infusible in the blowpipe flame. Only the fine ends of splinters are rounded
7	Quartz	1,710°	Infusible in the blowpipe flame

Reducing and oxidizing flames. Reduction consists essentially in taking oxygen away from a chemical compound, and oxidation consists in adding oxygen to it. These two opposite chemical reactions can be accomplished by means of either a Bunsen burner or a blowpipe flame. Cone b, Fig. 385, contains CO, carbon monoxide. This is a reducing agent, since, because of its strong tendency to take up oxygen to become CO_2, carbon dioxide, it will, if possible, take oxygen away from another substance in contact with it. For instance, if a small fragment of ferric oxide, Fe_2O_3, is held in this part of the blowpipe flame, it will be reduced by the removal of oxygen to ferrous oxide, FeO. In Fig. 385 cone b is the reducing part of the blowpipe flame, and if a reduction test is to be performed the mineral fragment is placed at r.

If oxidation is to be accomplished, the mineral must be placed entirely outside of the flame, where the oxygen of the air can have free access to it, but where it can still get in large degree the heat of the flame. Under these conditions, if the reaction is possible, oxygen will be added to the mineral and the substance will be oxidized. The oxidizing part of the blowpipe flame is at o (Fig. 385). Pyrite, FeS_2, for instance, if placed in the oxidizing flame, would be converted into ferric oxide, Fe_2O_3, and sulfur dioxide, SO_2.

Fig. 387. Charcoal Block with Antimony Oxide Coating.

Use of charcoal in blowpiping. Small charcoal blocks, about 4 inches long, 1 inch wide, and $\frac{1}{2}$ inch thick, are employed in a number of blowpipe tests (Fig. 387). The charcoal is used as a support upon

Metallic Globules Reduced on Charcoal

Element	Color and Character of Globule	Remarks
Gold Au	Yellow, soft, no coating, remains bright	Metallic gold can be easily reduced from the gold tellurides without a flux
Silver Ag	White, soft, no coating, remains bright	Usually necessary to use reducing mixture. To distinguish from other globules, dissolve in nitric acid, add hydrochloric acid to obtain white silver chloride precipitate
Tin Sn	White, soft, becomes dull on cooling. White coating of oxide film	Globules form with difficulty even with reducing mixture. The metallic globule is oxidized in nitric acid to a white hydroxide
Copper Cu	Red, soft, surface black when cold, difficultly fusible	Copper minerals should be roasted to drive off sulfur, arsenic, and antimony before mixing with reducing mixture
Lead Pb	Gray, soft, fusible. Bright in reducing flame, iridescent in oxidizing flame	The incandescent charcoal will reduce the lead. To distinguish from other globules dissolve in nitric acid, and from clear solution precipitate white lead sulfate by addition of sulfuric acid

NOTE: Easily fusible metallic beads are often obtained on heating metallic compounds containing sulphur, antimony, or arsenic. Such beads are always very brittle and often magnetic. Magnetic masses or globules are obtained when compounds of iron, nickel, and cobalt are heated on charcoal.

which various reactions are accomplished. For instance, some metals, indicated in the accompanying table, can be reduced from their minerals by means of the blowpipe flame, the experiment being performed upon the charcoal.

Sublimates on Charcoal

Element	Composition of Coating	Color and Character of Coating on Charcoal	Remarks
As	Arsenious oxide As_2O_3	White and volatile, depositing at some distance from the assay	Usually accompanied by garlic odor
Sb	Antimony oxides Sb_2O_3, Sb_2O_4	White and volatile, depositing close to the assay	Less volatile than arsenic oxide
Se	Selenium oxide SeO_2	Volatile white, tinged with red on outside; to gray near assay	Accompanied by a peculiar odor. Coating touched with reducing flame gives blue flame
Te	Tellurium oxide TeO_2	Dense white; volatile. On outside gray to brownish	In reducing flame coating gives bluish green flame color
Zn	Zinc oxide ZnO	If mixed with sodium carbonate on charcoal gives nonvolatile sublimate, yellow when hot, white when cold near assay	Coating moistened with cobalt nitrate and ignited turns green
Sn	Tin oxide SnO_2	Faint yellow when hot, white when cold. Nonvolatile in the oxidizing flame	Coating moistened with cobalt nitrate and ignited turns bluish green
Mo	Molybdenum oxide MoO_3	Pale yellow when hot, white when cold. May be crystalline. Volatile in the oxidizing flame. Red MoO_2 under assay	Coating touched for a moment by a reducing flame becomes dark blue
Pb	Lead oxide PbO	Yellow near the mineral and white farther away. Volatile	Coating may be composed of white sulfite and sulfate of lead in addition to the oxide
	Lead iodide PbI_2	Chrome yellow. Volatile	This reaction when lead minerals heated with iodide flux
Bi	Bismuth oxide Bi_2O_3	Yellow near the mineral and white farther away. Volatile	To be told from the lead oxide coating by iodide test
	Bismuth iodide BiI_3	Bright red with yellow ring near assay	This reaction when bismuth minerals heated with iodide flux

It is impossible to extract the metal from some minerals by ordinary blowpipe means. Other metals can be reduced by means of a flux, and a few can be reduced merely by heating on charcoal. A mixture of sodium carbonate and charcoal in equal proportions, called the *reducing mixture*, serves as a good flux for most reductions.

One of the important uses of the charcoal block is to obtain characteristic oxide coatings upon its surface. The table on page 214 gives a list of the elements which yield coatings when their minerals are heated in the oxidizing flame on charcoal. In some cases more characteristic coatings are obtained when the assay has had some chemical reagent added to it. The most important reagent is the so-called *iodide* or *bismuth flux,* a mixture of potassium iodide and sulfur. When this reagent is used colored iodide coatings may result.

Use of plaster of Paris tablets. In some cases it is preferable to collect sublimates on the surface of a plaster of Paris tablet rather than on charcoal. The material to be tested is placed in a small depression made near one end of the tablet and then heated before the

Sublimates on Plaster

Element	Composition of Coating	Color and Character of Coating on Plaster Tablet	Remarks
Se	Selenium oxide SeO_2	Red to crimson. Volatile	Volatilizes giving reddish fumes and characteristic odor
Te	Tellurium oxide TeO_2	Dark brown. Volatile	In reducing flame coating gives bluish green flame color
Cd	Cadmium oxide CdO	Greenish yellow with brown both near assay and at a distance	Nonvolatile
Pb	Lead iodide PbI_2	Chrome yellow with iodide flux	
Bi	Bismuth iodide BiI_3	Chocolate-brown with underlying red with iodide flux	Subjected to ammonia fumes coating becomes first orange-yellow then red
Mo	Molybdenum oxide MoO_3	White in oxidizing flame. Red MoO_2 under assay	Coating turns deep ultramarine blue if touched with reducing flame
	Molybdenum iodide, MoI_4	Ultramarine blue with iodide flux	
Sb	Antimony iodide SbI_3	Orange to red with iodide flux	Disappears when subjected to ammonia fumes

blowpipe exactly as on charcoal. The plaster tablet is used to bring out the color of sublimates poorly displayed on the black background of charcoal. The iodide coatings are especially marked on the plaster tablet.

Open-tube test. Tubing of hard glass is used in making what are known as open-tube tests. The tubing, with an internal diameter of

¼ inch, should be cut into approximately 6-inch lengths. A small amount of the mineral to be tested is powdered and placed in the tube at a point about one-third of its length from one end. The tube is then inclined at as sharp an angle as possible, with the mineral lying nearer the lower end. The tube is held over a Bunsen burner flame in such

Sublimates in the Open Tube

Element	Products of Oxidation		Remarks
	Composition	Color and Character	
S	Sulfur dioxide SO_2	SO_2, a colorless gas, issues from the upper end of the tube	The gas has a pungent and irritating odor. If a moistened strip of blue litmus paper is placed at the upper end of the tube, it becomes red, owing to the acid reaction of sulfurous acid
As	Arsenious oxide As_2O_3	White, highly volatile, and crystalline	The sublimate condenses at a considerable distance above the heated portion in small octahedral crystals
Sb	Antimonious oxide Sb_2O_3	White, volatile, and crystalline	The sublimate forms a white ring closer to the heated portion of the tube than the arsenious oxide. Is obtained from antimony compounds which do not contain sulfur
	Antimony tetraoxide Sb_2O_4	Pale yellow when hot, white when cold. Dense, non-volatile, amorphous	Sb_2O_4 obtained from antimony sulfide and sulfantimonites. Settles mostly on the bottom of the tube and usually is accompanied by Sb_2O_3
Mo	Molybdenum trioxide MoO_3	Pale yellow to white crystals form a network near heated portion	If crystals are touched with reducing flame they turn blue

a way that the flame plays on the upper part of the tube. This serves to convert the inclined tube into a chimney, up which a current of air flows. After a moment the tube is shifted so that the flame heats it at a point just above the mineral, or in some cases the flame may be directly beneath the mineral. The mineral is being heated under these conditions in a steady current of air, and it will be oxidized if such a reaction is possible. Various oxides may come off as gases and either escape at the end of the tube or be condensed as sublimates upon its walls. The table above gives a list of those elements which yield characteristic reactions in open tubes.

Closed-tube test. The closed tube made of soft glass should have a length of about $3\frac{1}{2}$ inches and an internal diameter from $\frac{1}{8}$ to $\frac{3}{16}$ inch. Two closed tubes can be made by fusing the center of a piece of tubing

7 inches in length and pulling it apart. The closed-tube test is used to determine what takes place when a mineral is heated in the absence of oxygen. In performing the test the mineral is broken into small fragments or powdered, placed in the closed end of the tube, and heated in the Bunsen burner flame.

Closed-Tube Tests

Element	Substance	Color and Character	Remarks
	Water H_2O	Colorless liquid, easily volatile	Minerals containing water of crystallization or hydroxyl give on moderate heating a deposit of drops of water on the cold upper walls of the tube. The water may be acid from hydrochloric, hydrofluoric, sulfuric, or other volatile acid
S	Sulfur S	Red when hot, yellow when cold. Volatile	Given only by native sulfur and those sulfides which contain a high percentage of sulfur
As	Arsenic As	Two rings around tube: one black amorphous material; the other near the bottom a silver gray crystalline material, the "arsenic mirror"	Given by native arsenic and some arsenides
	Arsenic sulfides AsS As_2S_3	Deep red liquid when hot, reddish yellow solid when cold	Given by realgar, AsS, and orpiment, As_2S_3, and some arsenic sulfides
Sb	Antimony oxysulfide Sb_2S_2O	Slight reddish brown coating near the bottom of the tube	Given by antimony sulfide and some antimony sulfides
Hg	Mercury sulfide HgS	Black amorphous sublimate	This test given when cinnabar, HgS, is heated alone
	Mercury Hg	Gray, metallic globules	Metallic mercury is obtained when cinnabar is mixed with sodium carbonate and heated

Flame test. Certain elements may be volatilized when minerals containing them are heated intensely and so impart characteristic colors to the flame. A flame test may be made by heating a small fragment of the mineral held in the forceps, but a more decisive test is usually obtained when the fine powder of the mineral is introduced into the Bunsen burner flame on a piece of platinum wire. Some minerals contain elements which normally impart a color to the flame

Flame Colorations

Element	Color of Flame	Remarks
Strontium Sr	Crimson	Strontium minerals which give the flame color also give alkaline residues after being heated
Lithium Li	Crimson	Lithium minerals which give the flame color do not give alkaline residues after being heated. (Difference from strontium)
Calcium Ca	Orange	In the majority of cases a distinct calcium flame will be obtained only after the assay has been moistened with HCl
Sodium Na	Intense yellow	A very delicate reaction. The flame should be very strong and persistent to indicate the presence of sodium in the mineral as an essential constituent
Barium Ba	Yellow-green	Minerals which give the barium flame also give alkaline residues after ignition
Molybdenum Mo	Yellow-green	Obtained from the oxide or sulfide of molybdenum
Boron B	Yellow-green	Minerals giving a boron flame rarely give alkaline residues after ignition. Many boron minerals will give a green flame only after they have been broken down by sulfuric acid or the "boron flux"
Copper Cu	Emerald-green	Obtained from copper oxide
	Azure-blue	Obtained from copper chloride. Any copper mineral will give the copper chloride flame after being moistened with hydrochloric acid
Chlorine Cl	Azure-blue (copper chloride flame)	If a mineral containing chlorine is mixed with copper oxide and introduced into the flame, the copper chloride flame results
Phosphorus P	Pale bluish green	A phosphorus mineral may not give the flame color until moistened with sulfuric acid. Not a decisive test
Zinc Zn	Bluish green	Appears usually as bright streaks in the flame
Antimony Sb	Pale green	Flame best observed when mineral is fused on charcoal. Color plays about assay
Lead Pb	Pale azure-blue	Flame may be observed to play about assay when a lead mineral is fused on charcoal
Potassium K	Violet	It may be necessary to decompose mineral with a flux of gypsum, $CaSO_4 \cdot 2H_2O$, to obtain flame color

but because of the nonvolatile nature of the chemical combination fail to give the characteristic flame until broken down by an acid or a flux.

Frequently a flame color is masked by the presence of a sodium flame. Although a mineral may contain no sodium, it may be coated with dust of a sodium compound ever present in the laboratory, and a yellow flame may result. A filter of blue glass held in front of the flame will completely absorb the yellow sodium flame and allow the characteristic flame colors of some other elements to be observed.

Color reactions with the fluxes. Some elements, when dissolved in certain fluxes, give a characteristic color to the fused mass. The fluxes that are most commonly used are borax, $Na_2B_4O_7 \cdot 10H_2O$; sodium carbonate, Na_2CO_3; and salt of phosphorus, $HNaNH_4PO_4 \cdot 4H_2O$. The operation is most satisfactorily performed by first fusing the flux on a small loop of platinum wire into the form of a lens-shaped bead. For best results the loop on the wire should have the shape and size shown in Fig. 388. After the flux has been fused into a bead on the wire, a small amount of the powdered mineral is introduced into it and is dissolved by further heating.[1] The color of the resulting bead may depend upon whether it was heated in the oxidizing or reducing flame.

Fig. 388. Loop in Platinum Wire.

In addition, *sodium carbonate* with oxide of manganese, when heated with a grain of niter in the oxidizing flame, gives a nontransparent bead, green when hot, bluish green when cold. When heated in the reducing flame, it gives a colorless bead.

Etch tests. A series of *etch tests* is used for the determination of fine-grained mixtures of metallic minerals. The specimen must first be polished and set in an appropriate mount so that the polished surface can be examined microscopically. When thus examined many minerals have a characteristic appearance and may be recognized by inspection. However, minerals which resemble one another on the polished surface can be differentiated by etching their surfaces with appropriate reagents. This method is used particularly by the economic geologist in the study of ore minerals. The technique has become so highly

[1] All metallic minerals should be roasted before being introduced into the bead, for it is the oxide of the metal that is desired. It is especially desirable to rid the mineral of arsenic, for even small amounts of this element make the platinum brittle and cause the end of the wire to break off.

developed and specialized that one must refer to specific books on the subject for an adequate treatment.

Microchemical reactions. Another method for the determination of the elements in minerals uses the microscope to observe chemical reactions and the products of such reactions. This microchemical method is particularly applicable to small quantities, and thus has a definite advantage over other methods if a limited amount of material is available. Its use, however, requires a petrographic microscope and

Color Reactions with the Fluxes[*]

(Bead Tests)

Oxides of	Borax Bead		Phosphorus Salt Bead	
	Oxidizing Flame	Reducing Flame	Oxidizing Flame	Reducing Flame
Titanium	Colorless to white	Brownish violet	Colorless	Violet
Tungsten	Colorless or white	Yellow to yellowish brown	Colorless	Fine blue
Molybdenum	Colorless or white	Brown	Colorless	Fine green
Chromium	Yellowish green	Fine green	Fine green	Fine green
Vanadium	Yellowish green almost colorless	Fine green	Yellow	Fine green
Uranium	Yellow	Pale green to nearly colorless	Pale greenish yellow	Fine green
Iron	Yellow	Pale bottle-green	Yellow to almost colorless	Almost colorless
Copper	Blue-green	Opaque red with much oxide	Blue	Opaque red
Cobalt	Blue	Blue	Blue	Blue
Nickel	Reddish brown	Opaque gray	Yellow to reddish yellow	Yellow to reddish yellow
Manganese	Reddish violet	Colorless	Violet	Colorless

[*] The colors given are those obtained after the bead is cold.

a knowledge of the optical properties of crystalline substances. Consequently, a discussion of this method, also, is beyond the scope of the present book, and the reader is referred to specialized books on the subject.

DESCRIPTIVE
MINERALOGY

INTRODUCTION

A description of about 200 minerals will be found on the following pages. This is a relatively small number, since approximately 1500 minerals have been described and recognized by mineralogists as bona fide species. This list of 200 includes all the common minerals and those that are of most importance economically. The names of some other minerals and their chemical compositions are given.

In the individual descriptions the crystallographic, chemical, and general physical properties are first considered, and then those features and tests which aid one in recognizing the mineral and distinguishing it from others. In addition a brief account of the mode of occurrence and characteristic mineral associations are given. The localities at which a mineral occurs in notable amount or quality are also mentioned. For those minerals that are found abundantly the world over, emphasis is placed on American localities. For minerals possessing economic value there are brief statements of their uses. When possible, the derivation of the mineral name is given. At the end of some of the individual descriptions is a heading "Similar species"; the similarity of the species listed to the mineral whose description precedes may be either on the basis of chemical composition or crystal structure.

Consequently the names of these minerals are not necessarily in those places where they would appear if this book were extended to include their descriptions.

The headings under which the various data are arranged for each mineral are:

Crystallography	Alteration
Physical properties	Occurrence
Composition	Use
Tests	Name
Diagnostic features	Similar species

The mineral classification used in this book[1] is based on chemical composition, the broadest divisions of which are the following classes:

1. Elements. About twenty elements in an uncombined form are found as minerals and are said to occur in the native state. Example, gold.

2. Sulfides. This class consists for the most part of combinations of the various metals with sulfur, selenium, or tellurium. The majority of the metallic ore minerals are in this class. Example, galena, PbS.

3. Sulfosalts. Minerals composed of lead, copper, or silver in combination with sulfur and antimony, arsenic, or bismuth are alone included in the sulfosalt class. Example, enargite, Cu_3AsS_4.

4. Oxides. *a. Simple* and *multiple Oxides.* The minerals of this class contain a metal in combination with oxygen. Example, hematite, Fe_2O_3.

b. Hydroxides. The mineral oxides that contain water or the hydroxyl (OH) as an important radical are included in this class. Example, brucite, $Mg(OH)_2$.

5. Halides. This class includes the natural chlorides, fluorides, bromides, and iodides. Example, fluorite, CaF_2.

6. Carbonates. The minerals whose formulas include the carbonate radical, CO_3, are in this class. Example, calcite, $CaCO_3$.

7. Nitrates. This class includes those minerals that can be considered salts of nitric acid and contain the NO_3 radical. Example, niter, KNO_3.

[1] The classification in this book is based upon that used in the following works:

1. C. Palache, H. Berman, C. Frondel, *Dana's System of Mineralogy,* 7th ed., Vol. I (1944), Vol. II (1952). John Wiley and Sons, New York. A critical discussion of all the minerals with the exception of the silicates.

2. H. Strunz, *Mineralogische Tabellen,* 3rd ed., Akademische Verlags., Leipzig, 1957. A listing and classification on crystal-chemical grounds of all the minerals and a brief summary of properties.

8. **Borates.** The borates contain the BO_3 group. Example, borax, $Na_2B_4O_7 \cdot 10H_2O$.

9. **Phosphates.** Minerals whose formulas include the phosphate radical, PO_4, are included in this class. Example, apatite, $Ca_5(F,Cl) - (PO_4)_3$.

10. **Sulfates.** Minerals whose formulas include the sulfate radical, SO_4, are in this class. Example, barite, $BaSO_4$.

11. **Tungstates.** The few minerals that are included in this class have the tungstate radical, WO_4, in their formulas. Example, scheelite, $CaWO_4$.

12. **Silicates.** The silicates form the largest chemical class among minerals. They contain various elements, the most common of which are sodium, potassium, calcium, magnesium, aluminum, and iron, in combination with silicon and oxygen, frequently forming very complex chemical structures.

The above classes are subdivided into *families* on the basis of chemical types, and the family in turn may be further divided into *groups* which show a close crystallographic and structural similarity. A group is made up of *species*, which may form *series* with each other, and finally a species may have several *varieties*. In each of the classes the minerals with the highest ratio of metal to nonmetal are given first, followed by those containing progressively less metal. Such a relatively small number of minerals are described in this book that often only one member of a group or family is represented, and thus a rigorous adherence to division and subdivision is impractical.

As an introduction to each of the chemical classes a few prefatory remarks are made regarding the crystal chemistry of the class. These discussions are in no way complete but are given as a basis for understanding the reasons for the similarities and differences of members of the class.

NATIVE ELEMENTS

With the exception of the free gases of the atmosphere, only about twenty elements are found in the native state. These elements can be divided into (1) metals; (2) semimetals; (3) nonmetals. The more common native metals constitute three isostructural groups: the *gold group*, gold, silver, copper, and lead; the *platinum group*, platinum, palladium, iridium, and osmium; and the *iron group*, iron and nickel-iron. In addition, mercury, tantalum, tin, and zinc have been found. The native semimetals form two isostructural groups: arsenic, antimony, and bismuth crystallize in the hexagonal-scalenohedral class, and the less common selenium and tellurium crystallize in the trigonal-trapezohedral class. The important nonmetals are carbon, in the form of diamond and graphite, and sulfur.

Native Metals

It is fitting that *descriptive mineralogy* begin with a discussion of the gold group, for man's knowledge of the properties and usefulness of metals arose from the chance discovery of nuggets and masses of

Fig. 389. Copper, Cu, Packing Model. The photograph shows copper atoms in 12-fold coordination (cubic closest packing) arranged in a face-centered cubic lattice. This structure is shared by silver, gold, and many other metals.

these minerals. Many relatively advanced early cultures, such as the Amerindian, were restricted in their use of metal to that found in the native state.

The elements of the gold group belong to the same family in the periodic classification of the elements, and, hence, their atoms have somewhat similar chemical properties; all are sufficiently inert to occur free in nature. When uncombined with other elements the atoms of these metals are united into crystal structures by the rather weak metallic bond. The minerals are isostructural and are built on the face-centered cubic lattice with identical atoms in 12-fold coordination (Fig. 389).

The similar properties of the members of this group arise from the common structure. All are rather soft; all are malleable, ductile, and sectile. All are excellent conductors of heat and electricity, display metallic luster and hackly fracture, and have rather low melting points. These are properties conferred by the metallic bond. All are isometric hexoctahedral and have unusually high densities. These properties arise from the very economical packing, called *cubic closest packing.*

Those properties with respect to which the minerals of this group differ arise from the properties of the atoms of the individual elements. Thus, the yellow of gold, the red of copper, and the white of silver are atomic properties. The specific gravities likewise depend on atomic properties and show a rough proportionality to the atomic weights.

The members of this group are isostructural, and the dominant factor controlling solid solution between them is atomic radius. Thus, gold and silver, which have the same atomic radii (1.44 Å), display complete mutual solid solubility but usually contain only small amounts of copper (atomic radius 1.28 Å). Conversely native copper carries only traces of gold and silver in solid solution.

The members of the platinum group, of which only platinum is discussed here, are harder and have higher melting points than the members of the gold group. Platinum is similar in its structure to gold.

Crystals of the iron group metals, although isometric, have a body-centered cubic lattice in which each atom touches eight others. Their structure is thus similar to that of cesium chloride (Fig. 376). Iron and nickel both have atomic radii of 1.24 Å, and thus nickel can and usually does substitute for some of the iron. This solid solution, nickel-iron, is particularly characteristic of iron meteorites and is believed to constitute a large part of the earth's core.

Native Metals

GOLD GROUP		PLATINUM GROUP	
Gold	Au	Platinum	Pt
Silver	Ag	IRON GROUP	
Copper	Cu	Iron	Fe

GOLD—Au

Crystallography. Isometric; hexoctahedral. Crystals are commonly octahedral (Fig. 390), rarely showing the faces of the dodecahedron, cube, and trapezohedron {113}. Often in arborescent crystal groups with crystals elongated in the direction of a 3-fold symmetry axis, or flattened parallel to an octahedron face. Crystals irregularly formed; passing into filiform, reticulated, and dendritic shapes (Fig. 391). Seldom shows crystal forms; usually in irregular plates, scales, or masses.

Physical properties. H $2\frac{1}{2}$–3. G 19.3 when pure. The presence of other metals decreases the specific gravity, which may be as low as 15. Very malleable and ductile. Opaque. Color various shades of yellow depending on the purity, becoming paler with the increase in the percentage of silver present.

Fig. 390. Malformed Gold Octahedron.

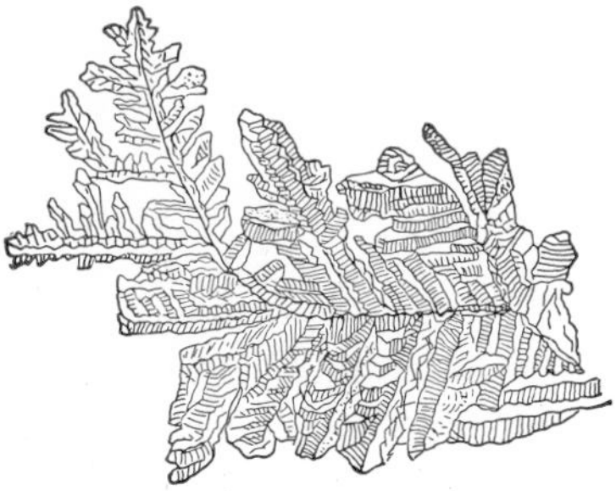

Fig. 391. Dendritic Gold.

Composition. Gold. A complete solid-solution series exists between gold and silver, and most gold contains some silver. California gold carries 10–15 per cent silver. When silver is present in amounts greater than 20 per cent, the alloy is known as *electrum*. Small amounts of copper and iron may be present as well as traces of bismuth, lead, tin, zinc, and the platinum metals. The purity or *fineness* of gold is expressed in parts per 1000. Most gold contains about 10 per cent of other metals and thus has a fineness of 900.

Tests. Fuses easily at 3 (1063° C). Insoluble in ordinary acids but soluble in *aqua regia* (a mixture of hydrochloric and nitric acids).

Diagnostic features. Gold is to be distinguished from certain yellow sulfides (particularly pyrite and chalcopyrite) and from yellow flakes of altered micas by its malleability, its insolubility in nitric acid, and its high specific gravity.

Occurrence. Although gold is a rare element, it occurs in nature widely distributed in small amounts. It is found most commonly in veins that bear a genetic relation to silicic types of igneous rocks. In places it has been found intimately associated with igneous rocks as in the Bushveld igneous complex in the Transvaal, South Africa. Most gold occurs as the native metal; tellurium and possibly selenium are the only elements that are combined with it in nature.

The chief source of gold is the so-called hydrothermal gold-quartz veins where, together with pyrite and other sulfides, gold was deposited from ascending mineral-bearing solutions. The gold is merely mechanically mixed with the sulfides and is not in any chemical combination. At and near the surface of the earth the gold-bearing sulfides are usually oxidized, thus setting free the gold and making its extraction easy. Such ores are called "free-milling" because their gold content can be recovered by amalgamation with mercury. Finely crushed ore is washed over copper plates coated with mercury. When sulfides are present in any quantity, not all the gold can be recovered by amalgamation, and either the cyanide or chlorination process must be used. In the cyanide process finely crushed ore is treated with a solution of potassium or sodium cyanide, forming a soluble cyanide. The gold is then recovered by precipitation with zinc or by electrolysis. The chlorination process renders the gold in a soluble form by treating the crushed and roasted ore with chlorine. In the majority of veins the gold is so finely divided and uniformly distributed that its presence in the ore cannot be detected with the eye. With the chemical processes of gold extraction ores carrying values as low as $1.00 per ton can be worked at a profit. It is interesting to note that, with the value of gold at $35 per troy ounce, such ore would contain about 0.0001 per cent gold by weight.

When gold-bearing veins are weathered, the gold liberated either remains behind in the soil mantle or is washed into the neighboring streams. In the soil, a residual concentration takes place, and in the streams placer deposits form. Because of its high specific gravity, gold is mechanically separated from the lighter material of the sands and gravels of the stream bed. In this way a concentration takes place behind projecting irregularities and in cavities on the stream floor, and a gold placer is formed. The gold is found in round or flattened grains and nuggets. Very fine flakes of gold may be carried long distances by the streams. Placer gold can be recovered by panning the sands by hand and washing away all but the heavy concentrate from which the gold can be easily separated. Sluices are used to operate on a larger scale. The gold-bearing sand is washed through sluices where the gold collects behind cross-bars or riffles and amalgamates with mercury placed behind the riffles for that purpose. Hydraulic mining is sometimes used to move great quantities of gravels through sluices. Most placer mining is today carried on with dredges, some of which are gigantic and can extract the gold from thousands of cubic yards of gravel a day. Some dredges can operate at a profit handling gravels which average no more than 10 cents in gold per cubic yard. Some alluvial gold deposits have been covered by lava flows and thus preserved as buried placers. Much of the placer gold of California has come from such deposits that now stand high on ridges between valleys owing to changes in elevation and rearrangement of the drainage.

The most important gold-producing states of the United States, in the order of the amount of gold produced at present, are: South Dakota, Utah, California, Alaska, Arizona, Colorado, Nevada, and Montana. For 100 years after gold was discovered in California in 1848, this state was the leading gold producer. It was not until 1949 that its production was exceeded by South Dakota and in 1950 by Utah. The most important gold-producing districts of California are those of the Mother Lode, a series of gold-quartz veins that lie along the western slope of the Sierra Nevada Mountains in Amador, Calaveras, Eldorado, Tuolumne, and Mariposa counties. Nearly one-half of California's gold comes from placer deposits worked mostly by dredging operations. Most of the gold mined in Alaska has come from placers. The largest single gold mine in the United States today is the Homestake mine at Lead, South Dakota.

Nearly 40 per cent of the world's gold production (over 14,000,000 ounces a year) comes from the Union of South Africa, chiefly from the Witwatersrand, "the Rand," near Johannesburg in the Transvaal. The gold is scattered through steeply dipping Precambrian quartz con-glomerates which extend for over 100 miles in an east-west direction. More recently similar deposits to the south in the Orange Free State have become major producers. The world's second largest gold pro-ducer is believed to be the U.S.S.R. Although no accurate figures are available, its production is estimated to be about 9,000,000 ounces a year. Most of it comes from placers in Siberia and from mines on the eastern slopes of the Ural Mountains. Other productive countries are: Canada, mostly from Ontario, Quebec, and Northwest Territories; Australia, especially Kalgoorlie (largely tellurides), Bendigo, and Ballarat; Philippine Islands; Mexico; Colombia; and India.

Use. The principal use of gold is a monetary standard. Other uses are in jewelry, scientific instruments, electroplating, gold leaf, and dental appliances.

SILVER—Ag

Crystallography. Isometric; hexoctahedral. Crystals commonly malformed and in branching, arborescent, or reticulated groups. Found usually in irregular masses, plates, and scales; in places as coarse or fine wire.

Physical properties. H $2\frac{1}{2}$–3. **G** 10.5 when pure, 10–12 when impure. Fracture hackly. Malleable and ductile. Luster metallic. Color and streak silver-white, often tarnished to brown or gray-black.

Composition. Silver, frequently containing alloyed mercury, copper, and gold, more rarely traces of platinum, antimony, and bismuth. *Amalgam* is a solid solution of silver and mercury.

Tests. Fusible at 2 (960.5° C) to bright globule. Soluble in nitric acid, giving on addition of hydrochloric acid a curdy white precipitate of silver chloride.

Diagnostic features. Silver can be told from similar-appearing minerals by its malleable nature, its color on a fresh surface, and its high specific gravity.

Occurrence. Native silver is widely distributed in small amounts, principally in the oxidized zone of ore deposits. The large deposits of native silver are probably the result of primary deposition of silver from hydrothermal solutions. There are three such types: native silver with sulfides and other silver minerals, with cobalt and nickel minerals, and with uraninite.

The mines at Kongsberg, Norway, worked for several hundred years, have produced magnificent specimens of crystallized wire silver. Other old and famous silver mines are at Freiberg and Schneeberg in Saxony. Native silver is also found in Bohemia, Alsace, Siberia, New South Wales at Broken Hill, and in Mexico.

In the United States native silver has been found with the native copper in the Lake Superior copper mines; in Montana at Butte and at the Elkhorn mine, Jefferson County; in Idaho at the Poorman mine, Silver City district; in Colorado at Aspen; and in Arizona at the Silver King mine. In Canada native silver has been found abundantly at Cobalt, Ontario (one slab weighing 1640 pounds was taken from there); in the Thunder Bay district on the north shore of Lake Superior, at Silver Islet; and associated with uraninite at Great Bear Lake, Northwest Territories.

Use. An ore of silver, although most of the world's supply comes from other minerals. Silver is used for ornamental purposes, coinage, and plating. It is usually alloyed with copper. The standard silver coin in the United States contains one part of copper to nine parts of silver.

COPPER—Cu

Crystallography. Isometric; hexoctahedral. Tetrahexahedron faces common (Fig. 392), also the cube, dodecahedron, and octahedron. Crystals usually malformed and in branching and arborescent groups

(Figs. 393 and 394). Usually in irregular masses, plates, and scales. In twisted and wirelike forms.

Physical properties. H $2\frac{1}{2}$–3. G 8.9. Highly ductile and malleable. Fracture hackly. Color copper-red on fresh surface, usually dark with dull luster because of tarnish.

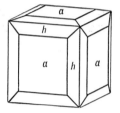

Fig. 392. Copper Crystal.

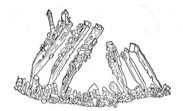

Fig. 393. Dendritic Copper.

Composition. Copper, often containing small amounts of silver, bismuth, mercury, arsenic, antimony.

Tests. Fuses at 3 (1083° C) to a globule. Dissolves readily in nitric acid, and the solution is colored a deep blue on addition of an excess of ammonium hydroxide.

Fig. 394. Native Copper, Keweenaw Peninsula, Michigan.

Diagnostic features. Native copper can be recognized by its red color on fresh surfaces, its hackly fracture, high specific gravity, and malleability.

Occurrence. Native copper is widely distributed in copper veins, but usually in small amounts. It is commonly found in the oxidized zones of copper deposits associated with cuprite, malachite, and azurite.

The most notable deposit of native copper known in the world is on Keweenaw Peninsula in northern Michigan, on the southern shore of Lake Superior. The region is occupied by a series of igneous flows of trap rock interbedded with conglomerates. The whole series dips toward the north. The copper is found in veins intersecting this rock series, in the amygdaloidal belts at the top of the various trap flows, and as a cementing material in the conglomerate. This last type has furnished the most important ore deposits, some of which have been worked for considerably over a mile in vertical depth. Not only does the copper act as a cement to bind the conglomerate together, but it has often penetrated the boulders of the rock to a depth of a foot or more. It is associated with such minerals as epidote, datolite, calcite, and various zeolites. The mines were worked superficially by the Indians and have been actively developed since the middle of the nineteenth century. Most of the copper of the district occurs in very small irregular specks, but notable large masses have been found; one weighing 420 tons was discovered in 1857.

Sporadic occurrences of copper similar to the Lake Superior district have been found in the sandstone areas of the eastern United States, notably in New Jersey, and in the glacial drift overlying a similar area in Connecticut. In Bolivia at Corocora, southwest of La Paz, there is a noted occurrence in sandstone. Native copper occurs in small amounts associated with the oxidized copper ores of Arizona, New Mexico, and northern Mexico.

Use. A minor ore of copper. Copper sulfides are today the principal ores of the metal. The greatest use of copper is for electrical purposes, mostly as wire. It is also extensively used in alloys, such as brass (copper and zinc), bronze (copper and tin with some zinc), and German silver (copper, zinc, and nickel). These and many other minor uses make copper second only to iron as a metal essential to modern civilization.

PLATINUM—Pt

Crystallography. Isometric; hexoctahedral. Cubic crystals are rare and commonly malformed. Usually found in small grains and scales. In places in irregular masses and nuggets of larger size.

Physical properties. H $4-4\frac{1}{2}$. (Unusually high for a metal.) G 21.45 when pure; 14–19 when native. Malleable and ductile. Color steel-gray, with bright luster. Magnetic when rich in iron.

Composition. Platinum, usually alloyed with several per cent of iron and with smaller amounts of iridium, osmium, rhodium, palladium; also copper, gold, nickel.

Tests. Infusible. Unattacked by ordinary reagents; soluble only in hot aqua regia, a mixture of hydrochloric and nitric acids.

Diagnostic features. Determined by its high specific gravity, malleability, infusibility, and insolubility.

Occurrence. Platinum is a rare metal which occurs almost exclusively in the native state; only one rare natural compound, *sperrylite*, $PtAs_2$, is known. Most platinum can be traced to ultrabasic rocks, especially dunites, as its source. When *in situ*, it is usually associated with olivine, chromite, pyroxene, and magnetite. It has been mined extensively in placers which are usually close to the platinum-bearing igneous rock.

Platinum was first discovered in the United States of Colombia, South America. It was taken to Europe in 1735 where it received the name *platina* from the word *plata* (Spanish for silver) because of its resemblance to silver. A small amount of platinum is still produced in Colombia from placers in two districts near the Pacific Coast. In 1822 platinum was discovered in placers on the Upper Tura River on the eastern slope of the Ural Mountains, U.S.S.R. From that time until 1934 most of the world's supply of platinum came from placers of that district, which centered around the town of Nizhne Tagil. In 1934 Canada became the leading producer of platinum. It is found there associated with the copper-nickel ore of the Sudbury, Ontario, district. Since 1954 the Union of South Africa has been the world's leading producer of platinum metals. Part of the production comes as a by-product from gold mining on the Rand, but the chief source is the Merensky Reef in the ultrabasic rocks of the Bushveld igneous complex. The Merensky Reef is a horizon of this layered intrusive about 12 inches thick extending for many miles with a uniform platinum content of about one-half ounce per ton of ore. The chief mining operations are near Rustenburg in the Transvaal. In smaller amounts platinum has come from Borneo, New South Wales, New Zealand, Brazil, Peru, and Madagascar.

In the United States small amounts of platinum have been recovered from the gold-bearing sands of North Carolina and from black-sand placers in California, Oregon, and Alaska. In Canada platinum is found in gold placers in several localities, but insignificant amounts compared with the relatively large quantity recovered from the nickel-copper ores of Sudbury.

Use. The uses of platinum depend chiefly upon its high melting point ($1755°$ C), resistance to chemical attack, and superior hardness.

It is used for chemical apparatus, electrical equipment, and jewelry. It is also used in dentistry, surgical instruments, pyrometry, and photography.

Similar species. *Iridium; iridosmine,* an alloy of iridium and osmium; and *palladium* are rare minerals of the platinum group associated with platinum.

Iron—Fe

Crystallography. Isometric; hexoctahedral. Crystals rare. Terrestrial: in blebs and large masses; meteoric: in plates and lamellar masses, frequently shows an octahedral pattern on etching polished surface; artificial: in octahedral, rarely cubic, crystals and dendritic growths.

Physical properties. Cleavage {010} poor. **H** $4\frac{1}{2}$. **G** 7.3–7.9. Fracture hackly. Malleable. Opaque. Luster metallic. Color steel-gray to black. Strongly magnetic.

Composition. Iron, always with some nickel and frequently small amounts of cobalt, copper, manganese, sulfur, carbon. The mineral *nickel-iron* contains about 76 per cent nickel.

Tests. Infusible. Soluble in hydrochloric acid. Red flocculent ferric hydroxide precipitated from acid solution by ammonium hydroxide.

Diagnostic Features. Iron can be recognized by its strong magnetism, its malleability, and the oxide coating usually on its surface.

Occurrence. Occurs sparingly as terrestrial iron and in meteorites. Terrestrial iron is regarded as a primary magmatic constituent or a secondary product formed by the reduction of iron compounds by assimilated carbonaceous material. The most important locality is on the west coast of Greenland where fragments ranging between small grains and masses of many tons are included in basalts. It was known in 1819 that the natives used it, but it was not until 1870 that the source became known. Terrestrial iron has been noted in a few other localities with a similar association.

Meteoric iron with a nickel content varying between 5 and 15 per cent makes up nearly the whole mass of iron meteorites and shows a hexagonal pattern on a polished and etched surface. Iron is found disseminated through stony meteorites in small grains. Meteorites are usually recognized by their fused and pitted surface and by a coating of ferric oxide.

Native Semimetals

The native semimetals form an isostructural group with similar properties. They belong to the hexagonal-scalenohedral class and have good basal cleavage. They are rather brittle and much poorer conductors of heat and electricity than the native metals. These properties reflect a bond type that is intermediate between true metallic and covalent; hence it is stronger and more directive in its properties, leading to lower symmetry. The structure may be pictured as a

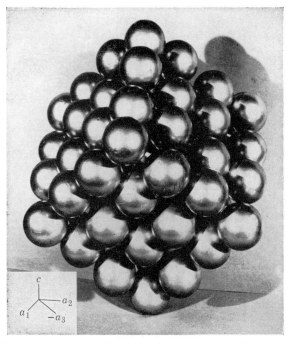

Fig. 395. Bismuth, Bi, Packing Model. The model shows the layered nature of the structure resulting from the fact that each atom is somewhat closer to three of its neighbors than to the other three.

modified type of 6-fold coordination in which each atom is more strongly bonded to three of its neighbors than to the other three (Fig. 395). The structure is thus made up of sheets of atoms strongly bonded to one adjacent sheet and weakly bonded to the other. The sheets are parallel to the base, and the weak bonding between sets of double sheets gives rise to the cleavage.

In addition to arsenic and bismuth, antimony is also found in the native state but is less common.

Native Semimetals

Arsenic   As   Bismuth   Bi

Arsenic—As

Crystallography. Hexagonal–*R;* scalenohedral. Pseudocubic crystals rare. Usually granular massive, reniform, and stalactitic.

Physical properties. Perfect {0001} cleavage. **H** $3\frac{1}{2}$. **G** 5.7. Luster nearly metallic on fresh surface. Color tin-white on fresh fracture, tarnishes to dark gray on exposure. Gray streak. Brittle.

Composition. Arsenic, often with antimony and traces of iron, silver, gold, bismuth.

Tests. Volatile without fusion. Before blowpipe on charcoal gives white volatile coating of arsenious oxide and odor of garlic. In the open tube gives volatile crystalline deposit of arsenious oxide.

Occurrence. Arsenic is a comparatively rare species found in veins in crystalline rocks associated with silver, cobalt, or nickel ores. Found in the silver mines of Freiberg, in Saxony; at Andreasberg in the Harz Mountains; in Bohemia; Rumania; and Alsace. Found sparingly in the United States.

Name. The name arsenic is derived from a Greek word meaning *masculine* from the belief that metals were of different sexes. The term was first applied to the sulfide of arsenic because of its potent properties.

Use. Very minor ore of arsenic. (See under arsenopyrite, page 272.)

Similar species. Allemontite, AsSb, an intermediate compound of arsenic and antimony.

Bismuth—Bi

Crystallography. Hexagonal–*R;* scalenohedral. Distinct crystals are rare. Usually laminated and granular; may be reticulated or arborescent. Artificial crystals pseudocubic {01$\overline{1}$2}.

Physical properties. Perfect {0001} cleavage. **H** $2-2\frac{1}{2}$. **G** 9.8. Sectile. Brittle. Luster metallic. Color silver-white with a decided reddish tone. Streak silver-white, shining.

Composition. Bismuth. Small amounts of arsenic, sulfur, tellurium, antimony may be present.

Tests. Fusible at 1 (271° C). Before blowpipe on charcoal gives metallic globule and yellow to white coating of bismuth oxide. The globule is somewhat malleable but cannot be hammered into as thin a sheet as lead. Mixed with potassium iodide and sulfur and heated on charcoal gives a brilliant yellow to red coating.

Diagnostic features. Bismuth is recognized chiefly by its laminated nature, its reddish-silver color, its perfect cleavage, and its sectility.

Occurrence. Bismuth is a comparatively rare mineral, occurring usually in connection with ores of silver, cobalt, nickel, lead, and tin. Found in the silver veins of Saxony; in Norway and Sweden; and at Cornwall, England. Important deposits are found in Australia, but the most productive deposits are in Bolivia. It is found in small veins associated with silver and cobalt minerals at Cobalt, Ontario, Canada. Found only sparingly in the United States.

Use. The chief ore of bismuth. Bismuth forms low-melting alloys with lead, tin, and cadmium, which are used for electric fuses and safety plugs in water sprinkling systems. About 75 per cent of the bismuth produced is for medicine and cosmetics. Bismuth nitrate is relatively opaque to x-rays and is taken internally when the digestive organs are to be photographed.

Name. Etymology in dispute; possibly from the Greek meaning *lead white.*

Native Nonmetals

Sulfur S   Diamond C   Graphite C

SULFUR—S

Crystallography. Orthorhombic; dipyramidal. Pyramidal in habit (Fig. 396), often with two dipyramids, first-order prism and base in combination (Fig. 397). Commonly in irregular masses imperfectly crystallized. Also massive reniform, stalactitic, as incrustations, earthy.

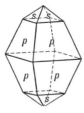

Fig. 396.

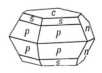

Fig. 397.

Sulfur Crystals.

There are three polymorphic forms of sulfur. The ordinary natural sulfur is orthorhombic; the other two are monoclinic and very rare as minerals.

Physical properties. Fracture conchoidal to uneven. Brittle. H $1\frac{1}{2}$–$2\frac{1}{2}$. G 2.05–2.09. Luster resinous. Color sulfur-yellow, varying with impurities to yellow shades of green, gray, and red. Transparent to translucent. Poor conductor of heat. When a crystal is held in the hand close to the ear it will be heard to crack. This is due to the expansion of the surface layers because of the heat from the hand, while the interior, on account of the slow heat conductivity, is un-affected. Crystals of sulfur should, therefore, be handled with care.

Composition. Sulfur; often impure with clay or asphalt. May contain small amounts of selenium.

Tests. Fusible at 1 (112.8° C) and burns with a blue flame to sulfur dioxide. Sublimates in closed tube, giving a red to dark yellow liquid when hot, yellow solid when cold.

Diagnostic features. Sulfur can be told by its yellow color and the ease with which it burns. The absence of a good cleavage distin-guishes it from orpiment.

Occurrence. Sulfur often occurs at or near the crater rims of active or extinct volcanoes where it has been derived from the gases given off in fumaroles. These may furnish sulfur as a direct sublima-tion product or by the incomplete oxidation of hydrogen sulfide gas. It is also formed by the reduction of sulfates, especially gypsum. It may be deposited from sulfur-bearing waters by the action of the so-called sulfur bacteria. Sulfur may be found in veins associated with metallic sulfides and formed by the oxidation of the sulfides. It is most commonly found in the Tertiary sedimentary rocks and most fre-quently associated with gypsum and limestone; often in clay rocks; frequently with bituminous deposits. The large deposits near Girgenti, Sicily, are noteworthy for the fine crystals associated with celestite, gypsum, calcite, aragonite. Sulfur is also found associated with the volcanoes of Mexico, Hawaii, Japan, and at Ollague, Chile, where it is mined at an elevation of 19,000 feet.

In the United States the most productive deposits are in Texas and Louisiana. Here the sulfur is associated with anhydrite, gypsum, and calcite in the cap rock of salt domes. At present over 80 per cent of the sulfur production of the United States is from Texas. There are several producing localities, but the largest output is from the Boling Dome. In Louisiana the chief production is at Grand Ecaille, Plaque-mines Parish. There are many other workable deposits of sulfur associated with salt domes. Sulfur is obtained from these deposits by what is known as the Frasch method. Superheated water is pumped down to the sulfur horizon, where it melts the sulfur; compressed air then forces the sulfur to the surface. Sulfur also occurs in Wyoming, Utah, and California.

Use. Sulfur is used in the chemical industry chiefly in the manu-facture of sulfuric acid. It is also used in fertilizers, insecticides, explosives, coal-tar products, rubber and in the preparation of wood pulp for paper manufacture.

DIAMOND AND GRAPHITE

Diamond and graphite, both elemental carbon, afford the most spectacular example of polymorphism. Both may be wholly burned to carbon dioxide at sufficiently high temperatures. Despite this chemical identity, diamond and graphite differ in almost every other regard, and the differences are directly traceable to the structures. Diamond has an exceptionally close-knit and strongly bonded structure in which each carbon atom is bound by powerful and highly directive covalent bonds to four carbon neighbors at the apices of a regular tetrahedron. The resulting structure, illustrated in Fig. 398, although strongly bonded, is not close packed, and only 34 per cent of the available space is filled. The presence in the structure of rather widely spaced

Fig. 398. Diamond Packing Model.   **Fig. 399.** Graphite Packing Model.

sheets of carbon atoms parallel to the (111) planes may be observed in Fig. 398. These sheets are the planes of maximum atomic population and account for the prominent {111} cleavage of diamond.

The structure of graphite, illustrated in Fig. 399, consists of sheets of six-membered rings in which each carbon atom has three near neighbors arranged at the apices of an equilateral triangle. Three of the four valence electrons in each carbon atom may be considered to be locked up in tight covalent bonds with its three close neighbors in the plane of the sheet. The fourth is free to wander over the surface of the sheet, creating a dispersed electrical charge which bestows on graphite its relatively high electrical conductivity. In contrast, diamond, in which all four valence electrons are locked up in covalent bonds, is among the best of electrical insulators.

The sheets composing the graphite crystal are stacked in such a way that alternate sheets are in identical position, with the intervening sheet translated a distance of one-half the identity period in the plane of the sheets. The distance between sheets is much greater than one atomic diameter, and van der Waals' binding forces perpendicular to the sheets are very weak. This wide separation and weak binding give rise to the perfect basal cleavage and easy gliding parallel to the sheets. Because of this open structure only about 21 per cent of the available space in graphite is filled, and the specific gravity is proportionately less than that of diamond. The relation

$$\frac{\% \text{ filling of space in graphite}}{\% \text{ filling of space in diamond}} = \frac{\text{specific gravity of graphite}}{\text{specific gravity of diamond}}$$

is very nearly numerically exact, indicating that the carbon-carbon bonds in the two structures are closely similar.

The synthesis of diamond in 1955 was the realization of an age-old dream and established firmly the stability relations between the dimorphs of carbon over a wide range of pressure and temperature. Figure 400, a phase diagram taken from the General Electric report, shows these relationships. Diamond, as is to be expected from its high specific gravity and fairly close packing, is the high-pressure dimorph. At low pressures or temperatures it is unstable with respect to graphite

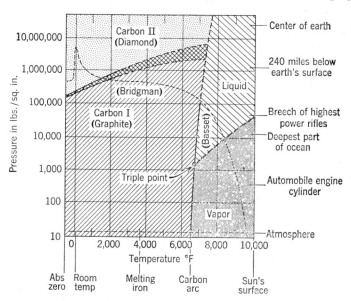

Fig. 400. Carbon Phase Diagram. (*Man-Made Diamonds.* General Electric Research Laboratory, Research Information Service, 1955.)

and may be converted to graphite at moderate temperatures in sealed containers. The reason that diamond and graphite can coexist at room temperatures and pressures is because the reaction is very sluggish. In order to permit inversion of graphite to diamond, extremely high temperatures are needed to cause the carbon atoms in the graphite lattice to break loose by thermal agitation and to make them available for building the diamond lattice. Such temperatures also increase the pressure required to bring about the inversion. Therefore, diamonds were not synthesized until an apparatus could be built that would simultaneously exert a very high pressure and withstand the high temperature. Such a press was built by General Electric engineers, and the first diamonds were synthesized in 1955 using pressures of 600,000 to 1,500,000 pounds per square inch and temperatures of 750 to 2750° C!

The success of the diamond syntheses encouraged experimentation with boron nitride, BN, whose structure is similar to graphite. In 1956 a high-pressure, high-temperature dimorph of boron nitride having the structure and hardness of diamond was prepared. This compound, known by the trade name of *Borazon* is expected to be of great industrial use. Borazon is not a mineral, but its synthesis illustrates the application to industrial problems of crystal chemical concepts first evolved and tested in minerals.

DIAMOND—C

Crystallography. Isometric; hextetrahedral, perhaps hexoctahedral. Crystals are usually octahedral in appearance with {111} and {1$\bar{1}$1} equally well developed. Flattened and elongated crystals are common. Curved faces, especially of the positive and negative hextetrahedron, or hexoctahedron (Figs. 401 and 402), are frequently observed. Cube and dodecahedron faces are rare. Rarely massive. Spinel twins, usually flattened parallel to the twin plane, are common (Fig. 403). *Bort*, a variety of diamond, has rounded forms and rough exterior resulting from a radial or cryptocrystalline aggregate. The term is also applied to badly colored or flawed diamonds without gem value.

Physical properties. Perfect {111} and {1$\bar{1}$1} cleavage. **H** 10 (hardest known mineral). **G** 3.5. Luster adamantine; uncut crystals have a characteristic greasy appearance. The very high refractive index, 2.42, and the strong dispersion of light account for the brilliancy and "fire" of the cut diamond. Usually pale yellow or colorless; also pale shades of red, orange, green, blue, and brown.

Deeper shades are rare. *Carbonado* or *carbon* is black or grayish black bort. It is noncleavable, opaque, and less brittle than crystals.

Composition. Pure carbon.

Tests. Insoluble in acids and alkalis. At a high temperature in oxygen will burn to CO_2 gas, leaving no ash.

Diagnostic features. Diamond is distinguished from similar-appearing minerals by its great hardness, adamantine luster, and cleavage.

 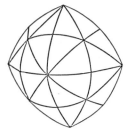 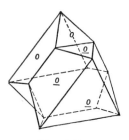

Fig. 401.	Fig. 402.	Fig. 403.

Diamond Crystals.

Occurrence. Diamonds have been discovered in many different localities but in only a few in notable amount. Most commonly the diamond is found in the sands and gravels of stream beds, where it has been preserved because of its inert chemical nature, its great hardness, and its fairly high specific gravity. In South Africa and more recently in other countries on the African continent as well as in Arkansas, diamonds have been found in an altered peridotite known as *kimberlite*. The four countries that up to the present time have furnished practically the entire world's output of diamonds are India, Brazil, Union of South Africa, and the Belgian Congo. The important diamond fields of India were located in the eastern and southern portions of the peninsula, but most of the famous mines are now abandoned. Only a few hundred carats a year are now produced from the gravels which during a period of 2000 years produced over 20,000,000 carats. Until the eighteenth century India remained the only source of diamonds, and many of the famous stones were found there.

Diamonds were discovered in Brazil in the first half of the eighteenth century and have since been mined there. At present, however, the production is comparatively small, about 250,000 carats a year. Diamonds are found in the stream gravels in several different districts, the two most important being located in the provinces of Minas Geraes and Bahia. The city of Diamantina, Minas Geraes, is situated in the center of the most productive field, the diamonds being found chiefly in the gravels of the Rio Jequitinhonha and Rio Doce. Extensive upland deposits of diamond-bearing gravels and clays are also worked. The black carbonado comes only from Bahia.

About 95 per cent of the world's output of diamonds comes at present from the African continent. The Belgian Congo is by far the largest producer and furnishes from placer deposits over 50 per cent of the world's supply. These Congo diamonds are mostly of industrial grade and represent only about 13 per cent of the total value of diamonds produced.

The first African diamonds were discovered in 1867 in the gravels of the Vaal River, South Africa. In 1871 diamonds were discovered imbedded in the rock of several volcanic necks or pipes located near the present town of Kimberley in Griqualand-West, south of the Vaal River, near the boundary of the Orange Free State. The diamonds in this district were first found in the soil resulting from the disintegration of the underlying altered peridotite. This soil was colored yellow by iron oxides and was known as "yellow ground."

The principal mines near the town of Kimberley are the Kimberley, Du Toitspan, De Beers, Wesselton, and Bultfontein. The Kimberley mine was developed to a depth of 3500 feet before it was abandoned. The mines were originally worked as open pits, but, as they increased in depth, underground methods were adopted. The early method of treatment was to crush the blue ground into coarse fragments and spread it out on platforms to disintegrate gradually under atmospheric influences. The present method is to crush the rock fine enough to permit immediate concentration. The diamonds are finally separated on shaking tables that have been coated with grease, to which the diamonds adhere, whereas the rest of the material is washed away.

In Cape Province on the desert coast just south of the mouth of the Orange River, terrace deposits containing high-quality stones were discovered in 1927. Later similar deposits were found along the coast north of the Orange River in South-West Africa extending 50 to 60 miles up the coast. Elsewhere in Africa alluvial diamonds have been found in French Angola, Ghana, French Equatorial Africa, and Sierra Leone. The most recent African discovery is in Tanganyika, which has made that country a major producer. For many years British Guiana and Venezuela have had a small production, but recently that from Venezuela has increased substantially.

Diamonds have been found sparingly in various parts of the United

States. Small stones have occasionally been discovered in the stream sands along the eastern slope of the Appalachian Mountains from Virginia south to Georgia. Diamonds have also been reported from the gold sands of northern California and southern Oregon. Sporadic occurrences of diamonds have been noted in the glacial drift in Wisconsin, Michigan, and Ohio. In 1906 the first diamond was found at a new locality situated near Murfreesboro, Pike County, Arkansas. The stones are found here not only in the detrital soil but also imbedded in the underlying peridotite rock in a manner quite similar to that of the South African occurrence. The Arkansas locality has yielded about 40,000 stones but is at present unproductive. In 1951 the old mine workings were opened to tourists who, for a fee, were permitted to look for diamonds. During the first six months, several small diamonds were thus found.

Use. *In Industry.* Fragments of diamond crystals are used to cut glass. The fine powder is employed in grinding and polishing diamonds and other gem stones. Wheels are impregnated with diamond powder for cutting rocks and other hard materials. Steel bits are set with diamonds, especially the cryptocrystalline variety, carbonado, to make diamond drills used in exploratory mining work. The diamond is also used in wire drawing and in tools for the truing of grinding wheels.

In Gems. The diamond is the most important of the gem stones, and only in modern times has it been put to other uses. Its value depends upon its hardness, its brilliancy, which is due to its high index of refraction, and to its "fire," which is due to its strong dispersion of light into the prismatic colors. In general the most valuable are those flawless stones which are colorless or possess a "blue-white" color. A faint straw-yellow color, which diamond often shows, detracts much from its value. Deep shades of yellow, red, green, or blue known as fancy stones are greatly prized, and fine stones of these colors bring very high prices. Diamonds can be colored deep shades of green by irradiation with high-energy nuclear particles, neutrons, deuterons, and alpha particles, and blue by exposing it to fast-moving electrons. A stone colored green by irradiation can be made a deep yellow by proper heat treatment. These artificially colored stones are difficult to distinguish from those of natural color.

The value of a cut diamond depends upon its color and purity, upon the skill with which it has been cut, and upon its size. A 1-carat stone weighs 200 milligrams, and if cut in the form of a brilliant would be 6.25 millimeters in diameter and 4 millimeters in depth. A 2-carat stone of the same quality would have a value three or four times as great.

Famous stones. The older famous diamonds include the following: the *Kohinoor,* weighing 106 carats, one of the crown jewels of Great Britain; the *Regent* or *Pitt,* weighing 137 carats, belonging to France; the *Orloff,* which is mounted in the Russian imperial scepter, weighing 199 carats; the *Florentine* yellow diamond, which weighs 137 carats; the *Star of the South,* weighing 129 carats.

Large stones found more recently in South Africa include the following: the *Victoria* or *Imperial,* which weighed 468 carats when found, and 236 when cut. It was later recut, however, its present weight being 190 carats. The *Stewart* weighed before and after cutting 296 and 123 carats, respectively. The *Tiffany* diamond, which is of a brilliant yellow color, weighed 287 carats before and 125 carats after cutting. The *Green Dresden* diamond weighs 50 carats, and the blue *Hope* diamond 45. The *Colenso* diamond, presented to the British Museum in 1887 by John Ruskin, weighs 133 carats. The *Excelsior* diamond, found at Jagersfontein in 1903, weighed 650 carats; it is now known as the *Jubilee,* and weighs 245 carats. The *Cullinan* or *Star of Africa* diamond found at the Premier mine, Transvaal, was the largest stone ever found, weighing 3106 carats or about 22 ounces, and measured 4 by $2\frac{1}{2}$ by 2 inches. This stone was presented to King Edward VII by the Transvaal Government and has been cut into nine large stones, and into ninety-six smaller brilliants, the largest two weighing 530 and 317 carats, respectively. The largest African stone found in recent years, known as the *Jonker* diamond, was discovered by Jacobus Jonker in 1934 in stream gravels near the Premier mine. It weighed 726.25 carats when found and has since been cut. The most recent find of a large stone was the discovery of the *Vargas* diamond in Brazil in 1938. It weighed about $\frac{1}{2}$ carat more than the Jonker diamond.

Artificial. For well over a century many experiments have been made with the hope of synthesizing diamond and many claims have been made for its synthesis. However, it was not until 1955 that the General Electric Company made authenticated diamonds. (See page 239.) So far the synthetic diamonds are small and not suitable for cutting into gems. However, they are being produced in competition with small natural industrial diamonds.

Name. The name diamond is a corruption of the Greek word *adamas,* meaning *invincible.*

GRAPHITE—C

Plumbago.   Black Lead

Crystallography. Hexagonal; dihexagonal-dipyramidal. In tabular crystals of hexagonal outline with prominent basal plane. Distinct faces of other forms very rare. Triangular markings on the base are the result of gliding along an undetermined second-order pyramid. Usually in foliated or scaly masses, but may be radiated or granular.

Physical properties. Perfect {0001} cleavage. **H** 1-2 (readily marks paper and soils the fingers). **G** 2.2. Luster metallic, sometimes dull earthy. Color black to steel-gray. Black streak. Greasy feel. Folia flexible but not elastic.

Composition. Carbon. Some graphite impure with iron oxide, clay, or other minerals.

Tests. Infusible, but may burn to CO_2 at a high temperature. Unattacked by acids.

Diagnostic features. Graphite is recognized by its color, foliated nature, and softness. Distinguished from molybdenite by its black color (molybdenite has a blue tone). On glazed porcelain graphite gives a black streak (molybdenite a greenish streak).

Occurrence. Graphite most commonly occurs in metamorphic rocks such as crystalline limestones, schists, and gneisses. It may be found as large crystalline plates inclosed in the rock or disseminated in small flakes in sufficient amount to form a considerable proportion of the rock. In these cases, it has probably been derived from carbon material of organic origin which has been converted into graphite during the metamorphism of the rock. Instances are known in which coal beds, under the influence of strong metamorphic action, such as the intrusion into them of an igneous rock, have in a greater or less degree been converted into graphite. Examples of such an occurrence are to be found in the graphite coals of Rhode Island and in the coal fields of Sonora, Mexico. Graphite also occurs in fissure veins associated with other minerals in the deposits at Ticonderoga, New York. Here the veins traverse a gneiss and, in addition to graphite, contain quartz, biotite, orthoclase, tourmaline, apatite, pyrite, and sphene. The graphite may have been formed in these veins from hydrocarbons introduced into them during the metamorphism of the region and derived from the surrounding carbon-bearing rocks. Graphite occurs occasionally as an original constituent of igneous rocks as in the basalts of Ovifak, Greenland, in a nepheline syenite in India, in a granite pegmatite in Maine. It is also found in some meteorites.

The most productive deposits of graphite at present are on the island of Ceylon, where coarsely foliated masses are found in veins in gneisses interbedded with limestones. It occurs in large amounts in various localities in Austria, Italy, India, Mexico, etc. Graphite is found in quantity with schistose rocks in Madagascar. The chief deposits in the United States are in the Adirondack region of New York, in

Essex, Warren, and Washington counties, particularly at Ticonderoga.

Artificial graphite is manufactured on a large scale in the electrical furnaces at Niagara Falls. Anthracite coal or petroleum coke with a small amount of evenly distributed ash is subjected to the intense heat of the electrical furnace and converted into graphite. The output of artificial graphite is considerably in excess of that of the natural mineral.

Use. Used in the manufacture of refractory crucibles for the steel, brass, and bronze industries. Most of the graphite for crucibles is imported from Ceylon. Used widely, when mixed with oil, as a lubricant. Mixed with fine clay, it forms the "lead" of pencils. Much of the graphite used in the United States for this purpose comes from Sonora, Mexico. Employed in the manufacture of a protective paint for structural iron and steel works. Used in the coating of foundry facings, for batteries, electrodes, stove polishes, in electrotyping, etc.

Name. Derived from the Greek word meaning *to write*, in allusion to its use in pencils.

SULFIDES

The sulfides form an important class of minerals which includes the majority of the ore minerals. With them are classed the similar but rarer selenides, tellurides, arsenides, and antimonides.

The general formula for the sulfides is given as A_mX_n in which A represents the metallic elements and X the nonmetallic element. The order of listing of the various minerals is in a decreasing ratio of $A:X$.

Sulfides

Argentite	Ag_2S	Cinnabar	HgS
Chalcocite	Cu_2S	Realgar	AsS
Bornite	Cu_5FeS_4	Orpiment	As_2S_3
Galena	PbS	Stibnite	Sb_2S_3
Sphalerite	ZnS	Bismuthinite	Bi_2S_3
Chalcopyrite	$CuFeS_2$	Pyrite	FeS_2
Stannite	Cu_2FeSnS_4	Cobaltite	$(Co,Fe)AsS$
Greenockite	CdS	Marcasite	FeS_2
Pyrrhotite	$Fe_{1-x}S$	Arsenopyrite	$FeAsS$
Niccolite	$NiAs$	Molybdenite	MoS_2
Millerite	NiS	Calaverite	$AuTe_2$
Pentlandite	$(Fe,Ni)_9S_8$	Sylvanite	$(Au,Ag)Te_2$
Covellite	CuS	Skutterudite	$(Co,Ni,Fe)As_3$

The sulfides can be divided into small structural groups, but no broad generalizations can be made regarding their structure. Many of the sulfides have ionic bonding, whereas others, displaying most of the properties of metals, have metallic bonding at least in part. Sphalerite has a structure similar to diamond and like diamond has a covalent bond.

Argentite—Ag_2S

Silver Glance

Crystallography. Isometric, hexoctahedral above 180° C; orthorhombic at ordinary temperatures. Crystals, paramorphs of the high-temperature form; most commonly show the cube, octahedron, and dodecahedron but frequently are arranged in branching or reticulated groups. Most commonly massive or as a coating.

Acanthite is the orthorhombic Ag_2S existing at ordinary temperatures.

Physical properties. H 2-$2\frac{1}{2}$. G 7.3. Very sectile; can be cut with a knife like lead. Luster metallic. Color and streak blackish lead-gray. Streak shining. Opaque. Bright on fresh surface but on exposure becomes dull black, owing to the formation of an earthy sulfide.

Composition. Silver sulfide, Ag_2S. Ag 87.1, S 12.9 per cent.

Tests. Fusible at $1\frac{1}{2}$ with intumescence. When fused on charcoal in the oxidizing flame gives off odor of sulfur dioxide and yields a globule of metallic silver.

Diagnostic features. Argentite can be distinguished by its color, sectility, and high specific gravity.

Occurrence. Argentite is an important primary silver mineral found in veins associated with native silver, the ruby silvers, polybasite, stephanite, galena, and sphalerite. It may also be of secondary origin. It is found in microscopic inclusions in so-called argentiferous galena. Argentite is an important ore in the silver mines of Guanajuato and elsewhere in Mexico; in Peru, Chile, and Bolivia. Important European localities for its occurrence are Freiberg in Saxony, Joachimsthal in Bohemia, Schemnitz and Kremnitz in Czechoslovakia, and Kongsberg in Norway. In the United States it has been an important ore mineral in Nevada, notably at the Comstock Lode and at Tonopah. It is also found in the silver districts of Colorado, and in Montana at Butte associated with copper ores.

Use. An important ore of silver.

Name. The name argentite comes from the Latin *argentum*, meaning silver.

CHALCOCITE—Cu₂S

Copper Glance

Crystallography. Orthorhombic; dipyramidal (below 105° C ortho-rhombic; above 105° C hexagonal). Crystals very rare, usually small and tabular with hexagonal outline; striated parallel to the *a* axis. (Figs. 404 and 405.) Commonly fine grained and massive.

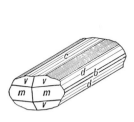
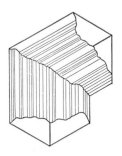

Fig. 404.   **Fig. 405.**

Chalcocite Crystals.

Physical properties. Fracture conchoidal. **H** 2½–3. **G** 5.5–5.8. Luster metallic. Imperfectly sectile. Color shining lead-gray, tarnishing to dull black on exposure. Streak grayish black. Some chalcocite is soft and sooty.

Composition. Cuprous sulfide, Cu₂S. Cu 79.8, S 20.2 per cent.

Tests. Fusible at 2–2½. Heated in the open tube on charcoal gives odor of sulfur dioxide. Roasted mineral, moistened with hydrochloric acid, gives azure-blue flame. Easily reduced to metallic copper on charcoal.

Diagnostic features. Chalcocite is distinguished by its lead-gray color and sectility.

Occurrence. Chalcocite is one of the most important copper-ore minerals. It occurs principally as a supergene mineral in enriched zones of sulfide deposits. The greatest copper mines in the United States today work what is called "porphyry copper" ore. In these deposits primary copper minerals disseminated through the rock, usually a porphyry, have been altered to chalcocite and thus enriched to form a workable ore body. The amount of copper in such deposits is small, rarely greater than 2 or 3 per cent and may be as low as 0.75 per cent. Chalcocite also occurs with bornite and other hypogene minerals in sulfide veins.

Fine crystals have been found at Cornwall, England, and at Bristol, Connecticut. Found as an ore at Monte Catini, Tuscany; Tsumeb, South-West Africa; French Congo; Mexico; Peru; and Chile. Found in large amounts in many mining districts in western United States such as Butte, Montana; Miami, Morenci, and Clifton, Arizona; Bingham, Utah; and Ely, Nevada. At Kennecott in the Copper River district, Alaska.

Use. An important copper ore.

Similar species. *Digenite,* Cu_9S_5, is blue to black, associated with chalcocite. *Stromeyerite,* $(Ag,Cu)_2S$, is a steel-gray mineral found in copper-silver veins.

BORNITE—Cu_5FeS_4

Purple Copper Ore. Peacock Ore

Crystallography. Isometric; hexoctahedral. Rarely in rough cubic and less commonly in dodecahedral and octahedral crystals. Usually massive.

Physical properties. H 3. G 5.06–5.08. Luster metallic. Color brownish bronze on fresh fracture but quickly tarnishing to variegated purple and blue and finally to almost black on exposure. Streak grayish black.

Composition. Copper iron sulfide, Cu_5FeS_4. Cu 63.3, Fe 11.2, S 25.5 per cent. Microscopic admixed blebs of other minerals cause the composition of what appears to be bornite to vary considerably, but analyses of pure material agree with the above formula.

Tests. Fusible at $2\frac{1}{2}$. Gives odor of sulfur dioxide on charcoal. Yields only a very little sulfur in the closed tube. Becomes magnetic in the reducing flame. If, after roasting, it is moistened with hydrochloric acid and heated, it gives an azure-blue flame (copper).

Diagnostic features. Bornite is distinguished by its characteristic bronze color on the fresh fracture and by the purple tarnish.

Alteration. Bornite alters readily to chalcocite and covellite.

Occurrence. Bornite is a widely occurring copper ore usually found associated with other copper minerals in hypogene deposits. It is much less frequently found as a supergene mineral, formed in the upper, enriched zone of copper veins through the action of descending copper-bearing solutions upon chalcopyrite. It is found disseminated in basic rocks, in contact metamorphic deposits, in replacement deposits, and in pegmatites. Bornite frequently occurs in intimate mixtures with chalcopyrite and chalcocite. Quantitatively it is not as important an ore of copper as chalcocite and chalcopyrite.

Good crystals of bornite have been found associated with crystals of chalcocite at Bristol, Connecticut, and at Cornwall, England. Found in large masses in Chile, Peru, Bolivia, and Mexico. In the United States it is found at Magma mine, Pioneer, Arizona; Butte, Montana; Engels mine, Plumas County, California; Halifax County, Virginia; and Superior, Arizona.

Use. An ore of copper.

Name. Bornite was named after the German mineralogist von Born (1742–1791).

GALENA—PbS

Crystallography. Isometric; hexoctahedral. The most common form is the cube, Fig. 406. The octahedron sometimes is present as truncations to the cube (Figs. 407 and 408). Dodecahedron and trisoctahedron rare. A group of galena crystals is shown in Fig. 409.

Galena has a NaCl type of structure with Pb in place of the Na and S in place of the Cl.

| Fig. 406. | Fig. 407. | Fig. 408. |

Galena Crystals.

Physical properties. Perfect {001} cleavage. **H** $2\frac{1}{2}$. **G** 7.4–7.6. Luster bright metallic. Color and streak lead-gray.

Composition. Lead sulfide, PbS. Pb 86.6, S 13.4 per cent. Silver is usually present, probably as admixtures of silver minerals such as argentite or tetrahedrite. Galena may also contain small amounts of zinc, cadmium, antimony, bismuth, and copper. Selenium may substitute for sulfur and a complete series from PbS–PbSe has been reported.

Tests. Fusible at 2. Reduced on charcoal to lead globule with formation of yellow to white coating of lead oxide. When galena is heated rapidly in the oxidizing flame the coating is heavier and consists chiefly of a white volatile combination of oxides of lead and sulfur, which resembles the antimony oxide coating. Odor of sulfur dioxide when roasted on charcoal.

Diagnostic features. Galena can be easily recognized by its good cleavage, high specific gravity, softness, and lead-gray streak.

Alteration. By oxidation galena is converted into the sulfate, anglesite and the carbonate, cerussite.

Fig. 409. Galena Crystals, Joplin, Missouri.

Occurrence. Galena is a very common metallic sulfide, found in veins associated with sphalerite, pyrite, marcasite, chalcopyrite, cerussite, anglesite, dolomite, calcite, quartz, barite, and fluorite. When found in veins that show a close connection with igneous rocks, galena is frequently found with silver minerals; it often contains silver itself and so becomes an important silver ore. A large part of the supply of lead comes as a secondary product from ores mined chiefly for their silver. A second type of galena deposit is associated with limestones, either as veins, open space fillings, or replacement deposits. The replacement deposits in limestone are commonly accompanied by a dolomitization of the rock and may have no apparent association with igneous rocks. Galena is also found in contact metamorphic deposits.

The most famous foreign localities are, Freiberg, Saxony; the Harz Mountains; Westphalia and Nassau; Příbram, Bohemia; Cornwall,

Derbyshire, and Cumberland, England; and Broken Hill, Australia.

In the United States there are many lead-producing districts; only the most important are mentioned here. In southeastern Missouri the ore occurs in the form of beds with galena disseminated through the limestone. In the tri-state district of Missouri, Kansas, and Oklahoma centering around Joplin, Missouri, the galena is associated with zinc ores and is found in irregular veins and pockets in limestone and chert. It is found in a similar manner but in smaller amount in Illinois, Iowa, and Wisconsin. The deposits of southeast Missouri are particularly productive. In Idaho, an important producing state, the lead is derived chiefly from lead-silver vein deposits located near Wallace in Shoshone County. Lead is produced in Utah at Brigham and from the silver deposits of the Tintic and Park City districts; and in Colorado, chiefly from the lead-silver ores of the Leadville district.

Use. Practically the only source of lead and an important ore of silver. Metallic lead is used chiefly as follows: for conversion into white lead (a basic lead carbonate), which is the principal ingredient of many white paints, or into the oxides (*litharge*, PbO, and *minium*, Pb_3O_4) used in making glass and in giving a glaze to earthenware; as pipe and sheets; and for shot. It is a principal ingredient of several alloys as solder (lead and tin), type metal (lead and antimony), and low-fusion alloys (lead, bismuth, and tin). Large amounts of metallic lead are used in storage batteries and as shielding in working with uranium and other radioactive substances.

Name. The name galena is derived from the Latin *galena*, a name originally given to lead ore.

Similar species. *Altaite*, PbTe, and *alabandite*, MnS, like galena, have a NaCl type of structure.

SPHALERITE—ZnS

Zinc Blende. Black Jack

Crystallography. Isometric; hextetrahedral. Tetrahedron, dodecahedron, and cube common forms (Figs. 410 and 411), but the crystals, frequently highly complex and usually malformed or in rounded aggregates, often show polysynthetic twinning. Usually found in cleavable masses, coarse to fine granular. Compact, botryoidal, cryptocrystalline.

The sphalerite structure is similar to that of diamond with one-half of the carbon atoms of diamond replaced by zinc and the other half by sulfur. Each zinc atom is surrounded by and bonded to four sulfur atoms and in turn each sulfur atom is bonded to four zinc atoms (Fig. 412).

The dimorphic form of ZnS, *wurtzite,* is hexagonal.

Physical properties. Perfect {011} cleavage, but sphalerite from some localities is too fine grained to show cleavage. **H** $3\frac{1}{2}$–4. **G** 3.9–4.1. Nonmetallic and resinous to submetallic luster; also adamantine.

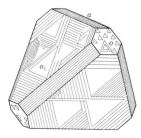
Fig. 410.

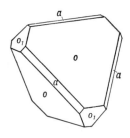
Fig. 411.

Sphalerite Crystals.

Color white when pure, and green when nearly so. Commonly yellow, brown to black, darkening with increase in the amount of iron present. Also red (ruby zinc). Transparent to translucent. Streak white to yellow and brown.

Composition. Zinc sulfide, ZnS. Zn 67, S 33 per cent when pure. Nearly always contains iron (Zn,Fe)S, the maximum iron content being about 36 per cent. It has been demonstrated[1] that in the presence of excess iron, the higher the temperature of formation, the greater the amount of iron present, up to 894° C when there is 36.5 per cent of FeS in solid solution (see Fig. 382). The amount of iron is thus an indication of the temperature of formation, and sphalerite becomes a geologic thermometer. Manganese and cadmium are usually present in small amounts in solid solution.

Tests. Pure zinc sulfide infusible; becomes fusible, but difficultly so, with increase in amount of iron. Gives odor of sulfur dioxide when heated on charcoal. When heated on charcoal with reducing mixture gives a coating of zinc oxide (yellow when hot, white when cold) which is nonvolatile in oxidizing flame.

Diagnostic features. Sphalerite can be recognized by its striking resinous luster and perfect cleavage. The dark varieties (black jack) can be told by the reddish brown streak.

---

[1] Kullerud, Gunnar, The FeS–ZnS system: a geological thermometer. *Norsk Geol. Tidssk.,* Vol. 32, pp. 81–147, 1953.

Occurrence. Sphalerite, the most important ore of zinc, is an extremely common mineral and is associated with galena, pyrite, marcasite, chalcopyrite, smithsonite, calcite, and dolomite. In its occurrence and mode of origin it is closely allied with galena, with which it is most commonly found. It is widely distributed but is chiefly in

Fig. 412. Sphalerite, ZnS, Packing Model. Zn (black) and S (white) are both in 4-fold coordination. Note sheets of atoms parallel to (111). If they are rotated 180° alternately, the wurtzite structure results.

veins and irregular replacement deposits in limestone. Sphalerite is also found in veins in igneous rocks and in contact metamorphic deposits.

The most noteworthy European occurrences are at Schemnitz and other localities in the gold- and silver-mining districts of Czechoslovakia and Rumania; at Alston Moor and other places in the lead-mining districts of northern England; and at Binnenthal, Switzerland, in fine crystals. Extensive mining of sphalerite is carried on in Australia, Canada, and Mexico. Large zinc deposits are found in the

United States in Missouri, Colorado, Montana, Wisconsin, Idaho, and Kansas. The chief locality for its production is the Joplin district in southwestern Missouri, and in adjacent districts in Kansas and Oklahoma.

Use. The most important ore of zinc. The chief uses for metallic zinc, or *spelter*, are in galvanizing iron; making brass, an alloy of copper and zinc; in electric batteries; and as sheet zinc. Zinc oxide, or zinc white, is used extensively for making paint. Zinc chloride is used as a preservative for wood. Zinc sulfate is used in dyeing and in medicine. Sphalerite also serves as the most important source of cadmium, indium, gallium, and germanium.

Name. Sphalerite from the Greek meaning *treacherous*. Blende because, although often resembling galena, it yielded no lead; from the German word meaning *blind* or *deceiving*.

CHALCOPYRITE—CuFeS$_2$

Copper Pyrites. Yellow Copper Ore

Crystallography. Tetragonal; scalenohedral. Commonly pseudo-tetrahedral in aspect with the sphenoidal faces {112} present (Fig. 413). Other forms shown in Figs. 414 and 415 rare. Usually massive.

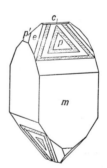

| Fig. 413. | Fig. 414. | Fig. 415. |

Chalcopyrite Crystals.

Physical properties. H 3½–4. G 4.1–4.3. Luster metallic. Brittle. Color brass-yellow; often tarnished to bronze or iridescent. Streak greenish black.

Composition. A sulfide of copper and iron, CuFeS$_2$. Cu 34.5, Fe 30.5, S 35.0 per cent. Analyses often show variations from the percentages given because of mechanical admixtures of other sulfides, chiefly pyrite.

Tests. Fusible at 2 to a magnetic globule. Gives odor of sulfur dioxide when heated on charcoal. Decrepitates and gives sulfur in the closed tube. After roasting, and moistening with hydrochloric acid, gives the azure-blue copper chloride flame.

Diagnostic features. Recognized by its brass-yellow color, greenish black streak, and softness. Distinguished from pyrite by being softer than steel and from gold by being brittle. Known as "fool's gold," a term which is also applied to pyrite.

Occurrence. Chalcopyrite is the most widely occurring copper mineral and one of the most important sources of that metal. Occurs widely distributed in metallic veins, especially of the high-temperature type. It is associated with pyrite, pyrrhotite, sphalerite, galena, quartz, calcite, dolomite, siderite, and various copper minerals. It is commonly of primary origin, and from it, by various alteration processes, many secondary copper minerals are derived. Also occurs as an original constituent of igneous rocks; in pegmatite dikes; in contact metamorphic deposits; and disseminated in schistose rocks. May carry gold or silver and become an ore of those metals. Often in subordinate amount with large bodies of pyrite, making them serve as low-grade copper ores.

A few of the localities at which chalcopyrite is the chief ore of copper are: Cornwall, England; Falun, Sweden; Schemnitz, Czechoslovakia; Schlaggenwald, Bohemia; Freiberg, Saxony; Rio Tinto, Spain; South Africa; northern Rhodesia; and Chile. Found widely in the United States but usually in connection with other copper minerals in equal or greater amount; found at Butte, Montana; Bingham, Utah; Jerome, Arizona; Ducktown, Tennessee; and various districts in California, Colorado, and New Mexico. In Canada the most important occurrences of chalcopyrite are at Sudbury, Ontario and at Rouyn district, Quebec.

Alteration. Chalcopyrite alters often to malachite, covellite, chalcocite, and iron oxides. Concentrations of copper in the zone of supergene enrichment are often the result of such alteration and removal of copper in solution with its subsequent deposition.

Use. Important ore of copper.

Name. Derived from Greek word meaning *brass* and from *pyrites*.

Stannite—Cu_2FeSnS_4

Crystallography. Tetragonal; scalenohedral. Appears pseudoisometric through twinning. Practically always massive.

Physical properties. H 4. G 4.4. Luster metallic. Color steelgray to iron-black. Streak black. Opaque.

Composition. A sulfide of copper, tin, and iron. S 29.9, Cu 29.5, Sn 27.5, Fe 13.1 per cent.

Tests. Fusible at 1½. Slightly magnetic after heating in the reducing flame. After roasting, and moistening with hydrochloric acid, gives when ignited the blue copper chloride flame.

Diagnostic features. Characterized by its low fusibility and tests for copper, tin, and iron.

Occurrence. Stannite occurs in tin-bearing veins associated with cassiterite, chalcopyrite, wolframite, pyrite, and quartz.

It is a rare mineral found in Bohemia, in various places in Cornwall, and in the tin ores of Bolivia.

Use. A minor ore of tin.

Name. From the Latin name for tin.

Greenockite—CdS

Crystallography. Hexagonal; dihexagonal-pyramidal. Crystals rare and small, showing prism faces, and terminated usually below with pedion and above with pyramids. Usually pulverulent, and as powdery incrustations.

Physical properties. H 3–3½. G 4.9. Luster adamantine to resinous, earthy. Color various shades of yellow and orange. Streak between orange-yellow and brick-red.

Composition. Cadmium sulfide, CdS. Cd 77.8, S 22.2 per cent. Wurtzite, ZnS, and greenockite are isostructural, and a complete solid-solution series exists between the two minerals.

Tests. Infusible. Yields odor of sulfur dioxide when heated on charcoal or in the open tube. Decomposed by hydrochloric acid with the evolution of hydrogen sulfide gas. Gives a reddish brown coating of cadmium oxide when heated with sodium carbonate on charcoal.

Diagnostic features. Characterized by its yellow color and pulverulent form and association with zinc ores.

Occurrence. Greenockite is the most common mineral containing cadmium but is found only in a few localities and in small amount, usually as an earthy coating on zinc ores, especially sphalerite.

Found in crystals at Bishopton, Renfrew, Scotland; Tsumeb, South-West Africa; and also in Bohemia and Carinthia. In the United States is found with the zinc ores of the tri-state district, in Arkansas, and in small amounts at Franklin, New Jersey.

Use. A source of cadmium. Cadmium is used in alloys for anti-friction bearings and low-melting alloys. Small amounts, less than 1.5 per cent, will harden copper and silver. The largest use is in electroplating other metals to form a coating resistant to chemical attack. Cadmium is also used in many pigments and chemicals.

Name. Named after Lord Greenock (later Earl Cathcart). The first crystal was found about 1810. It was over ½ inch across and was mistaken for sphalerite.

PYRRHOTITE—$Fe_{1-x}S$

Magnetic Pyrites

Crystallography. Hexagonal; dihexagonal-dipyramidal. Crystals usually tabular, in some cases pyramidal (Fig. 416). Practically always massive with granular or lamellar habit.

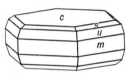

Fig. 416. Pyrrhotite.

Physical properties. H 4. G 4.58–4.65. Luster metallic. Color brownish bronze. Streak black. Magnetic, but varying much in intensity, the less magnetic kinds having more iron. Opaque.

Composition. Sulfide of iron, $Fe_{1-x}S$, with x between 0 and 0.2. The mineral *troilite* is close to FeS; most other pyrrhotites vary in composition but have a deficiency in iron.

Tests. Fusible at 3. Heated on charcoal or in the open tube gives odor of sulfur dioxide and becomes strongly magnetic. Little or no sulfur in the closed tube.

Diagnostic features. Recognized usually by its massive nature, bronze color, and magnetic properties.

Occurrence. Pyrrhotite is a common minor constituent of igneous rocks. It occurs in large masses associated with pentlandite, chalcopyrite, and other sulfides in basic igneous rocks from which it may have been segregated by some form of magmatic differentiation. It is also found in contact metamorphic deposits, in vein deposits, and in pegmatites.

Found in large quantities in Finland, Norway, and Sweden; and at Sudbury, Ontario, Canada. Nickel minerals are associated with it, and thus pyrrhotite is mined on a large scale for its associated nickel. In Germany from Andreasberg in the Harz Mountains; at Schneeberg, Saxony; and Bodenmais, Bavaria. In the United States in crystals from Standish, Maine; at the Gap mine, Lancaster County, Pennsylvania; and in considerable amount at Ducktown, Tennessee.

Use. It is mined for its associated nickel, particularly at Sudbury, Ontario.

Name. The name pyrrhotite comes from the Greek meaning *reddish*.

NICCOLITE—NiAs

Copper Nickel

Crystallography. Hexagonal; dihexagonal-dipyramidal. Rarely in crystals. Usually massive, reniform with columnar structure.

Physical properties. H 5–5½. **G 7.78.** Luster metallic. Color pale copper-red (hence called *copper nickel*), with gray to blackish tarnish. Streak brownish black. Opaque.

Composition. Nickel arsenide, NiAs. Ni 43.9, As 56.1 per cent. Usually with a little iron, cobalt, and sulfur. Arsenic frequently replaced in part by antimony.

Tests. Fusible at 2. When it is heated on charcoal a white volatile deposit of arsenious oxide forms and a garliclike odor is given off. Gives the nickel test with dimethylglyoxime.

Diagnostic features. Characterized by its copper-red color.

Alteration. Quickly alters to annabergite (nickel bloom) in moist atmosphere.

Occurrence. Niccolite, with other nickel arsenides and sulfides, pyrrhotite, and chalcopyrite, frequently occurs in, or is associated with, norites. Also found in vein deposits with cobalt and silver minerals.

Found in Germany in the silver mines of Saxony, the Harz Mountains, in Hessen-Nassau; and at Cobalt, Ontario.

Use. A minor ore of nickel.

Name. The first name of this mineral, *kupfernickel*, gave the name *nickel* to the metal. Niccolite is from the Latin for nickel.

Millerite—NiS

Capillary Pyrites

Crystallography. Hexagonal–R; scalenohedral. Usually in hairlike tufts and radiating groups of slender to capillary crystals. In velvety incrustations.

Physical properties. Cleavage $\{10\bar{1}1\}$ good. **H 3–3½. G 5.5 ± 0.2.** Luster metallic. Color pale brass-yellow; with a greenish tinge when in fine hairlike masses. Streak black, somewhat greenish.

Composition. Nickel sulfide, NiS. Ni 64.7, S 35.3 per cent.

Tests. Fusible at 1½–2 to magnetic globule. Gives odor of sulfur dioxide when heated on charcoal or in the open tube. The roasted mineral colors the borax bead reddish brown in the oxidizing flame. Gives nickel test with dimethylglyoxime.

Diagnostic features. Characterized by its capillary crystals and distinguished from minerals of similar color by nickel tests.

Occurrence. Millerite forms as a low-temperature mineral often in cavities and as an alteration of other nickel minerals, or as crystal inclusions in other minerals.

Occurs in various localities in Saxony, Westphalia, and Hessen-Nassau and in Bohemia. In the United States is found with hematite and ankerite at Antwerp, New York; with pyrrhotite at the Gap mine, Lancaster County, Pennsylvania; in geodes in limestone at St. Louis, Missouri; Keokuk, Iowa; and Milwaukee, Wisconsin.

Use. A subordinate ore of nickel.

Name. In honor of the mineralogist, W. H. Miller (1801–1880), who first studied the crystals.

Pentlandite—$(Fe,Ni)_9S_8$

Crystallography. Isometric; hexoctahedral. Massive, usually in granular aggregates.

Physical properties. Octahedral $\{111\}$ parting. **H** $3\frac{1}{2}$–4. **G** 4.6–5.0. Brittle. Luster metallic. Color yellowish bronze. Streak light bronze-brown. Opaque. Nonmagnetic.

Composition. A sulfide of iron and nickel $(Fe,Ni)_9S_8$. Usually with Fe:Ni close to 1:1. Usually contains small amounts of cobalt.

Tests. Fusible at $1\frac{1}{2}$–2. Gives odor of sulfur dioxide in the open tube; becomes magnetic on heating. Roasted mineral in the oxidizing flame colors borax bead reddish brown (nickel). Gives nickel test with dimethylglyoxime.

Diagnostic features. Pentlandite closely resembles pyrrhotite in appearance but can be distinguished from it by the octahedral parting and its lack of magnetism.

Occurrence. Pentlandite is almost always associated with pyrrhotite and usually occurs in basic rocks such as norites, and is perhaps derived from them by magmatic segregation. Also found with chalcopyrite and other iron and nickel minerals.

Found at widely separated localities in small amounts but its chief occurrences are in Canada, where, associated with pyrrhotite, it is the principal source of nickel at Sudbury, Ontario, and the Lynn Lake area, Manitoba. It is also an important ore mineral in similar deposits in the Petsamo district of U.S.S.R.

Use. The principal ore of nickel. The chief use of nickel is in steel. Nickel steel contains $2\frac{1}{2}$–$3\frac{1}{2}$ per cent nickel, which greatly increases the strength and toughness of the alloy, so that lighter machines can be made without loss of strength. Nickel is also an essential constituent of stainless steel. The manufacture of Monel metal (68 per cent nickel, 32 per cent copper) and Nichrome (38–85 per cent nickel) consumes a large amount of the nickel produced. Other alloys are German silver (nickel, zinc, and copper); metal for coinage—the 5-cent coin of the United States is 25 per cent nickel and 75 per cent copper—low-expansion metals for watch springs and other instruments. Nickel is used in plating; although chromium now largely replaces it for the surface layer, nickel is used for a thicker under-layer.

Name. After J. B. Pentland, who first noted the mineral.

Covellite—CuS

Crystallography. Hexagonal; dihexagonal-dipyramidal. Rarely in tabular hexagonal crystals. Usually massive as coatings or disseminations through other copper minerals.

Physical properties. Perfect {0001} cleavage giving flexible plates. H $1\frac{1}{2}$–2. G 4.6–4.76. Luster metallic. Color indigo-blue or darker. Streak lead-gray to black. Often iridescent. Opaque.

Composition. Cupric sulfide, CuS. Cu 66.4, S 33.6 per cent. A small amount of iron may be present.

Tests. Fusible at $2\frac{1}{2}$. Gives odor of sulfur dioxide on charcoal and in the open tube, and much sulfur in the closed tube. The roasted mineral, moistened with hydrochloric acid and ignited, gives the blue copper chloride flame.

Diagnostic features. Characterized by the indigo-blue color, micaceous cleavage yielding flexible plates, and association with other copper sulfides.

Occurrence. Covellite is not an abundant mineral but is found in most copper deposits as a supergene mineral, usually as a coating, in the zone of sulfide enrichment. It is associated with other copper minerals, principally chalcocite, chalcopyrite, bornite, and enargite, and is derived from them by alteration. Primary covellite is known but uncommon.

Found at Bor, Serbia; Yugoslavia; and Leogang, Austria. In large iridescent crystals from the Calabona mine, Alghero, Sardinia.

In the United States covellite is found in appreciable amounts at Butte, Montana; Summitville, Colorado; and La Sal district, Utah. Formerly found at Kennecott, Alaska.

Use. A minor ore of copper.

Name. In honor of N. Covelli (1790–1829), the discoverer of the Vesuvian covellite.

CINNABAR—HgS

Crystallography. Hexagonal–R; trigonal-trapezohedral. Crystals usually rhombohedral, often in penetration twins. Trapezohedral faces rare. Usually fine granular massive; also earthy, as incrustations and disseminations through the rock.

Physical properties. Perfect $\{10\bar{1}0\}$ cleavage. **H** $2\frac{1}{2}$. **G** 8.10. Luster adamantine when pure, to dull earthy when impure. Color vermilion-red when pure, to brownish red when impure. Streak scarlet. Transparent to translucent. *Hepatic cinnabar* is an inflammable variety with liver-brown color and in some cases a brownish streak, usually granular or compact.

Composition. Mercuric sulfide, HgS. Hg 86.2, S 13.8 per cent. Frequently impure from admixture of clay, iron oxide, bitumen.

Tests. Wholly volatile when free from impurities. Gives black sublimate of mercuric sulfide when heated alone in the closed tube. When heated in the closed tube with dry sodium carbonate gives globules of metallic mercury.

Diagnostic features. Recognized by its red color and scarlet streak, high specific gravity, and cleavage.

Occurrence. Cinnabar is the most important ore of mercury but is found in quantity at comparatively few localities. Occurs as impregnations and as vein fillings near recent volcanic rocks and hot springs and evidently deposited near the surface from solutions which were probably alkaline. Associated with pyrite, marcasite, stibnite, and sulfides of copper in a gangue of opal, chalcedony, quartz, barite, calcite, and fluorite.

The important localities for the occurrence of cinnabar are at Almaden, Spain; Idria in Gorizia, Italy; Huancavelica in southern Peru; and the provinces of Kweichow and Hunan, China. In the United States the important deposits are in California at New Idria in San Benito County, in Napa County, and at New Almaden in Santa Clara County. Also occurs in Nevada, Utah, Oregon, Arkansas, Idaho, and Texas.

Use. The only important source of mercury. The most important use of mercury has been in the amalgamation process for recovering gold and silver from their ores, but other methods of extraction have lessened its demand for this purpose. It is used in thermometers, barometers, and various scientific and electrical equipment, including the mercury cell, in drugs, and in the form of an amalgam with silver for dental work and with tin in "silvering" mirrors. Several plants in the United States utilize mercury vapor instead of steam for the generation of power. This is a great potential use for mercury. Important military applications include the manufacture of fulminate of mercury for detonating high explosives and of paint for ship bottoms.

Name. The name cinnabar is supposed to have come from India, where it is applied to a red resin.

REALGAR—AsS

Crystallography. Monoclinic; prismatic. Found in short, vertically striated, prismatic crystals (Fig. 417). Frequently coarse to fine granular and often earthy and as an incrustation.

Physical properties. Cleavage {010}. **H** $1\frac{1}{2}$–2. **G** 3.48. Sectile. Luster resinous. Color and streak red to orange. Translucent to transparent.

Composition. Arsenic monosulfide, AsS. As 70.1, S 29.9 per cent.

Tests. Fusible at 1. Heated on charcoal yields a volatile white sublimate of arsenious oxide with characteristic garlic odor. Roasted in the open tube gives volatile crystalline sublimate of arsenious oxide and odor of sulfur dioxide.

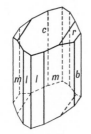

Fig. 417.
Realgar.

Diagnostic features. Realgar can be distinguished by its red color, resinous luster, and almost invariable association with orpiment. Its orange-red streak serves to distinguish it from other red minerals.

Occurrence. Realgar is found in veins of lead, silver, and gold ores associated with orpiment, other arsenic minerals, and stibnite. It also occurs as a volcanic sublimation product and as a deposit from hot springs.

Realgar is found associated with silver and lead ores in Hungary, Bohemia, Saxony. Found in good crystals at Nagyág, Transylvania; Binnenthal, Switzerland; and Allchar, Macedonia. In the United States realgar is found at Mercur, Utah; at Manhattan, Nevada; and deposited from the geyser waters in the Norris Geyser Basin, Yellowstone National Park.

Use. Realgar was used in fireworks to give a brilliant white light when mixed with saltpeter and ignited. Artificial arsenic sulfide is at present used for this purpose. It was formerly used as a pigment.

Name. The name is derived from the Arabic, Rahj al ghar, *powder of the mine.*

ORPIMENT—As_2S_3

Crystallography. Monoclinic; prismatic. Crystals small, tabular (Fig. 418) or short prismatic, and rarely distinct. Usually in foliated or columnar masses.

Physical properties. Perfect {010} cleavage. Cleavage laminae flexible but not elastic. Sectile. **H** 1½–2. **G** 3.49. Luster resinous, pearly on cleavage face. Color lemon-yellow. Translucent.

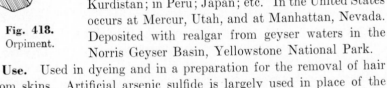

Composition. Arsenic trisulfide, As_2S_3. As 61, S 39 per cent.

Tests. Same as for realgar (see page 263).

Diagnostic features. Characterized by its yellow color and foliated structure. Distinguished from sulfur by its perfect cleavage.

Occurrence. Orpiment is a rare mineral, associated usually with realgar and formed under similar conditions. Found in various places in Rumania; in Kurdistan; in Peru; Japan; etc. In the United States occurs at Mercur, Utah, and at Manhattan, Nevada. Deposited with realgar from geyser waters in the Norris Geyser Basin, Yellowstone National Park.

Fig. 418.
Orpiment.

Use. Used in dyeing and in a preparation for the removal of hair from skins. Artificial arsenic sulfide is largely used in place of the mineral. Formerly both realgar and orpiment were used as pigments but are no longer, because of their poisonous nature.

Name. Derived from the Latin, *auripigmentum,* "golden paint," in allusion to its color and because the substance was supposed to contain gold.

STIBNITE—Sb_2S_3

Crystallography. Orthorhombic; dipyramidal. Slender prismatic habit, prism zone vertically striated. Crystals often steeply terminated (Fig. 419). Crystals sometimes curved or bent (Figs. 420 and 421). Often in radiating crystal groups or in bladed forms with prominent cleavage. Massive, coarse to fine granular.

Physical properties. Perfect {010} cleavage. **H** 2. **G** 4.52–4.62. Luster metallic, splendent on cleavage surfaces. Color and streak lead-gray to black. Opaque.

Composition. Antimony trisulfide, Sb_2S_3. Sb 71.4, S 28.6 per cent. May carry small amounts of gold, silver, iron, lead, and copper.

Tests. Fusible at 1. Heated on charcoal gives dense white coating of antimony trioxide and odor of sulfur dioxide. When roasted in the open tube gives nonvolatile white sublimate near bottom of tube and a white volatile sublimate as ring around tube.

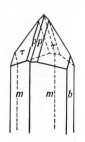

Diagnostic features. Characterized by its easy fusibility, bladed habit, perfect cleavage in one direction, lead-gray color, and soft black streak.

Occurrence. Stibnite is deposited by alkaline waters, usually in association with quartz. Found in quartz veins or beds in granite and gneiss with few other minerals present. May occur as a replacement in limestones and shales, probably owing its origin to

Fig. 419.
Stibnite.

hot-spring deposits. Often associated with intrusive rocks. Associated with other antimony minerals which have formed as the product of its decomposition, and with galena, cinnabar, sphalerite, barite, realgar, orpiment, and gold.

Found in various mining districts in Saxony, Rumania, Bohemia, Tuscany, and central France. Occurs in magnificent crystals in province of Iyo, Island of Shikoku, Japan. The world's most important producing district is in the province of Hunan, China. Occurs also in Borneo, Bolivia, Peru, and Mexico. Found in quantity at only a few localities in the United States, the chief deposits being in California, Nevada, and Idaho.

Use. The chief ore of antimony. The metal is used in various alloys, as antimonial lead for storage batteries, type metal, pewter, babbitt, britannia metals, and antifriction metal. The sulfide is employed in the manufacture of fireworks, matches, and percussion caps. Used in vulcanizing rubber. Used in medicine as tartar emetic and other compounds. Antimony trioxide is used as a pigment and for making glass.

Name. The name stibnite comes from an old Greek word that was applied to the mineral.

Bismuthinite—Bi_2S_3

Crystallography. Orthorhombic; dipyramidal. In acicular, striated crystals. Usually massive with foliated or fibrous texture.

Physical properties. Perfect {010} cleavage. **H** 2. **G** 6.78 ± 0.03. Luster metallic. Color and streak lead-gray. Opaque.

Composition. Bismuth trisulfide, Bi_2S_3. Bi 81.2, S 18.8 per cent. Often with antimony, lead, copper, iron.

Tests. Fusible at 1. Roasted in the open tube or on charcoal gives odor of sulfur dioxide. Mixed with iodide flux and heated on charcoal gives characteristic red coating.

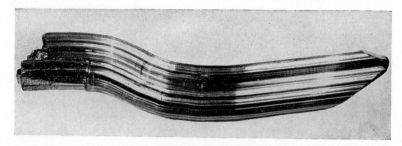

Fig. 420. Curved Stibnite Crystal, Ischinokowa, Japan.

Fig. 421. Group of Stibnite Crystals, Japan.

Diagnostic features. Resembles stibnite; recognized by the test for bismuth.

Occurrence. Bismuthinite is a rare mineral occurring commonly in veins that show definite relations to igneous rocks.

Found in Cornwall and Cumberland, England; Saxony; Sweden; Bohemia; Mexico. Important deposits associated with tin and tungsten ores occur in Bolivia. In the United States from Beaver County, Utah; Haddam, Connecticut; Delaware County, Pennsylvania; various localities in Colorado; and Manhattan, Nevada, with realgar and orpiment.

Use. An ore of bismuth.

PYRITE—FeS_2

Iron Pyrites

Crystallography. Isometric; diploidal. Frequently in crystals. The most common forms are the cube, the faces of which are usually striated, the striae on adjacent faces being perpendicular to each other (Fig. 422); the pyritohedron (Fig. 423); and the octahedron. Figures

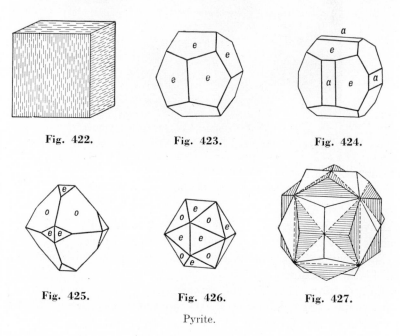

Fig. 422.   Fig. 423.   Fig. 424.

Fig. 425.   Fig. 426.   Fig. 427.

Pyrite.

424–426 show characteristic combinations of these forms. Figure 427 shows a penetration twin, known as the *iron cross* (with {011} the twin plane). Also massive, granular, reniform, globular, and stalactitic.

Pyrite has a modified type of NaCl structure (Fig. 428) with Fe occupying the position of Na and with S_2 groups occupying the position of Cl. The sulfur pairs are joined along the 3-fold axes, and each sulfur of a pair touches three iron atoms. Each iron atom is surrounded by six sulfur atoms. It will be noted that only one sulfur pair in four lies along a given 3-fold axis.

Fig. 428. Pyrite, FeS, Packing Model. Fe black; S white. Note that the sulfur pairs are aligned along the 3-fold symmetry axes.

Physical properties. Brittle. **H** 6–6½ (unusually hard for a sulfide). **G** 5.02. Luster metallic, splendent. Color pale brass-yellow; may be darker because of tarnish. Streak greenish or brownish black. Opaque.

Composition. Disulfide of iron, FeS_2. Fe 46.6, S 53.4 per cent. May contain small amounts of nickel and cobalt. Some analyses show considerable nickel, and a complete solid-solution series may exist between pyrite and *bravoite*, $(Ni,Fe)S_2$. Frequently carries minute quantities of gold and copper but presumably as microscopic impurities.

Tests. Fusible at 2½–3 to a magnetic globule. Yields much sulfur in the closed tube. Gives off sulfur dioxide when heated in the open tube or on charcoal.

Diagnostic features. Distinguished from chalcopyrite by its paler color and the fact that it cannot be scratched by steel, from gold by its brittleness and hardness, and from marcasite by its deeper color and crystal form.

Alteration. Pyrite is easily altered to oxides of iron, usually limonite. In general, however, it is much more stable than marcasite. Pseudomorphic crystals of limonite after pyrite are common. Pyrite veins are usually capped by a cellular deposit of limonite, termed *gossan*. Rocks that contain pyrite are unsuitable for structural purposes because the ready oxidation of the pyrite in them would serve both to disintegrate the rock and to stain it with iron oxide.

Occurrence. Pyrite is the most common and widespread of the sulfides. It has formed at both high and low temperatures, but the largest masses probably at high temperature. It occurs as direct magmatic segregation and as an accessory mineral in igneous rock, also in contact metamorphic and vein deposits. Pyrite is a common mineral in sedimentary rocks, being both primary and secondary in origin. It is associated with many minerals but found most frequently with chalcopyrite, sphalerite, galena.

Large and extensively developed deposits occur at Rio Tinto and elsewhere in Spain; also in Portugal. Important deposits of pyrite in the United States are in Prince William, Louisa, and Pulaski counties, Virginia, where it occurs in large lenticular masses which conform in position to the foliation of the inclosing schists; in St. Lawrence County, New York; at the Davis Mine, near Charlemont, Massachusetts; and in various places in California, Colorado, and Arizona.

Use. Pyrite is often mined for the gold or copper associated with it. Because of the large amount of sulfur present in the mineral it is used as an iron ore only in those countries where oxide ores are not available. It is chiefly used to furnish sulfur for sulfuric acid and *copperas* (ferrous sulfate). Sulfuric acid is perhaps the most important of all chemicals, being used for many different purposes, some of the more important being in the purification of kerosene and in the preparation of mineral fertilizers. The gas SO_2 derived either through burning sulfur or by roasting pyrite is used extensively in the preparation of wood pulp for manufacture into paper. Copperas is used in dyeing, in the manufacture of inks, as a preservative of wood, and for a disinfectant.

Name. The name *pyrite* is from a Greek word meaning *fire*, in allusion to the fact that when struck with steel it gives off brilliant sparks.

COBALTITE—(Co,Fe)AsS

Crystallography. Isometric; tetartoidal. Commonly in cubes or pyritohedrons with the faces striated as in pyrite. Also granular.

Physical properties. Perfect {001} cleavage. Brittle. **H** $5\frac{1}{2}$. **G** 6.33. Luster metallic. Color silver-white, inclined to red. Streak grayish black.

Composition. Sulfarsenide of cobalt with considerable iron (maximum about 10 per cent) and lesser amounts of nickel, (Co,Fe)AsS. *Gersdorffite*, NiAsS, and cobaltite form a complete solid-solution series, but intermediate members are rare.

Tests. Fusible at 2–3. On charcoal gives a volatile white sublimate of arsenious oxide with characteristic garlic odor. In the oxidizing flame in borax bead gives deep blue color (cobalt).

Diagnostic features. Although in crystal form cobaltite resembles pyrite, it can be distinguished by its silver color and cleavage.

Occurrence. Cobaltite is usually found in high-temperature deposits, as disseminations in metamorphosed rocks, or in vein deposits with other cobalt and nickel minerals. Notable occurrences of cobaltite are at Tunaberg, Sweden, and Cobalt, Ontario. The largest producer of cobalt today is the Belgian Congo, where oxidized cobalt and copper ores are associated.

Use. An ore of cobalt.

MARCASITE—FeS$_2$

White Iron Pyrites

Crystallography. Orthorhombic; dipyramidal. Crystals commonly tabular parallel to basal plane, showing also short vertical prisms and low first-order prisms (Fig. **429**). The first-order prisms usually striated parallel to the *a* axis. Often twinned, giving cockscomb and spear-shaped groups (Figs. **430** and **431**). Usually in radiating forms. Often stalactitic, having an inner core with radiating structure and covered on the outside with irregular crystal groups. Also globular and reniform.

Physical properties. **H** $6-6\frac{1}{2}$. **G** 4.89. Luster metallic. Color pale bronze-yellow to almost white on fresh fracture, yellow to brown tarnish. Streak grayish black. Opaque.

Composition. Iron disulfide, like pyrite, FeS$_2$. Fe 46.6, S 53.4 per cent.

Tests. Fusible at $2\frac{1}{2}$–3 to a magnetic globule. Heated on charcoal or in the open tube gives odor of sulfur dioxide. Much sulfur in the closed tube. When fine powder is treated with cold nitric acid, and the solution is allowed to stand until vigorous action ceases and is then boiled, the mineral is decomposed with separation of sulfur. Pyrite treated in the same manner would have been completely dissolved.

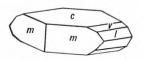

Fig. 429. Marcasite.

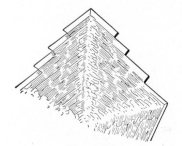

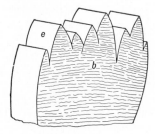

Fig. 430.   Fig. 431.

"Cockscomb" Marcasite.

Diagnostic features. Usually recognized and distinguished from pyrite by its pale yellow color, its crystals or its fibrous habit, and the above chemical test.

Alteration. Marcasite usually disintegrates more easily than pyrite with the formation of ferrous sulfate and sulfuric acid. The white powder that forms on marcasite is *melanterite*, $FeSO_4 \cdot 7H_2O$.

Occurrence. Marcasite is found in metalliferous veins, frequently with lead and zinc ores. Also in sedimentary rocks. It is less stable than pyrite, being easily decomposed, and is much less common. It is deposited at low temperatures from acid solutions and commonly formed under surface conditions as a supergene mineral. Marcasite most frequently occurs as replacement deposits in limestone, and often in concretions imbedded in clays, marls, and shales.

Found abundantly in clay near Carlsbad and elsewhere in Bohemia; in various places in Saxony; and in the chalk marl of Folkestone and Dover, England. In the United States marcasite is found with zinc and lead deposits of the Joplin, Missouri, district; at Mineral Point, Wisconsin; and at Galena, Illinois.

Use. Marcasite is used to a slight extent as a source of sulfuric acid.

Name. Derived from an Arabic word, at one time applied generally to pyrite.

ARSENOPYRITE—FeAsS

Mispickel

Crystallography. Monoclinic; prismatic. Crystals are commonly prismatic parallel to the *c* axis and less commonly parallel to the *b* axis (Fig. 432). The prism zone vertically striated, also *n* {101} striated as shown in Fig. 433. Twinning (1) on {100} and {001} produces pseudo-orthorhombic crystals; (2) on {101} as contact or penetration twins; may be repeated, as in marcasite; (3) on {012} to produce star-shaped trillings.

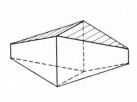
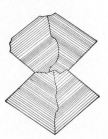

Fig. 432.   Fig. 433.

Arsenopyrite.

Physical properties. H $5\frac{1}{2}$–6.   G 6.07 ± 0.15.   Luster metallic. Color silver-white. Streak black. Opaque.

Composition. Essentially iron arsenide-sulfide, FeAsS. Fe 34.3, As 46, S 19.7 per cent. Cobalt may replace a part of the iron (*danaite*).

Tests. Fusible at 2 to magnetic globule. Heated on charcoal gives a volatile coating of arsenious oxide and a characteristic garlic odor. In the open tube gives odor of sulfur dioxide and a volatile ring of arsenious oxide. In the closed tube gives arsenic mirror.

Diagnostic features. Distinguished from marcasite by its silver-white color. Its crystal form and lack of cobalt test distinguish it from skutterudite.

Occurrence. Arsenopyrite is the most common mineral containing arsenic. It occurs with tin and tungsten ores in high-temperature deposits, in veins formed by deposition from hot waters, associated with silver and copper ores, galena, sphalerite, pyrite, chalcopyrite.

Frequently associated with gold. Often found sparingly in pegmatites, in contact metamorphic deposits, disseminated in crystalline limestones.

Arsenopyrite is a widespread mineral and is found in considerable abundance in many foreign localities, notably at Freiberg and Munzig, Saxony; with tin ores in Cornwall, England; from Tavistock, Devonshire; in various places in Bolivia. In the United States in fine crystals at Franconia, New Hampshire; from Roxbury, Connecticut; from Franklin, New Jersey. It is associated with gold at Lead, South Dakota. Large quantities occur at Deloro, Ontario.

Use. An ore of arsenic. Most of the arsenic produced is recovered in the form of the oxide as a by-product in the smelting of arsenical ores for copper, gold, lead, and silver. Metallic arsenic is used in some alloys, particularly with lead in shot metal. Arsenic is used chiefly, however, in the form of white arsenic or arsenious oxide in medicine, insecticides, preservatives, pigments, and glass. Arsenic sulfides are used in paints and fireworks.

Name. Arsenopyrite is a contraction of the older term *arsenical pyrites*.

MOLYBDENITE—MoS_2

Crystallography. Hexagonal; dihexagonal-dipyramidal. Crystals in hexagonal-shaped plates or short, slightly tapering prisms. Commonly foliated, massive or in scales.

Physical properties. Perfect basal {0001} cleavage. Laminae flexible but not elastic. Sectile. **H** 1–1½. **G** 4.62–4.73. Greasy feel. Luster metallic. Color lead-gray. Streak grayish black. Opaque.

Composition. Molybdenum sulfide, MoS_2. Mo 59.9, S 40.1 per cent.

Tests. Infusible. Heated before the blowpipe gives yellowish green flame. Roasted in the open tube gives odor of sulfur dioxide and deposit of thin plates of molybdic oxide, crossing the tube above the mineral. When heated with potassium iodide and sulfur on a plaster tablet gives a deep blue sublimate.

Diagnostic features. Resembles graphite but is distinguished from it by higher specific gravity; by a blue tone to its color, whereas graphite has a brown tinge; and by its reactions for sulfur and molybdenum. On glazed porcelain, molybdenite gives a greenish streak, graphite a black streak.

Occurrence. Molybdenite forms as an accessory mineral in certain granites; in pegmatites and aplites. Commonly in vein deposits associated with cassiterite, scheelite, wolframite, and fluorite. Also in contact metamorphic deposits with lime silicates, scheelite, and chalcopyrite.

Occurs with the tin ores of Bohemia; from various places in Norway and Sweden; from New South Wales; England; China; and Mexico. In the United States molybdenite is found in many localities: at Blue Hill, Maine; Westmoreland, New Hampshire; and in Okanogan County, Washington. From various places in Ontario, Canada. The bulk of the world's supply comes from Climax, Colorado, where molybdenite occurs in quartz veinlets in silicified granite with fluorite and topaz. Much molybdenum is produced at Bingham Canyon, Utah, as a by-product of the copper mining.

Use. An ore of molybdenum.

Name. The name molybdenite comes from the Greek word meaning *lead*.

Calaverite—$AuTe_2$

Crystallography. Monoclinic; prismatic. Rarely in distinct crystals which are elongated parallel to the b-axis; and the faces of this zone are deeply striated. Terminated at the ends of the b-axis with a large number of faces. Twinning frequent. Usually granular.

Physical properties. H $2\frac{1}{2}$. G 9.35. Luster metallic. Color brass-yellow to silver-white, in some cases with yellowish tarnish. Streak yellowish to greenish gray. Opaque. Very brittle.

Composition. Gold ditelluride, $AuTe_2$. Au 44.03, Te 55.97 per cent. Silver usually replaces the gold to a small extent.

Tests. Fusible at 1. On charcoal fuses with a bluish green flame, yielding globules of metallic gold. When decomposed in hot concentrated sulfuric acid the solution assumes a deep red color (tellurium), and a spongy mass of gold separates.

Diagnostic features. Distinguished from sylvanite by the presence of only a small amount of silver and by the lack of cleavage.

Occurrence. Calaverite is formed under conditions similar to those for sylvanite and is associated with it and other tellurides in the Cripple Creek district, Colorado, and at Kalgoorlie, West Australia.

Use. An ore of gold.

Name. Named from Calaveras County, California, where it was originally found in the Stanislaus mine.

Similar species. Other rare tellurides are *krennerite*, $AuTe_2$; *altaite*, $PbTe$; *hessite*, Ag_2Te; *petzite*, $(Ag,Au)_2Te$; and *nagyagite*, a sulfotelluride of lead and gold.

Sylvanite—(Au,Ag)Te$_2$

Crystallography. Monoclinic; prismatic. Distinct crystals rare. Usually bladed or granular. Often in skeleton forms deposited on rock surfaces and resembling writing in appearance.

Physical properties. Perfect {010} cleavage. **H** 1$\frac{1}{2}$–2. **G** 8–8.2. Luster brilliant metallic. Color silver-white. Streak gray. Opaque.

Composition. A ditelluride of gold and silver, (Au,Ag)Te$_2$. The ratio of the amounts of gold and silver varies somewhat; when Au:Ag = 1:1, Te 62.1, Au 24.5, Ag 13.4 per cent.

Tests. Fusible at 1. If a little of the powdered mineral is heated in concentrated sulfuric acid the solution assumes a deep red color (tellurium). When decomposed in nitric acid leaves a rust-colored, spongy mass of gold, and the solution with hydrochloric acid gives white precipitate of silver chloride. Heated on charcoal gives a gold-silver globule and test for tellurium.

Diagnostic features. Determined by above tests and its silver color, and distinguished from calaverite by its good cleavage.

Occurrence. Sylvanite is a rare mineral associated with calaverite and other tellurides, pyrite and other sulfides in small amounts, gold, quartz, chalcedony, fluorite, and carbonates. Usually in veins formed at low temperatures but may be in higher-temperature veins.

It is found at Offenbánya and Nagyág in Transylvania; at Kalgoorlie and Mulgabbie, West Australia. In the United States it is found sparingly at several localities in California and Colorado, but the most notable occurrence is at Cripple Creek, Colorado.

Use. An ore of gold and silver.

Name. Derived from Transylvania, where it was first found, and in allusion to *sylvanium,* one of the names first proposed for the element tellurium.

SKUTTERUDITE—(Co,Ni,Fe)As$_3$

Crystallography. Isometric; diploidal. Common crystal forms are cube and octahedron, more rarely dodecahedron and pyritohedron. Usually massive, dense to granular.

Physical properties. **H** 5$\frac{1}{2}$–6. **G** 6.5 ± 0.4. Brittle. Luster metallic. Color tin-white to silver-gray. Streak black. Opaque.

Composition. Essentially cobalt and nickel arsenide, (Co,Ni)As$_3$. Iron usually substitutes for some of the nickel or cobalt, so that the formula may be written (Co,Ni,Fe)As$_3$. The high nickel varieties are called *nickel-skutterudite*.

Tests. Fusible at $2-2\frac{1}{2}$. Before blowpipe on charcoal gives a volatile coating of arsenious oxide with garlic odor. In borax bead in oxidizing flame gives blue color (cobalt).

Diagnostic features. It is necessary to make the test for cobalt to distinguish skutterudite from massive arsenopyrite, for no physical properties distinguish the two.

Occurrence. Skutterudite is usually associated with cobaltite and niccolite in veins formed at moderate temperature. Native silver, bismuth, arsenopyrite, and calcite are also commonly associated with it.

Notable localities are Annaberg, Schneeberg, and Freiberg, in Saxony, and Cobalt, Ontario, where skutterudite is associated with silver ores.

Use. An ore of cobalt and nickel. Cobalt is chiefly used in alloys for making permanent magnets and high-speed tool steel. Cobalt oxide is used as blue pigment in pottery and glassware.

Name. Skutterudite from the locality, Skutterude, Norway.

Similar species. *Linnaeite,* Co_3S_4, associated with cobalt and nickel minerals. The name *smaltite* is common in the literature and probably refers to the mineral here described as skutterudite. The smaltite formula, $CoAs_2$, was probably based on analyses of impure material, for it has been shown that the diarsenide series does not exist.

SULFOSALTS

The term sulfosalt was originally proposed to indicate that a compound was a salt of one of a series of acids in which sulfur had replaced the oxygen of an ordinary acid. Since such acids may be purely hypothetical, it is perhaps misleading to endeavor to thus explain this class of minerals. Nevertheless, the term sulfosalt is serviceable and is retained for indicating a certain type of unoxidized sulfur mineral distinct from a sulfide.

The sulfides are those minerals in which a metal or a semimetal is combined with sulfur. If both a semimetal and a metal are present, the semimetal takes the place of sulfur in the structure, as in arseno-pyrite, $FeAsS$, and thus acts as an electronegative element. In the sulfosalts, the semimetals play a role more or less like that of metals in the structure, and thus, in a sense, the sulfosalts may be considered double sulfides. Enargite Cu_3AsS_4, may be considered as $3Cu_2S \cdot As_2S_5$. There are nearly 100 sulfosalts, but only a few are important enough to warrant description here.

Sulfosalts

Polybasite	$Ag_{16}Sb_2S_{11}$	Tetrahedrite	$(Cu,Fe,Zn,Ag)_{12}Sb_4S_{13}$
Stephanite	Ag_5SbS_4	Enargite	Cu_3AsS_4
Pyrargyrite	Ag_3SbS_3	Bournonite	$PbCuSbS_3$
Proustite	Ag_3AsS_3	Jamesonite	$Pb_4FeSb_6S_{14}$

Polybasite—$Ag_{16}Sb_2S_{11}$

Crystallography. Monoclinic; prismatic. Crystals are pseudo-rhombohedral in symmetry, occurring in short hexagonal prisms, often thin tabular. Basal planes show triangular markings. Also granular.

Physical properties. H 2–3. G 6.0–6.2. Luster metallic. Color steel-gray or iron-black. Streak black. Opaque.

Composition. Essentially a silver antimony sulfide, $Ag_{16}Sb_2S_{11}$. Ag 74.3, Sb 10.5, S 15.2 per cent. Copper substitutes for silver to about 30 atomic per cent. Arsenic may substitute for antimony to about 60 atomic per cent forming a partial series to *pearceite*, $(Ag,Cu)_{16}As_2S_{11}$.

Tests. Fusible at 1. On charcoal fuses, with spurting, to a globule and gives dense white coating of antimony trioxide with odor of sulfur dioxide.

Diagnostic features. To be distinguished from similar species chiefly by its crystals.

Occurrence. Polybasite is a comparatively rare silver mineral, associated with other silver sulfantimonides and with silver ores in general.

Found in the silver mines of Mexico, Chile, Saxony, and Bohemia. In the United States found at the Comstock Lode and Tonopah, Nevada; Ouray and Leadville, Colorado; and Silver City and Delamar, Idaho.

Use. An ore of silver.

Name. Name is in allusion to the *many metallic bases* contained in the mineral.

Stephanite—Ag_5SbS_4

Crystallography. Orthorhombic; pyramidal. Crystals usually small and short prismatic and tabular parallel to the base. Edges of crystals truncated by various pyramids. Vertical prism zone usually shows the four prism faces and the two of the side pinacoid, all making nearly 60° angles with each other and so giving the crystals a hexagonal aspect. Also twinned in pseudohexagonal crystals. Massive compact, or disseminated.

Physical properties. H 2–2$\frac{1}{2}$. G 6.2–6.3. Luster metallic. Brittle. Color and streak iron-black. Opaque.

Composition. Silver antimony sulfide, Ag_5SbS_4. Ag 68.5, Sb 15.2, S 16.3 per cent.

Tests. Fusible at 1. Before the blowpipe on charcoal gives dense white sublimate of antimony trioxide and odor of sulfur dioxide.

Diagnostic features. Recognized by its stout pseudohexagonal crystals and the above tests. Differs from argentite by being brittle and from tetrahedrite by being soft.

Occurrence. Stephanite is a rare silver mineral of primary origin and is usually one of the last minerals to form in silver veins. Associated with other silver sulfosalts, argentite, silver, tetrahedrite, and the commoner sulfides.

Notable localities for fine crystals are: Přibram, Czechoslovakia; Freiberg, Saxony; Mt. Narba, Sardinia; and Zacatecas, Mexico. In the United States an important ore mineral at the Comstock Lode and other silver deposits in Nevada. Also at Leadville, Colorado.

Use. An ore of silver.

Name. After the Archduke Stephan, formerly Mining Director of Austria.

PYRARGYRITE—Ag_3SbS_2

Dark Ruby Silver

Crystallography. Hexagonal–R; ditrigonal-pyramidal. Crystal prismatic with hemimorphic development, often with pyramidal terminations. Usually distorted and with complex development. Frequently twinned. Also massive, compact, in disseminated grains.

Physical properties. Cleavage, $\{10\bar{1}1\}$. H 2$\frac{1}{2}$. G 5.85. Luster adamantine. Translucent. Color deep red to black, in thin splinters deep ruby-red. Streak Indian-red.

Composition. Silver antimony sulfide, Ag_3SbS_3. Ag 59.7, Sb 22.5, S 17.8 per cent. May contain a small amount of arsenic. Compare proustite.

Test. Fusible at 1. On charcoal gives dense white coating of antimony trioxide. After prolonged heating, coating becomes tinged with a reddish color near assay due to a small amount of volatilized silver. Gives the odor of sulfur dioxide and coatings of antimony oxides when heated in the open tube.

Diagnostic features. Similar to proustite but of a deeper red color and less translucent.

Occurrence. Pyrargyrite is found in places as an important silver ore. It forms in silver veins at low temperatures as one of the last minerals to crystallize in the sequence of primary deposition. Associated with proustite and other silver sulfosalts, argentite, tetrahedrite, and silver.

Notable localities are: Andreasberg, Harz Mountains; Freiberg, Saxony; Příbram, Bohemia; Guanajuato, Mexico; and Chanarcillo, Chile; in Bolivia. In the United States is found in various silver veins in Colorado, Nevada, New Mexico, and Idaho. In Canada is found in the silver veins at Cobalt, Ontario.

Use. An ore of silver.

Name. Derived from two Greek words meaning *fire* and *silver*, in allusion to its color and composition.

PROUSTITE—Ag_3AsS_3

Light Ruby Silver

Crystallography. Hexagonal–R; ditrigonal-pyramidal. Crystals commonly prismatic with prominent steep pyramidal terminations. Often distorted and frequently complex in development. Commonly massive, compact, in disseminated grains.

Physical properties. Cleavage $\{10\bar{1}1\}$. **H** 2–2½. **G** 5.55. Brittle. Luster adamantine. Color ruby-red. Streak vermilion. Translucent, transparent to red light.

Composition. Silver arsenic sulfide, Ag_3AsS_3. Ag 65.4, As 15.2, S 19.4 per cent. May contain a small amount of antimony. Compare pyrargyrite.

Tests. Fusible at 1. Heated on charcoal gives volatile sublimate of arsenious oxide with characteristic garlic odor. In the open tube gives odor of sulfur dioxide and volatile crystalline sublimate of arsenious oxide. In the closed tube gives abundant sublimate of arsenic sulfide, reddish black when hot, reddish yellow when cold.

Diagnostic features. Characterized chiefly by its ruby-red color and vermilion streak and its brilliant luster. Distinguished from pyrargyrite by being lighter in color and by giving the test for arsenic.

Occurrence. Proustite is less common than pyrargyrite, but is found at the same localities and with similar mode of occurrence and associations.

Use. An ore of silver.

Name. In honor of the French chemist, J. L. Proust (1755–1826).

TETRAHEDRITE— $(Cu,Fe,Zn,Ag)_{12}Sb_4S_{13}$

Gray Copper. Fahlore

Crystallography. Isometric; hextetrahedral. Habit tetrahedral (Figs. 434 and 435); may be in groups of parallel crystals. Tetrahedron, tristetrahedron, dodecahedron, and cube the common forms. Frequently in crystals. Also massive, coarse or fine granular.

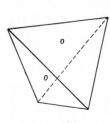
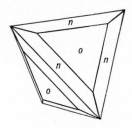

Fig. 434.   **Fig. 435.**

Tetrahedrite.

Physical properties. H $3–4\frac{1}{2}$. G 4.6–5.1 (with tennantite harder and of higher specific gravity than tetrahedrite). Luster metallic to submetallic, often splendent. Color grayish black to black. Streak black to brown. Opaque.

Composition. Essentially copper, iron, zinc, and silver antimony sulfide, $(Cu,Fe,Zn,Ag)_{12}Sb_4S_{13}$. Copper is always predominant, but considerable substitution takes place by iron and zinc, less commonly by silver, lead, and mercury. Arsenic may take the place of antimony in all proportions, and thus there exists a complete series from the pure antimony end member, *tetrahedrite,* to the pure arsenic end member, *tennantite.* The highly argentiferous variety is known as *freibergite.*

Tests. Fusible at $1\frac{1}{2}$. On charcoal or in the open tube gives tests for antimony or arsenic, or both. After roasting, and moistening with hydrochloric acid, gives azure-blue copper chloride flame. Decomposed by nitric acid with separation of sulfur and antimony trioxide; solution made alkaline with ammonia turns blue. Tetrahedrite and tennantite can be told apart only by testing for the presence of antimony and arsenic, and as both are often present in the same specimen a quantitative analysis may be necessary in order to determine positively to which end of the series it belongs.

Diagnostic features. Recognized by its tetrahedral crystals, or when massive by its brittleness, luster, and gray color.

Occurrence. Tetrahedrite, the most common member of the sulfo-salt group, is widespread in occurrence and varied in association. Tennantite is less widely distributed. Commonly found in hydro-thermal veins of copper or silver minerals formed at low to moderate temperatures. Rarely in higher-temperature veins or in contact meta-morphic deposits. Usually associated with chalcopyrite, pyrite, sphalerite, galena, and various other silver, lead, and copper min-erals. May carry sufficient silver to become an important ore of that metal.

Notable localities: Cornwall, England; the Harz Mountains, Ger-many; Freiberg, Saxony; Přibram, Bohemia; various places in Rumania; and the silver mines of Mexico, Peru, and Bolivia. Found in the United States in various silver and copper mines in Colorado, Montana, Nevada, Arizona, and Utah.

Use. An ore of silver and copper.

Name. Tetrahedrite in allusion to the tetrahedral form of the crystals. Tennantite after the English chemist, Smithson Tennant (1761–1815).

ENARGITE—Cu_3AsS_4

Crystallography. Orthorhombic; pyramidal. Crystals elongated parallel to c and vertically striated, also tabular parallel to {001}. Columnar, bladed, massive.

Physical properties. Cleavage perfect prismatic, {110}. **H** 3. **G** 4.43–4.45. Luster metallic. Color and streak grayish black to iron-black. Opaque.

Composition. Copper arsenic sulfide, Cu_3AsS_4. Cu 48.3, As 19.1, S 32.6 per cent. Antimony substitutes for arsenic up to 6 per cent by weight, and some iron and zinc are usually present.

Test. Fusible at 1. On charcoal gives volatile white sublimate of arsenious oxide and characteristic garlic odor. Roasted on charcoal, then moistened with hydrochloric acid and again ignited, gives azure-blue copper chloride flame.

Diagnostic features. Characterized by its color and its cleavage. Distinguished from stibnite by a test for copper.

Occurrence. Enargite is a comparatively rare mineral, found in vein and replacement deposits associated with pyrite, sphalerite, bornite, galena, tetrahedrite, covellite, chalcocite.

Notable localities: Bor, near Zajecar, Yugoslavia. Found abun-dantly at Morococha and Cerro de Pasco, Peru; also from Chile and Argentina; Island of Luzon, Philippines. In the United States is an important ore mineral at Butte, Montana, and to a lesser extent at

Bingham Canyon, Utah. Occurs in the silver mines of the San Juan Mountains, Colorado.

Use. An ore of copper. Arsenic oxide also obtained from it at Butte, Montana.

Name. From the Greek meaning *distinct,* in allusion to the cleavage.

Similar species. *Famatinite,* Cu_3SbS_4, is the antimony analogue of enargite, but the two minerals are not isostructural.

Bournonite—$PbCuSbS_3$

Cogwheel Ore

Crystallography. Orthorhombic; dipyramidal. Crystals usually short prismatic to tabular. May be complex with many vertical prism and pyramid faces. Frequently twinned, giving tabular crystals with recurring reentrant angles in the [001] zone (Fig. 436), whence the common name of *cogwheel ore*. Also massive; granular to compact.

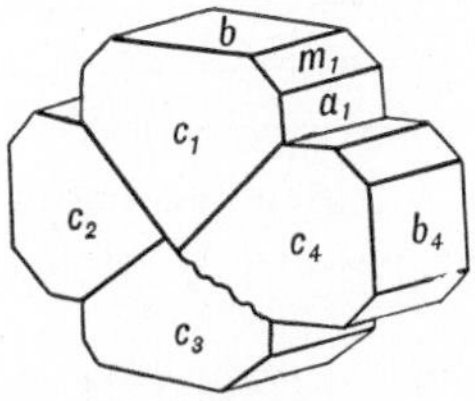

Fig. 436.
Bournonite.

Physical properties. H $2\frac{1}{2}$–3. G 5.8–5.9. Luster metallic. Color and streak steel-gray to black. Opaque.

Composition. A lead, copper, antimony sulfide, $PbCuSbS_3$. The percentages of the elements: Pb 42.4, Cu 13.0, Sb 24.9, S 19.7. Arsenic may substitute for antimony to about Sb : As = 4 : 1.

Test. Fusible at 1. Before the blowpipe on charcoal gives a combination coating of antimony and lead oxides. Roasted in the open tube gives sublimates of antimony oxides. Heated on charcoal with a mixture of potassium iodide and sulfur gives a chrome-yellow coating of lead iodide.

Diagnostic features. Recognized by its characteristic crystals, high specific gravity, and above tests.

Occurrence. Bournonite, one of the commonest of the sulfo-salts, occurs typically in hydrothermal veins formed at moderate temperature. It is associated with galena, tetrahedrite, chalcopyrite, sphalerite, pyrite. Frequently noted as microscopic inclusions in galena.

Notable localities are: the Harz Mountains; Kapnik and elsewhere in Rumania; Liskeard, Cornwall; also found in Australia, Mexico, and Bolivia. In the United States has been found in various places in

Arizona, Utah, Nevada, Colorado, and California, but not in notable amount or quality.

Use. An ore of copper, lead, and antimony.

Name. After Count J. L. de Bournon (1751–1825), French crystallographer and mineralogist.

Jamesonite—$Pb_4FeSb_6S_{14}$

Brittle Feather Ore

Crystallography. Monoclinic; prismatic. Usually in acicular crystals or in capillary forms with a featherlike appearance. Also fibrous to compact massive. Several different compounds are often designated "feather ore."

Physical properties. Cleavage {001}. Brittle. **H** 2–3. **G** 5.5–6. Luster metallic. Color and streak steel-gray to grayish black. Opaque.

Composition. Lead and iron antimony sulfide, probably Pb_4Fe-Sb_6S_{14}. Copper and zinc may be present in small amounts.

Tests. Fusible at 1. On charcoal gives a combination coating of lead and antimony oxides. Roasted in the open tube gives sublimates of antimony oxides. Heated on charcoal with iodide flux gives a chrome-yellow coating of lead iodide.

Diagnostic features. Recognized by its characteristic fibrous (feathery) appearance, and distinguished from stibnite by lack of good lengthwise cleavage. Difficult to distinguish from similar species (see below).

Occurrence. Jamesonite is found in ore veins formed at low to moderate temperatures. Associated with other lead sulfosalts, with galena, stibnite, tetrahedrite, sphalerite.

Found in Cornwall, England, and from various localities in Czechoslovakia, Rumania, and Saxony; from Tasmania and Bolivia. In the United States from Sevier County, Arkansas, and at Silver City, South Dakota.

Use. A minor ore of lead.

Name. After the mineralogist Robert Jameson (1774–1854), of Edinburgh.

Similar species. A number of minerals similar to jamesonite in composition and general physical characteristics are included under the term *feather ore*. These include such minerals as *zinkenite*, $Pb_6Sb_{14}S_{27}$; *boulangerite*, $Pb_5Sb_4S_{11}$; *meneghinite*, $Pb_{13}Sb_7S_{23}$. Other minerals of similar composition but different habit are: *plagionite*, $Pb_5Sb_8S_{17}$; *semseyite*, $Pb_9Sb_8S_4$; *geocronite*, $Pb_5(Sb,As)_2S_8$.

OXIDES

Oxides are classified as *simple oxides, multiple oxides, oxides containing hydroyxl,* and *hydroxides,* but because so few minerals are described here they are grouped merely as oxides and hydroxides. Within the framework of the classification there are a number of important *mineral groups,* notably the hematite, spinel, and rutile groups. Each of these contains one or more minerals of economic importance. Within the oxide class are the chief ores of iron (hematite and magnetite), chromium (chromite), manganese (pyrolusite, manganite, psilomelane), tin (cassiterite), and aluminum (bauxite).

A_2O type.[1] The solid oxide of hydrogen, ice, is a true mineral and a geologic substance of great importance. Unlike most minerals it is molecular, built of dipolar water molecules linked together so that each has four closest neighbors located at the apices of a nearly regular tetrahedron. The bonds joining these molecules are relatively weak, leading to low hardness, low melting point, and easy deformation by twinning and gliding. The ordered arrangement of water molecules characteristic of ice persists in part in the liquid state, up to 4° C above the melting point. At this temperature the rather open structure of ice becomes unstable and collapses into a more closely packed and more chaotic arrangement. On cooling of water the reverse process takes place and an ordering of the water molecules accounts for the anomalous expansion at 4° C.

AO_2 type. Dioxides fall in general into two structure types. One has the fluorite structure (see Fig. 467) in which each oxygen has four cation neighbors arranged about it at the apices of a more or less regular tetrahedron, whereas each cation has eight oxygens surrounding

Radius Ratios in the AO_2-Type Oxides (R_O = 1.32A)

R_A	R_A/R_O	Element	Mineral	Structure Type
0.60	0.45	Mn	Pyrolusite	Rutile
0.68	0.52	Ti	Rutile	Rutile
0.71	0.54	Sn	Cassiterite	Rutile
0.94	0.71	Ce	Cerianite	Fluorite
0.97	0.73	U	Uraninite	Fluorite
1.02	0.77	Th	Thorianite	Fluorite

[1] In this discussion of the oxides general formulas such as ABO_3 are used, in which A and B are cations and O is oxygen.

it at the corners of a cube. The oxides of 4-valent uranium, thorium, and cerium, now of considerable interest because of their connection with nuclear chemistry, have this structure. In general, all dioxides in which the radius ratio of cation to oxygen ($R_A : R_O$) lies within the limits for 8-fold coordination (0.732 − 1) may be expected to have this structure and be isometric hexoctahedral.

The second common AO_2 structure type is that typified by rutile. In this structure, the cation is smaller, with radius ratios of $R_A : R_O$ lying between the limits 0.732 to 0.414 and hence having 6-fold coordination. Accordingly, there are six oxygens grouped about each cation. Since the requirements for electrical neutrality dictate that there must be half as many cations as oxygens, only half the possible A sites are filled, and there are only three cations grouped about each oxygen (Fig. 437). The effect of this reduction in number of cations

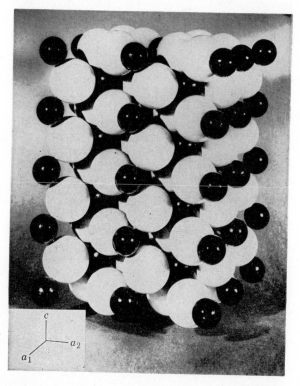

Fig. 437. Rutile, TiO_2, Packing Model. O (white) is in 6-fold coordination about Ti (black) and Ti is in 3-fold coordination about O. This structure is stable for AX_2 compounds in which the radius ratio is 0.414 − 0.732. Cassiterite SnO_2 and pyrolusite MnO_2 also have this structure. Compare Fig. 467 (fluorite).

is to warp the usual octahedral arrangement characteristic of 6-fold coordination into a configuration of lower symmetry. Hence the minerals of the rutile group are tetragonal with the prismatic habit reflecting the chainlike structure.

AB_2O_4 type. A large number of synthetic compounds as well as minerals have the general formula AB_2O_4 and fall into the spinel structure type. In this structure the A cation is larger than B, is generally divalent, and has a radius between 0.6 and 0.8 Å. The B cation is generally trivalent with radius between 0.5 and 0.7 Å. In the typical spinel structure, the A ions have four close oxygen neighbors, whereas the B ions have six (Fig. 438). This is an isodesmic structure, and the spinels are properly considered as multiple oxides.

Fig. 438. Spinel, $MgAl_2O_4$, Packing Model. A number of related minerals, including magnetite $FeFe_2O_4$, gahnite $ZnAl_2O_4$, and chromite $FeCr_2O_4$, also have this structure, in which Mg, Fe″ or Zn (small dark) is in 4-fold coordination and Al, Fe‴ or Cr (large dark) is in 6-fold coordination with O (white).

The spinel structure is built about a cubic lattice and gives rise to isometric hexoctahedral crystals of octahedral habit. The absence of cleavage, rather high specific gravities, and high hardness reflect the close packing and tight, uniform bonding.

Since all members of the spinel group are isostructural, ionic substitution is common within the limits imposed by the size of the ions involved. Proxying of one B ion for another is sensitive to ionic size and polarizing power, and solid solution with respect to the B ions is incomplete. Thus, although some ferric iron and trivalent chromium may occur in spinel and gahnite, there is no complete series between spinel, $MgAl_2O_4$, and magnesioferrite, $MgFe_2O_4$. On the other hand, there seems to be substantially complete solid solution with respect to the A cation. Hence, in the subgroup in which B is aluminum there is more or less complete substitution for each other of magnesium, ferrous iron, zinc, and divalent manganese.

This extensive solid solution gives rise to a wide range in the properties of the spinel group minerals such as color and specific gravity which depend chiefly on chemical composition. The crystal habit and those properties dependent on the geometry of the structure and the nature of the bond are, however, remarkably constant throughout the group.

Oxides

Cuprite	Cu_2O		
Ice	H_2O	GOETHITE GROUP	
Zincite	ZnO	Diaspore	$HAlO_2$
HEMATITE GROUP		Goethite	$HFeO_2$
Corundum	Al_2O_3	SPINEL GROUP	
Hematite	Fe_2O_3	Spinel	$MgAl_2O_4$
Ilmenite	$FeTiO_3$	Gahnite	$ZnAl_2O_4$
RUTILE GROUP		Magnetite	Fe_3O_4
Rutile	TiO_2	Franklinite	$(Zn,Fe,Mn)(Fe,Mn)_2O_4$
Pyrolusite	MnO_2	Chromite	$FeCr_2O_4$
Cassiterite	SnO_2	Chrysoberyl	$BeAl_2O_4$
Uraninite	UO_2	Columbite	$(Fe,Mn)(Nb,Ta)_2O_6$

Hydroxides

Brucite	$Mg(OH)_2$	Limonite	$FeO(OH) \cdot nH_2O$
Manganite	$MnO(OH)$	Bauxite	Al hydrates
Psilomelane	$BaMn''Mn^4{}_8O_{16}(OH)_4$		

CUPRITE—Cu_2O

Ruby Copper. Red Copper Ore

Crystallography. Isometric; hexoctahedral. Commonly in crystals showing the cube, octahedron, and dodecahedron, frequently in combination (Figs. 439 and 440). Sometimes in much elongated cubic crystals, capillary in size; known as "plush copper" or *chalcotrichite*. Frequently in fine-grained aggregates or massive.

Physical properties. H $3\frac{1}{2}$–4. G 6.1. Luster metallic-adamantine in clear crystallized varieties. Color red of various shades; ruby-red in transparent crystals. Streak brownish red, Indian-red.

Composition. Cuprous oxide, Cu_2O. Cu 88.8, O 11.2 per cent. Usually pure, but iron oxide may be present as an impurity.

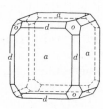

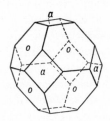

Fig. 439.

Fig. 440.

Cuprite.

Test. Fusible at 3. Azure-blue copper chloride flame obtained if cuprite is moistened with hydrochloric acid and then heated. Gives globule of copper on charcoal in the reducing flame. When dissolved in small amount of concentrated hydrochloric acid and solution diluted with cold water gives a white precipitate of cuprous chloride (tests for cuprous copper).

Diagnostic features. Usually distinguished from other red minerals by its crystal form, high luster, streak, and association.

Occurrence. Cuprite is an important supergene ore of copper. It is found in the upper oxidized portions of copper veins, associated with limonite and the other secondary copper minerals as native copper, malachite, azurite, and chrysocolla.

Noteworthy foreign countries where cuprite is an ore are Chile, Bolivia, Australia, and French Congo. Fine crystals have been found at Cornwall, England; Chessy, France; and the Ural Mountains. Found in the United States in excellent crystals in connection with the copper deposits at Bisbee, Arizona. Also found at Clifton and Morenci, Arizona.

Use. An ore of copper.

Name. Derived from the Latin *cuprum*, copper.

Similar species. *Tenorite* or *melaconite*, the cupric oxide, CuO, is a black supergene mineral.

ICE—H_2O

Water

Crystallography. Hexagonal; ditrigonal-pyramidal. Ice in the form of snow shows a great diversity of habit in the beautiful lacelike crystals. In countless crystals differing in detail, the hexagonal outline may be seen. Ice occurs most abundantly in massive and granular form.

Physical properties. H $1\frac{1}{2}$. G 0.917. Luster vitreous. Colorless to white.

Composition. H_2O. H 11.19, O 88.81 per cent. Frequently contains foreign material.

Occurrence. Ice forms on the surface of open water in cold regions, is precipitated in the form of snow and hail, and crystallizes in place as frost. In polar regions permanent ice exists, the largest masses today being in the icecaps of Greenland and Antarctica. Smaller amounts are to be found in mountain glaciers and, in the winter, on the surface of lakes and rivers and as snow on the land in more temperate zones.

ZINCITE—ZnO

Crystallography. Hexagonal; dihexagonal-pyramidal. Crystals are rare, terminated at one end by faces of a steep pyramid and the other with a pedion. (See Fig. 150.) Usually massive with platy or granular appearance.

Physical properties. Distinct $\{10\bar{1}0\}$ cleavage; $\{0001\}$ parting. H 4–$4\frac{1}{2}$. G 5.6. Luster subadamantine. Color deep red to orange-yellow. May be coated with a bluish black film. Streak orange-yellow. Translucent.

Composition. Zinc oxide, ZnO. Zn 80.3, O 19.7 per cent. Divalent manganese (Mn'') often present and probably colors the mineral; chemically pure ZnO is white.

Test. Infusible. Soluble in hydrochloric acid. When the finely powdered mineral is mixed with reducing mixture and intensely heated on charcoal it gives a nonvolatile coating of zinc oxide, yellow when hot, white when cold. Usually with borax bead in the oxidizing flame gives a reddish violet color (manganese).

Diagnostic features. Told chiefly by its red color, orange-yellow streak, and the association with franklinite and willemite.

Occurrence. Zincite is confined almost exclusively to the zinc deposits at Franklin, New Jersey, where it is associated with franklinite and willemite, often in an intimate mixture. (See frontispiece.) Also imbedded in pink calcite. Reported only in small amounts from other localities.

Use. An ore of zinc, particularly used for the production of zinc white (zinc oxide).

CORUNDUM—Al_2O_3

Crystallography. Hexagonal–R; scalenohedral. Crystals usually prismatic in habit or tapering hexagonal pyramids (Figs. 441 and 442). Often rounded into barrel shapes. Frequently with deep horizontal

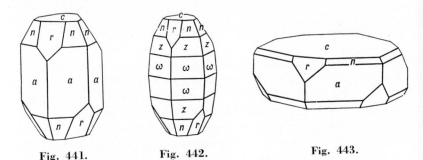

| Fig. 441. | Fig. 442. | Fig. 443. |

Corundum.

striations. May show rhombohedral faces (Fig. 443). Usually rudely crystallized or massive with parting planes nearly cubic in angle; coarse or fine granular.

Physical properties. Parting {0001} and {$10\bar{1}1$}, the latter giving nearly cubic angles; more rarely prismatic parting. **H** 9 (next to the diamond in hardness). Corundum may alter to mica, and care should be exercised in obtaining a fresh surface for hardness test. **G** 4.02 (unusually high for a nonmetallic mineral). Luster adamantine to vitreous. Transparent to translucent. Color various; usually some shade of brown, pink, or blue. May be white, gray, green, ruby-red, or sapphire-blue.

Color differences give rise to several varieties of gem corundum. The *ruby* is the deep red and the *sapphire* is the blue. Gem corundum of other colors is commonly named after other gems with the prefix *oriental*. Thus *oriental amethyst* is purple, *oriental topaz* is yellow, and *oriental emerald* is green. Although these are common terms, they are misleading, and their use is being discouraged by jewelers' organizations. Varieties of corundum having a stellate opalescence when viewed in the direction of the *c* crystal axis are termed asteriated, or *star sapphire* or *star ruby*.

Emery is a black granular corundum intimately mixed with magnetite, hematite, or hercynite.

Composition. Aluminum oxide, Al_2O_3. Al 52.9, O 47.1 per cent.

Tests. Infusible. Insoluble. Finely pulverized material moistened with cobalt nitrate and intensely ignited becomes blue (aluminum).

Diagnostic features. Characterized chiefly by its great hardness, high luster, specific gravity, and parting.

Occurrence. Corundum is common as an accessory mineral in the metamorphic rocks, such as crystalline limestone, mica-schist, gneiss. Found also as an original constituent of certain igneous rocks; usually those deficient in silica, as syenites and nepheline syenites. May be found in large masses in the zone separating peridotites from adjacent country rocks. It is disseminated in small crystals through certain lamprophyric dikes and is found in large crystals in pegmatites. Found frequently in crystals and rolled pebbles in detrital soil and stream sands, where it has been preserved through its hardness and chemical inertness. Associated minerals are commonly chlorite, micas, olivine, serpentine, magnetite, spinel, kyanite, and diaspore.

Rubies are found chiefly in Burma, Siam, and Ceylon. The most important locality in Burma is near Mogok, 90 miles north of Mandalay. The stones are found here chiefly in the soil resulting from the solution of a metamorphosed limestone. They have also been found *in situ* in the limestone. The rubies of Siam are found near Bangkok, on the Gulf of Siam, where they occur in a clay, derived from the decomposition of a basalt. The rubies of Ceylon are found with other gem stones in the stream gravels. In the United States a few rubies have been found in the gravels and in connection with the larger corundum deposits of North Carolina.

Sapphires are found associated with the rubies of Siam and Ceylon. They occur in Kashmir, India, and are found over an extensive area in central Queensland, Australia. In the United States small sapphires of fine color are found in various localities in Montana. They were first discovered in the river sands east of Helena during placer operations for gold, and have more recently been found imbedded in the rock of a lamprophyre dike at Yogo Gulch. The rock is mined and after exposure to the air for a time it gradually decomposes, setting the sapphires free. For economic reasons rather than from lack of sapphires, this mine ceased operation in 1929.

Common corundum is found in large crystals in the Transvaal, Union of South Africa. These crystals found loose in the soil or in pegmatites constitute the chief source of abrasive corundum imported into the United States. Common corundum is found in the United

States in various localities along the eastern edge of the Appalachian Mountains in North Carolina and Georgia. At one time it was extensively mined in southwestern North Carolina. It occurs here in large masses lying at the edges of intruded masses of an olivine rock (dunite) and is thought to have been a separation from the original magma. Found as an original constituent of a nepheline syenite in the Province of Ontario, Canada. In places the corundum is so abundant as to form more than 10 per cent of the rock mass.

Emery is found in large quantities on Cape Emeri on the island of Naxos and in various localities in Asia Minor, where it has been extensively mined for centuries. In the United States emery has been mined at Chester, Massachusetts, and Peekskill, New York.

Artificial. Artificial corundum is manufactured from bauxite on a large scale. This synthetic material together with other manufactured abrasives, notably silicon carbide, has largely taken the place of natural corundum as an abrasive.

Synthetic rubies and sapphires, colored with small amounts of chromium and titanium, have been manufactured since 1902 by the Verneuil process. Synthetic sapphires and rubies were made only in Switzerland, France, and Germany until 1940, when the Linde Air Products Company undertook their manufacture in the United States. The Linde Company was highly successful in corundum synthesis; their greatest achievement was the development of synthetic star rubies and sapphires. This was accomplished by introducing titanium which during proper heat treatment, exsolved as oriented rutile, TiO_2, to produce the star. The artificial rival the natural stones in beauty and it is difficult for the untrained person to distinguish them.

Before the Verneuil process small grains and chips of natural ruby were fused together into larger masses from which stones of two or three carats in size could be cut. These are known as reconstructed rubies.

Use. As a gem stone. The deep red ruby is one of the most valuable of gems, second only to emerald. The blue sapphire is also valuable, and stones of other colors may command good prices. Stones of gem quality are used as watch jewels and as bearings in scientific instruments. Corundum is used as an abrasive, either ground from the pure massive material or in its impure form as emery.

HEMATITE—Fe_2O_3

Crystallography. Hexagonal–R; hexagonal-scalenohedral. Crystals usually thick to thin tabular. Basal planes prominent, often showing triangular markings (Figs. 444 and 445). Edges of plates may be beveled with rhombohedral forms (Fig. 446). Thin plates may be grouped in rosette forms (iron roses) (Fig. 447). More rarely crystals are distinctly rhombohedral, often with nearly cubic angles. Usually earthy. Also in botryoidal to reniform shapes with radiating structure, *kidney ore.* (See Fig. 333, page 112.) May also be micaceous and foliated, *specular.* Called *martite* when in octahedral pseudomorphs after magnetite.

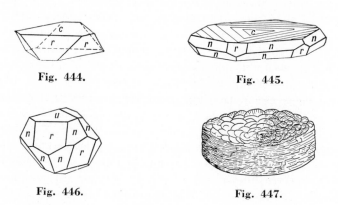

Fig. 444.

Fig. 445.

Fig. 446.

Fig. 447.

Hematite.

Physical properties. {0001} and {10$\bar{1}$1} parting with nearly cubic angles. **H** 5½–6½, **G** 5.26 for crystals. Luster metallic in crystals and dull in earthy varieties. Color reddish brown to black. Red earthy variety is known as *red ocher.* Streak light to dark Indian-red which becomes black on heating. Translucent.

Composition. Ferric oxide, Fe_2O_3. Fe 70, O 30 per cent. May contain titanium.

Tests. Infusible. Becomes strongly magnetic on heating in the reducing flame. Slowly soluble in hydrochloric acid; solution with potassium ferrocyanide gives dark blue precipitate (test for ferric iron).

Diagnostic features. Told chiefly by its characteristic Indian-red streak.

Occurrence. Hematite is a widely distributed mineral in rocks of all ages and forms the most abundant and important ore of iron. It may occur as a sublimation product in connection with volcanic activities. Occurs in contact metamorphic deposits and as an accessory mineral in feldspathic igneous rocks such as granite. Also replaces siliceous rocks on a large scale. Found from microscopic scales to enormous masses in connection with regionally metamorphosed rocks where it may have originated by the alteration of limonite, siderite, or magnetite. Like limonite, it may be formed in irregular masses and beds as the result of the weathering of iron-bearing rocks. The oölitic ores are of sedimentary origin and may occur in beds of considerable size. It is found in red sandstones as the cementing material that binds the quartz grains together.

Noteworthy localities for hematite crystals are the island of Elba; St. Gothard, Switzerland, in "iron roses"; in the lavas of Vesuvius; at Cleator Moor, Cumberland, England.

In the United States the columnar and earthy varieties are found in enormous beds that furnish a large proportion of the iron ore of the world. The chief iron-ore districts of the United States are grouped around the southern and northwestern shores of Lake Superior in Michigan, Wisconsin, and Minnesota. The chief districts, which are spoken of as iron ranges, are, from east to west, the Marquette in northern Michigan; the Menominee in Michigan to the southwest of the Marquette; the Penokee-Gogebic in northern Wisconsin. In Minnesota the Mesabi, northwest of Duluth; the Vermilion, near the Canadian boundary; and the Cuyuna, southwest of the Mesabi. The iron ore of these different ranges varies from the hard specular variety to the soft red earthy type. The ore is mined in part by underground methods, and in part, where it is soft and lies sufficiently near the surface, by means of large electric shovels in open pits.

Hematite is also found in the United States in the rocks of the Clinton formation, which extends from central New York south along the line of the Appalachian Mountains to central Alabama. The most important deposits of the series lie in eastern Tennessee and northern Alabama, near Birmingham. Hematite has been found at Iron Mountain and Pilot Knob in southeastern Missouri. Deposits of considerable importance are located in Wyoming in Laramie and Carbon counties.

Although the production of iron ore within the United States remains large, over 100,000,000 tons a year, the rich deposits are being rapidly worked out. In the future much of the iron must come from low-grade deposits or must be imported. After many years of experimentation, processes have been developed for the concentration of iron ore from *taconite*, the low-grade, silica-rich iron formation from which the high-grade deposits have been derived. The reserves of iron ore in taconite are far greater than were the original reserves of high-grade ore.

Exploration outside the United States has in recent years been successful in locating several large ore bodies with many hundreds of millions of tons of high-grade ore. These are notably in Venezuela, Brazil, and Canada. Brazil's iron mountain, Itabira, is estimated to have 15 billion tons of very pure hematite. Poor transportation over the 325 miles between the deposit and the sea has thus far prevented its major exploitation. In 1947 Cerro Bolivar in Venezuela was discovered as an extremely rich deposit of hematite and by 1954 ore was being shipped from there to the United States. In Canada several new iron ore deposits have been located, but the major ones lie along the boundary between Quebec and Labrador. A 350-mile railroad built into this previously inaccessible area began in 1954 to deliver iron ore to a St. Lawrence River port.

Use. Most important ore of iron. Also used in pigments, *red ocher* and as polishing powder.

Name. Derived from a Greek word meaning *blood,* in allusion to the color of the powdered mineral.

ILMENITE—FeTiO$_3$

Titanic Iron Ore.   Menaccanite

Crystallography. Hexagonal–R; rhombohedral. Crystals usually thick tabular with prominent basal planes and small rhombohedral truncations. Crystal constants close to those for hematite. Often in thin plates. Usually massive, compact; also in grains or as sand.

Physical properties. **H** 5$\frac{1}{2}$–6. **G** 4.7. Luster metallic to submetallic. Color iron-black. Streak black to brownish red. May be magnetic without heating. Opaque.

Composition. Iron titanium oxide, FeTiO$_3$. Fe 36.8, Ti 31.6, O 31.6 per cent. By the introduction of ferric oxide, the ratio between the titanium and iron often varies widely. The excess ferric oxide may be largely due to minute inclusions of hematite. Magnesium and manganese may replace the ferrous iron.

Tests. Infusible. Magnetic after heating. Fine powder fused in the reducing flame with sodium carbonate yields a magnetic mass. After fusion with sodium carbonate it can be dissolved in sulfuric acid and on the addition of hydrogen peroxide the solution turns yellow.

Diagnostic features. Ilmenite can be distinguished from hematite by its streak and from magnetite by its lack of strong magnetism. In doubtful cases, as in intergrowths with magnetite, it is necessary to apply the chemical tests.

Occurrence. Ilmenite occurs as beds and lenticular bodies enveloped in gneiss and other crystalline metamorphic rocks. Frequently found in veins or large masses as a product of magmatic segregation. Associated with magnetite. Also as an accessory mineral in igneous rocks. One of the constituents of black sands, associated with magnetite, rutile, zircon, and monazite.

Found in large quantities at Krägerö and other localities in Norway; in Finland; and in crystals at Miask in the Ilmen Mountains, U.S.S.R. It is mined in considerable quantities from beach sands, notably in India and Brazil. In the United States found at Washington, Connecticut; in Orange County, New York; and with many of the magnetite deposits of the Adirondack region, notably at Tahawus, Essex County, where it is actively mined. Also found at Bay St. Paul and Allard Lake, Quebec.

Use. As a source of titanium. Manufactured titanium dioxide is being used in increasingly large amounts as a paint pigment replacing older pigments, notably lead compounds. Much research work is being done on the use of metallic titanium as a structural material. Because of its high strength-to-weight ratio it is proving to be a desirable material for aircraft construction in both frames and engines. Ilmenite cannot be used as an iron ore because of difficulties in smelting it, but mixtures of ilmenite-magnetite and ilmenite-hematite are separated so that both titanium and iron can be recovered.

Name. From the Ilmen Mountains, U.S.S.R.

RUTILE—TiO_2

Crystallography. Tetragonal; ditetragonal-dipyramidal. Prismatic crystals with dipyramid terminations common (Fig. 448). Vertically striated. Frequently in elbow twins, often repeated (Figs. 449

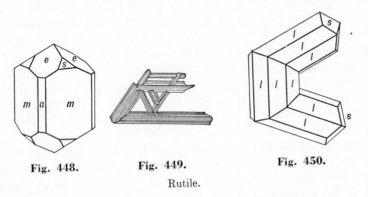

Fig. 448.   Fig. 449.   Fig. 450.

Rutile.

and 450). Twinning plane is dipyramid of second order {011} Crystals frequently slender acicular. Also compact massive.

Physical properties. H 6–6½. G 4.18–4.25. Luster adamantine to submetallic. Color red, reddish brown to black. Streak pale brown. Usually subtranslucent, may be transparent.

Composition. Titanium dioxide, TiO_2. Ti 60, O 40 per cent. A little iron is usually present and may amount to 10 per cent.

Tests. Infusible. Insoluble. After fusion with sodium carbonate it can be dissolved in sulfuric acid; the solution turns yellow on addition of hydrogen peroxide (titanium).

Diagnostic features. Characterized by its peculiar adamantine luster and red color. Lower specific gravity distinguishes it from cassiterite.

Occurrence. Rutile is found in granite, granite pegmatites, gneiss, mica schist, metamorphic limestone, and dolomite. It may be present as an accessory mineral in the rock, or in quartz veins traversing it. Often occurs as slender crystals penetrating quartz. Is found in considerable quantities in black sands associated with magnetite, zircon, and monazite.

Notable European localities are: Krägerö, Norway; Yrieix, near Limoges, France; in Switzerland; and the Tyrol. Rutile from mines in the coastal areas of northern New South Wales and southern Queensland makes Australia the largest producer of rutile. In the United States remarkable crystals come from Graves Mountain, Lincoln County, Georgia. Also found in Alexander County, North Carolina, and at Magnet Cove, Arkansas. Has been mined in Amherst and Nelson counties, Virginia, and derived in commercial quantities from the black sands of northeastern Florida.

Artificial. Single crystals of rutile have been manufactured by the Verneuil process. With the proper heat treatment they can be made transparent and nearly colorless, quite different from the natural mineral. Because of its high refractive index and dispersion, this synthetic material makes a beautiful cut gem stone with only a slight yellow tinge. It is sold under a variety of names, some of the better known are *titania, kenya gem,* and *miridis.*

Use. Most of the rutile produced is used as a coating of welding rods. Some titanium derived from rutile is used in alloys; for electrodes in arc lights; to give a yellow color to porcelain and false teeth. Manufactured oxide is used as a paint pigment. (See ilmenite.)

Name. From the Latin *rutilus,* red, in allusion to the color.

Similar species. *Octahedrite* or *anatase* (tetragonal) and *brookite* (orthorhombic) are polymorphous forms of TiO_2.

Perovskite, $CaTiO_3$, is an isometric titanium mineral found usually in metamorphic rocks.

PYROLUSITE—MnO_2

Crystallography. Tetragonal; ditetragonal-dipyramidal. Rarely in well-developed crystals, *polianite.* Many crystals pseudomorphous

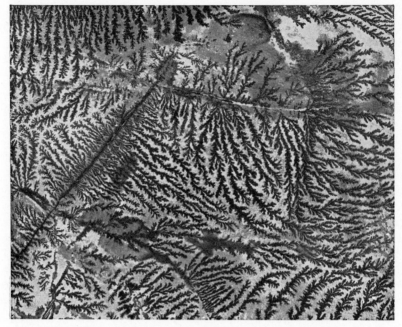

Fig. 451.   Dendrites of Pyrolusite on Limestone, Sardinia.

after manganite. Usually in radiating fibers or columns. Also granular massive; often in reniform coats and dendritic shapes (Fig. 451).

Physical properties. Cleavage {110}, perfect. H 1–2 (often soiling the fingers). For coarsely crystalline polianite the hardness is 6–6½. G 4.75. Luster metallic. Color and streak iron-black. Fracture splintery. Opaque.

Composition. Manganese dioxide, MnO_2. Mn 63.2, O 36.8 per cent. Commonly contains a little water.

Tests. Infusible. A small amount of powdered mineral gives a bluish-green opaque bead with sodium carbonate. Gives oxygen in the closed tube, which will cause a splinter of charcoal to ignite when placed in tube above the mineral and heated.

Diagnostic features. Characterized by and distinguished from other manganese minerals by its black streak, low hardness, and small amount of water.

Occurrence. Pyrolusite is a supergene mineral. Manganese is dissolved out of the crystalline rocks, in which it is almost always present in small amounts, and redeposited as various minerals, chiefly as pyrolusite. Dendritic coatings of pyrolusite are frequently observed on the surfaces of fractures and coating pebbles. Nodular deposits of pyrolusite are found on the sea bottom. Nests and beds of manganese ores are found inclosed in residual clays, derived from the decay of manganiferous limestones. It is thought that the manganese oxides were originally colloidal, having subsequent to deposition assumed a crystalline form. Also found in veins with quartz and various metallic minerals.

Pyrolusite is the most common manganese ore and is widespread in its occurrence. The chief manganese-producing countries are the U.S.S.R., Ghana, India, Union of South Africa, French Morocco, Brazil, and Cuba. In the United States, manganese ores are found in Virginia, West Virginia, Georgia, Arkansas, Tennessee, with the hematite ores of the Lake Superior districts, and in California.

Use. Most important manganese ore. Manganese is used with iron in the manufacture of *spiegeleisen* and *ferromanganese*, employed in making steel. Also used in various alloys with copper, zinc, aluminum, tin, and lead. Pyrolusite is used as an oxidizer in the manufacture of chlorine, bromine, and oxygen; as a disinfectant in potassium permanganate; as a drier in paints; as a decolorizer of glass; and in electric dry-cells and batteries. Manganese is also used as a coloring material in bricks, pottery, and glass.

Name. *Pyrolusite* is derived from two Greek words meaning *fire* and *to wash*, because it is used to free glass through its oxidizing effect of the colors due to iron.

Similar species. *Alabandite*, MnS, is comparatively rare, associated with other sulfides in veins.

Wad is the name given to manganese ore composed of a mixture of hydrous manganese oxides.

CASSITERITE—SnO_2

Tin Stone

Crystallography. Tetragonal; ditetragonal-dipyramidal. Common forms are prisms and dipyramids of first and second orders (Fig. 452). Frequently in elbow-shaped twins with a characteristic notch, giving rise to the miner's term *visor tin* (Fig. 453); the twin plane is the dipyramid of the second order, {011}. Usually massive granular; often in reniform shapes with radiating fibrous appearance, *wood tin*.

Physical properties. **H** 6–7. **G** 6.8–7.1 (unusually high for a mineral with nonmetallic luster). Luster adamantine to submetallic and dull. Color usually brown or black; rarely yellow or white. Streak white. Translucent, rarely transparent.

Composition. Tin dioxide, SnO_2. Sn 78.6, O 21.4 per cent. Small amounts of iron may be present.

Tests. Infusible. Gives globule of tin with coating of white tin oxide when finely powdered mineral is fused on charcoal with the reducing mixture. Insoluble. When fragments of cassiterite are

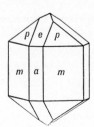

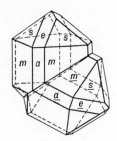

Fig. 452. **Fig. 453.**

Cassiterite.

placed in dilute hydrochloric acid together with a little metallic zinc the surface of the cassiterite is reduced and the specimen becomes coated with a dull gray deposit of metallic tin which becomes bright on rubbing.

Diagnostic features. Recognized by its high specific gravity, adamantine luster, and light streak.

Occurrence. Cassiterite is widely distributed in small amounts but is produced on a commercial scale in only a few localities. It has been noted as an original constituent of igneous rocks and pegmatites, but it is more commonly to be found in veins associated with quartz, in or near granitic rocks. Tin veins usually have minerals that contain fluorine or boron, such as tourmaline, topaz, fluorite, and apatite, and the minerals of the wall rocks are commonly much altered. Frequently associated with wolframite. Cassiterite is also found in the form of rolled pebbles in placer deposits, *stream tin*.

Most of the world's supply of tin ore comes from the Malay States, Bolivia, Indonesia, Belgian Congo, Nigeria. Cornwall, England, has produced large amounts of tin ore in the past. In the United States cassiterite is not found in sufficient quantities to warrant mining but is present in small amounts in numerous pegmatites.

Use. Principal ore of tin. The chief use of tin is in the manufacture of *tin plate* and *tern plate* for food containers. Tern plate is made by applying a coating of tin and lead instead of pure tin. Tin is also used with lead in solders, in babbitt metal with antimony and copper, and in bronze and bell-metal with copper. "Phosphor bronze" contains 89 per cent copper, 10 per cent tin, and 1 per cent phosphorus. Artificial tin oxide is a polishing powder.

Name. From the Greek word meaning *tin*.

Uraninite—UO_2

Pitchblende

Crystallography. Isometric. In octahedrons, also with dodecahedrons; less often showing cube faces. Crystals rare. Usually massive and botryoidal (*pitchblende*).

Physical properties. H $5\frac{1}{2}$. G 9–9.7 (unusually high); in the colloform varieties G 6.5–8.5. Luster submetallic to pitchlike, dull. Color black. Streak brownish black.

Composition. Uranium dioxide, UO_2. Uraninite is always partially oxidized, and thus the actual composition lies between UO_2 and U_3O_8. Thorium can substitute for uranium, and a complete series between uraninite and thorianite, ThO_2, has been observed in artificial preparations. Analyses usually show the presence of small amounts of lead and the rare elements radium, thorium, yttrium, nitrogen, helium, argon. The lead is present as the stable end product of the radioactive disintegration of both uranium and thorium. Two isotopes of lead are found: Pb^{206} results from the radioactive disintegration of the isotope of uranium U^{238}; and Pb^{207} results from the breakdown of U^{235}. In the disintegration ionized helium atoms (α particles) and electrons (β particles) are emitted. The helium is always found in uraninite. Since the radioactive disintegration proceeds at a uniform rate, the accumulation of both helium and lead can be used as a measure of the time elapsed since the mineral crystallized. Both the lead–uranium ratio and the helium–uranium ratio have been used by geologists to determine the age of rocks.

It was in the mineral uraninite that helium was first discovered on the earth, having been previously noted in the sun's spectrum. In it also radium was discovered.

Tests. Infusible. Imparts to the salt of phosphorus bead in the oxidizing flame a yellowish green and in the reducing flame a green color. These beads or a borax bead fluoresce under ultraviolet light. This is a very sensitive test for uranium. Because of its radioactivity, uraninite, as well as other uranium compounds, can be detected in small amounts by Geiger-Müller counters, ionization chambers, and similar instruments.

Diagnostic features Characterized chiefly by its pitchy luster, high specific gravity, color, and streak.

Occurrence. Uraninite occurs as a primary constituent of granitic rocks and pegmatites, also as a secondary mineral with ores of silver, lead, copper at Johanngeorgenstadt, Marienberg, and Schneeberg in Saxony; at Joachimsthal and Přibram in Bohemia; Rezbánya in Rumania; and Cornwall, England. Although these are old localities, active mining for uraninite is being carried on at many of them.

Many countries throughout the world are mining uraninite, but the most important producers are the Belgian Congo and Canada. The production from the Belgian Congo comes from the Shinkolobwe mine, where uraninite is associated with many brightly colored alteration minerals. Wilberforce, Ontario, has been a famous Canadian locality, but the present major sources are the mines on the shores of Great Bear Lake, Northwest Territory; the Beaverlodge region, Saskatchewan; and the Blind River area, Ontario. Uraninite is also recovered from the gold-bearing conglomerates of the Witwatersrand, Union of South Africa.

In the United States uraninite was early found in isolated crystals in pegmatites at Middletown, Glastonbury, and Branchville, Connecticut; and the mica mines of Mitchell County, North Carolina. A narrow vein of it was mined near Central City, Gilpin County, Colorado. Recent exploration has located many workable deposits of uraninite and associated uranium minerals on the Colorado Plateau in Arizona, Colorado, New Mexico, and Utah.

Use. In the fifteenth edition of this book, written in 1940, there was the statement, "Uranium has only a limited use." The author was unaware at that time of the great and growing interest in uranium as a source of atomic energy. Since that time, uraninite, as the chief source of uranium, has received more attention from both scientists and the general public than any other mineral. Until August 1945, when the first atomic bomb was dropped, the importance of uraninite was known to only a few, but since then people in all countries of the world have been made conscious of the major role that uranium will play in the future. As a result an intensive search for uranium minerals has been under way. Since 1945 41 new uranium minerals have been described and many old ones restudied. At present there are 85 known uranium minerals and 10 to 20 more partly described. Although uraninite remains the chief ore of uranium, other minerals are now important sources of the element such as carnotite (page 383), tyuyamunite (page 384), torbernite (page 382), and autunite (page 381).

Uranium has assumed such an important place among the elements because of its susceptibility to nuclear fission, a process by which the nuclei of uranium atoms are split apart with the generation of tremendous amounts of energy. This is the source of energy of the atomic bomb. Tremendous advances have been made in utilizing this energy for other purposes. Nuclear-power reactors are in operation generating electricity and nuclear-propulsion reactors are used in submarines and even in aircraft.

Uraninite is also the source of radium but contains it in very small amounts. Roughly, 750 tons of ore must be mined in order to furnish 12 tons of concentrates; chemical treatment of these concentrates yields about 1 gram of a radium salt. In the form of various compounds uranium has a limited use in coloring glass and porcelain, in photography, and as a chemical reagent.

Name. Uraninite in allusion to the composition.

Similar species. *Thorianite*, ThO_2, is dark gray to black with submetallic luster. Found chiefly in pegmatites and as water-worn crystals in stream gravels.

Diaspore—$HAlO_2$

Crystallography. Orthorhombic; dipyramidal. Usually in thin crystals, tabular parallel to {010}. Bladed, foliated massive, disseminated.

Physical properties. Perfect pinacoidal {010} cleavage. **H** $6\frac{1}{2}$–7. **G** 3.35–3.45. Luster vitreous except on cleavage face, where it is pearly. Color white, gray, yellowish, greenish. Transparent to translucent.

Composition. Hydrogen aluminum oxide, $HAlO_2$. Al_2O_3 85, H_2O 15 per cent.

Diaspore corresponds to the general formula type ABO_2 and differs from boehmite, $AlO(OH)$, in not having (OH) groups. The hydrogen acts as a cation in 2-fold coordination with oxygen.

Tests. Infusible. Insoluble. Decrepitates and gives water when heated in the closed tube. Ignited with cobalt nitrate turns blue (aluminum).

Diagnostic features. Characterized by its good cleavage, its bladed habit, and its hardness ($6\frac{1}{2}$–7).

Occurrence. Diaspore is commonly associated with corundum in emery rock, and with that mineral in dolomite and chlorite schist. Occurs in bauxite deposits and aluminous clays. Has been noted as an accessory mineral in metamorphic limestones.

Notable localities are the Ural Mountains; Schemnitz, Czechoslovakia; and Campolungo in Switzerland. In the United States is found in Chester County, Pennsylvania; at Chester, Massachusetts; with alunite, forming rock masses at Mt. Robinson, Rosita Hills, Colorado. It is found abundantly in the bauxite and aluminous clays of Arkansas, Missouri, and elsewhere in the United States.

Use. As a refractory.

Name. Derived from a Greek word meaning *to scatter*, in allusion to its decrepitation when heated.

Similar species. *Boehmite*, AlO(OH), and *gibbsite*, Al(OH)$_3$, are found in disseminated particles as constituents of bauxite.

Goethite—HFeO$_2$

Bog-Iron Ore

Crystallography. Orthorhombic; dipyramidal. Rarely in distinct prismatic, vertically striated crystals. Often flattened parallel to the side pinacoid. In acicular crystals. Also massive, reniform, stalactitic in radiating fibrous aggregates. Foliated. The so-called bog ore is generally loose and porous in texture.

Physical properties. Perfect {010} cleavage. H 5–5$\frac{1}{2}$. G 4.37; may be as low as 3.3 for impure material. Luster adamantine to dull; silky in certain fine scaly or fibrous varieties. Color yellowish brown to dark brown. Streak yellowish brown. Subtranslucent.

Composition. Hydrogen iron oxide, HFeO$_2$. Fe 62.9, O 27.0, H$_2$O 10.1 per cent. The hydrogen acts as a cation in 2-fold coordination with oxygen, and thus goethite differs from lepidocrocite, FeO(OH), in not having OH groups. Manganese is often present in amounts up to 5 per cent. The massive varieties often contain adsorbed or capillary water.

Tests. Difficultly fusible (5–5$\frac{1}{2}$). Becomes magnetic in the reducing flame. In the closed tube gives water and is converted to Fe$_2$O$_3$.

Diagnostic features. Told chiefly by the color of its streak and distinguished from limonite by its cleavage, radial growth, and other evidence of crystallinity. Most of the material formerly classed under limonite is now known to be goethite.

Occurrence. Goethite is one of the commonest minerals and is typically formed under oxidizing conditions as a weathering product of iron-bearing minerals. It also forms as a direct inorganic or biogenic precipitate from water and is widespread as a deposit in bogs and springs. Goethite with limonite forms the gossan or "iron hat" over metalliferous veins. Large quantities of goethite have been found as residual lateritic mantles resulting from the weathering of serpentine.

The very common pseudomorphs of so-called limonite after pyrite probably consist for the most part of goethite.

Deposits known as *bog-iron ore* are formed by the solution, transportation, and reprecipitation of pre-existing iron minerals through the agency of surface waters. Solution is brought about by small amounts of carbonic acid in the water. The iron is transported as a carbonate to the surface and then carried by the streams into marshes and stagnant pools. There the carbonate is changed to the oxide through evaporation of the water and the consequent loss of the carbonic acid, and through the agency of the reducing action of carbonaceous matter. The oxide separates and first collects as an iridescent scum on the surface of the water, and then later sinks to the bottom. This separation is also aided by the so-called iron bacteria which absorb the iron from the water and later deposit it as ferric hydroxide. In this way, under favorable conditions, beds of impure goethite can be formed in the bottom of marshes and bogs. Such deposits are very common but, because of associated foreign materials, are seldom of sufficient purity to be worked commercially.

Goethite deposits are also to be found with iron-bearing limestones. The iron content of the limestone may be gradually dissolved by circulating waters and under favorable conditions may, as goethite, replace the calcium carbonate of the rock. The gradual weathering and solution of the limestone may leave behind the iron content in the form of residual masses of ferric hydroxide, lying in clay above the limestone formation. Such deposits are often of considerable size and because of their greater purity are much more often mined than the bog-iron ores.

Goethite in some localities constitutes an important ore of iron. It is the principal constituent of the valuable minette ores of Alsace-Lorraine. Other notable European localities are: Eiserfeld in Westphalia; Přibram, Bohemia; and Cornwall, England. Large deposits of iron-rich laterites composed essentially of goethite are found in the Mayari and Moa districts of Cuba.

In the United States goethite is common in the Lake Superior hematite deposits, and has been obtained in fine specimens at Negaunee, near Marquette, Michigan. Goethite is to be found in iron-bearing limestones along the Appalachian Mountains, from western Massachusetts as far south as Alabama. Such deposits are particularly important in Alabama, Georgia, Virginia, and Tennessee. Finely crystallized material occurs with smoky quartz and microcline in Colorado at Fluorissant and in the Pikes Peak region.

Use. An ore of iron.

Name. In honor of Goethe, the German poet.

Similar species. *Turgite*, $2Fe_2O_3 \cdot H_2O$, is frequently associated with goethite but distinguished from it by the red streak. *Lepidocrocite*, $FeO(OH)$, is dimorphous with goethite and occurs with it.

SPINEL GROUP, AB$_2$O$_4$

As pointed out on page 286, the minerals of the spinel group with the general formula AB_2O_4 comprise a closely related isostructural group with solid solution between the members. There is nearly complete substitution of the divalent elements, magnesium, ferrous iron, zinc, and manganese in the A positions, but only limited substitution of the trivalent elements aluminum, ferric iron, and chromium in the B positions. The table below shows the relationship of the principal members of the group.

Spinel Group, AB$_2$O$_4$

A	B = Al		B = Fe		B = Cr	
Mg	Spinel	$MgAl_2O_4$	Magnesio-ferrite	$MgFe_2O_4$	Magnesio-chromite	$MgCr_2O_4$
Fe	Hercynite	$FeAl_2O_4$	Magnetite	$FeFe_2O_4$	Chromite	$FeCr_2O_4$
Zn	Gahnite	$ZnAl_2O_4$	Franklinite	$ZnFe_2O_4$		
Mn	Galaxite	$MnAl_2O_4$	Jacobsite	$MnFe_2O_4$		

SPINEL—MgAl$_2$O$_4$

Crystallography. Isometric; hexoctahedral. Usually in octahedral crystals (Fig. 454). In twinned octahedrons (spinel twins) (Fig. 456). Dodecahedron may be present as small truncations (Fig. 455). Other forms rare.

Physical properties. H 8. G 3.5–4.1. G 3.55 for the composition as given. Nonmetallic. Luster vitreous. Color various: white, red, lavender, blue, green, brown, black. Streak white. Usually translucent, may be clear and transparent.

Composition. $MgAl_2O_4$. MgO 28.2, Al_2O_3 71.8 per cent. Ferrous iron, zinc and less commonly manganese substitute for magnesium in all proportions. Ferric iron and chromium may substitute in part for aluminum. The clear red, nearly pure magnesium spinel is known as *ruby spinel*. *Pleonaste* is the iron spinel, dark green to black, and *picotite* is the chrome spinel, yellowish to greenish brown.

Tests. Infusible. The finely powdered mineral dissolves completely in the salt of phosphorus bead (proving the absence of silica).

Diagnostic features. Recognized by its hardness (8), its octa-hedral crystals, and its vitreous luster. The iron spinel can be distinguished from magnetite by its nonmagnetic character and white streak.

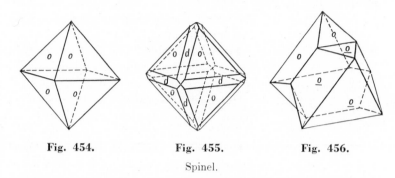

Fig. 454.   Fig. 455.   Fig. 456.

Spinel.

Occurrence. Spinel is a common metamorphic mineral occurring imbedded in crystalline limestone, gneisses, and serpentine. Occurs also as an accessory mineral in many dark igneous rocks. Spinel is frequently formed as a contact metamorphic mineral associated with phlogopite, pyrrhotite, chondrodite, and graphite. Found frequently as rolled pebbles in stream sands, where it has been preserved because of its resistant physical and chemical properties. The ruby spinels are found in this way, often associated with the gem corundum, in the sands of Ceylon, Siam, Upper Burma, and Madagascar. Ordinary spinel is found in various localities in New York and New Jersey.

Use. When transparent and finely colored is used as a gem. Usually red and known as the spinel ruby or *balas ruby*. Some stones are blue. The largest cut stone known weighs in the neighborhood of 80 carats. The stones usually are comparatively inexpensive.

Artificial. Synthetic spinel has been made by the Verneuil process (see corundum) in various colors rivaling the natural stones in beauty. Synthetic spinel is also used as a refractory.

Similar species. *Hercynite*, $FeAl_2O_4$, an iron spinel, is associated with corundum in some emery; also found with andalusite, sillimanite, and garnet. *Galaxite*, $MnAl_2O_4$, has not been found pure in nature; but *ferroan galaxite*, $(Mn,Fe)Al_2O_4$ has been reported.

Gahnite—$ZnAl_2O_4$

Zinc Spinel

Crystallography. Isometric; hexoctahedral. Commonly octahedral with faces striated parallel to the edge between the dodecahedron and octahedron (Fig. 457). Less frequently showing well-developed dodecahedrons and cubes.

Physical properties. H $7\frac{1}{2}$–8. **G** 4.55. Luster vitreous. Color dark green. Streak grayish. Translucent.

Composition. A zinc spinel, $ZnAl_2O_4$. Ferrous iron and manganese may substitute for zinc; and ferric iron for aluminum.

Tests. Infusible. The fine powder fused with sodium carbonate on charcoal gives a white nonvolatile coating of zinc oxide.

Diagnostic features. Characterized by crystal form (striated octahedrons) and hardness.

Occurrence. Gahnite is a rare mineral. It occurs in zinc deposits and also as a contact mineral in crystalline limestones. Found in large crystals at Bodenmais, Bavaria; in a talcose schist near Falun, Sweden. In the United States found at Charlemont, Massachusetts, and Franklin, New Jersey.

Fig. 457. Gahnite.

Name. After the Swedish chemist J. G. Gahn, the discoverer of manganese.

MAGNETITE—Fe_3O_4

Crystallography. Isometric; hexoctahedral. Frequently in crystals of octahedral habit (Fig. 458), occasionally twinned. More rarely in

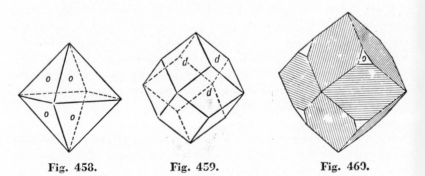

Fig. 458.   **Fig. 459.**   **Fig. 460.**

Magnetite.

dodecahedrons (Fig. 459). Dodecahedrons may be striated parallel to the intersection with the octahedrons (Fig. 460). Other forms rare. Usually granular massive, coarse or fine grained.

Physical properties. Octahedral parting on some specimens. H 6. G 5.18. Luster metallic. Color iron-black. Streak black. Strongly magnetic; may act as a natural magnet, known as *lodestone*. Opaque.

Composition. Fe_3O_4 or $FeFe_2O_4$. Fe 72.4, O 27.6 per cent. The composition of magnetite usually corresponds closely to that shown by the formula. However, some analyses show a few per cent of magnesium and divalent manganese.

Tests. Infusible. Slowly soluble in HCl, and solution reacts for both ferrous and ferric iron.

Diagnostic features. Characterized chiefly by its strong magnetism, its black color, and its hardness (6). Can be distinguished from magnetic franklinite by streak.

Occurrence. Magnetite is a common ore of iron. It is found disseminated as an accessory mineral through most igneous rocks. In certain types through magmatic segregation becomes one of the chief constituents, and may thus form large ore bodies. Such bodies are often highly titaniferous. Most commonly associated with crystalline metamorphic rocks, also frequently in rocks that are rich in ferromagnesian minerals, such as diorite, gabbro, and peridotite. Occurs also in immense beds and lenses, inclosed in old metamorphic rocks. Found in the black sands of the seashore. Occurs as thin plates and dendritic growths between plates of mica. Often intimately associated with corundum, forming the material known as *emery*.

The largest magnetite deposits in the world are in northern Sweden at Kiruna and Gellivare, and are believed to have formed by magmatic segregation. Other important foreign deposits are in Norway, Rumania, Ural Mountains. The most powerful natural magnets are found in Siberia, in the Harz Mountains, on the Island of Elba, and in the Bushveld complex, Transvaal.

In the United States has been found in commercial quantities in several localities in the Adirondack region in New York; Utah; California; New Jersey; and Pennsylvania. Found as lodestone and in crystals at Magnet Cove, Arkansas.

Use. An important iron ore.

Name. Probably derived from the locality Magnesia, bordering on Macedonia. A fable, told by Pliny, ascribes its name to a shepherd named Magnes, who first discovered the mineral on Mount Ida by noting that the nails of his shoes and the iron ferrule of his staff adhered to the ground.

Similar species. *Magnesioferrite*, $MgFe_2O_4$, is a rare mineral found chiefly in fumaroles. *Jacobsite*, $MnFe_2O_4$, is a rare mineral found at Langban, Sweden.

FRANKLINITE—$(Zn,Fe,Mn)(Fe,Mn)_2O_4$

Crystallography. Isometric; hexoctahedral. Habit strongly octahedral. Dodecahedron as truncations. Other forms rare. Crystals often rounded. Also massive, coarse or fine granular, in rounded grains.

Physical properties. H 6. G 5.15. Luster metallic. Color iron-black. Streak reddish brown to dark brown. Slightly magnetic.

Composition. Dominately $ZnFe_2O_4$ but always with substitution of ferrous iron and divalent manganese in the A position and trivalent manganese in the B position. Analyses show a wide variation in the proportions of the different elements.

Tests. Infusible. Becomes strongly magnetic on heating in the reducing flame. Gives a bluish green color to sodium carbonate bead in the oxidizing flame (manganese).

Diagnostic features. Resembles magnetite but is only slightly attracted by the magnet and has a dark brown streak. Usually identified by its characteristic association with willemite and zincite.

Occurrence. Franklinite, with only minor exceptions, is confined to the zinc deposits at Franklin, New Jersey, which are in the form of large lenses, inclosed in granular limestone. Associated chiefly with zincite and willemite, with which it is often intimately intergrown. (See frontispiece.)

Use. As an ore of zinc and manganese. The zinc is converted into zinc white, ZnO, and the residue is smelted to form an alloy of iron and manganese, *spiegeleisen*, which is used in the manufacture of steel.

Name. From Franklin, New Jersey.

CHROMITE—$FeCr_2O_4$

Crystallography. Isometric; hexoctahedral. Habit octahedral. Crystals small and rare. Commonly massive, granular to compact.

Physical properties. H $5\frac{1}{2}$. G 4.6. Luster metallic to submetallic; frequently pitchy. Color iron-black to brownish black. Streak dark brown. Subtranslucent.

Composition. $FeCr_2O_4$. FeO 32.0, Cr_2O_3 68.0 per cent. Some magnesium is always present substituting for iron. Some aluminum and ferric iron may substitute for chromium.

Tests. Infusible. When finely powdered and fused on charcoal with sodium carbonate gives a magnetic residue. Imparts a green color to the borax and salt of phosphorus beads (chromium).

Diagnostic features. The submetallic luster usually distinguishes chromite, but the green borax bead is diagnostic.

Occurrence. Chromite is a common constituent of peridotite rocks and the serpentines derived from them. One of the first minerals to separate from a cooling magma; large chromite ore deposits are thought to have been derived by such magmatic differentiation. Associated with olivine, serpentine, and corundum.

The important countries for its production are U.S.S.R., Union of South Africa, Turkey, Republic of the Philippines, Cuba, and Southern Rhodesia. Found only sparingly in the United States. Pennsylvania, Maryland, North Carolina, and Wyoming have produced it in the past. California, Alaska, and Oregon are small producers today, but the chief United States production comes from Montana, where bands of chromite are mined in the Stillwater igneous complex.

Uses. The only ore of chromium. Chromite ores are grouped into three categories—metallurgical, refractory, and chemical—on the basis of the chrome content and the chrome-iron ratio. As a metal chromium is used as a ferroalloy to give steel the combined properties of high hardness, great toughness, and resistance to chemical attack. Chromium is a major constituent in stainless steel. *Nichrome,* an alloy of nickel and chromium, is used for resistance in electrical heating equipment. Chromium is widely used in plating plumbing fixtures, automobile accessories, etc.

Because of the refractory character, chromite is made into bricks for the linings of metallurgical furnaces. The bricks are usually made of crude chromite and coal tar but sometimes of chromite with kaolin, bauxite, or other materials. Chromium is a constituent of certain green, yellow, orange, and red pigments and in K_2Cr_2O and $Na_2Cr_2O_7$, which are used as mordants to fix dyes.

Similar species. *Magnesiochromite,* $MgCr_2O_4$, is in both occurrence and appearance similar to chromite.

CHRYSOBERYL—$BeAl_2O_4$

Crystallography. Orthorhombic; dipyramidal. Usually in crystals tabular parallel to {100}, the faces of which are vertically striated. Commonly twinned, giving pseudohexagonal appearance (Fig. 461).

From its formula, $BeAl_2O_4$, it would appear that chrysoberyl is a member of the spinel group. However, because of the small size of the beryllium ion (Ion rad. 0.35 Å), chrysoberyl has a puckered structure of lower symmetry than the spinels.

Physical properties. Cleavage {110}. **H** $8\frac{1}{2}$ (unusually high). **G** 3.65–3.8. Luster vitreous. Color various shades of green, brown, yellow; may be red by transmitted light.

Alexandrite is an emerald-green variety, but red by transmitted light and generally also by artificial light. *Cat's-eye*, or *cymophane*, is a variety which when polished shows an opalescent luster, and across whose surface plays a long narrow beam of light, changing its position with every movement of the stone. This effect, known as chatoyancy, is best obtained when the stone is cut in an oval or round form *en cabochon*. This property of the mineral is thought to be due to numerous minute tubelike cavities, arranged in a parallel position. Chrysoberyl is the true *cat's-eye* and is not to be confused with various minerals possessing similar properties (e.g., quartz).

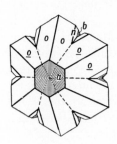

Fig. 461. Chrysoberyl.

Composition. Beryllium aluminum oxide, $BeAl_2O_4$. BeO 19.8, Al_2O_3 80.2 per cent. Be 7.1 per cent.

Tests. Infusible. Insoluble. The finely powdered mineral is wholly soluble in the salt of phosphorus bead (absence of silica). Mineral, moistened with cobalt nitrate and ignited, turns blue (aluminum).

Diagnostic features. Characterized by its extreme hardness, its yellowish to emerald-green color, and its twin crystals.

Occurrence. Chrysoberyl is a rare mineral. It occurs in granitic rocks and pegmatites and in mica schists. Frequently in river sands and gravels. The outstanding alluvial gem deposits are found in Brazil and Ceylon; the *alexandrite* variety comes from the Ural Mountains. In the United States chrysoberyl of gem quality is rarely found. It has been found in Oxford County and elsewhere in Maine; Haddam, Connecticut; and Greenfield, New York. Recently found in Colorado.

Use. Serves as a gem stone. The ordinary yellowish green stones are inexpensive; the varieties alexandrite and cat's-eye are of considerable value.

Name. *Chrysoberyl* means *golden beryl*. *Cymophane* is derived from two Greek words meaning *wave* and *to appear*, in allusion to the chatoyant effect of some of the stones. *Alexandrite* was named in honor of Alexander II of Russia.

Columbite-Tantalite—$(Fe,Mn)(Nb,Ta)_2O_6$

Crystallography. Orthorhombic; dipyramidal. Commonly in crystals. The habit is short prismatic or thin tubular; often in square prisms because of prominent development of the vertical pinacoids. Terminated by basal plane, pyramids, and horizontal prisms; frequently complex (Figs. 462–464). Also in heart-shaped twins.

Physical properties. Cleavage {010} good. **H** 6. **G** 5.2–7.9, varying with the composition, increasing with rise in percentage of tantalum
oxide present (Fig. 465). Luster submetallic. Color iron-black, frequently iridescent. Streak dark red to black. Subtranslucent.

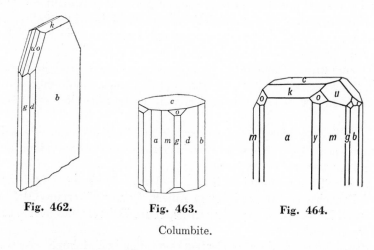

| Fig. 462. | Fig. 463. | Fig. 464. |

Columbite.

Composition. An oxide of niobium, tantalum, ferrous iron, and
manganese, $(Fe,Mn)(Nb,Ta)_2O_6$, which varies in composition from
pure *columbite* $(Fe,Mn)Nb_2O_6$, to pure *tantalite* $(Fe,Mn)Ta_2O_6$.

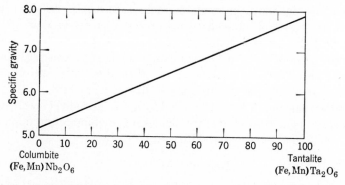

Fig. 465. Columbite-Tantalite. Variation of specific gravity with composition.

Often contains small amounts of tin and tungsten. A variety known
as *manganotantalite* is essentially a tantalite with divalent manganese
substituting for most of the ferrous iron.
Tests. Difficultly fusible $(5-5\frac{1}{2})$. Fused with borax; the bead dissolved in hydrochloric acid; the solution boiled with tin gives a blue

color (niobium). Generally when fused with sodium carbonate gives an opaque bluish green bead (manganese). Fused with sodium carbonate on charcoal yields a magnetic mass.

Diagnostic features. Recognized usually by its black color with lighter-colored streak, and high specific gravity. Distinguished from wolframite by having a lower specific gravity and less distinct cleavage; and from tourmaline by its orthorhombic crystal form and higher specific gravity.

Occurrence. Columbite occurs in granitic rocks and in pegmatite dikes, associated with quartz, feldspar, mica, tourmaline, beryl, spodumene, cassiterite, samarskite, wolframite, microlite, and monazite.

Notable localities for its occurrence are Belgian Congo; Nigeria; Brazil; near Moss, Norway; Bodenmais, Bavaria; Ilmen Mountains, U.S.S.R.; western Australia (*manganotantalite*); and Madagascar. In the United States found at Standish, Maine; Haddam, Middletown, and Branchville, Connecticut; in Amelia County, Virginia; Mitchell County, North Carolina; Black Hills, South Dakota; and near Canon City, Colorado.

Use. Source of the rare elements tantalum and niobium. Between 1903 and 1911 tantalum was used in making filaments for incandescent electric lamps. Because of its resistance to acid corrosion, tantalum is employed in chemical equipment, in surgery for skull plates and sutures, also in some tool steels and in electronic tubes. Niobium has its chief use in alloys in weldable high-speed steels, stainless steels, and alloys resistant to high temperatures, such as used in the gas turbine of the aircraft industry.

Name. *Columbite* from Columbia, a name for America, whence the original specimen was obtained. *Tantalite* from the mythical Tantalus in allusion to the difficulty in dissolving in acid.

Similar species. *Microlite*, $CaTa_2O_6$, is found in pegmatites; *pyrochlore* and *fergusonite* are oxides of niobium, tantalum, and rare earths found associated with alkalic rocks.

Brucite—$Mg(OH)_2$

Crystallography. Hexagonal–*R;* scalenohedral. Crystals usually tabular with prominent basal planes, which may show small rhombohedral truncations. Commonly foliated, massive.

Physical properties. Perfect {0001} cleavage. Folia flexible but not elastic. Sectile. **H** $2\frac{1}{2}$. **G** 2.39. Luster on base pearly, elsewhere vitreous to waxy. Color white, gray, light green. Transparent to translucent.

Composition. Magnesium hydroxide, $Mg(OH)_2$. MgO 69.0, H_2O 31.0 per cent. Iron and manganese may be present.

Tests. Infusible. Glows before the blowpipe. Gives water in the closed tube. Easily soluble in hydrochloric acid, and after solution has been made ammoniacal the addition of sodium phosphate gives a white granular precipitate of ammonium magnesium phosphate (test for magnesium).

Diagnostic features. Recognized by its foliated nature, light color, and pearly luster on cleavage face. Distinguished from talc by its greater hardness and lack of greasy feel, and from mica by being inelastic.

Occurrence. Brucite is found associated with serpentine, dolomite, magnesite, and chromite, as a decomposition product of magnesium silicates, especially serpentine. It is also found in crystalline limestone.

Notable foreign localities for its occurrence are at Unst, one of the Shetland Islands, and Aosta, Italy. In the United States found at Tilly Foster Iron Mine, Brewster, New York; at Wood's Mine, Texas, Pennsylvania; and Gabbs, Nevada.

Use. Brucite is used as a raw material for magnesia refractories.

Name. In honor of the early American mineralogist Archibald Bruce.

MANGANITE—MnO(OH)

Crystallography. Orthorhombic; dipyramidal. Crystals usually long prismatic with obtuse terminations, deeply striated vertically. Often twinned. Crystals often grouped in bundles or in radiating masses; also columnar.

Physical properties. Perfect {010} cleavage. **H** 4. **G** 4.3. Luster metallic. Color steel-gray to iron-black. Streak dark brown. Opaque.

Composition. MnO(OH). Mn 62.4, O 27.3, H_2O 10.3 per cent.

Tests. Infusible. Powdered mineral gives a bluish green bead with sodium carbonate. Much water when heated in the closed tube.

Diagnostic features. Told chiefly by its black color, prismatic crystals, hardness (4), and brown streak. The last two will serve to distinguish it from pyrolusite.

Occurrence. Manganite is found associated with other manganese oxides and has a similar origin. It frequently alters to pyrolusite. Found often in veins associated with the granitic igneous rocks, both filling cavities and as a replacement of the neighboring rocks. Barite and calcite are frequent associates.

Occurs at Ilfeld, Harz Mountains, in fine crystals; also at Ilmenau,

Thuringia, and Cornwall, England. In the United States at Negaunee, Michigan. In Nova Scotia.

Use. A minor ore of manganese.

PSILOMELANE—BaMn''Mn$^4{}_8$O$_{16}$(OH)$_4$

Crystallography. Orthorhombic. Massive, botryoidal, stalactitic. Appears amorphous.

Physical properties. H 5–6. G 3.7–4.7. Luster submetallic. Color black. Streak brownish black. Opaque.

Composition. BaMn''Mn$^4{}_8$O$_{16}$(OH)$_4$. Considerable substitution of magnesium, calcium, nickel, cobalt, and copper for barium and divalent manganese may take place.

Tests. Infusible. Fused with sodium carbonate gives an opaque bluish green bead. Gives much water in the closed tube.

Diagnostic features. Distinguished from the other manganese oxides by its greater hardness and apparent lack of crystal structure, and from limonite by its black streak.

Occurrence. Psilomelane occurs usually with pyrolusite, and its origin and associations are similar to those of that mineral.

Use. An ore of manganese. (See pyrolusite, page 299.)

Name. Derived from two Greek words meaning *smooth* and *black,* in allusion to its appearance.

Limonite—FeO(OH)·nH$_2$O

Brown Hematite. Bog-Iron Ore

Crystallography. Amorphous. In mammillary to stalactitic masses; also concretionary, nodular, earthy.

Physical properties. H 5–5$\frac{1}{2}$. Finely divided limonite may have an apparent hardness as low as 1. G 3.6–4. Luster vitreous. Color dark brown to black. Streak yellowish brown. Subtranslucent.

Composition. Largely FeO(OH)·nH$_2$O with some Fe$_2$O$_3$·nH$_2$O. Often impure with small amounts of hematite, clay minerals, and manganese oxides. The water content of limonite varies widely, and it is probable that the mineral is essentially an amorphous form of goethite with adsorbed and capillary water.

Tests. Difficultly fusible (5–5$\frac{1}{2}$). Strongly magnetic after heating in the reducing flame. Much water in the closed tube.

Diagnostic features. Characterized chiefly by its yellow-brown streak, and distinguished from goethite by its vitreous appearance and the absence of cleavage.

Occurrence. Limonite is always of supergene origin, formed through the alteration or solution of previously existing iron minerals. It may form in place as the result of direct oxidation or an inorganic or biogenic precipitation in water-lain deposits. Limonite and goethite are the chief constituents of the gossan or "iron hat" which is often the oxidized surface expression of sulfide veins. The principal mineral of most occurrences formerly listed under limonite is now known to be goethite. It is impossible to separate the localities of the two minerals on a mineralogical basis. (See goethite, page 304.) In addition to indicating the amorphous nature of the material, the name limonite may conveniently be retained as a field term to refer to natural hydrous iron oxides whose real identity is uncertain.

Limonite is the coloring material of yellow clays and soils, and mixed with fine clay makes what is known as *yellow ocher*. Limonite is commonly associated in its occurrence with goethite, hematite, turgite, pyrolusite, calcite, siderite.

Use. As a pigment, yellow ocher, and an ore of iron.

Name. Derived from the Greek word meaning *meadow*, in allusion to its occurrence in bogs.

BAUXITE[1]

Crystallography. A mixture. Pisolitic, in round concretionary grains; also massive, earthy, claylike.

Physical properties. H 1–3. G 2–2.55. Luster dull to earthy. Color white, gray, yellow, red. Translucent.

Composition. A mixture of hydrous aluminum oxides of indefinite composition. Some bauxites approach closely the composition of *gibbsite*, $Al(OH)_3$, but most are a mixture, and usually contain iron. As a result, bauxite has been discredited as a mineral species and in a rigid classification should be used only as a rock name. The principal constituents of the rock bauxite are *gibbsite; boehmite*, $AlO(OH)$; and *diaspore*, $HAlO_2$, any one of which may be dominant. *Cliachite* is the name proposed for the very fine-grained amorphous constituent of bauxite.

Tests. Infusible. Insoluble. Assumes a blue color when moistened with cobalt nitrate and then ignited (aluminum). Gives water in the closed tube.

Diagnostic features. Can usually be recognized by its pisolitic character.

[1] Bauxite has been discredited as a mineral species, but the name has been retained here since it has become so firmly fixed as the name of the important commercial substance.

Occurrence. Bauxite is of supergene origin, commonly produced under subtropical to tropical climatic conditions by prolonged weathering and leaching of silica from aluminum-bearing rocks. Also may be derived from the weathering of clay-bearing limestones. It has apparently originated as a colloidal precipitate. It may occur in place as a direct derivative of the original rock, or it may have been transported and deposited in a sedimentary formation. In the tropics deposits known as *laterites,* consisting largely of hydrous aluminum and ferric oxides, are found in the residual soils. These vary widely in composition and purity but may become valuable as sources of aluminum and iron.

Bauxite occurs over a large area in the south of France, an important district being at Baux, near Arles, France. The principal world producers are Surinam, Jamaica, and British Guiana. Other major producing countries are Indonesia, U.S.S.R., and Hungary. In the United States, the world's third largest producer, the chief deposits are found in Arkansas, Georgia, and Alabama. In Arkansas bauxite has formed by the alteration of a nepheline syenite.

Use. The ore of aluminum. Eighty-five per cent of the bauxite produced is consumed as aluminum ore. Because of its low density and great strength, aluminum has been adapted to many uses. Sheets, tubes, and castings of aluminum are used in automobiles, airplanes, and railway cars, where light weight is desirable. It is manufactured into cooking utensils, household appliances, and furniture. Aluminum is replacing copper to some extent in electrical transmission lines. Aluminum is alloyed with copper, magnesium, zinc, nickel, silicon, silver, and tin. Other uses are in paint, aluminum foil, and numerous salts.

The second largest use of bauxite is in the manufacture of Al_2O_3, which is used as an abrasive. It is also manufactured into aluminous refractories. Synthetic alumina is also used as the principal ingredient in heat-resistant porcelain such as spark plugs.

Name. From its occurrence at Baux, France.

HALIDES

The chemical class of halides is characterized by the dominance of the electronegative halogen ions, Cl^-, Br^-, F^- and I^-. These ions are large, feebly charged, and easily polarized. When they combine with relatively large, weakly polarized, cations of low valence, both cations and anions behave as almost perfectly spherical bodies. The packing of these spherical units leads to structures of the highest possible symmetry; and thus halite (Fig. 466), sylvite, and fluorite (Fig. 467) are all isometric hexoctahedral.

Because the weak electrostatic charges are spread over the entire surface of the nearly spherical ions, the halides are the most perfect examples of the pure ionic-bonding mechanism. The isometric halides all have relatively low hardness and moderate to high melting points

Fig. 466. Halite, NaCl, Packing Model. Na white, Cl gray.

and are poor conductors of heat and electricity in the solid state. Such conduction of electricity as takes place does so by electrolysis, that is, by transport of charges by ions rather than by electrons. As the temperature increases and ions are liberated by thermal disorder, electrical conductivity increases rapidly, becoming excellent in the molten state. Advantage is taken of this conductivity of halide melts in the commercial methods for the preparation of sodium and chlorine by electrolysis of molten sodium chloride in the Downs cell, and in the Hall process for the electrolytic preparation of aluminum using molten cryolite. These properties are those conferred by the ionic bond.

When the halogen ions are combined with smaller and more strongly polarizing cations than those of the alkali metals, structures of lower symmetry result, and the bond has somewhat more covalent properties.

In such structures, water and hydroxyl commonly enter as essential constituents, as in atacamite and carnallite.

Halides

Halite	NaCl	Fluorite	CaF_2
Sylvite	KCl	Atacamite	$Cu_2Cl(OH)_3$
Cerargyrite	AgCl	Carnallite	$KMgCl_3 \cdot 6H_2O$
Cryolite	Na_3AlF_6		

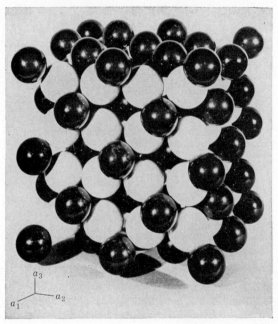

Fig. 467. Fluorite, CaF_2, Packing Model. F (white) is in 8-fold coordination about Ca (black). Because of requirements of electrical neutrality only half the possible Ca sites are filled and Ca is in 4-fold coordination about F. Compare with Fig. 437 (rutile). UO_2 also has the fluorite structure.

HALITE—NaCl

Rock Salt. Common Salt

Crystallography. Isometric; hexoctahedral. Habit cubic (Fig. 468). Some crystals hopper-shaped (Fig. 469). Other forms very rare. Found in crystals or granular crystalline masses showing cubic cleavage, known as *rock salt*. Also massive, granular to compact.

The crystal structure of halite was the first structure to be determined by x-rays (Fig. 466), and it typifies a large number of compounds with a radius ration between 0.41 and 0.73. It is also the classical example of a compound with ionic bond.

Physical properties. Perfect {001} cleavage. **H** $2\frac{1}{2}$. **G** 2.16. Luster transparent to translucent. Colorless or white, or when impure may have shades of yellow, red, blue, purple. Salty taste. Diathermanous.

Composition. Sodium chloride, NaCl. Na 39.3, Cl 60.7 per cent. Commonly contains impurities, such as calcium and magnesium sulfates and calcium and magnesium chlorides.

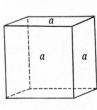

Fig. 468.

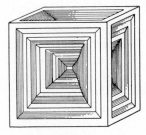

Fig. 469.

Halite.

Tests. Fusible at $1\frac{1}{2}$, giving strong yellow flame of sodium. With copper oxide in salt of phosphorus bead gives azure-blue copper chloride flame. Readily soluble in water; solution made acid with nitric acid gives with silver nitrate a white precipitate of silver chloride.

Diagnostic features. Characterized by its cubic cleavage and taste, and distinguished from sylvite by its yellow flame color and by less bitter taste.

Occurrence. Halite is a common and widely disseminated mineral, occurring often in extensive beds and irregular masses, precipitated from sea water and interstratified with sedimentary rocks. Associated with gypsum, sylvite, anhydrite, calcite, clay, and sand. Occurs also dissolved in the waters of salt springs, salt seas, and the ocean.

The deposits of salt have been formed by the gradual evaporation and ultimate drying up of inclosed bodies of salt water. The salt beds formed in this way have subsequently been covered by other sedimentary deposits and gradually buried beneath the rock strata formed from them. Salt beds range between a few feet and up to 100 feet in thickness and have been found at great depths. The history of the formation of these salt beds is as follows: River waters contain a small but appreciable amount of various soluble salts. When these waters are collected in a sea which has no outlet, or, in other words, a sea where the evaporation equals or exceeds the amount of water flowing in, there is a gradual concentration in the sea of the salts brought into it by the rivers. The sea water, therefore, in time becomes heavily charged with soluble salts, particularly sodium chloride. When the points of saturation of the various salts held in solution are reached, they will be deposited progressively upon the sea bottom, commencing with the most insoluble. This process may be interrupted by seasons of flood in which the sea water becomes freshened beyond the saturation point. Silt materials may be brought in at such times and deposited upon the bottom and so form beds of clay alternating with those of salt. Another theory of origin postulates that a body of sea water was separated from the ocean by the gradual growth of a sand bar, with the subsequent slow evaporation and concentration of the inclosed water. Such deposits of salt are now to be found buried in rock strata of all ages. At the present time similar deposits are being formed in the Great Salt Lake and the Dead Sea.

Important foreign countries for the production of salt are Austria, Poland, Czechoslovakia, Germany, Spain, U.S.S.R., and Great Britain.

In the United States salt is produced, on a commercial scale, in some fifteen states, either from rock-salt deposits or by evaporation of saline waters. Beds of rock salt are found in New York State from the Oatka Valley in Wyoming County east to Morrisville, Madison County, and south of this line wherever wells have been driven deep enough to reach the beds. The important producing localities are near Syracuse, Ithaca, Watkins, and Ludlowville, and at various places in Wyoming, Genesee, and Livingston counties. These beds continue into Michigan where salt is produced in Saginaw, Bay, Midland, Isabella, Detroit, Wayne, Manistee, and Mason counties. Notable deposits are also found in Ohio, Kansas, and New Mexico. Salt is obtained by the evaporation of sea waters in California and Texas and from the waters of the Great Salt Lake in Utah.

In Louisiana and Texas salt is produced extensively from *salt domes.* A salt dome is a nearly vertical pipelike mass of salt that appears to have punched its way upward to the surface from an underlying salt bed. Anhydrite, gypsum, and native sulfur are commonly associated with salt domes. More than a hundred salt domes have been located by geophysical prospecting in a search for petroleum, frequently associated with them. Some of them are under the waters of the Gulf of Mexico.

Use. Halite finds its greatest use in the chemical industry, where it serves as the source of sodium and chlorine. Some of the important manufactured alkali products are soda ash, bicarbonate of soda, caustic soda, sal soda, and modified sodas for the laundry, textile, lumber, and tanning trades. Metallic sodium, hydrochloric acid, and chlorine are produced from halite.

Salt is used extensively in the natural state in tanning hides, in fertilizers, in stock feeds, and as a weed killer. In addition to its familiar functions in the home, salt enters into the preparation of foods of many kinds, such as the preservation of butter, cheese, fish, and meat. It is also used as a refrigerant in refrigerator cars and in freezing and packing ice cream. There are many other uses for salt, but the above are the principal ones, and illustrate its importance in human activity.

Name. Halite comes from the Greek word meaning *salt*.

SYLVITE—KCl

Crystallography. Isometric; hexoctahedral. Cube and octahedron frequently in combination (Fig. 470). Usually in granular crystalline masses showing cubic cleavage; compact. Sylvite has the sodium chloride structure, but because of the difference in the ionic radii of the cations (Na 0.97 Å, K 1.33 Å) there is little solid solution.

Fig. 470.
Sylvite.

Physical properties. Perfect {010} cleavage. **H** 2. **G** 1.99. Transparent when pure. Colorless or white; also shades of blue, yellow, or red from impurities. Readily soluble in water. Salty taste but more bitter than that of halite.

Composition. Potassium chloride, KCl. K 52.4, Cl 47.6 per cent. May contain admixed sodium chloride.

Tests. Fusible at $1\frac{1}{2}$, giving violet flame of potassium, which may be obscured by yellow flame due to sodium present. The yellow sodium flame may be filtered out by means of a blue filter and the violet of the potassium rendered visible. Readily soluble in water; solution made acid with nitric acid gives with silver nitrate a heavy precipitate of silver chloride.

Diagnostic features. Distinguished from halite by the violet flame color of potassium and its more bitter taste.

Occurrence. Sylvite has the same origin, mode of occurrence, and associations as halite (page 320) but is much more rare. It remains in the mother liquor after precipitation of halite and is one of the last salts to be precipitated.

Found in some quantity and frequently well crystallized, associated with the salt deposits at Stassfurt, Prussia; from Kalusz in Galicia.

In the United States found in large amount in the Permian salt deposits near Carlsbad, New Mexico, and in western Texas.

Use. The chief source of potassium compounds, which are extensively used as fertilizers.

Name. Potassium chloride is the *sal digestivus Sylvii* of early chemistry, whence the name for the species.

Other potassium salts. Other potassium minerals commonly associated with sylvite and found in Germany and Texas in sufficient amount to make them valuable as sources of potassium salts are carnallite, $KMgCl_3 \cdot 6H_2O$ (see page 328); *kainite*, $MgSO_4 \cdot KCl \cdot 3H_2O$; *polyhalite*, $K_2SO_4 \cdot MgSO_4 \cdot 2CaSO_4 \cdot 2H_2O$.

CERARGYRITE—AgCl

Horn Silver

Crystallography. Isometric; hexoctahedral. Habit cubic but crystals rare. Usually massive, resembling wax; often in plates and crusts.

Physical properties. H 2–3. G 5.5±. Sectile, can be cut with a knife, like horn. Transparent to translucent. Color pearl-gray to colorless. Rapidly darkens to violet-brown on exposure to light.

Composition. Silver chloride, AgCl. Ag 73.3, Cl 24.7 per cent. A complete solid-solution series exists between AgCl and *bromyrite*, AgBr. Small amounts of iodine may be present in substitution for chlorine or bromine. Some specimens contain mercury.

Tests. Fusible at 1. Before the blowpipe on charcoal gives a globule of silver. With copper oxide in salt of phosphorus bead gives azure-blue copper chloride flame.

Diagnostic features. Distinguished chiefly by its horny or waxlike appearance and its sectility.

Occurrence. Cerargyrite is an important supergene ore of silver. It is to be found only in the upper, enriched zone of silver veins where descending waters containing small amounts of chlorine have acted upon the oxidized products of the primary silver ores of the vein. Found associated with other silver minerals and with native silver, cerussite, and secondary minerals in general.

Notable amounts have been found in New South Wales, Peru, Chile, Bolivia, and Mexico. In the United States cerargyrite was an important mineral in the mines at Leadville and elsewhere in Colorado, at the Comstock Lode in Nevada, and in crystals at the Poorman's Lode in Idaho.

Use. A silver ore.

Name. Cerargyrite is derived from two Greek words meaning *horn* and *silver*, in allusion to its hornlike appearance and characteristics.

Similar species. Other closely related silver minerals less common than cerargyrite, but formed under similar conditions, are *embolite*, Ag(Cl,Br); *bromyrite*, AgBr; *iodobromite*, Ag(Cl,Br,I); *iodyrite*, AgI.

CRYOLITE—Na_3AlF_6

Crystallography. Monoclinic; prismatic. Prominent forms are {001} and {110}. Crystals rare, usually cubic in aspect, and in parallel groupings growing out of massive material. Usually massive.

Physical properties. Parting in three directions nearly at right angles. **H** $2\frac{1}{2}$. **G** 2.95–3.0. Luster vitreous to greasy. Colorless to snow-white. Transparent to translucent. A low index of refraction gives the mineral an appearance of watery snow or of paraffin. Index of refraction near that of water, and thus powdered mineral almost disappears when immersed in water.

Composition. A fluoride of sodium and aluminum, Na_3AlF_6. Na 32.8, Al 12.8, F 54.4 per cent.

Tests. Fusible at $1\frac{1}{2}$ with strong yellow sodium flame. After intense ignition, residue gives alkaline reaction on moistened test paper.

Diagnostic features. Characterized by pseudocubic parting, white color, and peculiar luster; and for the Greenland cryolite, the association of siderite, galena, and chalcopyrite.

Occurrence. The only important deposit of cryolite is at Ivigtut, on the west coast of Greenland. Here it is found in a large veinlike mass in granite. Usually associated with the cryolite are siderite, galena, sphalerite, and chalcopyrite; and less commonly quartz, wolframite, fluorite, cassiterite, molybdenite, arsenopyrite, columbite. In the United States, found at the foot of Pikes Peak, Colorado.

Use. Cryolite is used for the manufacture of sodium salts, of certain kinds of glass and porcelain, and as a flux for cleansing metal surfaces. It was early used as a source of aluminum. When bauxite became the ore of aluminum, cryolite was used as a flux in the electrolytic process. Today most of the sodium aluminum fluoride used in the aluminum industry is produced artificially.

Name. Name is derived from two Greek words meaning *frost* and *stone*, in allusion to its icy appearance.

FLUORITE—CaF_2

Crystallography. Isometric; hexoctahedral. Habit cubic (Figs. 471 and 473), often in twinned cubes twinned on {111} as penetration twins (Fig. 472 and Fig. 477). Other forms are rare, but examples of all the forms of the hexoctahedral class have been observed; the tetra-hexahedron (Fig. 474) and hexoctahedron (Fig. 475) are characteristic. Usually in crystals or in cleavable masses. Also massive; coarse or fine granular; columnar.

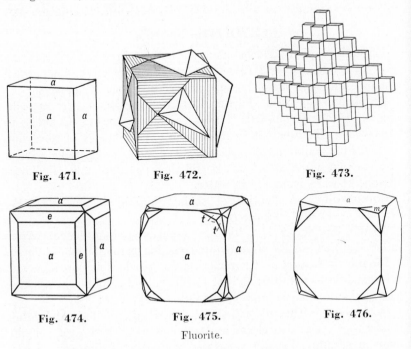

Fig. 471.   Fig. 472.   Fig. 473.

Fig. 474.   Fig. 475.   Fig. 476.

Fluorite.

Physical properties. Perfect {111} cleavage. **H** 4. **G** 3.18. Transparent to translucent. Luster vitreous. Color varies widely; most commonly light green, yellow, bluish green, or purple; also color-less, white, rose, blue, brown. The color in some fluorite results from the presence of a hydrocarbon. A single crystal may show varying bands of color; the massive variety is also often banded in color. The phenomenon of fluorescence (see page 165) is shown by some varieties of fluorite and hence receives its name.

Composition. Calcium fluoride, CaF_2. Ca 51.3, F 48.7 per cent. The rare earths, particularly yttrium and cerium, may substitute for calcium.

Tests. Fusible at 3, and residue gives alkaline reaction to moistened turmeric paper. Gives a reddish flame (calcium).

Diagnostic features. Determined usually by its cubic crystals and octahedral cleavage; also vitreous luster and usually fine coloring, and by the fact that it can be scratched with a knife.

Occurrence. Fluorite is a common and widely distributed mineral. Usually found either in veins in which it is the chief mineral or as a gangue mineral with metallic ores, especially those of lead and silver. Common in dolomites and limestone and has been observed also as a minor accessory mineral in various igneous rocks and pegmatites. Associated with many different minerals, as calcite, dolomite, gypsum, celestite, barite, quartz, galena, sphalerite, cassiterite, topaz, tourmaline, and apatite.

Fig. 477. Fluorite Crystals Coated with Quartz, Northumberland, England.

Fluorite is found in quantity in England, chiefly from Cumberland, Derbyshire, and Durham; the first two localities are famous for their magnificent crystallized specimens. Found commonly in the mines of Saxony. Fine specimens come from Switzerland, the Tyrol, Bohemia, and Norway. The large producers of commercial fluorite (fluorspar), aside from the United States, are Mexico, Canada, and Germany. The most important deposits in the United States are in southern Illinois near Rosiclare and Cave-in-Rock, and in the adjacent part of Kentucky. At Rosiclare fluorite which is without crystal form occurs in limestone, in fissure veins which in places are 40 feet in width. Twenty miles away at Cave-in-Rock the fluorite is in coarsely crystalline aggregates lining flat-lying open spaces. Fluorite is also mined in Colorado, New Mexico, Montana, and Utah.

Use. Fluorite is used mainly as a flux in the making of steel, in the manufacture of opalescent glass, in enameling cooking utensils, for the preparation of hydrofluoric acid, and occasionally as an ornamental material for vases and dishes. Small amounts of optical fluorite are used for lenses and prisms in various optical systems.

Name. From the Latin *fluere*, meaning to flow, since it melts more easily than other minerals with which it was, in the form of cut stones, confused.

Atacamite—$Cu_2Cl(OH)_3$

Crystallography. Orthorhombic; dipyramidal. Commonly slender prismatic in habit, with vertical striations. Also tabular parallel to the side pinacoid. Usually in confused crystalline aggregates; fibrous; granular. As "sand."

Physical properties. Cleavage perfect parallel to {010}. **H** 3–3½. **G** 3.75–3.77. Luster adamantine to vitreous. Color various shades of green. Transparent to translucent.

Composition. Basic copper chloride, $Cu_2Cl(OH)_3$. Cu 14.88, CuO 55.87, Cl 16.60, H_2O 12.65 per cent.

Tests. Fusible at 3–4, giving the azure-blue flame of copper chloride without the use of hydrochloric acid. Fused on charcoal with sodium carbonate gives globule of copper. Gives acid water in the closed tube.

Diagnostic features. Characterized by its green color and granular crystalline aggregates. Distinguished from malachite by its lack of effervescence in acids, and from brochantite and antlerite by its azureblue copper chloride flame.

Occurrence. Atacamite is a comparatively rare copper mineral. Found originally as sand in the province of Atacama in Chile. Occurs in arid regions as a supergene mineral in the oxidized zone of copper deposits. Is found with other copper ores in various localities in Chile, Bolivia, Mexico, and in some of the copper districts of South Australia. In the United States occurs sparingly in the copper districts of Arizona.

Use. A minor ore of copper.

Name. From the province of Atacama, Chile.

Carnallite—$KMgCl_3 \cdot 6H_2O$

Crystallography. Orthorhombic; dipyramidal. Crystals rare. Usually massive, granular.

Physical properties. H 1. **G** 1.6. Luster nonmetallic, shining, greasy. Color milk-white, often reddish, due to included hematite. Transparent to translucent. Taste bitter. Deliquescent.

Composition. A hydrous chloride of potassium and magnesium, $KMgCl_3 \cdot 6H_2O$. KCl 26.81, $MgCl_2$ 34.19, H_2O 39.0 per cent. Bromine may substitute for chlorine in small amounts.

Tests. Fusible at 1–1½ with violet flame. After ignition gives an alkaline reaction on moistened test paper. Gives much water in the closed tube. Easily and completely soluble in water; on addition of nitric acid and silver nitrate gives a white precipitate of silver chloride.

Diagnostic features. Carnallite is distinguished from associated salts by lack of cleavage and its deliquescent nature.

Occurrence. Carnallite is found associated with halite, sylvite, etc., in the salt deposits at Stassfurt, Germany. It is also found to a lesser extent in the potash deposits of western Texas and eastern New Mexico.

Use. A source of potassium compounds and magnesium.

Name. In honor of Rudolph von Carnall (1804–1874), Prussian mining engineer.

CARBONATES

When carbon unites with oxygen, it has a strong tendency to link to two oxygen atoms by sharing two of its four valence electrons with each and to form a stable chemical unit, a molecule of carbon dioxide. In nature, carbon also joins with oxygen to form the carbonate ion, $CO_3^=$. The ratio of the radii of carbon and oxygen (0.121) requires that three oxygen ions be coordinated by each carbon ion. Since oxygen has a charge of (-2) and carbon $(+4)$, the carbon-oxygen bond has a strength equal to $1\frac{1}{3}$ units of charge. This is greater than one-half the total charge of the oxygen ion, and, thus, each oxygen must be bonded to its coordinating carbon more strongly than it can possibly be bonded to any other ion in the structure. Further, oxygens are not shared between carbonate groups, and the carbon-oxygen triangles must be regarded as separate units of the structure. These flattened trefoil-shaped carbonate groups are the basic building units of all carbonate minerals and are largely responsible for the properties peculiar to the group.

Although the bond between the central carbon and its coordinated oxygens in the carbonate radical is strong, it is not as strong as the covalent bond in carbon dioxide. In the presence of the hydrogen ion, the carbonate radical becomes unstable and breaks down to yield carbon dioxide and water. This instability is the cause of the familiar "fizz" tests with acids, the widely used test for carbonates.

When divalent carbonate groups are combined with divalent cations, such that radius ratio considerations dictate 6-fold coordination, structures of simple geometry result. In this structure, which we may call the *calcite type* (Fig. 478), layers of metal cations and carbonate anions alternate. As described by Bragg, calcite may be thought of as having a distorted type of sodium chloride structure in which Na ions are replaced by calcium and chlorine ions by carbonate groups. We picture this structure oriented with a 3-fold axis vertical and then compressed along this axis so that the faces make angles of 74° 55′ with each other instead of the 90° in the cube. The vertical axis is now a unique 3-fold axis and perpendicular to the alternating layers of calcium and carbonate ions. The flattened carbonate groups in place of the spherical chlorine ions reduce the symmetry from isometric for halite to rhombohedral for calcite. Each calcium ion is coordinated to six oxygen ions, and each oxygen ion is coordinated to two calcium ions as well as to the carbon ion at the center of the carbonate groups. The cleavage characteristic of the calcite group, like the cleavage of halite, is parallel to the mostly widely spaced planes of maximum atomic population, but because of the reduction in symmetry cleavage is rhombohedral rather than cubic.

Although a very strong and partly covalent bonding is present within the carbonate ion, the bonds uniting it with the metal ions are simple ionic, and the properties of the individual members of the calcite

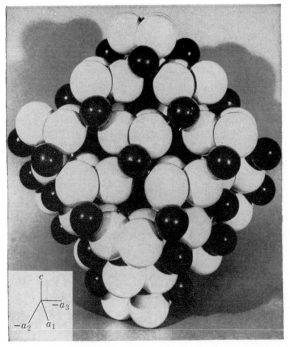

Fig. 478. Calcite, $CaCO_3$, Packing Model. Ca dark; O white; C at the center of the CO_3 triangle is not seen. The c axis is vertical. Note that horizontal layers of Ca'' ions alternate with horizontal layers of $CO_3^=$ ions. The structure of dolomite is similar but has layers of Mg'' ions alternating with layers of Ca'' ions.

group are largely conferred by the metal ions. Thus, the specific gravity of most of the members of the group is proportional to the atomic weight of the cation. The exception is magnesium, which is so much smaller than the rest that the closer packing permitted more than compensates for its low atomic weight. Hence its carbonate, magnesite, is denser than that of the heavier but much larger calcium ion.

Because all the members of the calcite group are isostructural, substitution of metal cations is possible with the limits set by their relative sizes. Thus, ferrous iron (R_A 0.74 Å), divalent manganese (R_A 0.80 Å), and magnesium (R_A 0.66 Å) all substitute for each other producing substances intermediate between the pure compounds, siderite, rhodochrosite, and magnesite; and whose physical properties vary in proportion to the amounts of the three ions. The substitution of these ions for calcium in calcite is not as complete nor as perfectly random because of the large size of the calcium ion (R_A 0.99 Å).

Substitution of magnesium for calcium or calcium for magnesium is particularly difficult because of the large differences in radii (33 per cent). If attempts are made to grow crystals of magnesite or calcite in the presence of large concentrations of both calcium and magnesium ions, extensive solid solution does not result. Instead layered crystals form consisting of sheets of carbonate ions alternating first with a sheet of magnesium ions and then a sheet of calcium ions. This is the mineral *dolomite*, an outstanding example of the mechanism of double-salt formation. The structure of dolomite is, thus, similar to that of calcite with cation layers normal to the *c* axis alternating with layers of carbonate ions. However, in dolomite the cation layers are alternately calcium and magnesium. The 2-fold symmetry axes in calcite intersect in the carbon ion at the center of the carbonate group with identical layers above and below. In dolomite these 2-fold axes do not exist because of the nonequivalence of the calcium and magnesium layers. The symmetry is thus reduced to that of the rhombohedral class, $\bar{3}$, having only a symmetry center and a 3-fold axis of rotary inversion.

When the carbonate ion combines with large divalent ions, the radius ratios do not permit stable 6-fold coordination, and orthorhombic structures result. This is the *aragonite* structure type (Fig. 479). As in calcite, the planar carbonate ions are in planes perpendicular to the *c* axis but with different coordination. In aragonite each calcium ion is coordinated to nine oxygen ions and each oxygen ion coordinated to three calcium ions. The cations have an arrangement in the structure approximating hexagonal closest-packing which gives rise to marked pseudohexagonal symmetry. This is reflected in both the crystal angles and in the pseudohexagonal twinning which is characteristic of all members of the group.

Solid solution within the aragonite group is somewhat more limited than in the calcite group, and it is interesting to note that calcium and barium, respectively the smallest and largest ions in the group, form a double salt closely analogous to dolomite. The differences in the physical properties of the minerals of the aragonite group are conferred largely by the cations. Thus the specific gravity is roughly proportional to the atomic weight of the metal ion. (See page 155.)

From the preceding discussion, it can be seen that the structure assumed by a carbonate is largely dependent on the radius of the cation, with the smaller ions entering into the rhombohedral structure

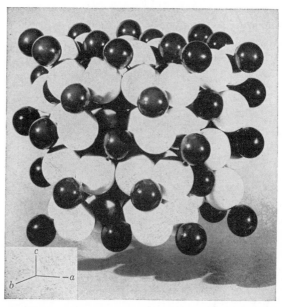

Fig. 479. Aragonite, $CaCO_3$, Packing Model. Ca dark; O white; C at the center of the CO_3 triangle is not seen. Each CO_3 group lies between six calcium ions.

and the larger ions entering into the orthorhombic structure. $CaCO_3$ is near the critical radius ratio of 0.73 between the two types and hence crystallizes with rhombohedral structure as calcite and with orthorhombic structure as aragonite.

Carbonates

Calcite Group		Aragonite Group	
Calcite	$CaCO_3$	Aragonite	$CaCO_3$
Dolomite	$CaMg(CO_3)_2$	Witherite	$BaCO_3$
Magnesite	$MgCO_3$	Strontianite	$SrCO_3$
Siderite	$FeCO_3$	Cerussite	$PbCO_3$
Rhodochrosite	$MnCO_3$		
Smithsonite	$ZnCO_3$		
Malachite	$Cu_2CO_3(OH)_2$		
Azurite	$Cu_3(CO_3)_2(OH)_2$		

The important anhydrous carbonates fall into the two isostructural groups, the *calcite group* and the *aragonite group*. Aside from the minerals of these groups the basic copper carbonates, azurite and malachite, are the only carbonates of importance.

CALCITE—$CaCO_3$

Crystallography. Hexagonal–R; hexagonal-scalenohedral. Crystals are extremely varied in habit, often highly complex. Over 300 different forms have been described. Three important habits: (1) prismatic, in long or short prisms, in which the prism faces are prominent,

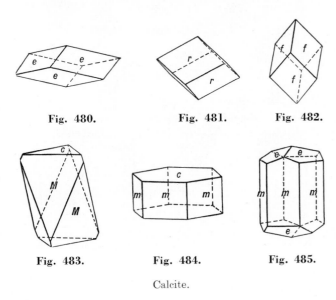

Fig. 480.   Fig. 481.   Fig. 482.

Fig. 483.   Fig. 484.   Fig. 485.

Calcite.

with basal pinacoid or rhombohedral terminations (Figs. 484 and 485); (2) rhombohedral, in which rhombohedral forms predominate, both low and steep rhombohedrons (Figs. 480, 482, 483); the unit (cleavage) form (Fig. 481) is not common; (3) scalenohedral, in which the scalenohedrons predominate (Fig. 486), often with prism faces and rhombohedral truncations (Figs. 487–490). The most common scalenohedron is $\{21\bar{3}1\}$. All possible combinations and variations of these types are found.

Twinning with the twin plane the negative rhombohedron, $\{01\bar{1}2\}$, very common (Fig. 491); often produces twinning lamellae which may as in crystalline limestones, be of secondary origin. This twinning may be produced artificially (see page 108). Twins with the basal pinacoid, $\{0001\}$, the twin plane common (Figs. 492 and 493). Twinning on the unit rhombohedron, $\{10\bar{1}1\}$, less common (Fig. 494).

Fig. 486. Calcite Crystals, Joplin, Missouri.

Calcite is usually in crystals or in coarse to fine granular aggregates. Also fine grained to compact, earthy, and in stalactitic forms.

Physical properties. Perfect $\{10\bar{1}1\}$ cleavage (cleavage angle = 74°55'). Parting along twin lamellae on $\{01\bar{1}2\}$. **H** 3 on cleavage, $2\frac{1}{2}$ on base. **G** 2.72. Luster vitreous to earthy. Color usually white or colorless, but may be variously tinted, gray, red, green, blue, yellow. Also, when impure, brown to black. Transparent to translucent. Shows strong double refraction (page 168), hence the name *doubly refracting spar*. The chemically pure and optically clear, colorless variety is known as *Iceland spar* because of its occurrence in Iceland.

Composition. Calcium carbonate, $CaCO_3$. CaO 56.0, CO_2 44.0 per cent. Manganese and ferrous iron may substitute for calcium, and a complete series extends to rhodochrosite and partial series towards smithsonite and siderite. Magnesium substitutes for calcium in only small amounts.

Tests. Infusible. After intense ignition, residue gives alkaline reaction to moistened test paper. Fragment moistened with hydrochloric

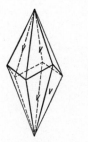 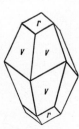 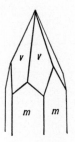 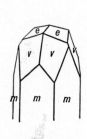

Fig. 487. Fig. 488. Fig. 489. Fig. 490.

Calcite.

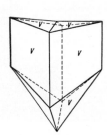

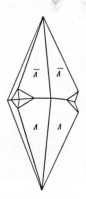

Fig. 491. Calcite Twinned on the Negative Rhombohedron.

Fig. 492. Calcite Twinned on the Base.

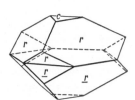

Fig. 493. Calcite Twinned on the Base.

Fig. 494. Calcite Twinned on the Unit Rhombohedron.

acid and heated gives orange-red flame. Fragments effervesce freely in cold dilute hydrochloric acid.

Diagnostic features. Distinguished by its hardness (3), its perfect cleavage, light color, vitreous luster. Distinguished from dolomite by the fact that fragments of calcite effervesce freely in cold hydrochloric acid, whereas those of dolomite do not. Distinguished from aragonite by having lower specific gravity and rhombohedral cleavage.

Occurrence. *As a Rock Mineral.* Calcite is one of the most common and widely diffused of minerals. It occurs as enormous and widespread sedimentary rock masses in which it is the predominant mineral; and in some limestones, it is the only mineral present. Crystalline metamorphosed limestones are known as *marbles.* Chalk is a fine-grained pulverulent deposit of calcium carbonate. Calcite is an important constituent of calcareous marls and calcareous sandstones. The limestone rocks have, in great part, been formed by the deposition on a sea bottom of great thicknesses of calcareous material in the form of shells and skeletons of sea animals. A smaller proportion of these rocks have been formed directly by precipitation of calcium carbonate.

As Cave Deposits, etc. Calcareous waters evaporating in limestone caves often deposit calcite in the form of stalactites, stalagmites, and incrustations. Such deposits are often beautiful and spectacular. The calcite is usually semitranslucent and of light yellow colors. Both hot and cold calcareous spring waters may form a deposit of calcite known as *travertine,* or *tufa,* around their mouths. Many deposits of cellular travertine are to be found in limestone regions. The deposit at Mammoth Hot Springs, Yellowstone Park, is more spectacular than most, but of similar origin. *Onyx marble,* known as Mexican onyx, is banded calcite and/or aragonite and is used as a decorative material. It comes mostly from Lower California, Mexico.

Siliceous Calcites. Calcite crystals may inclose considerable amounts of quartz sand (up to 60 per cent) and form what are known as sandstone crystals. Such occurrences are found at Fontainebleau, France (Fontainebleau limestone), and in the Bad Lands, South Dakota.

Calcite occurs as a secondary mineral in igneous rocks as a product of decomposition of lime silicates. It is found lining the amygdaloidal cavities in lavas. It occurs in many sedimentary and metamorphic rocks in greater or less proportion. It is the cementing material in some light-colored sandstones. Calcite is also one of the most common of vein minerals, occurring as a gangue material, with all sorts of metallic ores.

It would be quite impossible to specify all the important districts for the occurrence of calcite in its various forms. Some of the more notable localities in which finely crystallized calcite is found are as follows: Andreasberg in the Harz Mountains; various places in Saxony;

in Cumberland, Derbyshire, Durham, Cornwall, and Lancashire, England; Iceland; and Guanajuato, Mexico. In the United States at Joplin, Missouri; Lake Superior copper district; and Rossie, New York.

Use. The most important use for calcite is for the manufacture of cements and lime for mortars. Limestone is the chief raw material, which when heated to about 900° C, loses CO_2 and is converted into quicklime, CaO. This, when mixed with water, forms calcium hydrate (slaked lime), swells, gives off much heat, and hardens or, as commonly termed, "sets." Quicklime when mixed with sand forms common mortar.

The greatest consumption of limestone is in the manufacture of cements. The particular type known as Portland cement is most widely produced. It is composed of about 75 per cent calcium carbonate (limestone), 13 per cent silica, and 5 per cent alumina. Small amounts of magnesium carbonate and iron oxide are also present. This silica and alumina are contributed by clay or shale which is mixed with the limestone before "burning." When water is mixed with cement, hydrous calcium silicates and calcium aluminates are formed. Certain limestones have various clayey materials as impurities in the correct proportions and are known as *cement rocks*. Cements having the valuable property of hardening under water are known as hydraulic cements.

Chalk is used as a fertilizer, for whiting and whitewash, for crayons, etc. It is found in many places in Europe, the chalk cliffs of Dover being famous.

Limestone, particularly from Indiana, is quarried as a building stone. Great quantities of limestone are quarried each year as a flux for smelting various metallic ores. A fine-grained limestone is used in lithographing.

Marbles are used very extensively as ornamental and building material. The most important marble quarries in the United States are found in Vermont, New York, Georgia, and Tennessee.

Iceland spar is valuable for various optical instruments; its best known use is in the form of the Nicol prism to produce polarized light.

Name. From the Latin word, *calx*, meaning burnt lime.

DOLOMITE—CaMg(CO$_3$)$_2$

Crystallography. Hexagonal–R; rhombohedral. Crystals are usually the unit rhombohedron (Fig. 495), more rarely a steep rhombohedron and base (Fig. 497). Faces often curved, some so acutely as to form "saddle-shaped" crystals (Fig. 496). Other forms rare. In coarse, granular, cleavable masses to fine grained and compact.

Physical properties. Perfect $\{10\bar{1}1\}$ (cleavage angle $73°45'$). **H** $3\frac{1}{2}$–4. **G** 2.85. Luster vitreous; pearly in some varieties, *pearl spar.* Color usually some shade of pink, flesh color; may be colorless, white, gray, green, brown, or black. Transparent to translucent.

Composition. Carbonate of calcium and magnesium, $CaMg(CO_3)_2$. CaO 30.4, MgO 21.7, CO_2 47.9 per cent. In ordinary dolomite the proportion of $CaCO_3$ to $MgCO_3$ is $1:1$. However, calcium may substitute for magnesium up to about $Ca:Mg = 1:5$ in the magnesium

Fig. 495.	Fig. 496.	Fig. 497.

Dolomite.

positions, and magnesium may substitute for calcium up to about $Mg:Ca = 1:20$ in the calcium positions. Thus in dolomite the ratio of calcium to magnesium ranges between $58:42$ and $47\frac{1}{2}:52\frac{1}{2}$. Ferrous iron substitutes for magnesium, and when the amount of ferrous iron exceeds magnesium the mineral is called *ankerite*. Small amounts of divalent manganese, divalent cobalt, and zinc may substitute for magnesium and small amounts of lead for calcium.

Tests. Infusible. After intense ignition a fragment will give an alkaline reaction to moistened test paper. In cold dilute hydrochloric acid large fragments only slowly attacked, but powder readily soluble with effervescence. Large fragments soluble with effervescence in hot hydrochloric acid.

Diagnostic features. Crystallized variety told by its curved rhombohedral crystals and usually by its flesh-pink color. The massive rock variety is distinguished from limestone by the less vigorous reaction with hydrochloric acid.

Occurrence. Dolomite occurs chiefly in widely extended rock masses as dolomitic limestone and the crystallized equivalent, dolomitic marble. Occurrence same as for calcite rocks. Often intimately mixed with calcite. Dolomite as a rock mass is thought to be secondary in origin, having been formed from ordinary limestone by the replacement of calcium by magnesium. Occurs also as a vein mineral, chiefly in the lead and zinc veins that traverse limestone.

Found in large rock strata in the dolomite region of southern Tyrol; in crystals from the Binnenthal, Switzerland; Traversella in Piedmont; northern England; and Guanajuato, Mexico. In the United States is found as masses of sedimentary rock in many of the middle-western states, and in crystals in the Joplin, Missouri, district.

Use. As a building and ornamental stone. For the manufacture of certain cements. For the manufacture of magnesia used in the preparation of refractory linings of the converters in the basic steel process. Dolomite is a potential ore of metallic magnesium.

Name. In honor of the French chemist, Dolomieu (1750–1801).

Similar species. *Ankerite*, $Ca(Mg,Fe)(CO_3)_2$, is a rhombohedral carbonate analogous with dolomite structure in which ferrous iron replaces part of the magnesium.

MAGNESITE—$MgCO_3$

Crystallography. Hexagonal–R; hexagonal-scalenohedral. Rarely in crystals. Usually cryptocrystalline in white, compact, earthy masses; less frequently in cleavable granular masses, coarse to fine.

Physical properties. Perfect $\{10\bar{1}1\}$ cleavage (cleavage angle = $72°36'$). H $3\frac{1}{2}$–5. G 3.0–3.2. Luster vitreous. Color white, gray, yellow, brown. Transparent to translucent.

Composition. Magnesium carbonate, $MgCO_3$. MgO 47.8, CO_2 52.2 per cent. Ferrous iron substitutes for magnesium, and a complete series extends to siderite. Small amounts of calcium and manganese may be present.

Tests. Infusible. After intense ignition gives a faint alkaline reaction on moistened test paper. Scarcely acted upon by cold, but dissolves with effervescence in hot, hydrochloric acid.

Diagnostic features. Cleavable varieties are distinguished from dolomite only by the higher specific gravity and absence of abundant calcium. The white massive variety resembles chert and is distinguished from it by inferior hardness.

Occurrence. Magnesite is commonly in veins and irregular masses derived from the alteration of serpentine through the action of waters containing carbonic acid. Such magnesites are compact cryptocrystalline and often contain opaline silica. Beds of crystalline cleavable magnesite are (1) of metamorphic origin associated with talc schists, chlorite schists, and mica schists, and (2) of sedimentary origin formed as a replacement of calcite rocks by magnesium containing solutions, dolomite being formed as an intermediate product.

Notable deposits of the sedimentary type of magnesite are in Manchuria; at Satka in the Ural Mountains; and at Styria, Austria. The most famous deposit of the cryptocrystalline type is on the Island of Euboea, Greece.

In the United States the compact variety is found in irregular masses in serpentine in the Coast Range, California. Large masses of the sedimentary type are found at Chewelah in Stevens County, Washington, and in the Paradise Range, Nye County, Nevada. There are numerous minor localities in the eastern United States in which magnesite is associated with serpentine, talc, or dolomite rocks.

Use. Dead-burned magnesite, MgO, that is, magnesite that has been calcined at a high temperature and contains less than 1 per cent CO_2, is used in manufacturing bricks for furnace linings. Magnesite is the source of magnesia for industrial chemicals. It has also been used as an ore of metallic magnesium, but at present the entire production of magnesium comes from brines and sea water.

Name. Magnesite is named in allusion to the composition.

SIDERITE—$FeCO_3$

Spathic Iron. Chalybite

Crystallography. Hexagonal–R; hexagonal-scalenohedral. Crystals usually unit rhombohedrons (same as cleavage form), frequently with curved faces. Concretionary. In globular concretions. Usually cleavable granular. May be botryoidal, compact, and earthy.

Physical properties. Perfect rhombohedral $\{10\overline{1}1\}$ cleavage (cleavage angle = $73°\,0'$). **H** $3\frac{1}{2}$–4. **G** 3.96 for pure $FeCO_3$, but decreases with presence of divalent manganese and magnesium. Luster vitreous. Color usually light to dark brown. Transparent to translucent.

Composition. Ferrous carbonate, $FeCO_3$. FeO 62.1, CO_2 37.9 per cent. Fe 48.2 per cent. Divalent manganese and magnesium substitute for ferrous iron, and complete isomorphous series extend to rhodochrosite and magnesite. Calcium may be present in small amounts.

Tests. Difficultly fusible ($4\frac{1}{2}$–5). Becomes strongly magnetic on heating. Heated in the closed tube decomposes and gives a black magnetic residue. Soluble in hot hydrochloric acid with effervescence.

Diagnostic features. Distinguished from other carbonates by its color and high specific gravity, and from sphalerite by its rhombohedral cleavage.

Alteration. Pseudomorphs of limonite after siderite are common.

Occurrence. Siderite is frequently found as *clay ironstone*, impure by admixture with clay materials, in concretions with concentric layers. As *black-band ore* it is found, contaminated by carbonaceous material, in extensive stratified formations lying in shales and commonly associated with coal measures. These ores have been mined extensively in Great Britain in the past as the chief source of iron, but at present are mined only in North Staffordshire and Scotland. Clay ironstone is also abundant in the coal measures of western Pennsylvania and eastern Ohio, but it is not used to any great extent as an ore. Siderite is also formed by the replacement action of ferrous solutions upon limestones, and if such deposits are extensive they may be of economic value. The most notable occurrence of this type is in Styria, Austria, where siderite is mined on a large scale. Siderite, in its crystallized form, is a common vein mineral associated with various metallic ores containing silver minerals, pyrite, chalcopyrite, tetrahedrite, galena. When siderite predominates in such veins it may be mined, as in southern Westphalia, Germany.

Use. An ore of iron. Important in Great Britain and Austria, but of very subordinate value in the United States.

Name. From the Greek word meaning *iron.* The original name was *spherosiderite,* given to the concretionary variety and subsequently shortened to siderite to apply to the entire species. *Spathic ore* is a common name. *Chalybite,* used by some mineralogists, was derived from the Chalybes, who lived on the Black Sea, and were in ancient times workers in iron.

RHODOCHROSITE—$MnCO_3$

Crystallography. Hexagonal–R; hexagonal-scalenohedral. Only rarely in crystals of the unit rhombohedron; frequently with curved faces. Usually cleavable massive; granular to compact.

Physical properties. Perfect rhombohedral $\{10\bar{1}1\}$ cleavage (cleavage angle = $73°\,0'$). **H** $3\frac{1}{2}$–4. **G** 3.5–3.7. Luster vitreous. Color usually some shade of rose-red; may be light pink to dark brown. Streak white. Transparent to translucent.

Composition. Manganese carbonate, $MnCO_3$. MnO 61.7, CO_2 38.3 per cent. Ferrous iron and calcium substitute for manganese, and complete series extend to siderite and calcite. Only limited amounts of magnesium and zinc substitute for manganese.

Tests. Infusible. Soluble in hot hydrochloric acid with effervescence. Gives blue-green color to sodium carbonate bead. When heated on charcoal turns black but is nonmagnetic.

Diagnostic features. Told usually by its pink color, rhombohedral cleavage, and hardness (4). Distinguished by its hardness from rhodonite ($MnSiO_3$, **H** $5\frac{1}{2}$–$6\frac{1}{2}$).

Occurrence. Rhodochrosite is a comparatively rare mineral, occurring in veins with ores of silver, lead, and copper, and with other manganese minerals. Found in the silver mines of Rumania and Saxony. In the United States found at Branchville, Connecticut; Franklin, New Jersey; and Butte, Montana. In good crystals at Alicante, Lake County; Alma, Park County; and elsewhere in Colorado.

Use. A minor ore of manganese. Mined to a considerable extent at Butte, Montana.

Name. Derived from two Greek words meaning *rose* and *color*, in allusion to its rose-pink color.

SMITHSONITE—$ZnCO_3$

Dry-Bone Ore

Crystallography. Hexagonal–R; hexagonal-scalenohedral. Rarely in small rhombohedral or scalenohedral crystals. Usually reniform, botryoidal, or stalactitic, and in crystalline incrustations or in honeycombed masses known as *dry-bone ore*. Also granular to earthy.

Physical properties. Perfect rhombohedral $\{10\bar{1}1\}$ cleavage, which is seldom observed (cleavage angle = 72° 20′). **H** 4–4½ (unusually high for a carbonate). **G** 4.30–4.45. Luster vitreous. Color usually dirty brown. May be colorless, white, green, blue, pink. The yellow variety contains cadmium and is known as *turkey-fat ore*. Streak white. Translucent.

Composition. Zinc carbonate, $ZnCO_3$. ZnO 64.8, CO_2 35.2 per cent. Ferrous iron and divalent manganese may substitute for part of the zinc; also, less commonly, calcium, magnesium, cadmium, copper, cobalt, and lead.

Tests. Infusible. Soluble in cold hydrochloric acid with effervescence. A fragment heated in the reducing flame gives bluish green streaks in the flame, due to the burning of the volatilized zinc. Heated in the reducing flame on charcoal gives a nonvolatile coating of zinc oxide, yellow when hot, white when cold; if coating is moistened with cobalt nitrate and again heated it turns green.

Diagnostic features. Distinguished by its effervescence in acids, its tests for zinc, its hardness (5), and its high specific gravity.

Occurrence. Smithsonite is a zinc ore of supergene origin, usually found with zinc deposits lying in limestone rocks. Associated with sphalerite, galena, hemimorphite, cerussite, calcite, and limonite. Often found in pseudomorphs after calcite. *Dry-bone ore* is a honeycombed mass, with the appearance of dried bone, whose texture has resulted from the manner of deposition of the mineral. Some hemimorphite, the silicate of zinc, is included under the term. Found in places in translucent green or greenish blue material which is used for ornamental purposes. Laurium, Greece, is noted for this ornamental smithsonite; and Sardinia for yellow stalactites with concentric banding. Fine crystallized specimens have come from the Broken Hill mine, Northern Rhodesia, and from Tsumeb, South-West Africa. In the United States smithsonite occurs as an ore in the zinc deposits of Leadville, Colorado; Missouri; Arkansas; Wisconsin; and Virginia. Fine greenish blue material has been found at Kelly, New Mexico.

Use. An ore of zinc. A minor use is for ornamental purposes.

Name. Named in honor of James Smithson (1754–1829), who founded the Smithsonian Institution at Washington. English mineralogists formerly called the mineral calamine.

Similar species. *Hydrozincite*, $Zn_5(OH)_6(CO_3)_2$, occurs as a secondary mineral in zinc deposits.

ARAGONITE—CaCO₃

Crystallography. Orthorhombic; dipyramidal. Three habits of crystallization are common. (1) Acicular pyramidal; consisting of a vertical prism terminated by a combination of a very steep dipyramid

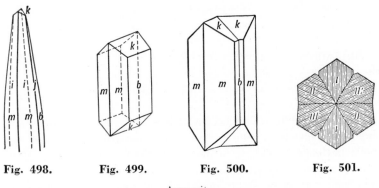

Fig. 498.   Fig. 499.   Fig. 500.   Fig. 501.

Aragonite.

and first-order prism (Fig. 498). Usually in radiating groups of large to very small crystals. (2) Tabular; consisting of prominent side-pinacoid faces modified by {110} and a low prism, k Fig. 499. Often twinned with {110} as the twinning plane (Fig. 500). (3) In pseudo-hexagonal twins (Fig. 501). This type shows a hexagonal-like prism terminated by a basal plane and is formed by an intergrowth of three individuals twinned on the prism face with basal planes in common. The crystals are distinguished from true hexagonal forms by noting that the basal plane is striated in three different directions and also by the fact that, because the prism angle of the simple crystals is not exactly 60°, but 63° 48', the composite prism faces for the twin will often show slight re-entrant angles. Also found in reniform, columnar, and stalactitic aggregates.

Physical properties. Cleavage {010} and {110} imperfect. Luster vitreous. Colorless, white, pale yellow, and variously tinted. Transparent to translucent. **H** $3\frac{1}{2}$–4. **G** 2.95 (harder and higher specific gravity than calcite).

Composition. Calcium carbonate, $CaCO_3$, polymorphous with calcite. CaO 56.0, CO_2 44.0 per cent. Strontium, lead and more rarely zinc may substitute for calcium. Aragonite is the unstable polymorph relative to calcite at ordinary temperatures and pressures. On heating in air aragonite begins to invert to calcite at 400° C. In contact with water or solutions containing dissolved $CaCO_3$, the inversion may take place at room temperature.

Tests. Infusible. Decrepitates. After intense ignition the powder gives an alkaline reaction on moistened test paper. Fragments fall to powder (change to calcite) when heated at low redness in the closed tube.

Diagnostic features. Distinguished from calcite by its higher specific gravity and lack of rhombohedral cleavage. Cleavage fragments of columnar calcite are terminated by a cross cleavage which is lacking in aragonite. Distinguished from witherite and strontianite by being infusible, of lower specific gravity, and in lacking a distinctive flame color.

Alteration. Paramorphs of calcite after aragonite are common. Calcium carbonate secreted by molluscs as aragonite is usually changed to calcite on the outside of the shell.

Occurrence. Aragonite is less stable than calcite and much less common. It is formed under a narrow range of physicochemical conditions, represented by low temperature, near surface deposits. Experiments have shown that carbonated waters containing calcium more often deposit aragonite when they are hot and calcite when they are cold. The pearly layer of many shells is aragonite. Aragonite is deposited by hot springs; found associated with beds of gypsum and deposits of iron ore, where it may occur in forms resembling coral, and is called *flos ferri* (flower of iron). It is found as fibrous crusts on serpentine and in amygdaloidal cavities in basalt.

Notable localities for the various crystalline types are as follows:

Pseudohexagonal twin crystals are found in Aragon, Spain; Bastennes, in the south of France; and at Girgenti, Sicily. The tabular type of crystals is found near Bilin, Bohemia. The acicular type is found at Alston Moor and Cleator Moor, Cumberland, England. Flos ferri is found in the Styrian iron mines. Some *onyx marble* from Lower California, Mexico, is aragonite. In the United States pseudohexagonal twins are found at Lake Arthur, New Mexico. The flos ferri variety occurs in the Organ Mountains, New Mexico, and in Bisbee, Arizona.

Name. From Aragon, Spain, where the pseudohexagonal twins were first recognized.

WITHERITE—BaCO$_3$

Crystallography. Orthorhombic; dipyramidal. Crystals always twinned on {110} forming pseudohexagonal pyramids by the intergrowth of three individuals. Crystals sometimes doubly terminated; often deeply striated horizontally and by a series of re-entrant angles have the appearance of one pyramid capping another. (Fig. 502.) Also botryoidal to globular; columnar or granular.

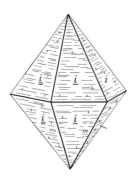

Fig. 502.
Witherite.

Physical properties. Poor {010} and {110} cleavage. H 3½. G 4.3. Luster vitreous. Colorless, white, gray. Translucent.

Composition. Barium carbonate, BaCO$_3$. BaO 77.7, CO$_2$ 22.3 per cent. Small amounts of strontium and calcium may substitute for barium.

Tests. Fusible at 2½–3, giving a yellowish green flame (barium). After intense ignition gives an alkaline reaction on moistened test paper. Soluble in cold hydrochloric acid with effervescence. All solutions, even the very dilute, give precipitate of barium sulfate with sulfuric acid (difference from calcium and strontium).

Diagnostic features. Witherite is characterized by high specific gravity and effervescence in acid. It can be distinguished from strontianite by the flame test and from barite by its effervescence in acid.

Occurrence. Witherite is a comparatively rare mineral, most frequently found in veins associated with galena. Found in England in fine crystals near Hexham in Northumberland and Alston Moor in Cumberland. Occurs at Leogang in Salzburg. In the United States found near Lexington, Kentucky, and in a large vein with barite at El Portal, Yosemite Park, California. Also at Thunder Bay, Lake Superior, Ontario.

Use. A minor source of barium.

Name. In honor of D. W. Withering (1741–1799), who discovered and first analyzed the mineral.

STRONTIANITE—$SrCO_3$

Crystallography. Orthorhombic; dipyramidal. Crystals usually acicular, radiating like type (1) under aragonite. Twinning on {110} frequent, giving pseudohexagonal aspect. Also columnar; fibrous and granular.

Physical properties. Good {110} cleavage. **H** $3\frac{1}{2}$–4. **G** 3.7. Luster vitreous. Color white, gray, yellow, green. Transparent to translucent.

Composition. Strontium carbonate, $SrCO_3$. SrO 70.2, CO_2 29.8 per cent. Calcium may be present in substitution for strontium.

Tests. Infusible, but on intense ignition swells and throws out fine branches and gives a crimson flame (strontium), and residue gives alkaline reaction on moistened test paper. Effervesces in hydrochloric acid, and the medium dilute solution will give precipitate of strontium sulfate on addition of a few drops of sulfuric acid.

Diagnostic features. Characterized by high specific gravity and effervescence in hydrochloric acid. Can be distinguished from witherite and aragonite by flame test; from celestite by poorer cleavage and effervescence in acid.

Occurrence. Strontianite is a low-temperature hydrothermal mineral associated with barite, celestite, and calcite in veins in limestone or marl, and less frequently in igneous rocks and as a gangue mineral in sulfide veins. Occurs in commercial deposits in Westphalia, Germany; Spain; Mexico; and England. In the United States found in geodes and veins with calcite at Schoharie, New York; in the Strontium Hills north of Barstow, California; and near La Conner, Washington.

Use. Source of strontium. Strontium has no great commercial application; used in fireworks, red flares, military rockets, in the separation of sugar from molasses, and in various strontium compounds.

Name. From Strontian in Argyllshire, Scotland, where it was originally found.

CERUSSITE—$PbCO_3$

Crystallography. Orthorhombic; dipyramidal. Crystals common of varied habit, and show many forms. Often tabular parallel to {010} (Fig. 503). Frequently twinned (Fig. 504); may form reticulated groups with the plates crossing each other at 60° angles (Fig. 505). May be pyramidal in habit; also twinned in pseudohexagonal pyramids, frequently with deep re-entrant angles in the vertical zone. Also in granular crystalline aggregates; fibrous; granular massive; compact; earthy.

Physical properties. Cleavage {110} good, {021} fair. **H** 3–3½. **G** 6.55 (high for a mineral with nonmetallic luster). Luster adamantine. Colorless, white, or gray. Transparent to subtranslucent.

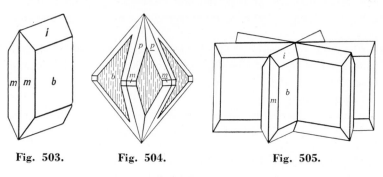

Fig. 503.   Fig. 504.   Fig. 505.

Cerussite.

Composition. Lead carbonate, $PbCO_3$. PbO 83.5, CO_2 16.5 per cent.

Tests. Fusible at 1½. With sodium carbonate on charcoal gives globule of lead and yellow to white coating of lead oxide. Soluble in warm dilute nitric acid with effervescence.

Diagnostic features. Recognized by its high specific gravity, white color, and adamantine luster. Crystal form and effervescence in nitric acid serve to distinguish it from anglesite.

Occurrence. Cerussite is an important and widely distributed supergene lead ore formed by the action of carbonated waters on galena in the upper zone of lead veins. Associated with the primary minerals galena and sphalerite, and various secondary minerals such as anglesite, pyromorphite, smithsonite, and limonite.

Notable localities for its occurrence are Ems in Nassau; Mies, Bohemia; Nerchinsk, Siberia; on the island of Sardinia; in Tunis; at Tsumeb, Otavi, South-West Africa; and Broken Hill, New South Wales. In the United States found at Phoenixville, Pennsylvania; Leadville, Colorado; various districts in Arizona; from the Organ Mountains, New Mexico; and in the Coeur d'Alene district in Idaho.

Use. An important ore of lead.

Name. From the Latin word meaning *white lead*.

Similar species. *Phosgenite,* a chlorocarbonate of lead $Pb_2Cl_2CO_3$, tetragonal in crystallization, is a rare anhydrous carbonate.

MALACHITE—$Cu_2CO_3(OH)_2$

Green Copper Carbonate

Crystallography. Monoclinic; prismatic. Crystals usually slender prismatic but seldom distinct. Crystals may be pseudomorphous after azurite. Usually in radiating fibers forming botryoidal or stalactitic masses. Often granular or earthy.

Physical properties. Perfect {001} cleavage, but rarely seen. H $3\frac{1}{2}$-4. G 3.9-4.03. Luster adamantine to vitreous in crystals; often silky in fibrous varieties; dull in earthy type. Color bright green. Translucent.

Composition. Basic carbonate of copper, $Cu_2CO_3(OH)_2$. CuO 71.9, CO_2 19.9, H_2O 8.2 per cent. Cu 57.4 per cent.

Tests. Fusible at 3, giving a green flame. With fluxes on charcoal gives copper globule. Soluble in hydrochloric acid with effervescence, yielding a green solution. Much water in the closed tube.

Diagnostic features. Recognized by its bright green color and botryoidal forms, and distinguished from other green copper minerals by its effervescence in acid.

Occurrence. Malachite is a widely distributed supergene copper ore. Found in the oxidized portions of copper veins associated with azurite, cuprite, native copper, iron oxides, and the various sulfides of copper and iron. Usually occurs in copper veins that lie in limestone.

Notable localities for its occurrence are at Nizhne Tagil in the Ural Mountains; at Chessy, near Lyons, France, associated with azurite; from Tsumeb, South-West Africa; from Rhodesia; Katanga, Belgian Congo; and South Australia. In the United States, formerly an important copper ore in the southwestern copper districts; at Bisbee, Morenci. and other localities in Arizona; and in New Mexico.

Use. An ore of copper. Has been used to some extent, particularly in Russia, as an ornamental material for vases, veneer for table tops, etc.

Name. Derived from the Greek word for *mallows*, in allusion to its green color.

AZURITE—$Cu_3(CO_3)_2(OH)_2$

Chessylite. Blue Copper Carbonate

Crystallography. Monoclinic; prismatic. Habit varied (Figs. 506 and 507). Crystals frequently complex in habit and malformed in development. Also in radiating spherical groups.

Physical properties. H $3\frac{1}{2}$–4. **G** 3.77. Luster vitreous. Color intense azure-blue. Transparent to translucent.

Composition. A basic carbonate of copper, $Cu_3(CO_3)_2(OH)_2$. CuO 69.2, CO_2 25.6, H_2O 5.2 per cent. Cu 55.3 per cent.

Tests. Same as for malachite (page 349).

Diagnostic features. Characterized chiefly by its azure-blue color and effervescence in hydrochloric acid.

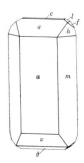

Fig. 506.

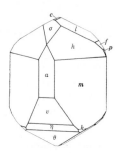

Fig. 507.

Azurite.

Alteration. Pseudomorphs of malachite after azurite commonly observed; less common after cuprite.

Occurrence. Azurite has the same origin and associations as malachite, but is much more frequently in crystals. Found in fine crystals at Chessy, near Lyons, France; Tsumeb, South-West Africa; in Rumania; Laurium, Greece; Siberia; and Broken Hill, New South Wales. In the United States at Copper Queen mine, Bisbee, and Morenci, Arizona. Widely distributed with copper ores. Not so common as malachite.

Use. A minor ore of copper.

Name. Named in allusion to its color.

Rare hydrous carbonates. *Aurichalcite*, a basic carbonate of zinc and copper, pale green to blue in monoclinic acicular crystals. *Gaylussite*, $Na_2Ca(CO_3)_2 \cdot 5H_2O$, monoclinic; *trona*, $Na_3H(CO_3)_2 \cdot 2H_2O$, monoclinic; both found in saline-lake deposits.

NITRATES

Five-valent nitrogen forms flattened trefoil-shaped ionic groups with oxygen, much like the carbonate group. These triangles are the monovalent nitrate radical, NO_3^- and are the dominant building block of the nitrates. Like carbon in the carbonate group, the highly charged and highly polarizing nitrogen ion binds its three coordinated oxygens into a close-knit group in which the strength of the oxygen-nitrogen bond ($1\frac{2}{3}$) is greater than any other possible bond in the crystal. Because of the greater strength of this N–O bond, nitrates are less readily decomposed by acids than carbonates.

When these nitrogen-oxygen triangles combine in one-to-one proportions with monovalent cations whose radii permits 6-fold coordination, structures analogous to those of the calcite group result. Thus, soda niter, $NaNO_3$, and calcite are isostructural with the same crystallography and cleavage and are homeomorphs. Because of the lesser charge, however, soda niter is softer than calcite and melts at a lower temperature and, because of the lower atomic weight of sodium, has a lower specific gravity. Niter, KNO_3 (Ion. rad. K = 1.33 Å), is similarly a precise structural analogue of aragonite, except for the monovalence of the ions.

It is particularly significant that soda niter, like calcite, has an orthorhombic polymorph isostructural with niter, thus making the analogy complete. The calcite structure is often alluded to as the $NaNO_3$ structure, and the aragonite structure as the KNO_3 structure type.

Nitrates

Soda Niter $NaNO_3$ Niter KNO_3

SODA NITER—$NaNO_3$

Chile Saltpeter

Crystallography. Hexagonal–R; hexagonal-scalenohedral. Rhombohedral crystals are rare. Usually massive, as an incrustation or in beds. Soda niter is homeomorphous with calcite and has similar crystal constants, cleavage, and optical properties.

Physical properties. Perfect $\{10\bar{1}1\}$ cleavage. **H** 1–2. **G** 2.29. Luster vitreous. Colorless or white, also reddish brown, gray, yellow. Transparent to translucent. Taste cooling. Deliquescent.

Composition. Sodium nitrate, $NaNO_3$. Na_2O 36.5, N_2O_5 63.5 per cent.

Tests. Fusible at 1, giving a strong yellow sodium flame. After intense ignition gives an alkaline reaction on moistened test paper. Easily and completely soluble in water. Heated in the closed tube with potassium disulfate gives off red vapors of nitrogen dioxide.

Diagnostic features. Distinguished by its cooling taste and its strong deliquescence.

Occurrence. Because of its solubility in water, soda niter is found only in arid and desert regions. Found in large quantities in the provinces of Tarapaca and Antofagasta, northern Chile, and the neighboring parts of Bolivia. Occurs over immense areas as a salt (caliche) bed interstratified with sand, beds of common salt, gypsum, etc. In the United States has been noted in Humboldt County, Nevada, and in San Bernardino County, California.

Use. In Chile it is quarried, purified, and used as a source of nitrates. Soda niter now competes with nitrogen "fixed" from the air. Nitrates are used in explosives and fertilizer.

Name. From the composition, the sodium analogue of *niter*, KNO_3.

NITER—KNO_3

Saltpeter

Crystallography. Orthorhombic; dipyramidal. Usually as thin encrustations or as silky acicular crystals. Twinning on {110} is common, giving pseudohexagonal groupings analogous to aragonite.

Physical properties. Perfect {011} cleavage. **H** 2. **G** 2.09–2.14. Luster vitreous. Color white. Translucent.

Composition. Potassium nitrate, KNO_3. K_2O 46.5, N_2O_5 53.5 per cent.

Tests. Fusible at 1, giving violet flame (potassium). After ignition gives alkaline reaction on moistened test paper. Heated in the closed tube with potassium disulfate gives red fumes of nitrogen dioxide. Easily soluble in water. Saline and cooling taste.

Diagnostic features. Characterized by its cooling taste; distinguished from soda niter by the potassium test and by being nondeliquescent.

Occurrence. Niter is found as delicate crusts, as an efflorescence, on surfaces of earth, walls, rocks, etc. Found as a constituent of certain soils. Also in the loose soil of limestone caves. Not as common as soda niter, but produced from soils in Spain, Italy, Egypt, Arabia, Persia, and India.

Use. Used as a source of nitrogen compounds.

BORATES

The borates are of great interest to the mineralogist because they, like the aluminofluorides and the silicates, are capable of forming polymerized anionic groups, having the form of chains, sheets, or isolated multiple groups. This fact arises from the circumstance that the very small, trivalent boron ion coordinates three oxygens in its most stable configuration. Since the charge on the central cation is $+3$, and there are three closest oxygen neighbors, the strength of the B–O bond must be one unit, equal to exactly one-half the binding energy of the oxygen ion. This permits a single oxygen to be shared between two boron ions thus linking the BO_3 triangles into a larger unit.

Substances are known in which the fundamental structure of the crystal is the BO_2^- chain, of unlimited length, formed by sharing of oxygens in each boron triangle, each of the shared oxygens uniting two adjacent triangles.

Most of the common borates seem to be built about interrupted sheets of BO_3 triangles in which all three oxygens are shared, the sheets being separated by layers of water molecules and joined together by sodium or calcium ions.

Although it is possible to prepare a three-dimensional boxwork made up of BO_3 triangles only and having the composition B_2O_3, such a configuration has a very low stability and disorders readily, yielding a glass. Because of the tendency to form somewhat disordered networks of BO_3 triangles, boron is regarded as a "network-former" in glass manufacture and is used in the preparation of special glasses of light weight and high transparency to energetic radiation.

Borates

Boracite	$Mg_3B_7O_{13}Cl$	Ulexite	$NaCaB_5O_9 \cdot 8H_2O$
Borax	$Na_2B_4O_7 \cdot 10H_2O$	Colemanite	$Ca_2B_6O_{11} \cdot 5H_2O$
Kernite	$Na_2B_4O_7 \cdot 4H_2O$		

Boracite—$Mg_3B_7O_{13}Cl$

Crystallography. Orthorhombic; pyramidal at ordinary temperatures, but crystals show isometric, hextetrahedral forms. The cube, tetrahedron, and dodecahedron are usually present in combination (Figs. 508 and 509). If boracite is heated to $265°$ C the structure reverts to isometric as required by the crystal form. Crystals usually isolated and disseminated in other minerals. Also massive.

Physical properties. H 7. **G** 2.9–3.0. Luster vitreous. Colorless, white, gray, green. Transparent to translucent.

Composition. $Mg_3B_7O_{13}Cl$. MgO 25.71, $MgCl_2$ 12.14, B_2O_3 62.15 per cent.

Tests. Fusible at 2 with green flame color (boron). Soluble in hydrochloric acid. Turmeric paper moistened with a solution of the mineral and then dried at 100° C turns reddish brown (boron).

Diagnostic features. Boracite is characterized by its high hardness, isometric crystals, and test for boron.

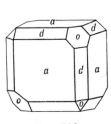
Fig. 508.

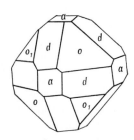
Fig. 509.

Boracite.

Occurrence. Boracite occurs associated with beds of halite, anhydrite, and gypsum, as one of the products formed by the evaporation of bodies of salt water. It is found at Stassfurt and other localities in Germany. In the United States it has been observed in the insoluble residues of salt wells in Louisiana.

Name. In allusion to the composition.

BORAX—$Na_2B_4O_7 \cdot 10H_2O$

Crystallography. Monoclinic; prismatic. Prismatic crystals, some large (Fig. 510). Also as massive cellular material or encrustations.

Physical properties. Perfect {100} cleavage. **H** 2–2½. **G** 1.7±. Luster vitreous. Colorless or white. Translucent. Sweetish-alkaline taste. Clear crystals effloresce and turn white with the formation of *tincalconite*, $Na_2B_4O_7 \cdot 5H_2O$.

Composition. Hydrous sodium borate, $Na_2B_4O_7 \cdot 10H_2O$. Na_2O 16.2, B_2O_3 36.6, H_2O 47.2 per cent.

Tests. Fusible at 1–1½ with much swelling and gives strong yellow flame (sodium). Fused with boron flux gives the bright green flame of boron. Readily soluble in water. Turmeric paper, moistened with a dilute hydrochloric acid solution of the mineral, turns reddish brown when dried at 100° C. Much water in the closed tube.

Diagnostic features. Characterized by its crystals and tests for boron.

Occurrence. Borax is the most widespread of the borate minerals. It is formed as a deposit from the evaporation of salt lakes and as an efflorescence on the surface of the ground in arid regions. The deposits in Tibet have furnished large amounts of borax, which has been exported to Europe in the crude state under the name of *tincal*. This was the first borax to reach western civilization. Obtained from brines and hot springs in northern Italy. In the United States was first found in Lake County, California, and later in the desert region of southeastern California, in Death Valley, Inyo County, and in San Bernardino County. Associated with kernite, it is mined from the bedded deposits near Kramer, California, and it is obtained commercially from the brines of Searles Lake at Trona, California. Occurs also in the adjacent parts of Nevada. Borax is associated with the other minerals deposited in similar manner, such as ulexite, hanksite, halite, gypsum, colemanite, and various rare borates.

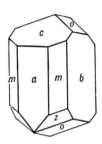

Fig. 510. Borax.

Use. Borax is used for washing and cleansing; as an antiseptic and preservative; in medicine; as a solvent for metallic oxides in soldering and welding; and as a flux in various smelting and laboratory operations. Borax and the other borate minerals are the source of boron, which appears to have ever-increasing uses. Elemental boron is used as a deoxidizer and alloy in nonferrous metals; in rectifiers and control tubes; and a neutron absorber in shields for atomic reactors. Boron is used in rocket fuels and as an additive in motor fuel. Boron carbide, harder than corundum, is used as an abrasive.

Name. Borax comes from an Arabic name for the substance.

KERNITE—$Na_2B_4O_7 \cdot 4H_2O$

Rasorite

Crystallography. Monoclinic; prismatic. Usually in coarse cleavable aggregates.

Physical properties. Perfect {001} and {100} cleavage. Cleavage fragments are thus elongated parallel to the *b* crystallographic axis. **H** 3. **G** 1.95. Luster vitreous to pearly. Colorless to white; colorless specimens become a chalky white on long exposure to the air, owing to a surface film of tincalconite.

Composition. Hydrous sodium borate, $Na_2B_4O_7 \cdot 4H_2O$. Na_2O 22.7, B_2O_3 51.0, H_2O 26.3 per cent.

Tests. Before the blowpipe swells and then fuses (at $1\frac{1}{2}$) to a clear glass. Slowly soluble in cold water.

Diagnostic features. Characterized by the long splintery cleavage fragments and low specific gravity.

Occurrence. The only locality at which kernite is found is on the Mohave Desert at Kramer, California. Here associated with borax in a bedded series of Tertiary clays it is present by the million tons. This deposit of sodium borates is 4 miles long, 1 mile wide, and 100 feet thick, and lies from 350 to 800 feet beneath the surface. The kernite is believed to have formed from borax by recrystallization caused by increased temperature and pressure.

Use. A major source of borax and boron compounds.

Name. From Kern County, California, where the mineral is found.

ULEXITE—$NaCaB_5O_9 \cdot 8H_2O$

Cotton-Balls

Crystallography. Triclinic; pinacoidal. Usually in rounded masses, loose in texture, consisting of fine fibers which are acicular or capillary crystals ("cotton-balls").

Physical properties. H $2\frac{1}{2}$; the aggregate has an apparent hardness of 1. G 1.96. Luster silky. Color white. Tasteless.

Composition. A hydrous sodium and calcium borate, $NaCaB_5O_9 \cdot 8H_2O$. Na_2O 7.7, CaO 13.8, B_2O_3 43.0, H_2O 35.5 per cent.

Tests. Fusible at 1, with intumescence to a clear blebby glass, coloring the flame deep yellow. Moistened with sulfuric acid gives momentarily the green flame of boron. Gives much water in closed tube.

Diagnostic features. The soft "cotton-balls" with silky luster are characteristic of ulexite.

Occurrence. Ulexite crystallizes in arid regions from brines which have concentrated in inclosed basins, as in playa lakes. Usually associated with borax. It occurs abundantly in the dry plains of northern Chile and in Argentina. In the United States it has been found abundantly in certain of the inclosed basins of Nevada and California and with colemanite in bedded Tertiary deposits.

Use. A source of borax.

Name. In honor of the German chemist, G. L. Ulex, who discovered the mineral.

COLEMANITE—$Ca_2B_6O_{11} \cdot 5H_2O$

Crystallography. Monoclinic; prismatic. In short prismatic crystals, highly modified. Cleavable massive to granular and compact.

Physical properties. Perfect {010} cleavage. **H** 4–4½. **G** 2.42. Luster vitreous. Colorless to white. Transparent to translucent.

Composition. Hydrous calcium borate, $Ca_2B_6O_{11} \cdot 5H_2O$. CaO 27.2, B_2O_3 50.9, H_2O 21.9 per cent.

Tests. Fusible at 1½. Before the blowpipe exfoliates, crumbles, and gives green flame (boron). Water in the closed tube.

Diagnostic features. Characterized by one direction of highly perfect cleavage and exfoliation on heating.

Occurrence. Colemanite deposits are interstratified with lake bed deposits of Tertiary age. Ulexite is usually associated, and the colemanite is believed to have originated by its alteration. Found in California in Los Angeles, Ventura, San Bernardino, and Inyo counties, and in Nevada in the Muddy Mountains and White Basin, Clark County.

Use. A source of borax which, at the time of the discovery of kernite, yielded over half of the world's supply.

Name. In honor of William T. Coleman, merchant of San Francisco, who marketed the product of the colemanite mines.

SULFATES AND CHROMATES

We have seen in the sulfide minerals that sulfur is important as the large, divalent sulfide anion. This ion results from the filling by captured electrons of the two vacancies in the outer, or valence, electron shell. The six electrons normally present in this shell may be lost, giving rise to a small, highly charged and highly polarizing positive ion. (Ion. rad. $= 0.30$ Å.) The ratio of the radius of this hexavalent sulfur ion to that of oxygen ($R_A : R_X = 0.226$) indicates that 4-fold, or tetrahedral, coordination will be stable. The sulfur to oxygen bond in such an ionic group is very strong and covalent in its properties and produces tightly bound groups that are not capable of sharing oxygens. These $SO_4^=$ groups, the sulfate radical of chemistry, are the fundamental structural units of the sulfate minerals.

The most important and most common of the anhydrous sulfates are members of the barite group, with large divalent cations coordinated with the sulfate ion. The rather simple structure leads to orthorhombic symmetry, with perfect {001} and {110} cleavage. The calcium sulfate, anhydrite, because of the smaller size of the calcium ion, has a slightly different structure and has three pinacoidal cleavages. The physical properties are in general conferred by the dominant cation. Specific gravity, for example, is directly proportional to atomic weight.

Among the hydrous sulfates, gypsum is most important and abundant. As is suggested by the highly perfect {010} cleavage, the structure is sheetlike, consisting of layers of calcium and sulfate ions separated by water molecules. Loss of these water molecules allows collapse of the structure into the anhydrite configuration with a large decrease in specific volume and loss of the perfect cleavage.

A large number of minerals belong to this class but only a few of them are common. The class can be divided into (1) the anhydrous sulfates and (2) the hydrous and basic sulfates.

Anhydrous Sulfates		Hydrous and Basic Sulfates	
Glauberite	$Na_2Ca(SO_4)_2$		
BARITE GROUP		Antlerite	$Cu_3(OH)_4SO_4$
Barite	$BaSO_4$	Polyhalite	$K_2Ca_2Mg(SO_4)_4 \cdot 2H_2O$
Celestite	$SrSO_4$	Gypsum	$CaSO_4 \cdot 2H_2O$
Anglesite	$PbSO_4$	Epsomite	$MgSO_4 \cdot 7H_2O$
Anhydrite	$CaSO_4$	Chalcanthite	$CuSO_4 \cdot 5H_2O$
Crocoite	$PbCrO_4$	Alunite	$KAl_3(OH)_6(SO_4)_2$

Glauberite—$Na_2Ca(SO_4)_2$

Crystallography. Monoclinic; prismatic. Crystals thin, tabular parallel to base.

Physical properties. Cleavage {001}. **H** $2\frac{1}{2}$–3. **G** 2.75–2.85. Luster vitreous. Color pale yellow or gray. Taste slightly saline. Transparent to translucent.

Composition. A sodium and calcium sulfate, $Na_2Ca(SO_4)_2$. Na_2O 22.3, CaO 20.1, SO_3 57.6 per cent.

Tests. Fusible at $1\frac{1}{2}$–2, giving yellow flame (sodium). After ignition, gives an alkaline reaction on moistened test paper. On long exposure deliquesces and falls to pieces.

Diagnostic features. Characterized by its thin tabular crystals, good cleavage and association.

Occurrence. Glauberite is a widespread constituent of saline deposits formed by the evaporation of salt lakes and is thus associated with other salts such as thenardite, halite, and polyhalite.

Found at Salzburg, Austria, and near Stassfurt, Germany. In the United States found in Yavapai County, Arizona, and at Borax Lake, San Bernardino County, California.

Name. Glauberite is so named because *Glauber's salt* (Na_2SO_4) is present in it.

BARITE GROUP

The sulfates of barium, strontium, and lead form an isostructural group. They crystallize in the orthorhombic system with closely related crystal constants and similar habits. The members of the group are: *barite, celestite,* and *anglesite.*

BARITE—$BaSO_4$

Barytes. Heavy Spar

Crystallography. Orthorhombic; dipyramidal. Crystals usually tabular parallel to base; often diamond-shaped because of the presence of a vertical prism (Fig. 511). Both first- and second-order prisms are usually present, either beveling the corners of the diamond-shaped crystals (Fig. 512) or, if the {110} faces are wanting, beveling the edges of the tables and forming rectangular prismatic crystals elongated parallel to either the *a* or *b* axis (Figs. 513 and 514). Crystals may be very complex. Frequently in divergent groups of tabular crystals forming "crested barite" or "barite roses." Also coarsely laminated; granular, earthy.

Physical properties. Cleavage perfect {001}, less perfect {210}. H 3–3½. G 4.5 (heavy for a nonmetallic mineral). Luster vitreous; on some specimens pearly on base. Colorless, white, and light shades of blue, yellow, red. Transparent to translucent.

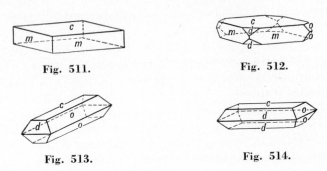

Fig. 511.

Fig. 512.

Fig. 513.

Fig. 514.

Barite.

Composition. Barium sulfate, $BaSO_4$. BaO 65.7, SO_3 34.3 per cent. Strontium substitutes for barium and a complete solid solution probably extends to celestite, but most material is near one end or the other of the series. A small amount of lead may substitute for barium.

Tests. Fusible at 4, giving yellowish green barium flame. After ignition gives an alkaline reaction on moistened test paper. Fused with reducing mixture gives a residue which, when moistened, produces a dark stain of silver sulfide on a clean silver surface.

Diagnostic features. Recognized by its high specific gravity and characteristic cleavage and crystals.

Occurrence. Barite is a common mineral of wide distribution. It occurs usually as a gangue mineral in metallic veins, associated especially with ores of silver, lead, copper, cobalt, manganese, and antimony. It is found in veins in limestone with calcite, or as residual masses in clay overlying limestone. Also in sandstone with copper ores. In places acts as a cement in sandstone. Deposited occasionally as a sinter by waters from hot springs.

Notable localities for the occurrence of barite crystals are in Westmoreland, Cornwall, Cumberland, and Derbyshire, England; Felsobanya and other localities, Rumania; Saxony; and Bohemia. In the United States at Cheshire, Connecticut; Dekalb, New York; and Fort Wallace, New Mexico. Massive barite, occurring usually as veins, nests, and irregular bodies in limestones, has been quarried in the

United States in Georgia, Tennessee, Missouri, and Arkansas. At El Portal, California, at the entrance to Yosemite Park, barite is found in a vein with witherite.

Use. More than 80 per cent of the barite produced is used in oil- and gas-well drilling. Barite is the chief source of barium for chemicals. A major use of barium is in *lithopone*, a combination of barium sulfide and zinc sulfate which combine to form an intimate mixture of zinc sulfide and barium sulfate. Lithopone is used in the paint industry and to a lesser extent in floor coverings and textiles. Precipitated barium sulfate, "blanc fixe," is employed as a filler in paper and cloth, in cosmetics, as a paint pigment, and for barium meals in medical radiology.

Name. From the Greek word meaning *heavy*, in allusion to its high specific gravity.

CELESTITE—SrSO$_4$

Crystallography. Orthorhombic; dipyramidal. Crystals resemble closely those of barite. Commonly tabular parallel to the base or prismatic parallel to the a or b axis with prominent development of the first- and second-order prisms (Fig. 515). Crystals that are

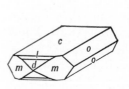

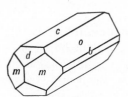

Fig. 515.   Fig. 516.

Celestite.

elongated parallel to the a axis are frequently terminated in front by four faces in nearly equal development, consisting of two faces of the third-order prism and two of the second-order prism (Fig. 516). Also radiating fibrous; granular.

Physical properties. Cleavage {001} perfect, {210} good. H 3–3½. G 3.95–3.97. Luster vitreous to pearly. Colorless, white, often faintly blue or red. Transparent to translucent.

Composition. Strontium sulfate, SrSO$_4$. SrO 56.4, SO$_3$ 43.6 per cent. Barium substitutes for strontium and a complete solid-solution series probably extends to barite.

Tests. Fuses at 3½–4 and colors the flame crimson (strontium). Usually decrepitates when touched with the blowpipe flame. After ignition gives an alkaline reaction on moistened test paper. Fused with sodium carbonate gives a residue which, when moistened, produces on a clean silver surface a dark stain of silver sulfide.

Diagnostic features. Closely resembles barite but of lower specific gravity. A flame test may be necessary to differentiate the two species positively.

Occurrence. Celestite is found usually disseminated through limestone or sandstone, or in nests and lining cavities in such rocks. Associated with calcite, dolomite, gypsum, halite, sulfur, fluorite. Also found as a gangue mineral in lead veins.

Notable localities for its occurrence are with the sulfur deposits of Sicily; at Bex, Switzerland; Yate, Gloucestershire, England; and Herrengrund, Slovakia. Found in the United States at Clay Center, Ohio; Put-in-Bay, Lake Erie; Mineral County, West Virginia; Lampasas, Texas; and Inyo County, California.

Use. Used in the preparation of nitrate of strontium for fireworks and tracer bullets, and other strontium salts used in the refining of beet sugar.

Name. Derived from *caelestis*, in allusion to the faint blue color of the first specimens described.

ANGLESITE—$PbSO_4$

Crystallography. Orthorhombic; dipyramidal. Frequently in crystals with habit often similar to that of barite but much more varied. Crystals may be prismatic parallel to any one of the crystal axes and frequently show many forms, with a complex development. Also massive, granular to compact. Frequently earthy, in concentric layers which may have an unaltered core of galena.

Physical properties. Cleavage {001} good, {210} imperfect. Fracture conchoidal. **H** 3. **G** 6.2–6.4 (unusually high). Luster adamantine when pure and crystalline, dull when earthy. Colorless, white, gray, pale shades of yellow. May be colored dark gray by impurities. Transparent to translucent.

Composition. Lead sulfate, $PbSO_4$. PbO 73.6, SO_3 26.4 per cent.

Tests. Fusible at $1\frac{1}{2}$. On charcoal with sodium carbonate reduced to a lead globule with yellow to white coating of lead oxide; the residue, when moistened, produces on clean silver surface a dark stain of silver sulfide.

Diagnostic features. Recognized by its high specific gravity, its adamantine luster, and frequently by its association with galena. Distinguished from cerussite in that it will not effervesce in nitric acid.

Occurrence. Anglesite is a common supergene lead mineral. It is formed through the oxidation of galena, either directly to the sulfate, as is shown by concentric layers of anglesite surrounding a core of unaltered galena, or by an intermediate solution and subsequent recrystallization. Found in the upper, oxidized portions of lead veins, associated with galena, cerussite, sphalerite, smithsonite, hemimorphite, and iron oxides.

Notable localities for its occurrence are Monte Poni, Sardinia; Island of Anglesey, Wales; Derbyshire; and Leadhills, Scotland. From Sidi-Amor-ben-Salem, Tunis; near Otavi, South-West Africa; Broken Hill, New South Wales; and Dundas, Tasmania. Is found in crystals at Los Lamentos, Chihuahua, Mexico, imbedded in sulfur. Occurs in the United States at Phoenixville, Pennsylvania; Tintic district, Utah; and Coeur d'Alene district, Idaho.

Use. A minor ore of lead.

Name. Named from the original locality on Island of Anglesey.

ANHYDRITE—CaSO₄

Crystallography. Orthorhombic; dipyramidal. Crystals rare; when observed are thick tabular, also prismatic parallel to the *b* axis. Usually massive or in crystalline masses resembling an isometric mineral with cubic cleavage. Also fibrous, granular, massive.

Physical properties. Distinct cleavage parallel to the three pinacoids {100}, {010}, {001} yields rectangular blocks. **H** $3-3\frac{1}{2}$. **G** 2.89–2.98. Luster vitreous to pearly on cleavage. Colorless to bluish or violet. Also may be white or tinged with rose, brown, or red.

Composition. Anhydrous calcium sulfate, $CaSO_4$. CaO 41.2, SO_3 58.8 per cent.

Tests. Fusible at 3. After ignition gives an alkaline reaction on moistened test paper. Moistened with hydrochloric acid and ignited gives orange-red flame of calcium. When fused with reducing mixture gives a residue that, when moistened with water, darkens silver.

Diagnostic features. Anhydrite is characterized by its three cleavages at right angles. It is distinguished from calcite by its higher specific gravity and from gypsum by its hardness. Some massive varieties are very difficult to recognize, and one should test for the sulfate radical.

Alteration. By the absorption of moisture anhydrite changes to gypsum, with an increase in volume, and in places large masses of anhydrite have been thus altered.

Occurrence. Anhydrite occurs in much the same manner as gypsum and is often associated with that mineral but is not nearly so common. Found in beds associated with salt deposits in the cap rock of salt domes, and in limestone rocks. Found in some amygdaloidal cavities in basalt.

Notable foreign localities are: Wieliczka, Poland; Aussee, Styria; Stassfurt, Prussia; Berchtesgaden, Bavaria; Hall near Innsbruck, Tyrol; and Bex, Switzerland. In the United States found in Lockport, New York; West Paterson, New Jersey; Nashville, Tennessee; New Mexico; and Texas. Found in large beds in Nova Scotia.

Name. Anhydrite is from the Greek meaning *without water*, in contrast to the more common calcium sulfate, gypsum, which contains much water.

Crocoite—$PbCrO_4$

Crystallography. Monoclinic; prismatic. Commonly in slender prismatic crystals, vertically striated and columnar aggregates. Also granular.

Physical properties. Imperfect {110} cleavage. **H** $2\frac{1}{2}$–3. **G** 5.9–6.1. Luster adamantine. Color bright hyacinth-red. Streak orange-yellow. Translucent.

Composition. Lead chromate, $PbCrO_4$. PbO 68.9, CrO_3 31.1 per cent.

Tests. Fusible at $1\frac{1}{2}$. Fused with sodium carbonate on charcoal gives a lead globule. With borax gives a green (chromium) bead in the oxidizing flame.

Diagnostic features. Characterized by its color, high luster, and high specific gravity. Crocoite may be confused with wulfenite, lead molybdate, but can be distinguished from it by its redder color, lower specific gravity, and crystal form.

Occurrence. Crocoite is a rare mineral found in the oxidized zones of lead deposits in those regions where lead veins have traversed rocks containing chromite. Associated with pyromorphite, cerussite, and wulfenite. Notable localities are: Dundas, Tasmania; Beresovsk near Sverdlovsk, Ural Mountains; and Rézbánya, Rumania. In the United States is found in small quantities in the Vulture district, Arizona.

Use. Not abundant enough to be of commercial value, but of historic interest, since the element chromium was first discovered in crocoite.

Name. From the Greek meaning *saffron*, in allusion to the color.

Antlerite—$Cu_3(OH)_4SO_4$

Crystallography. Orthorhombic; dipyramidal. Slender prismatic crystals, vertically striated, often acicular. May be tabular (Figs. 517 and 518). Also in parallel aggregates, reniform, massive.

Physical properties. Perfect {010} cleavage. **H** $3\frac{1}{2}$–4. **G** 3.9±.
Luster vitreous. Color emerald to blackish green. Streak pale green.
Transparent to translucent.

Composition. A basic sulfate of copper, $Cu_3(OH)_4SO_4$. CuO
67.3, SO_3 22.5, H_2O 10.2 per cent.

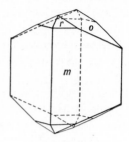
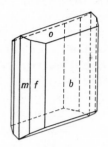

Fig. 517.   **Fig. 518.**

Antlerite.

Tests. Fusible at $3\frac{1}{2}$. Yields a copper globule when fused with
sodium carbonate on charcoal. Hydrochloric acid solution with barium
chloride gives white precipitate of barium sulfate. Yields water in the
closed tube and, at a high temperature, sulfuric acid.

Diagnostic features. Antlerite is characterized by its green color,
{010} cleavage, and associations. It will not effervesce in hydrochloric
acid and can thus be distinguished from malachite. It is impossible
to distinguish antlerite from atacamite or brochantite by inspection.
A positive test for chlorine will identify atacamite, but one must use
optical properties to distinguish antlerite from brochantite.

Occurrence. Antlerite is found in the oxidized portions of copper
veins, especially in arid regions. It was formerly considered a rare
mineral, but in 1925 it was recognized as the chief ore mineral at
Chuquicamata, Chile, the world's largest copper mine. It may form
directly as a secondary mineral on chalcocite, or the copper may go
into solution and later be deposited as antlerite, filling cracks. In the
United States is found at Bisbee, Arizona, and near Black Mountain,
Nevada. Also found at Kennecott, Alaska.

Use. An ore of copper.

Name. From the Antler mine, Arizona, from which locality it was
originally described.

Similar species. *Brochantite,* $Cu_4(OH)_6SO_4$, is similar in all its
properties to antlerite, but, although more widespread, is nowhere
abundant. Until 1925 it was considered to be the chief ore mineral
at Chuquicamata, Chile.

Polyhalite—$K_2Ca_2Mg(SO_4)_4 \cdot 2H_2O$

Crystallography. Triclinic; pinacoidal. Crystals very rare and usually twinned. Usually in compact granular, fibrous, or lamellar masses.

Physical properties. Distinct {10$\bar{1}$} cleavage. **H** 3–3$\frac{1}{2}$. **G** 2.78. Color gray, flesh- or brick-red. Luster resinous. Translucent. Taste bitter.

Composition. A hydrated sulfate of potassium, calcium, and magnesium, $K_2Ca_2Mg(SO_4)_4 \cdot 2H_2O$. K_2O 15.6, CaO 18.6, MgO 6.7, SO_3 53.1, H_2O 6.0 per cent.

Tests. Fusible at 1$\frac{1}{2}$, giving a violet flame color (potassium). Gives water in the closed tube. Readily soluble in hydrochloric acid, and solution made ammoniacal will, on the addition of ammonium oxalate, give a white precipitate of calcium oxalate. Filtrate with sodium phosphate gives white precipitate of ammonium magnesium phosphate.

Diagnostic features. Characterized by its red color, but not readily distinguished by inspection from other, associated and similar-appearing minerals.

Occurrence. Polyhalite occurs in bedded deposits associated with halite, sylvite, carnallite, etc. Notable localities are at Stassfurt, Germany, and Salzburg, Austria. In the United States is found associated with other potassium and magnesium salts in the Permian basin of western Texas and eastern New Mexico.

Use. A source of potassium.

Name. From the two Greek words meaning *many* and *salt*, in allusion to the several component salts present.

GYPSUM—$CaSO_4 \cdot 2H_2O$

Crystallography. Monoclinic; prismatic. Crystals are of prismatic habit (Figs. 519–521); tabular parallel to side pinacoid; diamond-shaped, with edges beveled by {110} and {111} faces. Other forms rare. Twins common, with the front pinacoid the twin plane (Fig. 522), often resulting in swallowtail twins. Cleavable massive; foliated; granular massive. *Satin spar* is a fibrous gypsum with silky luster. *Alabaster* is the fine-grained massive variety. *Selenite* is a variety that yields broad colorless and transparent cleavage folia.

Physical properties. Cleavage in four directions; perfect {010}, yielding easily thin folia; {100}, with conchoidal surface; {011}, with fibrous fracture. **H** 2 (can be scratched by the finger nail). **G** 2.32. Luster usually vitreous; also pearly and silky. Colorless, white, gray;

various shades of yellow, red, brown, from impurities. Transparent to translucent.

Composition. Hydrous calcium sulfate, $CaSO_4 \cdot 2H_2O$. CaO 32.6, SO_3 46.5, H_2O 20.9 per cent.

Tests. Fusible at 3. After intense ignition, residue gives alkaline reaction on moistened test paper. Soluble in hot dilute hydrochloric acid, and solution with barium chloride gives white precipitate of barium sulfate. In the closed tube turns white and yields much water.

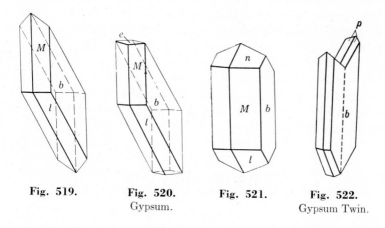

Fig. 519.   Fig. 520.   Fig. 521.   Fig. 522.
              Gypsum.   Gypsum Twin.

Diagnostic features. Characterized by its softness and its three unequal cleavages. Its solubility in acid and the presence of much water distinguish it from anhydrite.

Occurrence. Gypsum is a common mineral widely distributed in sedimentary rocks, often as thick beds. It frequently occurs interstratified with limestones and shales and is usually found as a layer underlying beds of rock salt, having been deposited there as one of the first minerals to crystallize on the evaporation of salt waters. May recrystallize in veins, forming *satin spar*. Occurs also as lenticular bodies or scattered crystals in clays and shales. Frequently formed by the alteration of anhydrite and under these circumstances may show folding because of increased volume. Found in volcanic regions, especially where limestones have been acted upon by sulfur vapors. Also common as a gangue mineral in metallic veins. Associated with many different minerals, the more common ones being halite, anhydrite, dolomite, calcite, sulfur, pyrite, and quartz.

Gypsum is the most common sulfate, and extensive deposits are found in many localities throughout the world. In the United States commercial deposits are found in many states, but the chief producers are located in New York, Michigan, Iowa, Texas, Nevada, and California. Gypsum is found in large deposits in Arizona and New Mexico in the form of wind-blown sand.

Use. Gypsum is used chiefly for the production of plaster of Paris. In the manufacture of this material, the gypsum is ground and then heated at 190–200° C until about 75 per cent of the water has been driven off. This plaster, when mixed with water, slowly absorbs the water, crystallizes, and thus hardens or "sets." Plaster of Paris is used extensively for "staff," the material from which temporary exposition buildings are built, for gypsum lath, wall board, and for molds and casts of all kinds. Gypsum is employed in making adamant plaster for interior use. Serves as land plaster, for a fertilizer. Uncalcined gypsum is used as a retarder in Portland cement. Satin spar and alabaster are cut and polished for various ornamental purposes but are restricted in their uses because of their softness.

Name. From the Greek name for the mineral, but more especially for the calcined mineral.

Epsomite—$MgSO_4 \cdot 7H_2O$

Epsom Salt

Crystallography. Orthorhombic; disphenoidal. Rarely in crystals. Usually in botryoidal masses and delicately fibrous crusts.

Physical properties. Perfect {010} cleavage. **H** 2–2$\frac{1}{2}$. **G** 1.68. Luster vitreous to earthy. Colorless to white. Transparent to translucent. Taste very bitter.

Composition. Hydrous magnesium sulfate, $MgSO_4 \cdot 7H_2O$. MgO 16.3, SO_3 32.5, H_2O 51.2 per cent.

Tests. In the closed tube gives much acid water, and liquefies in its water of crystallization. Soluble in water.

Diagnostic features. Characterized by its mode of occurrence in delicate fibrous and capillary aggregates, its easy solubility in water, and its bitter taste.

Occurrence. Epsomite is usually deposited as an efflorescence on the rocks in mine workings and on the walls of caves. More rarely it is found in lake deposits; associated with other soluble salts as at Stassfurt, Germany. In the United States it is found on the floors of limestone caves in Kentucky, Tennessee, and Indiana, and in abandoned mines in California and Colorado. Found in lake deposits in Stevens County, Washington.

Use. The mineral epsomite has little use in itself, for commercial epsom salt is manufactured from other magnesium minerals.

Name. Epsomite was named from the original locality of Epsom, England.

Chalcanthite—$CuSO_4 \cdot 5H_2O$

Blue Vitriol

Crystallography. Triclinic; pinacoidal. Found in crystals commonly tabular parallel to $\{\bar{1}\bar{1}1\}$. Also massive, stalactitic, and reniform; may have fibrous appearance.

Physical properties. H $2\frac{1}{2}$. G 2.12–2.30. Luster vitreous. Color deep azure-blue. Transparent to translucent. Taste metallic.

Composition. Hydrous copper sulfate, $CuSO_4 \cdot 5H_2O$. CuO 31.8, SO_3 32.1, H_2O 36.1 per cent.

Tests. Infusible. Gives copper globule when fused with sodium carbonate on charcoal. Soluble in water. Turns white and gives much water in the closed tube.

Diagnostic features. Characterized by its blue color, metallic taste, and solubility in water.

Occurrence. Chalcanthite is rare, found only in arid regions as a supergene mineral, occurring near the surface in copper veins, and derived from the original copper sulfides by oxidation. Often deposited on iron from the waters in copper mines.

Chalcanthite is found abundantly at Chuquicamata and other arid localities in Chile, where it has served as an important ore mineral. Other occurrences are unimportant commercially.

Use. A minor ore of copper. The artificial blue vitriol is used in calico printing, in galvanic cells, as an insecticide, and for industrial purposes.

Name. From two Greek words meaning *brass* and *flower*.

Alunite—$KAl_3(OH)_6(SO_4)_2$

Alumstone

Crystallography. Hexagonal–R; ditrigonal-pyramidal. Crystals usually a combination of positive and negative trigonal pyramids resembling rhombohedrons with nearly cubic angles (90° 50′). May be tabular parallel to $\{0001\}$. Commonly massive or disseminated.

Physical properties. Imperfect {0001} cleavage. **H** 4. **G** 2.6–2.8. Color white, gray, or reddish. Transparent to translucent.

Composition. Basic potassium aluminum sulfate, $KAl_3(OH)_6$-$(SO_4)_2$. K_2O 11.4, Al_2O_3 37.0, SO_3 38.6, H_2O 13.0 per cent. Sodium may replace potassium in part, giving *natro-alunite*.

Tests. Infusible and decrepitates before the blowpipe, giving a potassium flame. Heated with cobalt nitrate solution turns a fine blue color. In the closed tube gives acid water. Soluble in sulfuric acid.

Diagnostic features. Alunite is usually massive and in that form is difficult to distinguish by inspection from rocks such as limestone and dolomite, and other massive minerals such as anhydrite and granular magnesite. A positive test for acid water will serve to distinguish alunite from similar-appearing minerals.

Occurrence. Alunite is usually formed by sulfuric acid solutions acting on rocks rich in potash feldspar, and in some places large masses have thus been formed. Found in smaller amounts about volcanic fumeroles. In the United States it is found at Red Mountain in the San Juan district, Colorado; Goldfield, Nevada; and Marysvale, Utah.

Use. In the production of alum. At Marysvale, Utah, alunite has been mined and treated in such a way as to recover potassium and aluminum.

Name. From the Latin meaning *alum*.

Similar species. *Jarosite*, $KFe_3(OH)_6(SO_4)_2$, the iron analogue of alunite, is a secondary mineral found as crusts and coatings on ferruginous ores.

PHOSPHATES, ARSENATES, AND VANADATES

Five-valent phosphorus is only slightly larger than six-valent sulfur and, hence, like sulfur, forms a tetrahedral ionic group with oxygen. This group, the PO_4^{-3} tetrahedron, is, like the sulfate tetrahedron, a separate radical that cannot share oxygen or form polymerized groups. All phosphates are built about this phosphate ion as the fundamental building unit. Similar units, having the same configuration of the oxygens, the same kind and intensity of the binding forces, are built about the five-valent arsenic and vanadium ions. Phosphorus, arsenic, and vanadium may substitute for each other as the central coordinating ion in the tetrahedral oxygen group.

This freedom of substitution of phosphorus, arsenic, and vanadium is best shown in the pyromorphite subgroup of the apatite group. Pyromorphite, mimetite, and vanadinite are isostructural, and all gradations of composition between the pure compounds may exist.

Apatite, the most important and abundant phosphate, displays solid solution with respect to anions both by substitution of chlorine and hydroxyl for the common fluorine and more rarely by substitution of carbonate groups for phosphate. Manganese, strontium, and other cations may substitute for calcium. This complex ionic substitution is typical of the phosphates, which have involved chemical relationships and generally rather complicated structures.

This mineral class, composed mostly of phosphates, is very large, but most of its members are so rare that they need not be mentioned

Phosphates, Arsenates, and Vanadates

Monazite	$(Ce,La,Y,Th)PO_4$
Triphylite	$LiFePO_4$
Apatite Group	
Apatite	$Ca_5(F,Cl,OH)(PO_4)_3$
Pyromorphite	$Pb_5Cl(PO_4)_3$
Mimetite	$Pb_5Cl(AsO_4)_3$
Vanadinite	$Pb_5Cl(VO_4)_3$
Amblygonite	$LiAlFPO_4$
Lazulite	$MgAl_2(OH)_2(PO_4)_2$
Scorodite	$FeAsO_4 \cdot 2H_2O$
Wavellite	$Al_3(OH)_3(PO_4)_2 \cdot 5H_2O$
Turquoise	$CuAl_6(PO_4)_4(OH)_8 \cdot 2H_2O$
Autunite	$Ca(UO_2)_2(PO_4)_2 \cdot 10-12H_2O$
Vivianite	$Fe_3(PO_4)_2 \cdot 8H_2O$
Erythrite	$Co_3(AsO_4)_2 \cdot 8H_2O$
Carnotite	$K_2(UO_2)_2(VO_4)_2 \cdot 3H_2O$

here. Of the minerals listed, apatite is the only one that can be considered common.

Monazite—$(Ce,La,Y,Th)PO_4$

Crystallography. Monoclinic; prismatic. Crystals rare and usually small, often flattened on {100}, or elongated parallel to the b crystal axis. Usually in granular masses, frequently as sand.

Physical properties. Cleavage {100} poor. Parting {001}. H 5–$5\frac{1}{2}$. G 5.0–5.3. Luster resinous. Color yellowish to reddish brown. Translucent.

Composition. A phosphate of the rare-earth metals, essentially $(Ce,La,Y,Th)PO_4$. Thorium is present between a few per cent and 20 per cent ThO_2. Silica is usually present and has been ascribed to *thorite*, $ThSiO_4$.

Tests. Infusible. Insoluble in hydrochloric acid. After fusion with sodium carbonate, dissolve in nitric acid, and add solution to excess of ammonium molybdate solution; a yellow precipitate forms (test for a phosphate). Decomposed by heating with concentrated sulfuric acid; solution after dilution with water and filtering gives with ammonium oxalate a precipitate of the oxalates of the rare earths.

Diagnostic features. In large specimens may be distinguished from zircon by crystal form and inferior hardness, and from sphene by crystal form and higher specific gravity. On doubtful specimens it is usually well to make the chemical phosphate test.

Occurrence. Monazite is a comparatively rare mineral occurring as an accessory mineral in granites, gneisses, aplites, and pegmatites, and as rolled grains in the sands derived from the decomposition of such rocks. It is concentrated in sands because of its resistance to chemical attack and because of its high specific gravity, and is thus associated with other resistant and heavy minerals such as magnetite, ilmenite, rutile, and zircon.

The bulk of the world's supply of monazite comes from sands in the provinces of Espirito Santo and Bahia, Brazil, and from the coasts of India and Australia. A dikelike body of massive granular monazite is mined near VanRhynsdorp, Cape Province, South Africa. Found in the United States in North Carolina, both in gneiss and in the stream sands, and in the beach sands of Florida.

Use. Monazite is the chief source of thorium oxide, which it contains in amounts varying between 1 and 20 per cent; commercial monazite usually contains between 3 and 9 per cent. Thorium oxide is used in the manufacture of mantles for incandescent gas lights.

Thorium is a radioactive element and is receiving considerable attention as a source of atomic energy. The natural isotope of thorium, Th-232, can be converted by neutron bombardment, first to Th-233, and then to U-233, a fissionable isotope.

Name. The name *monazite* is derived from a Greek word meaning *to be solitary,* in allusion to the rarity of the mineral.

Triphylite—$LiFePO_4$

Crystallography. Orthorhombic; dipyramidal. Crystals rare. Commonly in cleavable masses. Also compact.

Physical properties. Cleavage {001} nearly perfect, {010} imperfect. **H** $4\frac{1}{2}$–5. **G** 3.42–3.56. Luster vitreous to resinous. Color bluish gray in triphylite to salmon-pink or clove-brown with the increased amount of manganese. May be stained black by manganese oxide. Translucent.

Composition. Phosphate of lithium and ferrous iron, $LiFePO_4$. With substitution of manganese for ferrous iron a complete series extends to *lithiophilite,* $LiMnPO_4$.

Tests. Fusible at $2\frac{1}{2}$, giving red lithium flame. Triphylite becomes magnetic on heating in the reducing flame. Some manganese is usually present, and therefore it gives an opaque bluish green bead with sodium carbonate.

Diagnostic features. Characterized by two cleavages at right angles, resinous luster, and association.

Occurrence. Triphylite is a rare mineral occurring in granite pegmatites associated with other phosphates, spodumene, and beryl. Notable localities are Rabenstein, Bavaria, and Finland. In the United States found at Huntington, Massachusetts; Peru, Maine; Grafton, North Grafton, and Newport, New Hampshire; and the Black Hills, South Dakota. Lithiophilite is found at Branchville and Portland, Connecticut.

Name. From the Greek words meaning *three* and *a tribe,* because it contains the three bases iron, lithium, and manganese.

APATITE GROUP

APATITE—$Ca_5(F,Cl,OH)(PO_4)_3$

Crystallography. Hexagonal; dipyramidal. Commonly in crystals of long prismatic habit; some short prismatic or tabular. Usually terminated by prominent pyramid of first order and frequently a basal plane (Figs. 523 and 524). Some crystals show faces of a hexagonal dipyramid (μ, Fig. 525) which reveals the true symmetry. Also in massive granular to compact masses.

Physical properties. Cleavage {0001} poor. **H** 5 (can just be scratched by a knife). **G** 3.15–3.20. Luster vitreous to subresinous. Color usually some shade of green or brown; also blue, violet, colorless. Transparent to translucent.

Composition. Calcium fluophosphate, $Ca_5F(PO_4)_3$, *fluorapatite;* more rarely $Ca_5Cl(PO_4)_3$, *chlorapatite,* and $Ca_5(OH)(PO_4)_3$, *hydrox-*

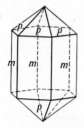

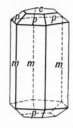

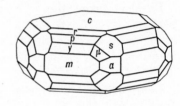

| Fig. 523. | Fig. 524. | Fig. 525. |

Apatite.

ylapatite. Fluorine, chlorine, and OH can substitute for each other, giving complete series. CO_3 may substitute for PO_4 giving *carbonate-apatite.* Manganese can substitute in part for calcium.

Collophane. The name collophane has been given to the massive, cryptocrystalline types of apatite that constitute the bulk of phosphate rock and fossil bone. X-ray study shows that collophane is essentially apatite and does not warrant designation as a separate species. In its physical appearance collophane is usually dense and massive with a concretionary or colloform structure. It is usually impure and contains small amounts of calcium carbonate.

Tests. Difficultly fusible (5–5½). Soluble in acids. Gives a yellow precipitate of ammonium phosphomolybdate when dilute nitric acid solution is added to large excess of ammonium molybdate solution.

Diagnostic features. Recognized usually by its crystals, color, and hardness. Distinguished from beryl by the prominent pyramidal terminations of its crystals and by its being softer than a knife blade.

Occurrence. Apatite is widely disseminated as an accessory constituent in all classes of rocks—igneous, sedimentary, and metamorphic. It is also found in pegmatite and other veins, probably of hydrothermal origin. Found in titaniferous magnetite bodies. Occasionally concentrated into large deposits or veins associated with alkalic rocks.

Apatite occurs in large amounts along the southern coast of Norway, between Lagnesund and Arendal, where it is found in veins and pockets associated with gabbro. It is distributed through the magnetite iron ore at Kiruna, Sweden. Apatite occurs in commercial amount in Ontario and Quebec, Canada. Unusually fine crystals have come from Renfrew County, Ontario. It is found there in crystals and masses inclosed in crystalline calcite and in veins and irregular nests along the contact of the limestone with igneous rocks.

The world's largest deposit of apatite is located on the Kola Peninsula, near Kirovsk, U.S.S.R. It is found there in a great lens between two types of alkalic rocks. The apatite is in granular aggregates intimately associated with nepheline and sphene.

Finely crystallized apatite occurs at various localities in the Tyrol; in Switzerland; and Jumilla, Spain. In the United States at Auburn, Maine; St. Lawrence County, New York; Alexander County, North Carolina; and San Diego County, California.

The variety collophane is an important constituent of the rock *phosphorite* or *phosphate rock*. Bone is calcium phosphate, and large bodies of phosphorite are derived from the accumulation of animal remains as well as chemical precipitation from sea water. Commercial deposits of phosphorite are found in northern France, Belgium, Spain, and especially in northern Africa in Tunisia, Algeria, and Morocco. In the United States high-grade phosphate deposits are found in western middle Tennessee and in Wyoming and Idaho. Nodular deposits of phosphate rock are found at intervals all along the Atlantic coast from North Carolina to Florida, the chief deposits being in Florida.

Use. Crystallized apatite has been used extensively for fertilizer, but today only the deposits on the Kola Peninsula are of importance. The phosphorite deposits supply most of the phosphorus for fertilizer. The calcium phosphate is treated with sulfuric acid and changed to superphosphate to render it more soluble in the dilute acids that exist in the soil.

Transparent varieties of apatite of fine color are occasionally used for gems. The mineral is too soft, however, to allow its extensive use for this purpose.

Name. From the Greek word *to deceive*, since the gem varieties were confused with other minerals.

Pyromorphite—$Pb_5Cl(PO_4)_3$

Crystallography. Hexagonal; dipyramidal. Prismatic crystals with basal plane (Fig. 526). Rarely shows pyramid truncations. Often in rounded barrel-shaped forms. Sometimes cavernous, the crystals being hollow prisms. Also in parallel groups. Frequently globular, reniform, fibrous, and granular.

Physical properties. H $3\frac{1}{2}$–4. **G** 6.5–7.1. Luster resinous to adamantine. Color usually various shades of green, brown, yellow; rarely orange-yellow, gray, white. Subtransparent to translucent.

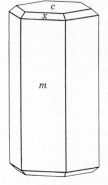

Fig. 526.
Pyromorphite.

Composition. Lead chlorophosphate, $Pb_3Cl(PO_4)_3$. Pb 82.2, Cl 2.6, P_2O_5 15.7 per cent. AsO_4 substitutes for PO_4 and a complete series extends to mimetite. Calcium may substitute in part for lead.

Tests. Fusible at 2. Gives a lead globule with sodium carbonate. When fused alone on charcoal gives a globule which on cooling appears to show crystal forms. The addition of a few drops of the nitric acid solution to ammonium molybdate solution gives a yellow precipitate of ammonium phosphomolybdate.

Diagnostic features. Characterized by its crystal form, high luster, and high specific gravity.

Occurrence. Pyromorphite is a supergene mineral found in the oxidized portions of lead veins, associated with other lead minerals.

Notable localities for its occurrence are the lead mines of Poullaouen and Huelgoat, Brittany; at Ems in Nassau; at Zschopau, Saxony; Příbram, Bohemia; Beresovsk, Ural Mountains; and in Cumberland and at Leadhills, Scotland. In the United States found at Phoenixville, Pennsylvania; Davidson County, North Carolina; and Idaho.

Use. A subordinate ore of lead.

Name. Derived from two Greek words meaning *fire* and *form*, in allusion to the apparent crystalline form it assumes on cooling from fusion.

Mimetite—$Pb_5Cl(AsO_4)_3$

Crystallography. Hexagonal; dipyramidal. Crystals prismatic, showing basal plane and pyramids. Usually in rounded barrel- to globular-shaped forms. Also in rounded crystals, mammillary crusts. Nearly identical to pyromorphite in appearance.

Physical properties. H $3\frac{1}{2}$. **G** 7–7.2. Luster resinous to adamantine. Colorless, yellow, orange, brown. Subtransparent to translucent.

Composition. Lead chloroarsenate, $Pb_5Cl(AsO_4)_3$. PbO 74.9, Cl 2.4, As_2O_5 23.2 per cent. PO_4 substitutes for AsO_4, and a complete series extends to pyromorphite. Calcium may substitute for some lead.

Tests. Fusible at $1\frac{1}{2}$. Gives globules of lead when fused with sodium carbonate on charcoal. A fragment placed in the closed tube and heated in contact with a splinter of charcoal gives deposit of metallic arsenic on walls of tube.

Diagnostic features. Difficult to distinguish from pyromorphite without a blowpipe or chemical test.

Occurrence. Mimetite is a comparatively rare supergene mineral occurring in the oxidized portions of lead veins associated with other lead minerals. Notable localities for its occurrence are in Cornwall and Cumberland, England; Johanngeorgenstadt, Saxony; and Nerchinsk, Siberia. In the United States found at Phoenixville, Pennsylvania, and Eureka, Utah.

Use. A minor ore of lead.

Name. Derived from the Greek for *imitator*, in allusion to its resemblance to pyromorphite.

Vanadinite—$Pb_5Cl(VO_4)_3$

Crystallography. Hexagonal; dipyramidal. Prism with base. May have small pyramidal faces, rarely the hexagonal dipyramid. In rounded crystals; in some cases cavernous. Also in globular forms. As incrustations.

Physical properties. H 3. **G** 6.9. Luster resinous to adamantine. Color ruby-red, orange-red, brown, yellow. Transparent to translucent.

Composition. Lead chlorovanadate, $Pb_5Cl(VO_4)_3$. PbO 78.7, Cl 2.5, V_2O_5 19.4 per cent. PO_4 and AsO_4 may substitute in small amounts for VO_4. In the variety *endlichite*, intermediate between vanadinite and mimetite, the proportion of V_2O_5 to As_2O_5 is nearly 1 : 1.

Tests. Fusible at $1\frac{1}{2}$. Gives globule of lead on charcoal when fused with sodium carbonate. Gives an amber color in the oxidizing flame to salt of phosphorus bead (vanadium). Dilute nitric acid solution gives with silver nitrate a white precipitate of silver chloride.

Diagnostic features. Characterized by crystal form, high luster, and high specific gravity; distinguished from pyromorphite and mimetite by color.

Occurrence. Vanadinite is a rare mineral of secondary origin found in the oxidized portion of lead veins associated with other lead minerals. Found in fine crystals near Oudjda, Morocco, and Grootfontein, South-West Africa. In the United States occurs in various districts in Arizona and New Mexico.

Use. Source of vanadium and minor ore of lead. Vanadium is obtained chiefly from other ores, such as *patronite*, a substance of indefinite composition formerly thought to be the sulfide; the vanadate *carnotite;* and a vanadium mica, *roscoelite.* Vanadium is used chiefly as a steel-hardening metal. Metavanadic acid, HVO_3, is a yellow pigment, known as vanadium bronze. Vanadium oxide is a mordant in dyeing.

AMBLYGONITE—$LiAlFPO_4$

Crystallography. Triclinic; pinacoidal. Usually in coarse, cleavable masses. Crystals are rare, equant, and usually rough when large.

Physical properties. Cleavage {100} perfect, {110} good. **H** 6. **G** 3.0–3.1. Luster vitreous, pearly on {100} cleavage. Color white to pale green or blue. Translucent.

Composition. Lithium aluminum fluophosphate, $LiAlFPO_4$. Li_2O 10.1, Al_2O_3 34.4, F 12.9, P_2O_5 47.9 per cent. Hydroxyl (OH) substitutes for fluorine and sodium for lithium. When OH > F the mineral is *montebrasite.*

Tests. Fusible at 2 with intumescence, giving a red flame (lithium). Insoluble in acids. After fusion with sodium carbonate and dissolving in nitric acid, solution with excess of ammonium molybdate solution gives yellow precipitate (test for phosphate).

Diagnostic features. Cleavage fragments may be confused with feldspar, but are much more easily fusible and yield a red flame.

Occurrence. Amblygonite is a rare mineral found in granite pegmatite with spodumene, tourmaline, lepidolite, and apatite. Found at Montebras, France. In the United States occurs at Hebron, Paris, Auburn, and Peru, Maine; Pala, California; and Black Hills, South Dakota.

Use. A source of lithium.

Name. From the two Greek words meaning *blunt* and *angle,* in allusion to the angle between the cleavages.

LAZULITE—$MgAl_2(OH)_2(PO_4)_2$

Crystallography. Monoclinic; prismatic. Crystals showing steep fourth-order prisms rare. Usually massive, granular to compact.

Physical properties. Indistinct prismatic {110} cleavage. **H** 5–$5\frac{1}{2}$. **G** 3.0–3.1. Luster vitreous. Color azure-blue. Translucent.

Composition. A basic magnesium aluminum phosphate, $MgAl_2(OH)_2(PO_4)_2$. Ferrous iron replaces magnesium, and a complete series exists between lazulite and the iron end member, *scorzalite.*

Tests. Infusible. Before the blowpipe it swells, loses its color, and falls to pieces. In the closed tube whitens and yields water. Insoluble. After fusion with sodium carbonate, a nitric acid solution added to an excess of ammonium molybdate solution gives a yellow precipitate of ammonium phosphomolybdate.

Diagnostic features. If crystals are lacking, lazulite is difficult to distinguish from other blue minerals without a chemical or blowpipe test.

Occurrence. Lazulite is a rare mineral. It is usually found in quartzites associated with kyanite, andalusite, corundum, rutile. Notable localities for its occurrence are Salzburg, Austria; Krieglach, Styria; and Horrsjoberg, Sweden. In the United States found with corundum on Crowder's Mountain, Gaston County, North Carolina; with rutile on Graves Mountain, Lincoln County, Georgia; and with andalusite in the White Mountains, Inyo County, California.

Use. A minor gem stone.

Name. Lazulite derived from an Arabic word meaning *heaven*, in allusion to the color of the mineral. Scorzalite after E. P. Scorza, Brazilian mineralogist.

Scorodite—FeAsO$_4$·2H$_2$O

Crystallography. Orthorhombic; dipyramidal. Usually in pyramidal crystals, resembling octahedrons; also prismatic. Crystals in irregular groups and aggregates. Also earthy and compact.

Physical properties. Cleavage {201} imperfect. **H** 3½–4. **G** 3.1–3.3. Luster vitreous to adamantine. Color pale green to liver-brown. Translucent.

Composition. A hydrous ferric arsenate, FeAsO$_4$·2H$_2$O. Fe$_2$O$_3$ 34.6, As$_2$O$_5$ 49.8, H$_2$O 15.6 per cent. Aluminum substitutes for ferric iron, and a complete series probably extends to *mansfieldite*, AlAsO$_4$·2H$_2$O.

Tests. Fusible at 2. Magnetic when heated in the reducing flame. Heated intensely with splinter of charcoal in the closed tube gives arsenic mirror. Water in the closed tube. Soluble in hydrochloric acid, and reacts for ferric iron.

Diagnostic features. No outstanding diagnostic property, but crystal habit, luster, and test for arsenic are usually sufficient to identify the mineral.

Occurrence. Scorodite occurs in oxidized portions of metallic veins as an alteration of arsenic-containing minerals. It is also deposited by certain hot springs. Notable localities are: Adun Chilon Mountains, Siberia; Laurium, Greece; Lolling, Carinthia; and Cornwall, England. In the United States scorodite occurs at several localities in Nevada, notably at Eureka and in the Tintic district of Utah; and as a deposit of hot springs at Yellowstone National Park.

Name. From the Greek word meaning *garlic*, in allusion to the odor obtained on heating.

Wavellite—$Al_3(OH)_3(PO_4)_2 \cdot 5H_2O$

Crystallography. Orthorhombic; dipyramidal. Crystals rare. Usually in radiating spherulitic and globular aggregates.

Physical properties. Cleavage {110} and {101} good. **H** $3\frac{1}{2}$–4. **G** 2.33. Luster vitreous. Color white, yellow, green, and brown. Translucent.

Composition. A hydrous basic aluminum phosphate, $Al_3(OH)_3$-$(PO_4)_2 \cdot 5H_2O$. Al_2O_3 38.0, P_2O_5 35.2, H_2O 26.8 per cent. Fluorine may substitute for OH.

Tests. Infusible, but on heating swells and splits into fine particles. Insoluble. Yields much water in the closed tube. Decomposed by fusion with sodium carbonate and dissolved in nitric acid gives yellow precipitate when solution is added to excess of ammonium molybdate (test for phosphoric acid). When moistened with cobalt nitrate and then ignited assumes a blue color (aluminum).

Diagnostic features. Characterized almost invariably by radiating globular aggregates.

Occurrence. Wavellite is a rare mineral of secondary origin. Frequently in small amounts in crevices in aluminous, low-grade metamorphic rocks and in limonite and phosphorite deposits. Although it occurs in many localities, it never is found in quantity. In the United States wavellite occurs in a number of localities in Pennsylvania and near Avant, Arkansas.

Name. After Dr. William Wavel, who discovered the mineral.

Turquoise—$CuAl_6(PO_4)_4(OH)_8 \cdot 2H_2O$

Crystallography. Triclinic; pinacoidal. Rarely in minute crystals, usually cryptocrystalline. Massive compact, reniform, stalactitic. In thin seams, incrustations and disseminated grains.

Physical properties. **H** 6. **G** 2.6–2.8. Luster waxlike. Color blue, bluish green, green. Transmits light on thin edges.

Composition. A basic hydrous phosphate of aluminum, $CuAl_6$-$(PO_4)_4(OH)_8 \cdot 2H_2O$. Ferric iron can substitute for aluminum, and a complete series exists between turquoise and *chalcosiderite* in which iron exceeds aluminum.

Tests. Infusible. When moistened with hydrochloric acid and heated gives blue copper chloride flame. Soluble in hydrochloric acid after ignition. Solution gives a yellow precipitate with an excess of ammonium molybdate solution (test for a phosphate). Gives a momentary green flame. In the closed tube turns dark and gives water.

Diagnostic features. Turquoise can be easily recognized by its color. It is harder than chrysocolla, the only common mineral which it resembles.

Occurrence. Turquoise is a mineral of secondary origin, usually found in the form of small veins and stringers traversing more or less decomposed volcanic rocks. The famous Persian deposits are found in trachyte near Nishâpûr in the province of Khorasan. In the United States it is found in a much altered trachytic rock in the Los Cerillos Mountains, near Santa Fe, and elsewhere in New Mexico. Turquoise has also been found in Arizona, Nevada, and California.

Use. As a gem stone. It is always cut in round or oval forms. Much turquoise is cut which is veined with the various gangue materials, and such stones are sold under the name of *turquoise matrix*.

Name. Turquoise is French and means *Turkish*, the original stones having come into Europe from the Persian locality through Turkey.

Autunite—$Ca(UO_2)_2(PO_4)_2 \cdot 10$–$12H_2O$

Crystallography. Tetragonal; ditetragonal-dipyramidal. Crystals tabular parallel to {001}; subparallel growths are common; also foliated and scaly aggregates.

Physical properties. Perfect {001} cleavage. **H** 2–$2\frac{1}{2}$. **G** 3.1–3.2. Luster vitreous, pearly on {001}. Color lemon yellow to pale green. Streak yellow. In ultraviolet light fluoresces strongly yellow-green.

Composition. A hydrated phosphate of calcium and uranium, $Ca(UO_2)_2(PO_4)_2 \cdot 10$–$12H_2O$. Small amounts of barium and magnesium may substitute for calcium. On slight heating autunite passes reversibly to *meta-autunite I* with $6\frac{1}{2}$–$2\frac{1}{2}$ H_2O; on heating to about $80°$ C autunite passes irreversibly to *meta-autunite II* with 0–6 H_2O.

Tests. Fusible at 2–3. Soluble in acids. A soda bead with dissolved torbernite fluoresces in ultraviolet light.

Diagnostic features. Autunite is characterized by yellow-green tetragonal plates and strong fluorescence in ultraviolet light.

Occurrence. Autunite is a secondary mineral found chiefly in the zone of oxidation and weathering derived from the alteration of uraninite or other uranium minerals. Notable localities are near Autun, France; Sabugal and Vizeu, Portugal; Johanngeorgenstadt district and Falkenstein, Germany; Cornwall, England; and Katanga district, Belgian Congo. In the United States autunite is found in many pegmatites, notably at the Ruggles mine, Grafton Center, New Hampshire; Black Hills, South Dakota; and Spruce Pine, Mitchell County, North Carolina. The finest specimens have come from the Daybreak mine, Spokane County, Washington.

Use. An ore of uranium (see uraninite, page 301).

Name. From Autun, France.

Similar species. *Torbernite*, $Cu(UO_2)_2(PO_4)_2 \cdot 8-12H_2O$, is iso-structural with autunite, but there is no evidence of a solid-solution series. Color green, nonfluorescent. Associated with autunite.

Vivianite—$Fe_3(PO_4)_2 \cdot 8H_2O$

Crystallography. Monoclinic; prismatic. Prismatic crystals, vertically striated; often in radiating groups. Also nodular and earthy.

Physical properties. Perfect {010} cleavage. **H** $1\frac{1}{2}$–2. **G** 2.58–2.68. Luster vitreous; pearly on cleavage face. Colorless when unaltered; blue to green when altered. Transparent when fresh, becoming translucent on exposure.

Composition. Hydrous ferrous phosphate, $Fe_3(PO_4)_2 \cdot 8H_2O$. FeO 43.0, P_2O_5 28.3, H_2O 28.7 per cent.

Tests. Fusible at 2 to a magnetic globule. Nitric acid solution added to an excess of ammonium molybdate solution gives yellow precipitate (test for phosphate). Water in the closed tube.

Diagnostic features. Usually altered, and in this state characterized by blue to green color. Cleavage lamellae flexible.

Occurrence. Vivianite is a rare mineral of secondary origin, associated with pyrrhotite and pyrite in copper and tin veins and forms as a weathering product from primary iron-manganese phosphates in pegmatites. Found also in beds of clay; may be associated with limonite; often in cavities of fossils.

Name. In honor of the eighteenth-century English mineralogist J. G. Vivian, the discoverer of the mineral.

Similar species. *Variscite*, $Al(PO_4) \cdot 2H_2O$, is a massive, bluish green mineral somewhat resembling turquoise. It has been found in nodules in a large deposit at Fairfield, Utah.

Erythrite—$Co_3(AsO_4)_2 \cdot 8H_2O$

Cobalt Bloom

Crystallography. Monoclinic; prismatic. Crystals prismatic and vertically striated. Usually as crusts in globular and reniform shapes. Also pulverulent and earthy.

Physical properties. Perfect {010} cleavage. **H** $1\frac{1}{2}$–$2\frac{1}{2}$. **G** 3.06. Luster adamantine to vitreous, pearly on cleavage. Color crimson to pink. Translucent.

Composition. Hydrous cobalt arsenate, $Co_3(AsO_4)_2 \cdot 8H_2O$. CoO 37.5, As_2O_5 38.4, H_2O 24.1 per cent. Nickel substitutes for cobalt to form a complete series to annabergite, $Ni_3(AsO_4)_2 \cdot 8H_2O$. *Annabergite*, or *nickel bloom*, is light green in color.

Tests. Fusible at 2 to a gray bead. When heated on charcoal gives arsenical odor. Imparts a deep blue to the borax bead (cobalt). Soluble in hydrochloric acid, giving a red solution.

Diagnostic features. The association of erythrite with other cobalt minerals and its pink color are usually sufficient to distinguish it from all other minerals.

Occurrence. Erythrite is a rare secondary mineral which occurs as an alteration product of cobalt arsenides. It is rarely present in large amounts and usually forms as crusts or fine aggregates filling cracks. Notable localities are at Schneeberg, Saxony, and Cobalt, Ontario.

Use. Although erythrite has no economic importance it is used by the prospector as a guide to other cobalt minerals and associated native silver.

Name. From the Greek word meaning *red*.

Carnotite—$K_2(UO_2)_2(VO_4)_2 \cdot 3H_2O$

Crystallography. Orthorhombic. Only rarely in imperfect microscopic crystals flattened on {001}. Usually found as a powder or as loosely coherent aggregates; disseminated.

Physical properties. Perfect basal {001} cleavage. The specific gravity has not been measured but has been calculated as **G** 5.03. Luster dull or earthy. Color bright yellow to greenish yellow.

Composition. A hydrated basic vanadate of potassium and uranium, $K_2(UO_2)_2(VO_4)_2 \cdot 3H_2O$. The water content varies with humidity at ordinary temperatures; the $3H_2O$ is for fully hydrated material. Small amounts of calcium, barium, magnesium, iron, and sodium have been reported.

Tests. Infusible. Soluble in acids. A soda bead with dissolved carnotite fluoresces in ultraviolet light (test for uranium).

Diagnostic features. Carnotite is characterized by its yellow color, its pulverant nature, and its occurrence. Unlike many secondary uranium minerals, carnotite will not fluoresce.

Occurrence. Carnotite is of secondary origin, and its formation is usually ascribed to the action of meteoric waters on pre-existing uranium and vanadium minerals. It has a strong pigmenting power and when present in a sandstone in amounts even less than 1 per cent will color the rock yellow. It is found principally in the plateau region of southwestern Colorado and in adjoining districts of Utah where it occurs disseminated in a cross-bedded sandstone. Concentrations of relatively pure carnotite are found around petrified tree trunks.

Use. Carnotite is an ore of vanadium and, in the United States, a principal ore of uranium.

Name. After Marie-Adolphe Carnot (1839–1920), French mining engineer and chemist.

Similar species. *Tyuyamunite*, $Ca(UO_2)_2(VO_4)_2 \cdot 3H_2O$, is the calcium analogue of carnotite and similar in physical properties except for a slightly more greenish color and yellow-green fluorescence. It is found in almost all carnotite deposits. Named from Tyuya Muyum, Southeastern Turkistan, U.S.S.R., where it is mined as a uranium ore.

TUNGSTATES AND MOLYBDATES

The six-valent ions of tungsten and molybdenum (Ion. rad. of both = 0.62 Å) are considerably larger than those of six-valent sulfur and five-valent phosphorus. Hence, when these ions enter into aniso-desmic ionic groups with oxygen, the four coordinated oxygen ions do not occupy the apices of regular tetrahedra, as is the case in the sulfates and phosphates, but form a somewhat flattened grouping of square outline. Although W 184 has a much greater atomic weight than Mo 96, both belong to the same family of the periodic table and, because of the lanthanide contraction, have the same ionic radii. As a result, each may freely substitute for the other as the coordinating cation in the warped tetrahedral oxygen groupings. In nature, however, the operation of the processes of geochemical differentiation often separate these elements, perhaps because of their very different atomic weights, and it is not uncommon to find primary tungstates almost wholly free of molybdenum, and vice versa. In secondary minerals, the two elements are more commonly associated in solid-solution relations with each other.

The minerals of this chemical class fall in the main into two isostructural groups. The wolframite group consists of fairly small divalent cations such as iron, manganese, magnesium, nickel, and cobalt in 6-fold coordination with tungstate ions. Complete solid solution between ferrous iron and divalent manganese is observed in minerals.

The scheelite group contains compounds of larger divalent ions such as calcium and lead in 8-fold coordination with tungstate and molybdate ions. Tungsten and molybdenum may substitute for each other forming partial series between *scheelite*, $CaWO_4$, and *powellite*, $CaMoO_4$; and *stolzite*, $PbWO_4$, and *wulfenite*, $PbMoO_4$. The substitution of calcium and lead for one another forms partial series between scheelite and stolzite and between powellite and wulfenite.

Tungstates and Molybdates

Wolframite	$(Fe,Mn)WO_4$
Scheelite	$CaWO_4$
Wulfenite	$PbMoO_4$

WOLFRAMITE—$(Fe,Mn)WO_4$

Crystallography. Monoclinic; prismatic. Crystals commonly tabular parallel to the front pinacoid (Fig. 527), giving bladed forms.

[001] zone vertically striated. In bladed, lamellar, or columnar forms. Massive granular.

Physical properties. Cleavage {010} perfect. **H** 4-4½. **G** 7.0-7.5, higher with higher iron content. Luster submetallic to resinous. Color black in *ferberite* to brown in *huebnerite*. Streak from nearly black to brown.

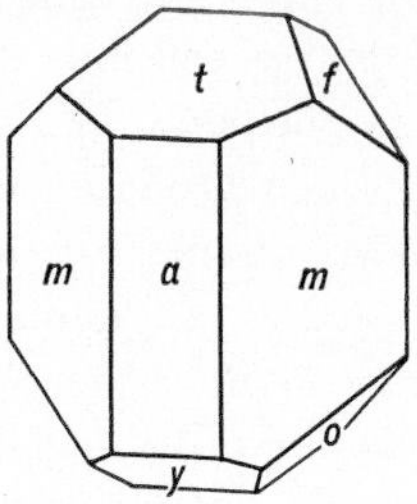

Composition. Ferrous and manganous tungstate, $(Fe,Mn)WO_4$. Ferrous iron and divalent manganese substitute for each other in all proportions and a complete solid-solution series exists between *ferberite*, $FeWO_4$, and *huebnerite*, $MnWO_4$. The percentage of WO_3 is 76.3 in ferberite and 76.6 in huebnerite.

Fig. 527. Wolframite.

Tests. Fusible at 3-4 to a magnetic globule. Insoluble in acids. Fused with sodium carbonate, dissolves in hydrochloric acid; tin added and solution boiled gives a blue color (tungsten). In the oxidizing flame with sodium carbonate gives bluish green bead (manganese).

Diagnostic features. The dark color, one direction of perfect cleavage, and high specific gravity serve to distinguish wolframite from other minerals.

Occurrence. Wolframite is a comparatively rare mineral found usually in pegmatite dikes and high-temperature quartz veins associated with granites. More rarely in sulfide veins. Minerals commonly associated include cassiterite, scheelite, bismuth, quartz, pyrite, galena, sphalerite, and arsenopyrite. In some veins wolframite may be the only metallic mineral present.

Found in fine crystals from Schlaggenwald and Zinnwald, Bohemia, and in the various tin districts of Saxony and Cornwall. Important deposits occur in China, Burma, New South Wales, and Bolivia. Nearly half of the world's supply of tungsten comes, as wolframite, from China. Wolframite occurs in the United States in the Black Hills, South Dakota. Ferberite has been mined extensively in Boulder County, Colorado. Huebnerite is found near Silverton, Colorado; Mammoth district, Nevada; and Black Hills, South Dakota.

Use. Chief ore of tungsten. Tungsten is used as hardening metal in the manufacture of high-speed tool steel, valves, springs, chisels, files, etc. Its high melting point (3410° C) requires a special chemical process for reduction of the metal which is produced in the form of a powder. By powder-metallurgy, pure metal products such as lamp filaments are fabricated. A large use for tungsten is in the manufacture of carbides, harder than any natural abrasives, and are used for cutting tools, rock bits, and hard facings. Sodium tungstate is used in fireproofing cloth and as a mordant in dyeing.

Name. Wolframite is derived from an old word of German origin.

SCHEELITE—$CaWO_4$

Crystallography. Tetragonal; dipyramidal. Crystals usually simple dipyramids of the first order. The second-order dipyramid closely resembles the octahedron in angles (Fig. 528). Faces of the tetragonal dipyramid are small and rare. Also massive granular.

Physical properties. Cleavage {011}. **H** $4\frac{1}{2}$–5. **G** 5.9–6.1 (unusually high for a mineral with nonmetallic luster). Luster vitreous to adamantine. Color white, yellow, green, brown. Translucent; some specimens transparent. Most scheelite will fluoresce.

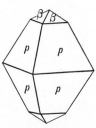

Composition. Calcium tungstate, $CaWO_4$. CaO 19.4, WO_3 80.6 per cent. Molybdenum is usually present, replacing a part of the tungsten.

Tests. Difficultly fusible (5). Decomposed by boiling in hydrochloric acid, leaving a yellow residue of tungstic oxide, which, when tin is added to the solution and boiling continued, turns first blue and then brown.

Fig. 528. Scheelite.

Diagnostic features. Recognized by its high specific gravity and crystal form. The test for tungsten may be necessary for identification.

Occurrence. Scheelite is found in granite pegmatites, contact metamorphic deposits, and high-temperature ore veins which are associated with granitic rocks. Associated with cassiterite, topaz, fluorite, apatite, molybdenite, and wolframite. Found in places with gold. Occurs in connection with the tin deposits of Bohemia, Saxony, and Cornwall; and in quantity in New South Wales and Queensland. In the United States scheelite is mined near Mill City and Mina, Nevada; near Atolia, San Bernardino County, California; and in lesser amounts in Arizona, Utah, and Colorado.

Use. An ore of tungsten. Wolframite furnishes most of the world's supply of tungsten, but scheelite is more important in the United States.

Name. After K. W. Scheele, the discoverer of tungsten.

WULFENITE—$PbMoO_4$

Crystallography. Tetragonal; pyramidal. Crystals usually square tabular in habit with prominent base (Fig. 529). Some crystals very thin. Edges of tables beveled with faces of low second-order pyramid (Fig. 530). More rarely pyramidal in habit. Also massive granular, coarse to fine.

Physical properties. H 3. **G** 6.8±. Luster vitreous to adamantine. Color yellow, orange, red, gray, white. Streak white. Transparent to subtranslucent.

Composition. Lead molybdate, $PbMoO_4$. PbO 60.8, MoO_3 39.2 per cent. Calcium may replace some of the lead.

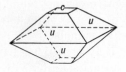   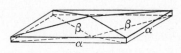

Fig. 529.   Fig. 530.

Wulfenite.

Tests. Fusible at 2. Gives a lead globule when fused with sodium carbonate on charcoal. With salt of phosphorus in the reducing flame gives green bead; in the oxidizing flame, yellowish green when hot to almost colorless when cold.

Diagnostic features. Wulfenite is characterized by its tabular crystals, orange to yellow color, high luster, and association with other lead minerals. Distinguished from crocoite by test for molybdenum.

Occurrence. Wulfenite is found in the oxidized portion of lead veins with other secondary lead minerals, especially vanadinite and pyromorphite. Found in the United States at Phoenixville, Pennsylvania, and in a number of places in Utah, Nevada, Arizona, and New Mexico. Found in beautiful crystals at Red Cloud, Arizona.

Use. A minor source of molybdenum. Molybdenite is the chief ore.

Name. After X. F. Wulfen, Austrian mineralogist.

SILICATES

The silicate mineral class is of greater importance than any other, for about 25 per cent of the known minerals and nearly 40 per cent of the common ones are silicates. With a few minor exceptions all the igneous rock-forming minerals are silicates, and they thus constitute well over 90 per cent of the earth's crust.

Of every 100 atoms in the crust of the earth, more than 60 are oxygen, over 20 silicon, and 6 to 7 aluminum. Iron, calcium, magnesium, sodium, and potassium each account for about two more atoms. With the possible exception of titanium, all other elements are volumetrically insignificant in the architecture of the earth's crust. Since our approach to the nature of minerals in this book is structural rather than stoichiometric, it is entirely proper that we should think of the constituents of the crust in terms of the space they occupy rather than their percentages by weight. If we do so, we are led to picture the crust as a boxwork of oxygen ions bound into configurations of greater or lesser complexity by the small, highly charged silicon and aluminum ions. The interstices of this more or less continuous oxygen-silicon-aluminum network are occupied by ions of magnesium, iron, calcium, sodium, and potassium in coordination states proper to their individual radii. This startling simplification of the composition of the earth's crust results from consideration of *atomic proportions* rather than weight per cents, the form in which the composition of rocks and minerals is usually stated.

The dominant minerals of the crust are thus shown to be the silicates and oxides, whose properties depend upon the chemical and physical conditions of origin. Of the different assemblages of silicate minerals, which characterize igneous, sedimentary, and metamorphic rocks, ore veins, pegmatites, weathered rocks, and soils, each tells something of the environment in which it was formed. If the rocks are the pages in the book of geologic history, the minerals are the characters in which the book is printed and only with an understanding of them and their structures does the document become readable.

We have a further deep and compelling reason for the study of the silicates. The soil from which our food is ultimately drawn is made up in large part of silicates. The brick, stone, concrete, and glass used in the construction of our buildings are either silicates or largely derived from silicates. The silicates are the most important ceramic materials and contribute in a host of ways to our culture and standard of living. Even with the coming of the space age, we need not fear obsolescence of our studies of the silicates, but rather an enlargement of their scope, since we have every reason to believe that the moon and all the planets of our solar system have rocky crusts made of silicates and oxides much like those of Earth.

The ratio of the radius of the four-valent silicon ion (Rad. = 0.42 Å) to that of the oxygen ion (Rad. = 1.32Å) is 0.318. This radius ratio indicates that 4-fold coordination will be the stable state of silicon-oxygen groupings. The fundamental unit on which the structure of all silicates is based consists of four oxygen ions at the apices of a regular tetrahedron surrounding and coordinated by the four-valent silicon ion (Fig. 531). The powerful bond which unites the oxygen and silicon ions is literally the cement that holds the earth's crust together. This bond may be estimated by use of Pauling's (page 190) electronegativity concept as 50% ionic 50% covalent. That is, although the bond arises in part from the attraction of oppositely charged ionic units, it also involves sharing of electrons and interpenetration of the electronic super-structures of the ions involved. The bond is strongly localized in the vicinity of these shared electrons.

Fig. 531. SiO_4 Tetrahedra.

Although electron sharing is present in the silicon-oxygen bond, the total bonding energy of the silicon ion is still distributed equally among its four closest oxygen neighbors. Hence, the strength of any single silicon-oxygen bond is equal to just one-half the total bonding energy available in the oxygen ion. Each oxygen ion has, therefore, the potentiality of bonding to another silicon ion and entering into another tetrahedral grouping, thus uniting the tetrahedral groups through the shared oxygen. This sharing may involve one, two, three, or all four of the oxygen ions in the tetrahedron, giving rise to a diversity of structural configurations. In no case, however, are three or even two oxygens shared between two adjacent tetrahedra in nature. Such sharing would place two highly charged positive silicon ions close together and the repulsion between them renders the structure unstable. Sharing of one oxygen between any two adjacent tetrahedra may, if all four oxygens are so shared, give rise to structures with a very high degree of connectivity, such as the quartz structure. We may call this linking of tetrahedra by sharing of oxygens *polymerization*, to borrow a term from organic chemistry, and the capacity for polymerization is the origin of the great variety of silicate structures.

There is a simple and highly significant relation between the conditions of origin of silicate minerals and the degree of polymerization. All other things being equal, *the higher the temperature of formation, the lower the degree of polymerization and vice versa.* This relation is subject to the disturbing effect of a host of external factors, chief among which are pressure and chemical concentration. Within a single geological body such as a mass of crystallizing igneous rock, the generalization seems to be supported by observation. It has long been noted that the silicate minerals in igneous rocks display a fairly regular and predictable sequence of crystallization, beginning with olivine and progressing through pyroxene to amphibole and thence to micas. Although calcium-rich feldspar may appear very early in the sequence of crystallization, alkali-rich feldspar and quartz are generally very late. N. L. Bowen[1] and his associates at the Geophysical Laboratory in Washington, D. C., during nearly half a century of phase equilibrium studies of silicates observed a very similar sequence of appearance of silicate minerals with reduction in temperature. This sequence is in the order of increasing polymerization of the silicate tetrahedra.

Next to oxygen and silicon the most important constituent of the crust is aluminum. Aluminum is trivalent and has an ionic radius of 0.51 Å. Hence the ratio of its radius to that of oxygen is 0.386, corresponding to a normal coordination number with oxygen of four. However, the radius ratio is sufficiently close to the upper limit for 4-fold coordination so that 6-fold coordination is also possible and almost as stable as 4-fold. It is this capacity for playing a double role in silicate minerals that gives aluminum its outstanding significance in the crystal chemistry of the silicates. When aluminum coordinates four oxygens arranged at the apices of a regular tetrahedron, the resultant grouping occupies the same space as a silicon-oxygen tetrahedron and may link with silicon tetrahedra in polymerized groupings. On the other hand, aluminum in 6-fold coordination may serve to link the tetrahedral groupings together through simple ionic bonds, much weaker than those which unite the ions in the tetrahedra. It is thus possible to have aluminum in silicate structures both in the tetrahedral sites, substituting for silicon, and in the octahedral sites with 6-fold coordination, involved in solid-solution relations with magnesium and divalent and trivalent iron.

Magnesium, divalent iron, trivalent iron, divalent manganese, alumi-

[1] N. L. Bowen, *The evolution of the igneous rocks.* Princeton University Press, Princeton, N. J., 1928. (Reprinted 1956 by Dover Publications, New York.)

num, and tetravalent titanium all tend to occur in silicate structures in 6-fold coordination with respect to oxygen. Although divalent, trivalent, and tetravalent ions are included here, all have about the same space requirements and about the same radius ratio relations with oxygen and, hence, tend to occupy the same type of atomic site. Since one of the inviolate rules of crystal structures is that of electrical neutrality, solid-solution relations between ions of such diverse valence introduces a problem of electrical compensation. Thus, if a tetravalent cation is substituted for a trivalent, such as titanium for ferric iron, gaining one positive charge, then somewhere in the crystal another substitution must be made in which a positive charge is lost or a negative charge gained.

The larger and more weakly charged cations, calcium and sodium, of ionic radii 0.99 Å and 0.97 Å respectively, generally enter sites having 8-fold, or cubic, coordination with respect to oxygen. It is again obvious that substitution of divalent calcium for monovalent sodium creates a problem of electrical unbalance that must be solved by concomitant coupled substitution elsewhere in the structure. If, for instance, every time an aluminum ion substitutes for a silicon ion in a tetrahedral site, resulting in a loss of one positive charge, a calcium ion substitutes for a sodium ion in an 8-fold site, electrical balance will be maintained. It is by just this mechanism that electrical neutrality is preserved in the sodium-calcium feldspars, the scapolite group and other groups in which sodium and calcium substitute freely for each other.

Coordination of Important Elements in Silicates

	Coordination Number	Ion	Ionic Radius (Å)
Z	4	Si^{+4}	0.42
	4	Al'''	0.51
Y	6	Al'''	0.51
	6	Fe'''	0.64
	6	Mg''	0.66
	6	Ti^{+4}	0.68
	6	Fe''	0.74
	6	Mn''	0.80
X	8	Na'	0.97
	8	Ca''	0.99
X	8–12	K'	1.33
	8–12	Ba''	1.34
	8–12	Rb'	1.47

The largest ions common in silicate structures are those of potassium, rubidium, barium, and the rarer alkalis and alkali earths. These ions generally do not enter readily into sodium-calcium sites and are found in high-coordination-number sites of unique type. Hence, solid-solution relations between these ions and the common ions are limited and are generally confined to high-temperature crystallization, where solid solution is favored.

Ionic substitution is generally common and extensive between elements whose symbols lie between a pair of horizontal lines in the table, page 392, but it is rare and difficult between elements separated by a horizontal line. This generalization of the role played by the commonest elements in the structure of the silicates permits us to write a general formula for all silicates:

$$X_m Y_n (Z_p O_q) W_r$$

where X represents large, weakly charged ions in 8-fold or higher coordination with oxygen; Y represents medium sized, two to four valent ions in 6-fold coordination; Z represents small, highly charged ions in tetrahedral coordination; O is oxygen; and W represents additional anionic groups such as (OH) or anions such as Cl^-, F^-, etc. The ratio $p:q$ depends on the degree of polymerization of the silicate framework, and the other subscript variables, m, n, and r, depend on the condition of electrical neutrality. Any common silicate may be expressed by suitable substitution in this general formula.

Depending on the degree of polymerization and the extent of oxygen-sharing between tetrahedra, the silicate framework may consist of separate tetrahedra, separate multiple tetrahedral groups, chains, double chains or bands, sheets or three-dimensional boxworks. The silicate framework governs the ratio of $p:q$ in the general formula, the stoichiometric proportion of the oxides, and to a large extent the physical properties and chemical stability of the mineral. Hence, it is appropriate that this criterion should be used as a basis for the classification of the silicates.

Up to the 1930's, the analyses of silicates were interpreted and their formulas generally written in terms of a number of hypothetical oxyacids of silicon. Thus, olivine, Mg_2SiO_4, was termed an "ortho-silicate" and considered to be a salt of orthosilicic acid H_4SiO_4; enstatite, $MgSiO_3$, was called a "metasilicate" and considered to be a salt of metasilicic acid H_2SiO_3. In some simple cases this theory of the silicates worked fairly well, and some of these acids could be prepared. We now know that, because of the peculiar nature of the hydrogen bond, such acids have no significance for the silicates whatsoever.

However, when an analysis indicated a ratio of silicon to oxygen of $4:11$, as in the amphiboles, and contained excess water as well, there was a strong temptation to blame the departure from a ratio of $1:3$ on the imperfections of the analysis or the impurity of the sample and to assign the inconvenient water to the same source. This is what happened, and textbooks as late as 1932 wrote the formula of amphibole as "near that of a metasilicate, $RSiO_3$" and gave the formula $CaMg_3(SiO_3)_4$ for tremolite in spite of the fact that many of the available analyses calculate out precisely as $Ca_2Mg_5Si_8O_{22}(OH)_2$, the formula now accepted as in agreement with the structure. It is little wonder that the chemistry of the silicates was regarded as a chaotic morass of uncertainty. Into this chaos the structural determinations of the Braggs brought order. It is this scheme, summarized in 1937 by Berman[1] and revised and elaborated on by Strunz[2] (1957), that is followed in this book.

Silicate Classification*

Class	Arrangement of SiO_4 Tetrahedra	Ratio $Si:O$	Mineral Example
Nesosilicates	Isolated	$1:4$	Olivine, $(Mg,Fe)_2SiO_4$
Sorosilicates	Double	$2:7$	Hemimorphite $Zn_4(Si_2O_7)(OH)\cdot H_2O$
Cyclosilicates	Rings	$1:3$	Beryl, $Be_3Al_2(Si_6O_{18})$
Inosilicates	Chains (single)	$1:3$	Enstatite, $Mg_2(Si_2O_6)$
	Chains (double)	$4:11$	Tremolite, $Ca_2Mg_5(Si_8O_{22})(OH)_2$
Phyllosilicates	Sheets	$2:5$	Talc, $Mg_3(Si_4O_{10})(OH)_2$
Tectosilicates	Frameworks	$1:2$	Quartz, SiO_2

* The names of the silicate classes are those proposed by H. Strunz in *Mineralogische Tabellen*, 1941 and 1957. The prefixes are from the Greek: *neso*, island; *soro*, group; *cyclo*, ring; *ino*, chain or thread; *phyllo*, sheet; *tecto*, framework.

[1] Harry Berman, *Constitution and classification of the natural silicates.* Am. Min. 22, pp. 342–408, 1937.
[2] Hugo Strunz, *Mineralogische Tabellen.* Akademische Verlagsgesellschaft, Leipzig, 1957.

Nesosilicates

In the nesosilicates, the SiO_4 tetrahedra, common to all silicate structures, are isolated (Fig. 531) and bound to each other only by ionic bonds through interstitial cations. Their structures depend chiefly upon the size and charge of these interstitial cations. The simplest structures are found in those minerals in which there is only one type of cation site. If the cation is divalent, a compound of formula type A_2SiO_4, represented by phenacite and olivine, results. When the A cation is sufficiently small, such as Be^{+2} (0.35 Å), only 4-fold coordination with oxygen is permitted. The difficulty of arranging SiO_4 tetrahedra in such a way that each A cation coordinates only four oxygens, while maintaining electrical neutrality, leads to the rather complex phenacite structure (hexagonal rhombohedral). Willemite, Zn_2SiO_4, also has this structure.

Magnesium and divalent iron characteristically have 6-fold coordination with oxygen. When these ions enter into a compound of A_2SiO_4 type, a structure of rather high symmetry results consisting of SiO_4 tetrahedra arranged around A type sites so that each A ion coordinates six oxygens. This, the olivine structure, can be thought of as a regular stacking together of alternating tetrahedra and octahedra, with the apices of the tetrahedra pointing alternately up and down. The octahedral sites may be occupied by either magnesium or ferrous iron in random arrangement, giving rise to a complete solid-solution series between Mg_2SiO_4 and Fe_2SiO_4. Manganese may also enter the octahedral sites in the olivine structure, giving rise to solid solution between Fe_2SiO_4 and Mn_2SiO_4, *tephroite*.

Larger ions such as calcium and lead do not readily substitute for magnesium and ferrous iron in the olivine structure, and the silicates of calcium and lead have a different structure with higher coordination of the cations with respect to oxygen. If a A_2SiO_4 silicate containing large amounts of either calcium or lead in addition to magnesium, ferrous iron, or divalent manganese is caused to crystallize, an ordered layer-type double salt like dolomite will be formed, with the larger and smaller cations separated into layers. Several minerals of this type, such as *monticellite* and *larsenite*, are known.

The minerals of the olivine group are geologically very important. They are known to comprise several per cent of the superficial crustal rocks and are thought to predominate in the heavier and deeper seated rocks of the subcrustal zone. They are high-temperature minerals, in general forming early from silicate melts, and are frequently replaced by later minerals. They are common in extra-terrestrial stony meteorites and, hence, are probably important in all planets with a stony crust or mantle.

The mineral chondrodite typifies a group of related silicates made up of layers of the olivine structure alternating with structurally homologous brucite, $Mg(OH)_2$, sheets. Fluorine may substitute for hydroxyl in the octahedrally coordinated brucite layers. The minerals of this class are differentiated from each other by the relative proportions of olivine and brucite layers, having the general formula $Mg_{2n+1}(SiO_4)_n(F,OH)_2$ where $n = 1, 2, 3$, and 4, equal to the number of olivine layers to each brucite layer.

Silicates of zirconium, thorium, and uranium have the formula $ASiO_4$. These rather large cations enter stable 8-fold coordination with oxygen; and the resulting structure may be thought of as an alternation of tetrahedra and distorted cubes, giving rise to tetragonal symmetry. This is the zircon structure type, which is shared by thorite and coffinite, the silicates of thorium and uranium respectively. Some ionic substitution of the rare elements hafnium, yttrium, and cerium may take place, sometimes in appreciable amounts. Partial replacement of SiO_4 tetrahedra by $(OH)_4$ groupings is common.

The garnet group, with its striking uniformity of crystal morphology, its great diversity of chemical composition, and its strict dependence of physical properties upon composition, presents the finest example of an isostructural group. The structure consists of isolated SiO_4 tetrahedra united by oxygen-cation-oxygen bonds through two structurally distinct types of cation sites. One of these sites, A, is occupied by rather large divalent ions, the other, B, by smaller trivalent ions leading to the formula $A_3B_2(SiO_4)_3$. The structural arrangement is such that the atomic population of the $\{100\}$ and $\{111\}$ families of planes is much depleted. As a result, the cube and octahedron, common on most isometric hexoctahedral crystals, are rarely found on garnet crystals. Within the framework of this structure type, there is ready and substantially complete interchange of magnesium, ferrous iron, and divalent manganese in the A cation sites. Calcium substitutes less readily for the foregoing ions in the A sites. In the B sites there is limited substitution with respect to aluminum, ferric iron, and chromium.

Because of size considerations in the filling of the A cation sites, we may expect a fairly well-defined division of the garnets into those with calcium and those with the easily interchangeable magnesium, ferrous iron, and divalent manganese. Likewise, because of the limited substitution of the B ions, we may expect a separation of garnets into aluminum, ferric iron, and chromium bearing. These two trends are both well marked and have each given rise to a mode of classification of the garnets. The first, proposed by Winchell,[1] on the basis of the A ion, divides the garnets into two groups:

Pyralspite		Ugrandite	
Pyrope	MgAl	Uvarovite	CaCr
Almandine	FeAl	Grossularite	CaAl
Spessartine	MnAl	Andradite	CaFe

This classification serves as an excellent mnemonic aid for the names and formulas. The second grouping, on the basis of the B ion, yields three unequal groups:

Aluminum Garnets	Ferri-garnets	Chrome-garnets
Pyrope	Andradite	Uvarovite
Almandine		
Spessartine		
Grossularite		

$(OH)_4$ may substitute to a limited extent for SiO_4 groups in the *hydro-garnets*, such as hydrogrossularite, and titanium may enter the B sites concomitant with replacement of calcium by sodium in the A sites, producing the black *melanite*.

The three polymorphs of Al_2SiO_5 have rather complex chain or fiberlike structures; in all of them one of the two aluminum ions is consistently coordinated to six oxygens. In sillimanite the other aluminum is in 4-fold coordination producing a true chain structure of alternating silicon and aluminum tetrahedra, much resembling the structure of pyroxene. It is significant that sillimanite has the most fibrous and needlelike habit of the three polymorphs. In andalusite the second aluminum has a coordination number of five with respect to oxygen, and in kyanite both aluminums have a coordination number of six with respect to oxygen. As a result, andalusite and kyanite have a more columnar or bladed habit.

All three minerals are characteristic of metamorphic rocks. The stability relations between the three polymorphs are shown by the pressure-temperature diagram Fig. 532. All three may, however, occur in the same rock, because the transformations are sluggish.

Topaz, staurolite, datolite, and dumortierite have structures complicated by the presence of hydroxyl, fluorine, and boron. In the struc-

---

[1] N. H. Winchell and A. N. Winchell, *Elements of Optical Mineralogy.* John Wiley and Sons, New York, 1927.

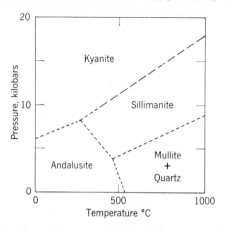

Fig. 532. Al_2SiO_5 Phase Diagram. (Clark, Robertson, and Birch, *Am. Jour. Sci.*, 255, 1957.)

Nesosilicates

PHENACITE GROUP
Phenacite $Be_2(SiO_4)$
Willemite $Zn_2(SiO_4)$

OLIVINE GROUP
Forsterite $Mg_2(SiO_4)$
Fayalite $Fe_2(SiO_4)$

GARNET GROUP $A_3B_2(SiO_4)_3$
Pyrope   Spessartite   Andradite
Almandine   Grossularite   Uvarovite

ZIRCON GROUP
Zircon $Zr(SiO_4)$

Al_2SiO_5 GROUP*
Andalusite $Al^{[6]}Al^{[5]}O(SiO_4)$
Sillimanite $Al^{[6]}Al^{[4]}O(SiO_4)$
Kyanite $Al^{[6]}Al^{[6]}O(SiO_4)$

Topaz $Al_2(SiO_4)(F,OH)_2$
Staurolite $Fe_2Al_9O_7(SiO_4)_4(OH)$

CHONDRODITE GROUP
Chondrodite $Mg_5(SiO_4)_2(OH,F)_2$

Datolite $CaB(SiO_4)(OH)$
Sphene $CaTiO(SiO_4)$
Dumortierite $(Al,Fe)_7O_3(BO_3)(SiO_4)_3$

* Numbers in square brackets equal the coordination number of the aluminum ion.

ture of sphene, $CaTiSiO_5$, one of the oxygens appearing in the formula is not a part of the isolated tetrahedral silicon-oxygen groups. Titanium is linked to six oxygens at the apices of a fairly regular octahedron, whereas the calcium ions have the unusual coordination number of seven with respect to oxygen.

Phenacite—$Be_2(SiO_4)$

Crystallography. Hexagonal-R; rhombohedral. Crystals usually rhombohedral in form. Short prisms may be present. Often with complex development.

Physical properties. Imperfect $\{11\bar{2}0\}$ cleavage. **H** $7\frac{1}{2}$–8. **G** 2.97–3.00. Luster vitreous. Colorless, white. Transparent to translucent.

Composition. Beryllium silicate, $Be_2(SiO_4)$. BeO 45.6, SiO_2 54.4 per cent.

Tests. Infusible and insoluble. Fused with sodium carbonate yields a white enamel.

Diagnostic features. Characterized by its crystal form and great hardness.

Occurrence. Phenacite is a rare mineral, found in pegmatite dikes associated with topaz, chrysoberyl, beryl, and apatite. Fine crystals are found at the emerald mines in the Ural Mountains, U.S.S.R., and in Minas Geraes, Brazil. In the United States found at Mount Antero, Colorado.

Use. Occasionally cut as a gem stone.

Name. From the Greek meaning *a deceiver*, in allusion to its having been mistaken for quartz.

WILLEMITE—$Zn_2(SiO_4)$

Crystallography. Hexagonal-R; rhombohedral. In hexagonal prisms with rhombohedral terminations. Usually massive to granular. Rarely in crystals.

Physical properties. Cleavage $\{0001\}$. **H** $5\frac{1}{2}$. **G** 3.9–4.2. Luster vitreous to resinous. Color yellow-green, flesh-red, and brown; white when pure. Transparent to translucent. Most willemite from Franklin, New Jersey, fluoresces. (See frontispiece.)

Composition. Zinc silicate, $Zn_2(SiO_4)$. ZnO 73.0, SiO_2 27.0 per cent. Manganese often replaces a considerable part of the zinc (manganiferous variety called *troostite*); iron may also be present in small amount.

Tests. Pure willemite infusible, troostite difficultly fusible ($4\frac{1}{2}$–5). Gives a coating of zinc oxide (yellow when hot, white when cold) when heated with sodium carbonate on charcoal; coating moistened with cobalt nitrate and heated turns green. When heated on charcoal with cobalt nitrate assay turns blue. Troostite will give reddish violet color to the borax bead in the oxidizing flame (manganese).

Diagnostic features. Willemite from Franklin, New Jersey, can usually be recognized by its association with franklinite and zincite. Other specimens must be identified by the above tests. Distinguished from hemimorphite by absence of water.

Occurrence. Willemite is found in crystalline limestone and may be the result of metamorphism of earlier hemimorphite or smithsonite. It is also found sparingly as a secondary mineral in the oxidized zone of zinc deposits.

Found at Altenberg, near Moresnet, Belgium; Algeria; French Congo; Northern Rhodesia; South-West Africa; and Greenland. The most important locality is in the United States at Franklin, New Jersey, where willemite occurs associated with franklinite and zincite and as grains imbedded in calcite. It has also been found at the Merritt mine, New Mexico, and Tiger, Arizona.

Use. A valuable zinc ore.

Name. In honor of the King of the Netherlands, William I.

OLIVINE—$(Mg,Fe)_2(SiO_4)$

Chrysolite. Peridot

Crystallography. Orthorhombic; dipyramidal. Crystals usually a combination of the three prisms, the three pinacoids, and dipyramid.

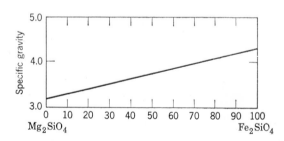

Fig. 533. Specific Gravity of Olivine.

Often flattened parallel to either the front or the side pinacoid. Usually in imbedded grains or in granular masses.

Physical properties. Fracture conchoidal. **H** $6\frac{1}{2}$–7. **G** 3.27–4.37, increasing with increase in iron content. (See Fig. 533.) Luster vitreous. Olive to grayish green, brown. Transparent to translucent.

Composition. Silicate of magnesium and ferrous iron, $(Mg,Fe)_2$-(SiO_4). A complete solid-solution series exists, grading from *forsterite*, $Mg_2(SiO_4)$ to *fayalite*, $Fe_2(SiO_4)$. The more common olivines are richer in magnesium than in iron.

Tests. Infusible. Rather slowly soluble in hydrochloric acid and yields gelatinous silica upon evaporation. Solution gives tests for iron and magnesium.

Diagnostic features. Distinguished usually by its glassy luster, conchoidal fracture, green color, and granular nature.

Occurrence. Olivine is a rather common rock-forming mineral, varying in amount from that of an accessory to that of a main constituent of the rock. It is found principally in the dark-colored ferromagnesian igneous rocks such as gabbro, peridotite, and basalt. A rock known as *dunite* is made up almost wholly of olivine. Found also as glassy grains in meteorites. Occasionally in crystalline dolomitic limestones. Associated often with pyroxene, calcic plagioclase feldspar, magnetite, corundum, chromite, and serpentine.

The transparent green variety is known as *peridot*. It was used as a gem in ancient times in the East, but the exact locality for the stones is not known. At present peridot is found in Burma, on St. John's Island in the Red Sea, and in rounded grains associated with pyrope garnet in the surface gravels of Arizona and New Mexico. Crystals of olivine are found in the lavas of Vesuvius. Larger crystals, altered to serpentine, come from Snarum, Norway. Olivine occurs in granular masses in volcanic bombs in the Eifel district, Germany, and in Arizona. Dunite rocks are found at Dun Mountain, New Zealand, and with the corundum deposits of North Carolina.

Alteration. Very readily altered to serpentine and less commonly to *iddingsite*. Magnesite and iron oxides may form at the same time as a result of the alteration.

Use. As the clear green variety, peridot, it has some use as a gem.

Name. Olivine derives its name from the usual olive-green color of the mineral and is the term usually given to the species when speaking of it as a rock-forming mineral. Peridot is an old name for the species.

Similar species. Other members of the olivine group which are rarer in occurrence are *monticellite*, $CaMgSiO_4$; *tephroite*, Mn_2SiO_4; *larsenite*, $PbZnSiO_4$.

GARNET GROUP

The garnet group includes a series of subspecies that crystallize in the hexoctahedral class of the isometric system and are similar in crystal habit. They all correspond to the same general formula although the elements present differ widely. (See page 397.)

Crystallography. Isometric; hexoctahedral. Common forms dodecahedron (Fig. 534) and trapezohedron (Fig. 535), often in combination (Figs. 536 and 537). Hexoctahedron observed occasionally (Fig. 538). Other forms rare. Usually distinctly crystallized; also in rounded grains; massive granular, coarse or fine.

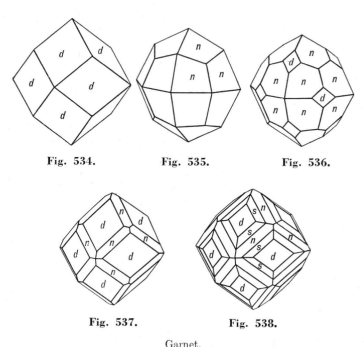

Fig. 534.   Fig. 535.   Fig. 536.

Fig. 537.   Fig. 538.

Garnet.

Physical properties. H $6\frac{1}{2}$–$7\frac{1}{2}$. G 3.5–4.3, varying with the composition (see page 403). Luster vitreous to resinous. Color varying with composition; most commonly red, also brown, yellow, white, green, black. White streak. Transparent to translucent.

Composition. The garnets are silicates which conform to the general formula $A_3B_2(SiO_4)_3$. A may be calcium, magnesium, ferrous iron, or divalent manganese; B may be aluminum, ferric iron, titanium, or chromium. The formulas of the chief subspecies are given, with the specific gravity for the pure compound; many of them, however, grade more or less into each other.

Pyrope. Precious garnet in part. Calcium and iron usually present. Color deep red to nearly black. Often transparent and then used as a

Subspecies	Composition	Specific Gravity
Pyrope	$Mg_3Al_2(SiO_4)_3$	$3.51\pm$
Almandite	$Fe_3Al_2(SiO_4)_3$	$4.25\pm$
Spessartite	$Mn_3Al_2(SiO_4)_3$	$4.18\pm$
Grossularite	$Ca_3Al_2(SiO_4)_3$	$3.53\pm$
Andradite	$Ca_3Fe_2(SiO_4)_3$	$3.75\pm$
Uvarovite	$Ca_3Cr_2(SiO_4)_3$	$3.77\pm$

gem. Name derived from Greek, meaning *firelike*. *Rhodolite* is the name given to a pale rose-red or purple garnet, corresponding in composition to two parts of pyrope and one of almandite.

Almandite. Precious garnet in part, common garnet in part. Ferric iron may replace aluminum, and magnesium, ferrous iron. Color fine deep red, transparent in precious garnet; brownish red, translucent in common garnet. Name derived from Alabanda, where in ancient times garnets were cut and polished.

Spessartite. Ferrous iron usually replaces some of the manganese and ferric iron some of the aluminum. Color brownish to red.

Grossularite (Essonite, Cinnamon Stone). Often contains ferrous iron replacing calcium and ferric iron replacing aluminum. Color, white, green, yellow, cinnamon-brown, pale red. Name derived from the botanical name for gooseberry, in allusion to the light green color of the original grossularite.

Andradite. Common garnet in part. Aluminum may replace ferric iron; ferrous iron, manganese, and magnesium may replace calcium. Color various shades of yellow, green, brown to black. *Demantoid* is a green variety with a brilliant luster, used as a gem. Named after the Portuguese mineralogist, d'Andrada.

Uvarovite. Calcium-chromium garnet. Color emerald-green. Named after Count Uvarov.

Tests. With the exception of uvarovite, all garnets fuse at $3-3\frac{1}{2}$; uvarovite is almost infusible. The iron garnets, almandite and andradite, fuse to magnetic globules. Spessartite when fused with sodium carbonate gives a bluish green bead (manganese). Uvarovite gives a green color to salt of phosphorus bead (chromium).

Diagnostic features. Garnets are usually recognized by their characteristic isometric crystals, their hardness, and their color. Specific gravity, refractive index, and unit-cell dimension taken together serve to distinguish members of the group.

Occurrence. Garnet is a common and widely distributed mineral, occurring as an accessory constituent of metamorphic and in some igneous rocks. Its most characteristic occurrence is in mica schists, hornblende schists, and gneisses. Found in pegmatite dikes, more rarely in granitic rocks. Grossularite is found chiefly as a product of contact or regional metamorphism in crystalline limestones. Almandite is especially characteristic of the mica schists. Pyrope is often found in peridotite rocks and the serpentines derived from them. Spessartite occurs in the igneous rock, rhyolite. *Melanite*, a black variety of andradite, occurs mostly in certain igneous rocks. Uvarovite is found in serpentine associated with chromite. Garnet frequently occurs as rounded grains in stream- and sea-sands.

Almandite, of gem quality, is found in northern India, Ceylon, and Brazil. Fine crystals, although for the most part too opaque for cutting, are found in a mica schist on the Stikine River, Alaska. Pyrope of gem quality is found associated with clear grains of olivine (peridot) in the surface sands near Fort Defiance, close to the Utah-Arizona line. A locality near Meronitz, Bohemia, is famous for pyrope gems. Grossularite is used only a little in jewelry, but essonite or cinnamon stones of good size and color are found in Ceylon.

Alteration. Garnet often alters to other minerals, particularly talc, serpentine, and chlorite.

Use. Chiefly as a rather inexpensive gem stone. A green andradite, known as *demantoid*, comes from the Ural Mountains, U.S.S.R., and yields fine gems known as *Uralian emeralds*. Considerable amounts of garnet are ground and used, on account of its hardness, for abrading purposes, as for sawing and grinding stone, or for making garnet paper.

Name. *Garnet* is derived from the Latin *granatus*, meaning like a grain.

ZIRCON—Zr(SiO$_4$)

Crystallography. Tetragonal; ditetragonal-dipyramidal. Crystals usually show a simple combination of prism and dipyramid of the first order (Figs. 539 and 540). The prism of the second order and a ditetragonal dipyramid also observed (Fig. 541). Base very rare. Usually in crystals; also in irregular grains.

Physical properties. H 7$\frac{1}{2}$. G 4.68. Luster adamantine. Color commonly some shade of brown; also colorless, gray, green, red. Streak uncolored. Usually translucent; in some cases transparent.

Composition. Zirconium silicate, Zr(SiO$_4$). ZrO$_2$ 67.2, SiO$_2$ 32.8 per cent.

Tests. Infusible, insoluble. When intensely ignited glows and gives off a white light. If zircon is fused with sodium carbonate and the fusion is then dissolved in dilute hydrochloric acid, the solution will turn a piece of turmeric paper to an orange color (zirconium).

Diagnostic features. Recognized usually by its characteristic crystals, color, luster, hardness, and high specific gravity.

Occurrence. Zircon is a common and widely distributed accessory mineral in all types of igneous rocks. It is especially frequent in the more silicic types such as granite, granodiorite, syenite, and monzonite.

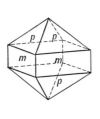 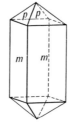 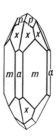

Fig. 539.	Fig. 540.	Fig. 541.

Zircon.

Very common in nepheline syenite. It is usually the first silicate to crystallize out from a cooling magma. Found also commonly in crystalline limestone, in gneiss, schist, etc. Found frequently as rounded grains in stream and beach sands, often with gold. Zircon has been produced from beach sands in Australia, Brazil, and Florida.

Gem zircons are found in the stream sands at Matura, Ceylon, and in the gold gravels in the Ural Mountains and Australia. In large crystals from Madagascar. Found in the nepheline syenites of Norway. Found in the United States at Litchfield, Maine, and in Orange and St. Lawrence counties, New York; in considerable quantity in the sands of Henderson and Buncombe counties, North Carolina. Large crystals have been found in Renfrew County, Ontario, Canada.

Use. When transparent serves as a gem stone. It is colorless in some specimens, but more often of a brownish and red-orange color, called *hyacinth* or *jacinth*. Blue is not a natural color for zircon but is produced by heat treatment. The colorless, yellowish, or smoky stones are called *jargon*, because although resembling the diamond they have little value; and thence the name *zircon*. Serves as the source of zirconium oxide, which is one of the most refractory substances known. Platinum, which fuses at 1755° C, can be melted in crucibles of zirconium oxide.

Overshadowing its other uses since 1945 is the use of zircon as the source of metallic zirconium. Pure zirconium metal is used in the construction of nuclear reactors. Its low neutron-absorption cross section, coupled with retention of strength at high temperatures and excellent corrosion resistance, makes it a most desirable metal for this purpose.

Similar species. *Thorite,* $Th(SiO_4)$, is like zircon in form and structure; usually hydrated and black in color.

ANDALUSITE—$AlAlO(SiO_4)$

Crystallography. Orthorhombic; dipyramidal. Usually in coarse, nearly square prisms terminated by the basal pinacoid.

Physical properties. H $7\frac{1}{2}$. G 3.16–3.20. Luster vitreous. Color flesh-red, reddish brown, olive-green. The variety *chiastolite* has dark-colored carbonaceous inclusions arranged in a regular manner forming a cruciform design (Fig. 542). Transparent to translucent. In some cases strongly dichroic, appearing, in transmitted light, green in one direction and red in another.

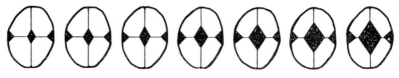

Fig. 542. Successive Cross Sections through a Chiastolite Crystal.

Composition. Aluminum silicate, $AlAlO(SiO_4)$. Al_2O_3 63.2, SiO_2 36.8 per cent.

Tests. Infusible. Insoluble. When fine powder is made into a paste with cobalt nitrate and intensely ignited it turns blue (aluminum).

Diagnostic features. Characterized by the nearly square prism, hardness, and infusibility. Chiastolite is readily recognized by the symmetrically arranged inclusions.

Alteration. Pseudomorphs of fine-grained muscovite (sericite) after andalusite are common.

Occurrence. Andalusite is formed usually by the metamorphism of aluminous shales and slate. It may be the result of regional metamorphism or a contact mineral found especially in connection with granitic intrusions.

Notable localities are in Andalusia, Spain; the Austrian Tyrol; in water-worn pebbles from Minas Geraes, Brazil. Crystals of chiastolite are found at Bimbowrie, South Australia. In the United States found in the White Mountains near Laws, California; at Standish, Maine;

and Delaware County, Pennsylvania. Chiastolite is found at West-ford, Lancaster, and Sterling, Massachusetts.

Use. Andalusite has been mined in large quantities in California for use in the manufacture of spark plugs and other porcelains of a highly refractory nature. When clear and transparent may serve as a gem stone.

Name. From Andalusia, a province of Spain.

SILLIMANITE—AlAlO (SiO₄)

Fibrolite

Crystallography. Orthorhombic; dipyramidal. Occurs in long slender crystals without distinct terminations; often in parallel groups; frequently fibrous.

Physical properties. Perfect pinacoidal {010} cleavage. **H** 6–7. **G** 3.23. Luster vitreous. Color brown, pale green, white. Transparent to translucent.

Composition. An aluminum silicate like andalusite, AlAlO (SiO₄). Al₂O₃ 63.2, SiO₂ 36.8 per cent.

Tests. Infusible. Insoluble. The finely ground mineral turns blue when heated with cobalt nitrate solution.

Diagnostic features. Characterized by slender crystals with one direction of cleavage.

Occurrence. Sillimanite is a comparatively rare mineral, found as a constituent of gneiss and schist in the highest grade of metamorphic rocks; rarely a contact metamorphic mineral. Often occurs with corundum.

Notable localities for its occurrence are Maldau, Bohemia; Fassa, Austrian Tyrol; Bodenmais, Bavaria; Freiberg, Saxony; and water-worn masses in diamantiferous sands of Minas Geraes, Brazil. In the United States found at Worcester, Massachusetts; at Norwich and Willimantic, Connecticut; and New Hampshire.

Name. In honor of Benjamin Silliman (1779–1864), professor of chemistry at Yale University.

KYANITE—AlAlO (SiO₄)

Crystallography. Triclinic; pinacoidal. Usually in long, tabular crystals, rarely terminated. In bladed aggregates.

Physical properties. Perfect pinacoidal {100} cleavage. **H** 5 parallel to length of crystals, 7 at right angles to this direction. **G** 3.55–3.66. Luster vitreous to pearly. Color usually blue, often of darker shade toward the center of the crystal. Also, in some cases, white, gray, or green. Color may be in irregular streaks and patches.

Composition. Aluminum silicate, like andalusite and sillimanite, $AlAlO(SiO_4)$. Al_2O_3 63.2, SiO_2 36.8 per cent.

Tests. Infusible. Insoluble. A fragment moistened with cobalt nitrate solution and ignited assumes a blue color.

Diagnostic features. Characterized by its bladed crystals, good cleavage, blue color, and the fact that it is softer than a knife in the direction parallel to the length of the crystals but harder than a knife in the direction at right angles.

Occurrence. Kyanite is an accessory mineral in gneiss and mica schist, often associated with garnet, staurolite, and corundum. Notable localities for its occurrence are St. Gothard, Switzerland; the Austrian Tyrol; and Pontivy and Morbihan, France. In the United States found at Chesterfield, Massachusetts; Litchfield, Connecticut; Gaston, Lincoln, and Yancey counties, North Carolina, and northern Georgia.

Use. Kyanite is mined in North Carolina and Georgia for use in spark plugs and other highly refractory porcelains.

Name. Derived from a Greek word meaning *blue*.

Similar species. *Mullite*, $Al_6Si_2O_{13}$, is rare as a mineral but common in artificial melts, and it forms when kyanite, andalusite, and sillimanite are heated to high temperatures.

TOPAZ—$Al_2(SiO_4)(F,OH)_2$

Crystallography. Orthorhombic, dipyramidal. In prismatic crystals terminated by dipyramids, first- and second-order prisms and

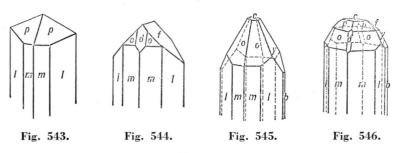

| Fig. 543. | Fig. 544. | Fig. 545. | Fig. 546. |

Topaz.

basal pinacoid. (Figs. 543–545.) Often highly modified (Fig. 546). Vertical prism faces frequently striated. Usually in crystals but also in crystalline masses; granular, coarse or fine.

Physical properties. Perfect {001} cleavage. **H** 8 (unusually high). **G** 3.4–3.6. Luster vitreous. Colorless, straw-yellow, pink, wine-yellow, bluish, greenish. Transparent to translucent.

Composition. An aluminum fluosilicate, $Al_2(SiO_4)(F,OH)_2$.

Tests. Infusible. Insoluble. With cobalt nitrate solution the pulverized mineral gives a fine blue on heating (aluminum).

Diagnostic features. Recognized chiefly by its crystals, its basal cleavage, its hardness (8), and its high specific gravity.

Occurrence. Topaz is a mineral formed through the agency of fluorine-bearing vapors given off during the last stages of the solidification of igneous rocks. Found in cavities in rhyolite lavas and granite; a characteristic mineral in pegmatite dikes, especially in those carrying tin. Associated with tourmaline, cassiterite, apatite, and fluorite; also with beryl, quartz, mica, and feldspar. Found in some localities as rolled pebbles in stream sands.

Notable localities for its occurrence are in the U.S.S.R. in the Nerchinsk district in Siberia in large wine-yellow crystals, and in Mursinsk, Ural Mountains, in pale blue crystals; in Saxony from various tin localities; from Minas Geraes, Brazil; Omi and Mino provinces, Japan; and San Luis Potosí, Mexico. In the United States found at Pikes Peak, near Florissant and Nathrop, Colorado; Thomas Range, Utah; Streeter, Texas; San Diego County, California; Stoneham and Topsham, Maine; Amelia, Virginia; and Jefferson, South Carolina.

Use. As a gem stone. A number of other inferior stones are also frequently called topaz, or *oriental topaz*. The color of the stones varies, being colorless, wine-yellow, golden brown, pale blue, and pink. The pink color is usually artificial, being produced by gently heating the dark yellow stones.

Name. Derived from Topazion, the name of an island in the Red Sea, but originally probably applied to some other species.

STAUROLITE—$Fe_2Al_9O_7(SiO_4)_4(OH)$

Crystallography. Orthorhombic. Habit prismatic, showing usually a combination of {110} with large angle (130°), {010}, {001}, and {101} (Fig. 547). Cruciform twins very common, of two types: (1) with {032} the twin plane, in which the two individuals cross at nearly 90° (Fig. 548); (2) with {232} the twin plane, in which they cross at nearly 60° (Fig. 549). In some cases both types are combined in one twin group. Usually in crystals; rarely massive.

Physical properties. H $7-7\frac{1}{2}$. G 3.65–3.75. Luster resinous to vitreous, for pure and fresh material; often dull to earthy when altered or impure. Color red-brown to brownish black. Translucent.

Composition. Ferrous iron aluminum silicate, $Fe_2Al_9O_7(SiO_4)_4$- (OH) FeO 16.7, Al_2O_3 53.3, SiO_2 27.9, H_2O 2.0 per cent. Often very impure.

Tests. Infusible. Insoluble. On intense ignition in the closed tube yields a little water.

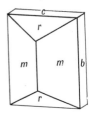

Fig. 547.

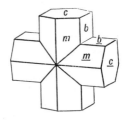

Fig. 548.

Staurolite.

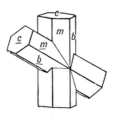

Fig. 549.

Diagnostic features. Recognized by its characteristic crystals and twins. Distinguished from andalusite by its obtuse prism.

Occurrence. Staurolite is an accessory mineral in crystalline schists, slates, and in some cases gneisses. Often associated with garnet, kyanite, and tourmaline. May grow on kyanite in parallel orientation. In some localities may include carbonaceous impurities.

Notable localities for its occurrence are Monte Campione, Switzerland; Goldenstein, Moravia; Aschaffenburg, Bavaria; and in large twin crystals in Brittany and Scotland. In the United States found at Windham, Maine; Franconia and Lisbon, New Hampshire; Chesterfield, Massachusetts; Macon, Madison, and Clay counties, North Carolina; Fannin County, Georgia; Ducktown, Tennessee; and also in Virginia, New Mexico, and Montana.

Use. Occasionally a transparent stone from Brazil is cut as a gem.

Name. Derived from a Greek word meaning *cross*, in allusion to its cruciform twins.

Chondrodite—$Mg_5(SiO_4)_2(F,OH)_2$

Crystallography. Monoclinic; prismatic. Crystals are frequently complex with many forms. Usually in isolated grains. Also massive.

Physical properties. H $6-6\frac{1}{2}$. G 3.1–3.2. Luster vitreous to resinous. Color light yellow to red. Translucent.

Composition. A magnesium fluosilicate, $Mg_5(SiO_4)_2(F,OH)_2$. Hydroxyl replaces part of the fluorine, and iron often takes the place of magnesium. Chondrodite is the most common member of the *chondrodite group.* The species in the group and their compositions are:

Norbergite	$Mg_3(SiO_4)_1(F,OH)_2$
Chondrodite	$Mg_5(SiO_4)_2(F,OH)_2$
Humite	$Mg_7(SiO_4)_3(F,OH)_2$
Clinohumite	$Mg_9(SiO_4)_4(F,OH)_2$

Tests. Infusible. Yields water in the closed tube. Gelatinizes with acids.

Diagnostic features. Characterized by its light yellow to red color and its mineral associations in crystalline limestone. The members of the *chondrodite group* cannot be distinguished from one another without optical tests.

Occurrence. Chondrodite occurs most commonly in metamorphosed dolomitic limestones of Archean age. The mineral association including phlogopite, spinel, pyrrhotite, and graphite is highly characteristic. Noteworthy localities of chondrodite are Monte Somma, Italy; Paragas, Finland; and Kafveltorp, Sweden. In the United States is found abundantly at the Tilly Foster magnetite deposit near Brewster, New York.

Name. Chondrodite is from the Greek meaning *a grain,* alluding to its occurrence as isolated grains. Humite is named in honor of Sir Abraham Hume.

DATOLITE—$CaB(SiO_4)(OH)$

Crystallography. Monoclinic; prismatic. Crystals usually nearly equidimensional in the three axial directions and often complex in development (Fig. 550). Usually in crystals. Also coarse to fine granular. Compact and massive, resembling unglazed porcelain.

Physical properties. H 5–$5\frac{1}{2}$. G 2.8–3.0. Luster vitreous. Colorless, white, often with faint greenish tinge. Transparent to translucent.

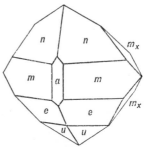

Fig. 550. Datolite.

Composition. A basic silicate of calcium and boron, $CaB(SiO_4)(OH)$. CaO 35.0, B_2O_3 21.8, SiO_2 37.6, H_2O 5.6 per cent.

Tests. Fuses at 2–$2\frac{1}{2}$ to a clear glass and colors the flame green (boron). Gives a little water in the closed tube.

Diagnostic features. Characterized by its glassy luster, pale green color, and its crystals with many and usually irregularly developed faces. Distinguished from quartz by ease of fusibility and boron flame.

Massive datolite is difficult to recognize, and blowpipe and chemical tests are necessary for its identification.

Occurrence. Datolite is a mineral of secondary origin, found usually in cavities in basalt lavas and similar rocks. Associated with zeolites, prehnite, apophyllite, and calcite. Notable foreign localities are Andreasberg, Harz Mountains; in Italy near Bologna; from Seiser Alpe and Theiso, Trentino; and Arendal, Norway. In the United States occurs associated with the trap rocks of Massachusetts, Connecticut, and New Jersey, particularly at Westfield, Massachusetts, and Bergen Hill, New Jersey. Found associated with the copper deposits of Lake Superior.

Name. Derived from a Greek word meaning *to divide*, in allusion to the granular character of a massive variety.

SPHENE—CaTiO(SiO$_4$)

Titanite

Crystallography. Monoclinic. Crystals varied in habit. Often with prominent basal plane which is steeply inclined and which in combination with short vertical prism and fourth-order prism gives a thin wedge-shaped crystal (Figs. 551 and 552). Usually well crystallized or lamellar.

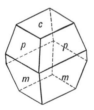
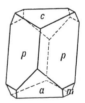

Fig. 551.   **Fig. 552.**

Sphene.

Physical properties. Cleavage {110}. Parting parallel to {221} may be present. H 5–5½. G 3.4–3.55. Luster resinous to adamantine. Color gray, brown, green, yellow, black. Transparent to translucent.

Composition. Calcium titanosilicate, CaTiO(SiO$_4$). CaO 28.6, TiO$_2$ 40.8, SiO$_2$ 30.6 per cent. Iron is usually present in small amounts.

Tests. Fusible at 4 with slight intumescence to a dark mass. Fused with sodium carbonate, fusion dissolved in sulfuric acid, solution turns yellow to amber on addition of hydrogen peroxide (titanium).

Diagnostic features. Characterized by its wedge-shaped crystals and high luster. Hardness is less than that of staurolite and greater than that of sphalerite. The reaction for titanium is distinctive.

Occurrence. Sphene is a rather common accessory mineral in igneous rocks, being found as small crystals in granites, granodiorites, diorites, syenites, and nepheline syenites. Also found in crystals of considerable size imbedded in the metamorphic rocks, gneiss, chlorite schist, and crystalline limestone. Very commonly associated with chlorite. Also found with iron ores, pyroxene, amphibole, scapolite, zircon, apatite, feldspar, and quartz.

The most notable locality for its occurrence is on the Kola Peninsula, U.S.S.R., where it is associated with apatite and nepheline in connection with large intrusions of nepheline syenite. It is mined there extensively as a granular aggregate. It is found in crystals at Tavetsch, Binnental, and St. Gothard, Switzerland; Zillertal, Tyrol; Ala, Piedmont; Vesuvius; and Arendal, Norway. In the United States in Diana, Rossie, Fine, Pitcairn, Edenville, and Brewster, New York; and Riverside, California. Also in various places in Ontario and Quebec, Canada.

Use. As a source of titanium for use as a paint pigment.

Name. *Sphene* comes from a Greek word meaning *wedge*, in allusion to a characteristic development of the crystals.

Similar species. *Benitoite* is a blue, hexagonal, barium titanium silicate associated with *neptunite* in San Benito, California. *Astrophyllite, aenigmatite, lamprophyllite, ramsayite, fersmannite* are rare titanium-bearing silicates found associated with alkalic rocks.

Dumortierite— $(Al,Fe)_7O_3(BO_3)(SiO_4)_3$

Crystallography. Orthorhombic. Rarely in distinct crystals. Usually in fibrous to columnar aggregates, frequently radiating.

Physical properties. Poor {100} cleavage. **H** 7. **G** 3.26–3.36. Luster vitreous. Color blue, greenish blue, violet, pink. Transparent to translucent.

Composition. An aluminum borosilicate, $(Al,Fe)_7O_3(BO_3)-(SiO_4)_3$.

Tests. Infusible; loses color on ignition. Heated with cobalt nitrate solution turns blue (aluminum).

Diagnostic features. Characterized by fibrous habit, but difficult to identify positively without optical tests.

Occurrence. Dumortierite is found in schists and gneisses and, more rarely, in pegmatite dikes. Notable localities are Lyons, France; Wolfschau, Silesia; Madagascar; Rio de Janeiro, Brazil; and Nacozari, Mexico. In the United States is found at Dehesa, California; at

Oreana, Nevada; and over a large area in the Rochester, Nevada, mining district.

Use. Dumortierite is mined in Nevada for use in the manufacture of high-grade porcelain.

Name. In honor of the French paleontologist, Eugene Dumortier.

Sorosilicates

The sorosilicates are characterized by isolated double tetrahedral groups formed by two SiO_4 tetrahedra sharing a single apical oxygen between them (Fig. 553). The ratio of silicon to oxygen resulting from this arrangement is $2:7$.

The most important sorosilicates are those of the *epidote group*. Both isolated SiO_4 tetrahedra and Si_2O_7 groups occur in the rather complex structure of epidote, which, like that of garnet, has two different kinds of cation sites. One, which we may call the X cation sites, customarily is occupied by rather large weakly charged ions such as calcium or sodium; and, second, sites occupied by smaller, more highly charged ions which we may call the Y cations, including aluminum, ferric iron, trivalent manganese, and rarely divalent manganese. The general formula may hence be written

Fig. 553. Si_2O_7 Group.

$$X_2Y_3O(SiO_4)(Si_2O_7)(OH)$$

All members of the group are isostructural and form monoclinic crystals characteristically elongate in the direction of the b axis. Orthorhombic zoisite has a structure which may be derived from that of its monoclinic polymorph, clinozoisite, by a simple twinlike doubling of the cell along the a axis. As a result of the generally consistent structure, the crystal chemistry of this group is chiefly concerned with the kind and degree of solid-solution relations. In the principal members of the group, the ions in the X and Y sites are chiefly:

	X	Y
Clinozoisite	Ca	Al
Epidote	Ca	Al,Fe'''
Piedmontite	Ca	Al,Fe''',Mn'''
Allanite	Ca,Ce,La,Na	Al,Fe''',Be,Mg,Mn'''

X may further be constituted in part by divalent manganese, lead, or strontium; and Y may be in part chromium. Most common epidote contains little manganese and almost none of the rarer ions listed and has a composition that may be represented fairly well by a simple ratio of aluminum to ferric iron. The common metamorphic mineral idocrase has a composition closely analogous to that of epidote and a similar structure containing both isolated SiO_4 and Si_2O_7 groups. Magnesium and ferrous iron occur in variable proportions, replacing each other freely.

Sorosilicates

Hemimorphite	$Zn_4(Si_2O_7)(OH)_2 \cdot H_2O$
Lawsonite	$CaAl_2(Si_2O_7)(OH)_2 \cdot H_2O$
EPIDOTE GROUP	
Clinozoisite	$Ca_2Al_3O(SiO_4)(Si_2O_7)(OH)$
Epidote	$Ca_2(Al,Fe)Al_2O(SiO_4)(Si_2O_7)(OH)$
Allanite	$X_2Y_3O(SiO_4)(Si_2O_7)(OH)$
Idocrase	$Ca_{10}(Mg,Fe)_2Al_4(SiO_4)_5(Si_2O_7)_2(OH)_4$
Prehnite	$Ca_2Al_2(Si_3O_{10})(OH)_2$

HEMIMORPHITE—$Zn_4(Si_2O_7)(OH)_2 \cdot H_2O$

Calamine

Crystallography. Orthorhombic; pyramidal. Crystals usually tabular parallel to {010}. They show prism faces and are terminated above usually by a combination of domes and pedion, and below by a pyramid (Fig. 554). Usually in crystal groups with the individuals attached at their lower (pyramidal) ends and lying with their {010} faces in common. Crystals often divergent, giving rounded groups with slight re-entrant notches between the individual crystals, forming knuckle or coxcomb masses. Also mammillary, stalactitic, massive, and granular.

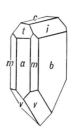

Fig. 554.
Hemimorphite.

Physical properties. Cleavage {110}. **H** $4\frac{1}{2}$–5. **G** 3.4–3.5. Luster vitreous. Color white, in some cases with faint bluish or greenish shade; also yellow to brown. Transparent to translucent. Strongly pyroelectric.

Composition. Hydrous silicate of zinc, $Zn_4(Si_2O_7)(OH)_2 \cdot H_2O$. ZnO 67.5, SiO_2 25.0, H_2O 7.5 per cent. Small amounts of aluminum and iron may be present.

Tests. Fusible with difficulty at 5. Fused on charcoal with sodium carbonate gives a nonvolatile coating of zinc oxide (yellow when hot, white when cold). Fused with cobalt nitrate on charcoal turns blue. Water in the closed tube.

Diagnostic features. Characterized by the grouping of crystals. Resembles prehnite but higher specific gravity. Distinguished from smithsonite by its crystal aggregates.

Occurrence. Hemimorphite is a mineral of secondary origin, found in the oxidized portion of zinc deposits, associated with smithsonite, sphalerite, cerussite, anglesite, and galena.

Notable localities for its occurrence are at Moresnet, Belgium; Aix-la-Chapelle, Germany; Carinthia; Rumania; Sardinia; Cumberland and Derbyshire, England; Algeria; and Chihuahua, Mexico. In the United States is found at Sterling Hill, Ogdensburg, New Jersey; Friedensville, Pennsylvania; Wythe County, Virginia; with the zinc deposits of southwestern Missouri; Leadville, Colorado; Organ Mountains, New Mexico; and Elkhorn Mountains, Montana.

Use. An ore of zinc.

Name. From the hemimorphic character of the crystals.

Lawsonite—$CaAl_2(Si_2O_7)(OH)_2 \cdot H_2O$

Crystallography. Orthorhombic; usually in tabular or prismatic crystals. Frequently twinned polysynthetically on {110}.

Physical properties. Cleavage good {010} and {110}. **H** 8. **G** 3.09. Colorless, pale blue to bluish gray. Luster vitreous to greasy. Translucent.

Composition. Calcium aluminum silicate, $CaAl_2(Si_2O_7)(OH)_2 \cdot H_2O$. It is interesting to note that the composition of lawsonite is the same as that of anorthite plus water.

Tests. Fuses to a blebby glass but once fused is not again fusible. On intense ignition in the closed tube yields water.

Diagnostic features. Lawsonite is characterized by its high hardness and its tendency to yield water in the closed tube.

Occurrence. Lawsonite is found in gneisses and schists in well-formed grains as well as in veins in metamorphic rocks. The type locality is on the Tiburon Peninsula, San Francisco Bay, California. Lawsonite is also found in schists in France and New Caledonia.

Name. In honor of Professor Andrew Lawson of the University of California.

Similar species. *Ilvaite*, $CaFe''Fe'''O(Si_2O_7)(OH)$, is related to lawsonite with a similar although not identical structure. A combination of ferrous iron and ferric iron in ilvaite seems to be roughly structurally equivalent to aluminum in lawsonite; $Fe''Fe'''(OH)$ for $Al_2(OH)_2$.

EPIDOTE GROUP

The epidote group is made up of several complex calcium aluminum silicates corresponding to the general formula $X_2Y_3O(SiO_4)(Si_2O_7)$-(OH). With the exception of the comparatively rare *zoisite*, the minerals of the epidote group are monoclinic and have similar crystallographic properties.

Clinozoisite—$Ca_2Al_3O(SiO_4)(Si_2O_7)(OH)$

Crystallography. Monoclinic; prismatic. Crystals have prismatic aspect parallel to the *b* axis. Striated parallel to the *b* axis. Columnar, massive granular.

Physical properties. H 6–6½. G 3.25–3.37. Luster vitreous. Color grayish white, green, pink. Transparent to translucent.

Composition. A hydrous calcium aluminum silicate, Ca_2Al_3O-$(SiO_4)(Si_2O_7)(OH)$. Clinozoisite and epidote form a solid solution series. Manganese is present in the pink variety, *thulite*.

Tests. Fuses at 3–4 with intumescence to a light-colored slag. Yields a little water on intense ignition in the closed tube.

Diagnostic features. Characterized by the columnar habit and intumescence on fusion. Distinguished from epidote by its lighter color.

Occurrence. Clinozoisite is usually found in crystalline schists which have been derived by the metamorphism of a dark igneous rock containing calcic feldspar. Commonly accompanies an amphibole. In igneous rocks it is present as an alteration of plagioclase.

Name. Clinozoisite is so named because it is the monoclinic modification of zoisite. Zoisite is named after the Austrian Baron Zois von Edelstein.

Similar species. *Zoisite* (orthorhombic) is dimorphous with clinozoisite. It is similar in appearance and occurrence to, but less common than, clinozoisite.

EPIDOTE—$Ca_2(Al,Fe)Al_2O(SiO_4)(Si_2O_7)(OH)$

Crystallography. Monoclinic; prismatic. Crystals are often much elongated parallel to the *b* axis, with a prominent development of the faces of the {010} zone, giving them a prismatic aspect. Striated parallel to the *b* axis. Terminated usually only at one end of the *b* axis and most commonly by the two faces of a fourth-order prism (Figs. 555 and 556). Some crystals twinned with {100} the twin plane. Usually coarse to fine granular; also fibrous.

Physical properties. Perfect cleavage on {001} and imperfect on {100}. **H** 6–7. **G** 3.35–3.45. Luster vitreous. Color usually pistachio-green or yellowish to blackish green, in some specimens gray or black. Transparent to translucent. Transparent varieties often show strong dichroism, appearing dark green in one direction and brown in a direction at right angles.

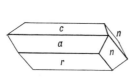 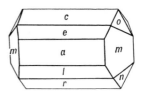

Fig. 555.   **Fig. 556.**

Epidote.

Composition. Hydrous calcium aluminum-iron silicate, $Ca_2(Al,Fe)Al_2O(SiO_4)(Si_2O_7)(OH)$. The ratio of aluminum to iron varies from 6:1 to 3:2.

Tests. Fuses at 3–4 with intumescence to a black slag; once formed, this slag is not again fusible. On intense ignition in the closed tube yields a little water. When previously ignited, gelatinizes with acid.

Diagnostic features. Characterized by its peculiar green color and one perfect cleavage. The slag formed on fusing which is again infusible is diagnostic.

Occurrence. Epidote occurs commonly in the crystalline metamorphic rocks, as gneiss, amphibolite, and various schists, where it is the product of alteration of such minerals as feldspar, pyroxene, amphibole, and biotite. Often associated with chlorite. Is formed frequently also during the metamorphism of an impure limestone, and is especially characteristic of contact metamorphic deposits in limestone.

Epidote is a widespread mineral. Notable localities for its occurrence in fine crystals are Knappenwand, Untersulzbachthal, Salzburg, Austria; Bourg d'Oisans, Isère, France; and the Ala Valley and Traversella, Piedmont. In the United States found at Haddam, Connecticut; Riverside, California; and Blueberry Mountain, Woburn, Massachusetts. In Alaska on Prince of Wales Island.

Name. From the Greek meaning *increase*, since the base of the vertical prism has one side longer than the other.

Similar species. *Piedmontite*, similar in crystal structure and chemical composition to epidote but contains trivalent manganese; occurs in crystalline schists and with manganese ores.

Allanite

Orthite

Crystallography. Monoclinic; prismatic. Habit of crystals often similar to epidote. Commonly massive and in imbedded grains.
Physical properties. H $5\frac{1}{2}$–6. G 3.5–4.2. Luster submetallic to pitchy and resinous. Color brown to pitch-black. Often coated with a yellow-brown alteration product. Subtranslucent, will transmit light on thin edges. Slightly radioactive.
Composition. A silicate of variable composition, $X_2Y_3O(SiO_4)$-$(Si_2O_7)(OH)$ where X = Ca, Ce, La, Na, and Y = Al, Fe, Mn, Be, Mg.
Tests. Fuses at $2\frac{1}{2}$ with intumescence to a black magnetic glass. Gelatinizes in acids if not previously ignited.
Diagnostic features. Characterized by its black color, pitchy luster, and association with granitic rocks.
Occurrence. Allanite occurs as a minor accessory constituent in many igneous rocks, such as granite, syenite, diorite, and pegmatites. Frequently associated with epidote. Has been noted in limestone as a contact mineral. Found in some magnetic bodies.

Notable localities are at Miask, Ural Mountains, U.S.S.R.; Greenland; Falun, Ytterby, and Sheppsholm, Sweden; and Madagascar. In the United States allanite is found at Moriah, Monroe, and Edenville, New York; Franklin, New Jersey; Amelia Court House, Virginia; and Barringer Hill, Texas.
Name. In honor of Thomas Allan, who first observed the mineral.

IDOCRASE—$Ca_{10}(Mg,Fe)_2Al_4(SiO_4)_5(Si_2O_7)_2(OH)_4$

Vesuvianite

Crystallography. Tetragonal; ditetragonal-dipyramidal. Crystals prismatic in habit, often vertically striated. Common forms are prisms of first {110} and second {100} orders, dipyramid of first order {111}, and base {001} (Figs. 557 and 558). Some crystals show a more complex development with other prisms, dipyramids, and ditetragonal forms. Frequently found in crystals, but striated columnar aggregates more common. Also granular, massive.
Physical properties. H $6\frac{1}{2}$. G 3.35–3.45. Luster vitreous to resinous. Color usually green or brown; also yellow, blue, red. Subtransparent to translucent. Streak white.

Composition. Essentially a hydrous calcium aluminum silicate, but with magnesium and iron, $Ca_{10}(Mg,Fe)_2Al_4(SiO_4)_5(Si_2O_7)_2(OH)_4$. Boron or fluorine is present in some varieties. Beryllium has been reported in some analyses.

Tests. Fuses at 3 with intumescence to a greenish or brownish glass. Water in the closed tube.

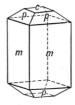

Fig. 557.

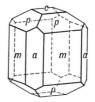

Fig. 558.

Idocrase.

Diagnostic features. Brown tetragonal prisms and striated columnar masses are characteristic of idocrase.

Occurrence. Idocrase is usually found in crystalline limestones formed as the result of contact metamorphism. Associated with other contact minerals, such as garnet, wollastonite, diopside, and tourmaline. Was originally discovered in the ancient ejections of Vesuvius and in the dolomitic blocks of Monte Somma.

Important localities are Zermatt, Switzerland; Ala, Piedmont; Monzoni, Trentino; Vesuvius; Christiansand, Norway; Achmatovsk, Ural Mountains, and River Vilui, Siberia, U.S.S.R.; and Morelos and Chiapas, Mexico. In the United States found at Auburn and Sanford, Maine; near Amity, New York; and Franklin, New Jersey. Found at many contact metamorphic deposits in western United States. A compact green variety resembling jade found in Siskiyou, Fresno, and Tulare counties, California, is known as *californite*. In Quebec, Canada, found at Litchfield, Pontiac County; and at Templeton, Ottawa County.

Use. The variety californite is used to a small extent as a semiprecious stone. An attempt has been made to mine beryllium-bearing idocrase as a source of beryllium.

Name. From two Greek words meaning *form* and *a mixture* because the crystal forms present appear to be a combination of those found on different minerals.

PREHNITE—$Ca_2Al_2(Si_3O_{10})(OH)_2$

Crystallography. Orthorhombic. Distinct crystals rare, commonly tabular parallel to the base {001}. Usually reniform, stalactitic, and in rounded groups of tabular crystals.

Physical properties. H 6–6½. G 2.8–2.95. Luster vitreous. Color usually light green, passing into white. Translucent.

Composition. Hydrous calcium aluminum silicate, Ca_2Al_2-$(Si_3O_{10})(OH)_2$. CaO 27.1, Al_2O_3 24.8, SiO_2 43.7, H_2O 4.4 per cent. Some iron may replace aluminum.

Tests. Fuses at 2½ with intumescence to a white enamel. Yields water in the closed tube.

Diagnostic features. Characterized by its green color and crystalline aggregates forming reniform surfaces. Resembles hemimorphite but is of lower specific gravity and fuses easily. Ease of fusion also distinguishes it from quartz and beryl.

Occurrence. Prehnite occurs as a mineral of secondary origin lining cavities in basalt and related rocks. Associated with zeolites, datolite, pectolite, and calcite. In the United States occurs at Farmington, Connecticut; Paterson and Bergen Hill, New Jersey; Westfield, Massachusetts; and Lake Superior copper district. Found in good crystals at Coopersburg, Pennsylvania.

Name. In honor of Colonel Prehn, who brought the mineral from the Cape of Good Hope.

Cyclosilicates

The cyclosilicates are built about rings of linked SiO_4 tetrahedra having a ratio of $Si : O = 1 : 3$. Three possible closed cyclic configurations of this kind may exist as shown in Figs. 559–561. The simplest is the Si_3O_9 ring, represented among minerals only by the rare titanosilicate *benitoite*, $BaTiSi_3O_9$. The Si_4O_{12} ring occurs together with BO_3 triangles and (OH) groups in the complex structure of the triclinic mineral *axinite*. The Si_6O_{18} ring, however, is the basic framework of the structures of the common and important minerals, beryl and tourmaline.

The hexagonal Si_6O_{18} rings are arranged, in the structure of beryl, in planar sheets parallel to {0001}. These sheets are so firmly bonded by the small beryllium and aluminum ions with their high surface density of charge and high polarizing power that only poor cleavage results. The very simple crystal morphology of beryl is an outward expression of the simple, firmly bonded architecture of the crystals.

Beryllium is in 4-fold coordination with oxygen, whereas the slightly larger aluminum is in 6-fold coordination. The silicon-oxygen rings are so arranged as to be nonpolar; that is, a symmetry plane can be pictured as passing through the tetrahedra in the plane of the ring

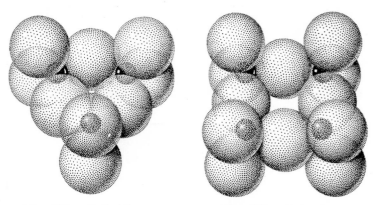

Fig. 559. Si_3O_9 Ring.   **Fig. 560.** Si_4O_{12} Ring.

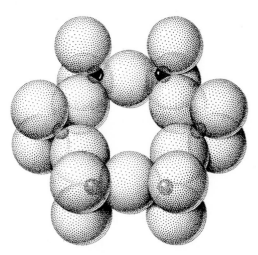

Fig. 561. Si_6O_{18} Ring.

(Fig. 561). The bonds extending from oxygens to beryllium and aluminum ions have the same total strength viewed in either direction along the c axis. Rings are positioned one above the other in the basal sheets so that the central holes correspond, forming prominent channels parallel to the c axis. In these channels a wide variety of ions, neutral atoms and molecules may be trapped. Hydroxyl, fluorine, atomic helium, water, and ions of lithium, rubidium, cesium, sodium,

are housed in beryl in this way. Atoms and ions so trapped in the
c-axis channels have little effect on the cell dimensions or other
properties of the mineral. Cordierite has a structure similar to beryl
but forms orthorhombic pseudohexagonal crystals in which some of the
aluminum enters tetrahedrally coordinated silicon sites in the rings
and some is in 6-fold coordination.

Tourmaline, whose structure long remained a mystery because of its
complexity, has now been shown to be built about Si_6O_{18} rings. In
tourmaline, however, the rings are polar; that is, the net strength of
bonds to one face of the ring is not the same as the strength of bonds
extending to the other, looking first in one direction, then in the other
along the c axis (Fig. 562). This polarity of the fundamental structural unit leads to the well-known polar
character of the tourmaline crystal. In
the structure of tourmaline, in addition
to the Si_6O_{18} rings, there are independent
BO_3 triangles and (OH) groups. All
these structural units are bound together
by ionic bonds through X- and Y-type
cations. X-type ions may be sodium or
calcium, and Y-type ions may be magnesium, ferrous iron, aluminum, ferric iron,
divalent manganese, and lithium, much
as in other silicates considered earlier.
The varieties are determined by the rela-
tive proportions of different X and Y ions, and ionic substitution
follows the usual pattern, with extensive mutual substitution of
magnesium, ferrous iron, and divalent manganese in Y sites, and of
sodium and calcium in the X sites accompanied by concomitant
coupled substitution to maintain electrical neutrality.

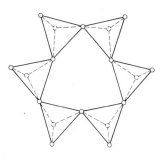

Fig. 562. Si_6O_{18} Ring in Tourmaline.

Cyclosilicates

Axinite	$Ca_2(Fe,Mn)Al_2(BO_3)(Si_4O_{12})(OH)$
BERYL GROUP	
Beryl	$Be_3Al_2(Si_6O_{18})$
Cordierite	$Mg_2Al_3(AlSi_5O_{18})$
Tourmaline	$XY_3Al_6(BO_3)_3(Si_6O_{18})(OH)_4$
Chrysocolla	$CuSiO_3 \cdot nH_2O$

Axinite—$Ca_2(Fe,Mn)Al_2(BO_3)(Si_4O_{12})(OH)$

Crystallography. Triclinic; pedial. Axinite is the only common
mineral crystallizing in this class. Crystals usually thin with sharp
edges but varied in habit (Fig. 563). Frequently in crystals and crystalline aggregates; also massive, lamellar to granular.

Physical properties. H $6\frac{1}{2}$–7. **G** 3.27–3.35. Luster vitreous. Color clove-brown, violet, gray, green, yellow. Transparent to translucent.

Composition. A hydrous aluminum borosilicate with varying amounts of calcium, manganese, and ferrous iron, $Ca_2(Fe,Mn)Al_2$-$(BO_3)(Si_4O_{12})(OH)$.

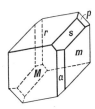

Tests. Fusible at $2\frac{1}{2}$–3 with intumescence. When mixed with boron flux and the mixture heated on platinum wire gives a green flame (boron). Gives water in the closed tube.

Diagnostic features. Characterized by the triclinic crystals with very acute angles.

Occurrence. Axinite occurs in cavities in gran-

Fig. 563. Axinite. ite, and in the contact zones surrounding granitic intrusions. Notable localities for its occurrence are Bourg d'Oisans, Isère, France; various points in Switzerland; St. Just, Cornwall; and Obira, Japan. In the United States at Luning, Nevada, and a yellow manganous variety at Franklin, New Jersey.

Name. Derived from a Greek word meaning *axe*, in allusion to the wedgelike shape of the crystals.

BERYL—$Be_3Al_2(Si_6O_{18})$

Crystallography. Hexagonal; dihexagonal-dipyramidal. Strong prismatic habit. Frequently vertically striated and grooved. Cesium beryl frequently flattened on {0001}. Forms usually present consist only of {$10\bar{1}0$} and base {0001} (Fig. 564). Dihexagonal forms are

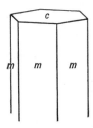

Fig. 564. Beryl.

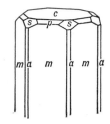

Fig. 565. Epidote.

rare (Fig. 565). Crystals frequently of considerable size with rough faces. At Albany, Maine, a tapering crystal **27** feet long weighed over **25** tons.

Physical properties. H $7\frac{1}{2}$–8. **G** 2.75–2.8. Cleavage {0001} imperfect. Luster vitreous. Color commonly bluish green or light yellow;

may be deep emerald-green, gold-yellow, pink, white, or colorless. Transparent to translucent. Frequently the larger, coarser crystals show a mottled appearance due to the alternation of clear transparent spots with cloudy portions.

Color serves as the basis for several variety names of beryl. *Aquamarine* is the pale greenish blue transparent variety. *Morganite*, or *rose beryl*, is pale pink to deep rose. *Emerald* is the deep green transparent beryl. *Golden beryl* is a clear golden-yellow variety.

Composition. Beryllium aluminum silicate, $Be_3Al_2(Si_6O_{18})$. BeO 14.0, Al_2O_3 19.0, SiO_2 67.0 per cent. Small amounts of the alkalis, often in part consisting of cesium, frequently present.

Tests. Fuses with difficulty at $5-5\frac{1}{2}$ to an enamel. Yields a little water on intense ignition. Insoluble in acids.

Diagnostic features. Recognized usually by its hexagonal crystal form and color. Distinguished from apatite by greater hardness.

Occurrence. Beryl, although containing the rare element beryllium, is rather common and widely distributed. It occurs usually in granitic rocks, either in druses or in pegmatic dikes. It is also found in mica schists and associated with tin ores. Emeralds of gem quality occur in a dark bituminous limestone at Muso, 65 miles northwest of Bogotá, Colombia. This locality has been worked almost continually since the middle of the sixteenth century and has furnished the greater part of the emeralds of the world. Another famous locality for emeralds is in Siberia on the river Takowaja, 45 miles east of Sverdlovsk. There they occur in a mica schist associated with phenacite, chrysoberyl, and rutile. Rather pale emeralds have been found in small amount in Alexander County, North Carolina, associated with the green variety of spodumene, hiddenite. Beryl of the lighter aquamarine color is much more common and is found in gem quality in Brazil and Siberia and also in Madagascar. In the United States gem beryls, chiefly aquamarine, have been found in various places in Maine, New Hampshire, Massachusetts, Connecticut, North Carolina, and Colorado. Golden beryl has been found in Maine, Connecticut, North Carolina, and Pennsylvania; also in Siberia and Ceylon. Rose-colored beryl has been found in San Diego County, California, associated with pink tourmaline and the pink spodumene, kunzite. A similar occurrence in Madagascar has furnished magnificent rose-colored stones.

Use. Used as a gem stone of various colors. The emerald ranks as the most valuable of stones and may have a much greater value than the diamond. Beryl is also the major source of beryllium, a light metal similar to aluminum in many of its properties. One of its chief uses is as an alloy with copper. One and one-half per cent of beryllium in copper greatly increases the hardness, tensile strength, and fatigue resistance. Beryllium oxide has been an important phosphor in fluorescent lamps, but because of its poisonous nature its use has been discontinued.

Name. The name beryl is of ancient origin, derived from the Greek word which was applied to green gem stones.

Similar species. *Euclase*, $BeAl(SiO_4)(OH)$, and *gadolinite*, $YFe''Be_2(SiO_4)_2O_2$, are rare beryllium silicates.

Cordierite—$Mg_2Al_3(AlSi_5O_{18})$

Iolite. Dichroite

Crystallography. Orthorhombic; dipyramidal. Crystals usually short prismatic pseudohexagonal twins. Also as imbedded grains and massive.

Physical properties. Pinacoidal cleavage {010} poor. **H** $7-7\frac{1}{2}$. **G** 2.60–2.66. Luster vitreous. Color different shades of blue. Transparent to translucent. Shows pleochroism.

Composition. A silicate of magnesium and aluminum, $Mg_2Al_3(AlSi_5O_{18})$. Ferrous iron and manganese may replace part of the magnesium, and ferric iron part of the aluminum. Water may also be present.

Tests. Fusible at $5-5\frac{1}{2}$. Only partially attacked by acids.

Diagnostic features. Cordierite resembles quartz and is distinguished from it with difficulty. Unlike quartz, it is fusible on thin edges. Distinguished from corundum by lower hardness. Pleochroism is characteristic if observed.

Alteration. Most commonly altered to some form of mica, chlorite, or talc and is then various shades of grayish green.

Occurrence. Cordierite is found as an accessory mineral in granite, gneiss (cordierite gneiss), schists, and in contact metamorphic zones. Notable localities for its occurrence are Bavaria, Finland, Greenland, and Madagascar. Gem material has come from Ceylon. In the United States is found chiefly in Connecticut and New Hampshire.

Use. Transparent cordierite of good color has been used as a gem known by jewelers as *saphir d'eau*.

Name. After the French geologist P. L. A. Cordier (1777–1861).

TOURMALINE

Crystallography. Hexagonal–R; ditrigonal-pyramidal. Crystals usually prismatic, with a prominent trigonal prism and subordinate second-order hexagonal prism. The tendency of the prism faces to be vertically striated and to round into each other gives the crystals a cross section like a spherical triangle (Fig. 566). Crystals are commonly terminated by a pedion and low positive and negative trigonal pyramids; ditrigonal pyramids may be present. When doubly terminated, crystals usually show different forms at the opposite ends of the vertical axis (Fig. 568). Usually in crystals. Some massive compact; also coarse to fine columnar, either radiating or parallel.

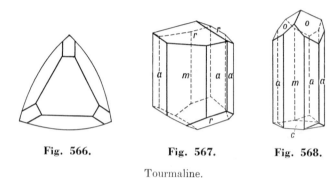

| Fig. 566. | Fig. 567. | Fig. 568. |

Tourmaline.

Physical properties. H 7–$7\frac{1}{2}$. G 3.0–3.25. Luster vitreous to resinous. Color varied, depending upon the composition.

The most common tourmaline is black (*schorlite*) and contains much iron; brown tourmaline is magnesium bearing. The rare lithium-bearing varieties are light colored in fine shades of red, pink, green, blue, and yellow. Rarely white or colorless *achroite*. A single crystal may show several different colors arranged either in concentric bands about the center of the crystal or in transverse layers along its length. Strongly pyroelectric and piezoelectric. Some tourmaline crystals show a strong dichroism; i.e., light traversing the crystal in the direction of the c axis may be of quite a different color or shade of color from that traversing the crystal in a direction at right angles.

Composition. A complex silicate of boron and aluminum, whose composition can be expressed by the general formula $XY_3Al_6(BO_3)_3$-$(Si_6O_{18})(OH)_4$, where $X = Na,Ca$ and $Y = Al,Fe''',Li,Mg$.

Tests. Fusibility varies with composition: magnesium varieties fusible at 3; iron varieties fusible with difficulty; lithium varieties infusible. Fused with boron flux gives momentary green flame of boron.

Diagnostic features. Recognized usually by the characteristic rounded triangular cross section of the crystals and conchoidal fracture. Distinguished from hornblende by absence of prismatic cleavage.

Occurrence. The most common and characteristic occurrence of tourmaline is in granite pegmatites and in the rocks immediately surrounding such deposits. The bulk of the tourmaline in pegmatites is black, but the lighter-colored gem varieties are also found there. The characteristic association is with the ordinary pegmatite minerals, microcline, albite, quartz, and muscovite; also with lepidolite, beryl,

Fig. 569. Tourmaline Crystals with Quartz and Cleavelandite, Pala, California.

apatite, fluorite, and rarer minerals (see Fig. 569). Found also as an accessory mineral in igneous rocks and in metamorphic rocks, such as gneisses, schists, and crystalline limestones.

Famous localities for the occurrence of the gem tourmalines are the Island of Elba; the state of Minas Geraes, Brazil; Ural Mountains near Sverdlovsk; and Madagascar. In the United States found at Paris and Auburn, Maine; Chesterfield, Massachusetts; Haddam Neck, Connecticut; and Mesa Grande, Pala, Rincon, and Ramona in San Diego County, California. Brown crystals are found near Gouverneur, New York, and fine black crystals at Pierrepont, New York.

Use. Tourmaline forms one of the most beautiful of the semi-precious gem stones. The color of the stones varies, the principal shades being olive-green, pink to red, and blue. Sometimes a stone is so cut as to show different colors in different parts. The green-colored stones are usually known by the mineral name, tourmaline, or as *Brazilian emeralds.* The red or pink stones are known as *rubellite,* and the rarer dark blue stones are called *indicolite.*

Because of its strong piezoelectric property, tourmaline is used in the manufacture of pressure gauges.

Name. *Tourmaline* comes from *turamali,* a name given to the early gems from Ceylon.

CHRYSOCOLLA—$CuSiO_3 \cdot nH_2O$

Crystallography. Cryptocrystalline. Has been observed in small, acicular crystals but commonly cryptocrystalline or amorphous. Massive compact. In some cases earthy.

Physical properties. Fracture conchoidal. **H** 2–4. **G** 2.0–2.4. Luster vitreous to earthy. Color green to greenish blue; brown to black when impure.

Composition. Hydrous copper silicate, whose formula is near $CuSiO_3 \cdot nH_2O$. CuO 45.2, SiO_2 34.3, H_2O 20.5 per cent when $n = 2$. Varies considerably in composition and is often impure.

Tests. Infusible. Gives a copper globule when fused with sodium carbonate on charcoal. In the closed tube darkens and gives water.

Diagnostic features. Characterized by its green or blue color and conchoidal fracture. Distinguished from turquoise by inferior hardness.

Occurrence. Chrysocolla is a mineral of secondary origin, occurring in the oxidized zones of copper veins. Associated with malachite, azurite, cuprite, native copper, etc. Found in the copper districts of Arizona and New Mexico. In microscopic crystals in Mackay, Idaho.

Use. A minor ore of copper.

Name. Chrysocolla, derived from two Greek words meaning *gold* and *glue,* which was the name of a similar-appearing material used to solder gold.

Similar species. *Dioptase,* $Cu_6(Si_6O_{18}) \cdot 6H_2O$, is a rhombohedral hydrous copper silicate occurring in well-defined green rhombohedral crystals.

Inosilicates

SiO_4 tetrahedra may be linked into chains by sharing oxygens with adjacent tetrahedra (Fig. 570). Such simple chains may then be joined side by side by further sharing of oxygens in some of the tetrahedra to form bands or double chains (Fig. 571). These configurations characterize the *inosilicates.* In the simple chain structure, two of the four oxygens in each SiO_4 tetrahedron are shared with neighboring tetrahedra, whereas in the band structure, half the tetrahedra share

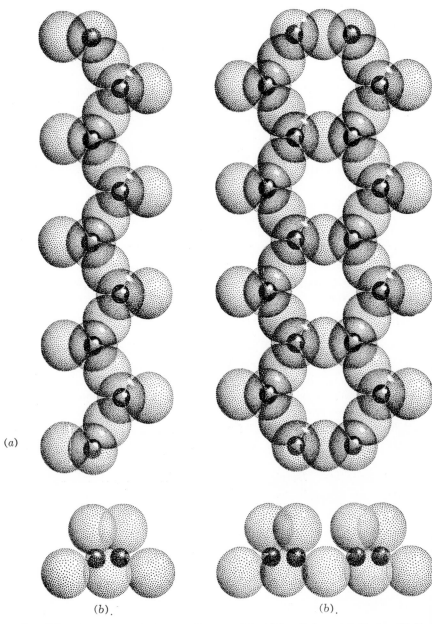

(a)

(b).

(b).

Fig. 570. SiO_3. (a) Chain; (b) Cross section.

Fig. 571. Si_4O_{11}. (a) Chain; (b) Cross section.

three oxygens and the other half share only two. These configurations lead to ratios of silicon to oxygen of 1 : 3 for the simple chain and 4 : 11 for the double chain or band.

The simple chain structure is best represented by the pyroxenes, the general formula for which is $XY(Si_2O_6)$. The structure may be visualized as one of parallel silicon-oxygen chains extending indefinitely in the direction of the c axis, bound together by ionic bonds through the X and Y cations. The X cations are large and weakly charged, generally sodium or calcium, and are bound to eight oxygen neighbors.

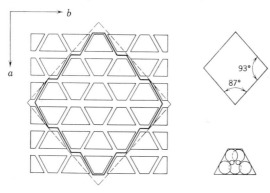

Fig. 572. Section of pyroxene structure at right angles to c axis showing how it controls cleavage (modified from Bragg).

The Y cations are smaller, leading to 6-fold coordination with oxygen, and may be magnesium, ferrous or ferric iron, aluminum, divalent or trivalent manganese, or even lithium or four-valent titanium. The introduction of an ion of greater or lesser charge may be compensated for by a simultaneous substitution, as aluminum for silicon in the tetrahedral sites.

Pyroxenes are, in general, monoclinic when X and Y sites are occupied by large and small ions respectively. If, however, both X and Y sites are occupied by small ions, an orthorhombic symmetry results. This symmetry is produced by a twinlike reflection across (100) accompanied by a doubling of the a_0-cell dimension. The occupation of both X and Y sites by larger ions may result in a triclinic lattice, as is the case in rhodonite, $Mn(SiO_3)$, and wollastonite, $Ca(SiO_3)$. All pyroxenes display the prominent near-90° {110} cleavage parallel to the SiO_3 chains (Fig. 572) and generally have prominent parting parallel to {100} and {001}.

In accord with the principles set forth above, we find that when both X and Y sites are occupied by magnesium or ferrous iron, as in enstatite-hypersthene, orthorhombic symmetry results. Magnesium and ferrous iron are free to substitute for each other in all proportions with random distribution resulting in a linear change of properties with composition. Under certain conditions of pressure and temperature, these compounds may form monoclinic polymorphs (clinoenstatite-clinohypersthene) with half the a_0-cell dimension of the orthorhombic modification.

When the X sites are occupied by calcium ions in 8-fold coordination and Y sites by magnesium, ferrous iron, or divalent manganese in 6-fold coordination, a member of the *diopside series* results. Within this series there can be substantially complete mutual substitution of magnesium, ferrous iron, and divalent manganese resulting in minor but nearly linear changes in cell dimensions and properties.

Occupation of the X sites by a moderate to large-sized monovalent alkali metal ion and the Y sites by a small trivalent cation, results in a member of the *spodumene series,* spodumene, jadeite, or aegirine. Solid solution, not only within this series but also between this series and the diopside series, is possible and gives rise to many varieties and variety names.

The common pyroxenes of the igneous and metamorphic rocks contain both calcium and sodium in the X sites, magnesium, ferrous

Ions in Common Pyroxenes and Amphiboles

X	Y	Pyroxene	Amphibole
Mg	Mg	Enstatite	Anthophyllite
		Clinoenstatite	Kupfferite
Mg,Fe	Mg,Fe	Bronzite, hypersthene	Anthophyllite
		Clinohypersthene	Cummingtonite
Ca	Mg	Diopside	Tremolite
Ca	Fe	Hedenbergite	Actinolite
Ca	Mn	Johannssenite	
Na	Al	Jadeite	Glaucophane
Na	Fe'''	Aegirine	Riebeckite
			Arfvedsonite
Li	Al	Spodumene	
Ca,Na	Mg,Fe, Mn,Al, Fe''', Ti	Augite	Hornblende

iron, aluminum, ferric iron and some four-valent titanium in the Y sites, as well as some aluminum substituting for silicon in the tetra-

hedral sites. The proportions of these constituents vary depending
on the environment of formation. The name "common augite" is used
to cover pyroxenes of variable and complex composition of this kind.

Among the most abundant and important of rock-making minerals
are the *amphiboles*, constituting a mineral family closely paralleling
the pyroxenes. All the members have as their basic structure the
Si_4O_{11} double chain or band. These double chains may be regarded

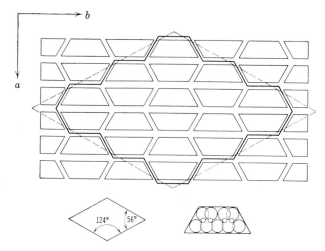

Fig. 573. Section of amphibole structure at right angles to cleavage showing
how it controls cleavage (modified from Bragg).

as of indefinite extent parallel to the perfect cleavage and the c axis.
When the double chains are viewed end on, i.e., in the direction of the
c axis (Fig. 573), it can be seen how they account for the cleavage
angles near 56° and 124°. Cleavage serves as the best means of rapid
visual distinction between the amphiboles and the pyroxenes, for not
only do the cleavage angles differ but the amphibole cleavage is better
than that of the pyroxenes.

The chains are bound together, as in the pyroxenes, by ionic bonds
through two types of cation sites, generally occupied by ions of X and
Y type, as defined above. OH ions occupy the open spaces resulting
from the joining of single chains side by side to form the double chain.
A geometry of arrangement is such that the larger X cations are in
8-fold coordination, whereas the smaller Y cations are in 6-fold.
Consistent with the requirement of electrical neutrality a general
formula for the amphiboles may be writtens as:

$$X_{0-7}Y_{7-14}Z_{16}O_{44}(OH)_4$$

There is considerable latitude in the interpretation of even so general a formula. X ions are generally sodium and calcium with minor potassium. Y ions include magnesium, ferrous and ferric iron, aluminum, divalent and trivalent manganese, and titanium as in the pyroxenes. Essentially complete ionic substitution may take place between sodium and calcium and among magnesium, ferrous iron, and divalent manganese. There is limited substitution between ferric iron and aluminum, and between titanium and other Y-type ions; and partial substitution of aluminum for silicon in the Z-type sites within the double chains, as required for valence compensation and electrical neutrality. Partial substitution of fluorine and oxygen for OH in the hydroxyl sites is also common. In the common rock-forming amphibole hornblende, many if not all of the above substitution possibilities take place leading to a complex formula.

Some amphiboles, like some pyroxenes, are dimorphous, having orthorhombic and monoclinic members. The orthorhombic members have a structure which may be derived from the monoclinic structure by reflection across (100) and accordingly show doubling of the cell dimension a_0. This doubling of the unit cell occurs in those members in which both X- and Y-type sites are occupied by the smaller cations such as magnesium and ferrous iron, thus producing amphiboles analogous to the enstatite series of pyroxenes. These amphiboles are assigned to the *anthophyllite series,* and their monoclinic dimorphs to the *cummingtonite series.* The resemblance between the pyroxene and amphibole analogues can not be carried further, for it has been shown that the limits of ionic substitution are not identical in anthophyllite and cummingtonite, whereas complete solid solution is possible in both enstatite-ferrosilite and clinoenstatite-clinoferrosilite.

The pyroxenes crystallize at higher temperatures than their amphibole analogues and hence are generally formed earlier in a cooling igneous magma. Frequently early formed pyroxene alters to amphibole at a later stage in the history of an igneous rock. The experiments of N. L. Bowen indicated that olivine, crystallized from a silicate melt resembling natural magmas in composition, would react, as the temperature was slowly decreased, with residual liquid melt to form pyroxene. If water is present, this pyroxene may then react with residual liquid at still lower temperatures to form amphibole.

PYROXENE FAMILY

The pyroxenes include a number of species that crystallize in the orthorhombic and monoclinic systems and yet are closely related in

Inosilicates

PYROXENE FAMILY	
Enstatite Series	
Enstatite	$Mg_2(Si_2O_6)$
Hypersthene	$(Fe,Mg)_2(Si_2O_6)$
Diopside Series	
Diopside	$CaMg(Si_2O_6)$
Hedenbergite	$CaFe(Si_2O_6)$
Spodumene Series	
Spodumene	$LiAl(Si_2O_6)$
Jadeite	$NaAl(Si_2O_6)$
Aegirite	$NaFe(Si_2O_6)$
Augite Series	
Augite	$XY(Z_2O_6)$
Rhodonite	$Mn(SiO_3)$
Wollastonite	$Ca(SiO_3)$
Pectolite	$Ca_2NaH(SiO_3)_3$
AMPHIBOLE FAMILY	
Anthophyllite	$(Mg,Fe)_7(Si_8O_{22})(OH)_2$
Tremolite Series	
Tremolite	$Ca_2Mg_5(Si_8O_{22})(OH)_2$
Actinolite	$Ca_2(Mg,Fe)_5(Si_8O_{22})(OH)_2$
Riebeckite Series	
Riebeckite	
Arfvedsonite	$Na_3Mg_4Al(Si_8O_{22})(OH,F)_2$
Hornblende Series	$X_{2-3}Y_{5-7}Z_8O_{22}(O,OH,F)_2$

crystal structure. They all have poor prismatic cleavage that makes angles of about $87°$ and $93°$ (Fig. 574). (Compare with amphibole, Fig. 579, page 443.) The pyroxenes form a series in which members are closely analogous chemically to the members of the amphibole group. (See page 443.) The following species are here described as members of the pyroxene family.

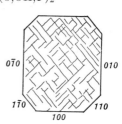

Fig. 574. Pyroxene Cleavage.

Enstatite	Jadeite
Diopside	Aegirite
Spodumene	Augite

ENSTATITE—$Mg_2(Si_2O_6)$

Crystallography. Orthorhombic; dipyramidal. Prismatic habit, crystals rare. Usually massive, fibrous, or lamellar.

Physical properties. Good {110} cleavage at angles of $87°$ and $93°$. Frequently good parting on {100}, less common on {001}.

H $5\frac{1}{2}$. **G** 3.2–3.5. Luster vitreous to pearly on cleavage surfaces; a variety with a submetallic, bronzelike luster is known as *bronzite*. Color grayish, yellowish, or greenish white to olive-green and brown. Translucent.

Composition. Magnesium silicate, $Mg_2(Si_2O_6)$. MgO 40.0, SiO_2 60.0 per cent. Rarely pure and may contain up to 5 per cent ferrous iron. Ferrous iron may substitute for magnesium in all proportions up to the ratio of $Mg:Fe = 1:1$. If the amount of FeO lies between 5 and 13 per cent, the variety is called *bronzite;* if over 13 per cent, the mineral is called *hypersthene.* Aluminum may also be present. The name *ferrosilite* is given to pure $Fe_2(Si_2O_6)$.

Tests. Almost infusible; thin edges will become slightly rounded. Fuses more easily with increasing amounts of iron.

Diagnostic features. Usually recognized by its color and unusual luster. Varieties high in iron are black and difficult to distinguish from augite without optical tests.

Occurrence. Enstatite is common in pyroxenites, peridotites, gabbros, norites, and basalts, and is thus a widespread mineral. A common mineral in both metallic and stony meteorites.

Enstatite is found in the United States at the Tilly Foster mine, Brewster, New York, and at Edwards, St. Lawrence County, New York; at Texas, Pennsylvania; Bare Hills, near Baltimore, Maryland; and Webster, North Carolina. Hypersthene occurs in New York in the norites of the Cortland region, on the Hudson River, and in the Adirondack region.

Name. Enstatite is named from the Greek word meaning *opponent* because of its refractory nature. Hypersthene is named from two Greek words meaning *very* and *strong* because its hardness is greater than that of hornblende.

Similar species. *Clinoenstatite* is a monoclinic, dimorphic form of $Mg_2(Si_2O_6)$, and *clinoferrosilite* is the dimorph of $Fe_2(Si_2O_6)$.

DIOPSIDE—CaMg(Si$_2$O$_6$)

Crystallography. Monoclinic; prismatic. In prismatic crystals showing square or eight-sided cross section. Also granular massive, columnar, and lamellar. Frequently twinned polysynthetically on {001}. Less commonly twinned on {100}.

Physical properties. Imperfect prismatic {110} cleavage. Frequently parting parallel to the basal pinacoid {001}, and less commonly parallel to {100}. Parting on the front pinacoid is characteristic of the variety *diallage.* **H** 5–6. **G** 3.2–3.3. Color white to light green; deepens with increase of iron. Luster vitreous. Transparent to translucent.

Composition. Calcium-magnesium silicate, $CaMg(Si_2O_6)$. CaO 25.9, MgO 18.5, SiO_2 55.6 per cent. Ferrous iron may substitute for magnesium in all proportions, and a complete series exists between diopside and *hedenbergite*, $CaFe(Si_2O_6)$.

Tests. Fusible at 4 to a green glass. Insoluble in acids. With fluxes gives tests for calcium and magnesium.

Diagnostic features. Characterized by its crystal form, light color, and imperfect prismatic cleavage at 87° and 93°.

Occurrence. Diopside is characteristically found as a contact metamorphic mineral in crystalline limestones. In such deposits it is associated with tremolite, scapolite, idocrase, garnet, and sphene. It is also found in regionally metamorphosed rocks. The variety diallage is frequently found in gabbros, peridotites, and serpentines.

Fine crystals have been found in Ural Mountains, U.S.S.R.; Austrian Tyrol; Binnenthal, Switzerland; and Piedmont, Italy. At Nordmark, Sweden, fine crystals range between diopside and hedenbergite. In the United States found at Canaan, Litchfield County, Connecticut; and DeKalb Junction and Gouverneur, St. Lawrence County, New York.

Use. Transparent varieties of diopside have been cut and used as gem stones.

Name. From two Greek words meaning *double* and *appearance*, since the vertical prism zone can apparently be oriented in two ways.

SPODUMENE—$LiAl(Si_2O_6)$

Crystallography. Monoclinic; prismatic. Prismatic crystals, flattened frequently parallel to {100}. Deeply striated vertically. Crystals usually coarse and with roughened faces; some very large. Occurs also in cleavable masses. Twinning on {100} common.

Physical properties. Perfect {110} cleavage at angles of 87° and 93°. Usually a well-developed parting parallel to {100}. **H** $6\frac{1}{2}$–7. **G** 3.15–3.20. Luster vitreous. Color white, gray, pink, yellow, green. Transparent to translucent.

The clear lilac-colored variety is called *kunzite*, and the clear emerald-green variety *hiddenite*.

Composition. Lithium aluminum silicate, $LiAl(Si_2O_6)$. Li_2O 8.0, Al_2O_3 27.4, SiO_2 64.6 per cent. Usually has a small amount of sodium substituting for lithium.

Tests. Fusible at $3\frac{1}{2}$, throwing out fine branches at first, and then fusing to a clear glass. Gives crimson flame (lithium). Insoluble.

Diagnostic features. Characterized by its vertical prismatic cleavage and front pinacoid parting. The angle formed by one cleavage direction and the {100} parting resembles the cleavage angle of tremolite. A careful angular measurement or a lithium flame is necessary to distinguish them.

Alteration. Spodumene very easily alters to other species, becoming dull. The alteration products include albite, eucryptite, $LiAl(SiO_4)$, muscovite, microcline.

Occurrence. Spodumene is a comparatively rare species, but it is found occasionally in very large crystals in pegmatite dikes. Occurs in Goshen, Chesterfield, Huntington, and Sterling, Massachusetts; Branchville, Connecticut; Newry, Maine; Dixon, New Mexico; and Etta mine, Black Hills, South Dakota, in crystals measuring as much as 40 feet in length and weighing many tons. Spodumene is mined as a source of lithium in the Black Hills, South Dakota; Kings Mountain district, North Carolina; and Gunnison County, Colorado. Hiddenite occurs with emerald beryl at Stony Point, Alexander County, North Carolina. Kunzite is found with pink beryl at Pala, San Diego County, California, and at various localities in Madagascar.

Use. As a source of lithium. Lithium's largest use is in greases to which it is added to help them retain their lubricating properties over a wide range of temperatures. It is used in ceramics, storage batteries, air conditioning, and as a welding flux. The gem varieties of spodumene, hiddenite, and kunzite furnish very beautiful gem stones but are limited in their occurrence.

Names. *Spodumene* comes from a Greek word meaning *ash colored*. *Hiddenite* is named for W. E. Hidden, *kunzite* for G. F. Kunz.

Jadeite—$NaAl(Si_2O_6)$

Crystallography. Monoclinic; prismatic. Rarely in isolated crystals. Usually fibrous in compact massive aggregates.

Physical properties. Cleavage {110} at angles of $87°$ and $93°$. Extremely tough and difficult to break. **H** $6\frac{1}{2}$–7. **G** 3.3–3.5. Color apple-green to emerald-green, white. May be white with spots of green. Luster vitreous, pearly on cleavage surfaces.

Composition. Sodium aluminum silicate, $NaAl(Si_2O_6)$. Na_2O 15.4, Al_2O_3 25.2, SiO_2 59.4 per cent. Contains some ferric iron, calcium, magnesium.

Tests. Fuses at $2\frac{1}{2}$ to a transparent blebby glass. Insoluble in acids.

Diagnostic features. Characterized by its green color and tough aggregates of compact fibers. Distinguished from nephrite by its ease of fusion.

Occurrence. Jadeite occurs in large masses in serpentine apparently formed by the metamorphism of a nepheline-albite rock. It is found chiefly in eastern Asia in Upper Burma. It is also found in Tibet and southern China.

Use. Jadeite has long been highly prized in the Orient, especially in China, where it is worked into ornaments and utensils of great variety and beauty. It was also used by early man for various weapons and implements.

Name. Jadeite is so named because it was found to make up many jade specimens. Under the term *jade* are included both the amphibole nephrite, and the pyroxene jadeite.

Aegirite—NaFe'''(Si_2O_6)

Crystallography. Monoclinic; prismatic. Slender prismatic crystals with steep terminations. Often in fibrous aggregates. Faces often imperfect.

Physical properties. Imperfect {110} cleavage at angles of 87° and 93°. **H** 6–6½. **G** 3.40–3.55. Luster vitreous. Color brown or green. Translucent.

Composition. Essentially a sodium-ferric iron silicate, NaFe'''-(Si_2O_6). Na_2O 13.4, Fe_2O_3 34.6, SiO_2 52.0 per cent. A mineral with this exact composition is known as *acmite* and is rarely found. Usually some calcium substitutes for sodium and some magnesium and aluminum for ferric iron. Some vanadium may be present.

Tests. Fusible at 3, giving yellow sodium flame. Fused globule slightly magnetic. With fluxes gives tests for iron.

Diagnostic features. The slender prismatic crystals, brown to green color, and associations are characteristic. However, it is not easily distinguished without optical tests.

Occurrence. Aegirite is a comparatively rare rock-forming mineral found chiefly in rocks rich in soda and poor in silica, such as nepheline syenite and phonolite. Associated with orthoclase, feldspathoids, augite, and soda-rich amphiboles. It occurs in the nepheline syenites and related rocks of Norway; southern Greenland; Kola Peninsula, U.S.S.R. In the United States is found in fine crystals at Magnet Cove, Arkansas. Found in Montana at Libby and in the Highwood and Bear Paw Mountains.

Name. From *Aegir*, the Icelandic god of the sea.

AUGITE—(Ca,Na) (Mg,Fe″,Fe‴,Al) (Si,Al)$_2$O$_6$

Crystallography. Monoclinic; prismatic. Crystals prismatic in habit; vertical prism faces make angles of 87° and 93° with each other. The vertical zone commonly shows the prism faces truncated by both {100} and {010}, so that the crystals, when viewed parallel to the c axis, show a rectangular cross section with truncated corners. {100} $\wedge$ {010} = 90°; {110} $\wedge$ {1$\bar{1}$0} = 93°; {010} $\wedge$ {110} = 43$\frac{1}{2}$°. Thus, the interfacial angles in the prism zone are either exactly or very

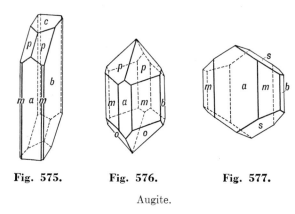

Fig. 575.   **Fig. 576.**   **Fig. 577.**

Augite.

close to 90° and 45°. The terminations vary, being made up frequently of a combination of the basal plane with first-order and fourth-order prisms (Figs. 575–577). Often lamellar and coarse to fine granular. Twinning on {001} and {100} common.

Physical properties. Cleavage {110} may be good, often interrupted. Frequently basal parting observed, often shown by twinning lamellae. H 5–6. G 3.2–3.4. Luster vitreous. Color dark green to black. Translucent, transmits light only on thin edges.

Composition. (Ca,Na) (Mg,Fe″,Fe‴,Al) (Si,Al)$_2$O$_6$. Augite can be considered an intermediate member in the diopside-hedenbergite series in which aluminum has taken the place of some of the silicon and magnesium.

Tests. Fusible from 4 to 4$\frac{1}{2}$. Insoluble in hydrochloric acid.

Diagnostic features. Recognized usually by its characteristic crystals with four- or eight-sided cross section. Distinguished from diopside by its darker color and from hornblende by its cleavage.

Occurrence. Augite is the most common pyroxene and an important rock-forming mineral. It is found chiefly in the dark-colored igneous rocks, especially those whose magmas were rich in iron, calcium, and magnesium. Seldom found in rocks that contain much quartz. Augite is found in basaltic lavas, and in the dark-colored intrusions known generally as trap, in gabbros and peridotites. Found in some syenites and similar rocks and in some gneisses. In igneous rocks augite is associated with orthoclase, the plagioclase feldspars, nepheline, olivine, leucite, hornblende, and magnetite.

Some of the notable localities, particularly for fine crystals, are the following: in the lavas of Vesuvius; at Val di Fassa, Trentino, Italy; and Bilin, Bohemia.

Name. Augite comes from a Greek word meaning *luster*. The name pyroxene, *stranger to fire*, is a misnomer and was given to the mineral because it was thought that it did not occur in igneous rocks.

RHODONITE—Mn(SiO$_3$)

Crystallography. Triclinic; pinacoidal. Crystallographically closely related to the pyroxenes. Crystals commonly tabular parallel to {001} (Fig. 578); often rough with rounded edges. Commonly massive, cleavable to compact; in imbedded grains.

Physical properties. Cleavage {110} and {1$\bar{1}$0} at about 88° and 92°. H 5$\frac{1}{2}$–6. G 3.4–3.7. Luster vitreous. Color rose-red, pink, brown; frequently with black exterior of manganese oxide. Transparent to translucent.

Composition. Manganese silicate, Mn(SiO$_3$). MnO 54.1, SiO$_2$ 45.9 per cent. Calcium substitutes in part for manganese.

Tests. Fusible at 3 to a nearly black glass. Insoluble in hydrochloric acid. Gives a blue-green color to the sodium carbonate bead.

Fig. 578.
Rhodonite.

Diagnostic features. Characterized by its pink color and prismatic cleavage. Distinguished from rhodochrosite by its greater hardness and insolubility and from feldspar by its higher specific gravity.

Occurrence. Rhodonite is found at Långban, Sweden, with other manganese minerals and iron ore; in large masses near Sverdlovsk in the Ural Mountains, U.S.S.R.; and from Broken Hill, New South Wales. In the United States a zinciferous variety, known as *fowlerite*, occurs in good-sized crystals in crystalline limestone with franklinite, willemite, zincite, etc., at Franklin, New Jersey.

Use. Some rhodonite is polished for use as an ornamental stone. This material is obtained chiefly from the Ural Mountains.

Name. Derived from the Greek word for *a rose*, in allusion to the color.

Similar species. *Tephroite,* Mn_2SiO_4, is a red to gray mineral associated with rhodonite.

WOLLASTONITE—$Ca(SiO_3)$

Crystallography. Triclinic; pinacoidal. Usually in tabular crystals, with either {001} or {100} prominent. Commonly massive, cleavable to fibrous; also compact.

Pseudowollastonite, $Ca(SiO_3)$, is formed above 1200° C; it is monoclinic, pseudohexagonal with different properties from wollastonite.

Physical properties. Perfect {001} and {100} cleavage, giving cleavage fragments an elongation parallel to the *b* crystallographic axis. **H** 5–5½. **G** 2.8–2.9. Luster vitreous, pearly on cleavage surfaces. May be silky when fibrous. Colorless, white, or gray. Translucent.

Composition. Calcium silicate, $Ca(SiO_3)$. CaO 48.3, SiO_2 51.7 per cent.

Tests. Fusible at 4 to a white, almost glassy globule. Decomposed by hydrochloric acid, with the separation of silica but without the formation of a jelly.

Diagnostic features. Characterized by its two perfect cleavages at about 84° and 96°. It resembles tremolite but is distinguished from it by the cleavage angle and solubility in acid.

Occurrence. Wollastonite occurs chiefly as a contact metamorphic mineral in crystalline limestones. It is associated with calcite, diopside, andradite and grossularite garnet, tremolite, calcium feldspars, idocrase, and epidote.

In places may be so plentiful as to constitute the chief mineral of the rock mass. Such wollastonite rocks are found in the Black Forest, in Brittany; Willsboro, New York; in California; and Mexico. Crystals of the mineral are found at Csiklova in Rumania; Harz Mountains, Germany; and Chiapas, Mexico. In the United States found in New York at Diana, Lewis County, and also in Orange and St. Lawrence counties. In California at Crestmore, Riverside County.

Use. Wollastonite is mined in those places where it constitutes a major portion of the rock mass and is used in the manufacture of tile.

Name. In honor of the English chemist, W. H. Wollaston (1766–1828).

Pectolite—$Ca_2NaH(SiO_3)_3$

Crystallography. Triclinic; pinacoidal. Crystals usually elongated parallel to the *b* axis. Usually in aggregates of acicular crystals. Frequently radiating, with fibrous appearance. In compact masses.

Physical properties. Perfect cleavage parallel to the basal {001} and front {100} pinacoids. **H** 5. **G** 2.7–2.8. Luster vitreous to silky. Colorless, white, or gray.

Composition. Hydrous calcium-sodium silicate, Ca_2NaH $(SiO_3)_3$. CaO 33.8, Na_2O 9.3, SiO_2 54.2, H_2O 2.7 per cent.

Tests. Fuses quietly at $2\frac{1}{2}$–3 to a glass; colors flame yellow (sodium). Decomposed by hydrochloric acid, with the separation of silica but without the formation of a jelly. Water in the closed tube.

Diagnostic features. Characterized by two directions of perfect cleavage yielding sharp acicular fragments. Resembles wollastonite but gives test for water and sodium. Distinguished from similar-appearing zeolites by absence of aluminum.

Occurrence. Pectolite is a mineral of secondary origin similar in its occurrence to the zeolites. Found lining cavities in basalt, associated with various zeolites, prehnite, calcite, etc. Found at Bergen Hill and West Paterson, New Jersey.

Name. From the Greek word meaning *compact,* in allusion to its habit.

AMPHIBOLE FAMILY

The more common minerals of the amphibole family crystallize in the orthorhombic and monoclinic systems. Rarer amphiboles crystallize in the triclinic system, but the crystal structures of the different species are closely similar. Chemically they form a group parallel to the pyroxene family (page 435). The amphiboles, however, contain hydroxyl. The amphiboles and pyroxenes closely resemble one another and are distinguished by cleavage. The {110} cleavage angle of amphiboles is about 56° and 124° (Fig. 579), whereas the poorer pyroxene cleavage angle is about 87° and 93° (Fig. 574).

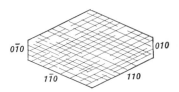

Fig. 579. Amphibole Cleavage.

Anthophyllite—$(Mg,Fe)_7(Si_8O_{22})(OH)_2$

Crystallography. Orthorhombic, corresponding to the orthorhombic pyroxene group, enstatite-hypersthene. Rarely in distinct crystals. Commonly lamellar or fibrous.

Physical properties. Perfect {110} cleavage. **H** $5\frac{1}{2}$–6. **G** 2.85–3.2. Color gray to various shades of green and brown. Luster vitreous. Translucent.

Composition. Magnesium-iron silicate, $(Mg,Fe)_7(Si_8O_{22})(OH)_2$. *Gedrite* is a variety in which aluminum is present in considerable amount.

Tests. Fusible at 5 to a black magnetic enamel. Insoluble in acids. Yields water in the closed tube.

Diagnostic features. Characterized by its clove-brown color but unless in crystals cannot be distinguished from other amphiboles without optical tests.

Occurrence. Anthophyllite is a comparatively rare mineral, occurring in the crystalline schists and thought to have been derived from the metamorphism of olivine. Occurs at Kongsberg, Norway; in many localities in southern Greenland. In the United States is found at several localities in Pennsylvania and Montana and at Franklin, North Carolina.

Use. *Amosite,* an iron-rich anthophyllite, occurs in long, flexible fibers and is used as asbestos. It is mined for this purpose in South Africa.

Name. From the Latin *anthophyllum,* meaning *clove,* in allusion to the clove-brown color.

Similar species. *Cummingtonite,* a monoclinic amphibole, has the same composition as anthophyllite but is usually relatively higher in iron.

TREMOLITE—$Ca_2Mg_5(Si_8O_{22})(OH)_2$

Crystallography. Monoclinic; prismatic. Crystals prismatic in habit; the vertical prism faces make angles of 56° and 124° with each other. The termination of the crystals is almost always formed by the

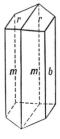
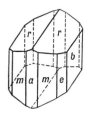

Fig. 580.   **Fig. 581.**

Tremolite.

two faces of a low first-order prism (Figs. 580 and 581). Tremolite is often bladed and frequently in radiating columnar aggregate. In some cases in silky fibers. Coarse to fine granular. Compact.

Physical properties. Perfect {110} cleavage at an angle of 56° often yielding a splintery surface. **H** 5–6. **G** 3.0–3.3. Luster vitreous. Often with silky sheen in the prism zone. Color varying from white to light green in actinolite (see under "Composition"). Color deepens with increase in the amount of iron present. Transparent to translucent. A felted aggregate of tremolite fibers goes under the name of *mountain leather* or *mountain cork*. A tough, compact variety which supplies much of the material known as *jade* is called *nephrite* (see also under "Jadeite").

Composition. $Ca_2Mg_5(Si_8O_{22})(OH)_2$, usually contains some ferrous iron in ionic substitution for magnesium. When iron is present in amounts greater than 2 per cent, the mineral is called *actinolite*.

Diagnostic features. Characterized by slender prisms and good prismatic cleavage. Distinguished from pyroxenes by the cleavage angle and from hornblende by lighter color.

Occurrence. Tremolite is most frequently found in impure, crystalline, dolomitic limestones where it has formed on the recrystallization of the rock during metamorphism. It is also found in talc schists. Actinolite commonly occurs in the crystalline schists, being often the chief constituent of green-colored schists and greenstones. Frequently the actinolite of such rocks has had its origin in the pyroxene contained in the igneous rock from which the metamorphic type has been derived.

Notable localities for crystals of tremolite are: Ticino, Switzerland; in the Tyrol; and in Piedmont, Italy. In the United States from Russell, Gouverneur, Amity, Pierrepont, DeKalb, and Edwards, New York. Crystals of actinolite are found at Greiner, Zillerthal, Tyrol. Actinolite frequently is fibrous and is the material to which the name *asbestos* was originally given. The asbestos form of actinolite has been found in the metamorphic rocks in various states along the Appalachian Mountains. Nephrite has been found near Lander, Wyoming. A famous locality for nephrite is in the Kuen Lun Mountains, on the southern border of Turkestan.

Use. The fibrous variety is used to some extent as asbestos material. The fibrous variety of serpentine furnishes more and usually a better grade of asbestos. The compact variety nephrite is used largely for ornamental material by oriental peoples.

Names. Tremolite is derived from the Tremola Valley near St. Gothard, Switzerland. Actinolite comes from two Greek words meaning *a ray* and *stone*, in allusion to its frequently somewhat radiated habit.

Arfvedsonite—$Na_3Mg_4Al(Si_8O_{22})(OH,F)_2$

Crystallography. Monoclinic; prismatic. Crystals long prismatic, often tabular parallel to {010}. Found in prismatic aggregates as well as in isolated crystals.

Physical properties. Perfect {110} cleavage at angles of 56° and 124°. **H** 6. **G** 3.45. Luster vitreous. Color deep green to black. Translucent, will transmit light only on thin edges.

Composition. A sodium-rich amphibole, $Na_3Mg_4Al(Si_8O_{22})$-$(OH,F)_2$ essentially. Considerable ionic substitution is present: calcium for sodium, ferrous iron and titanium for magnesium, ferric iron for aluminum, and aluminum for silicon.

Tests. Fusible at 2 with intumescence to a black magnetic globule. Colors flame yellow (sodium). Insoluble in acid.

Diagnostic features. Characterized by its dark green to black color and its presence in igneous rocks poor in silica. More easily fusible than hornblende and actinolite.

Occurrence. Arfvedsonite and other sodium-rich amphiboles are rock-forming minerals of igneous rocks poor in silica, such as nepheline syenites. Large crystals are found in pegmatite dikes associated with such rocks as in the Julianehaab district of southern Greenland. Also occurs in the nepheline syenites and related rocks near Oslo, Norway, and on the Kola Peninsula, U.S.S.R.

Name. In honor of the Swedish chemist, Prof. J. A. Arfvedson.

Similar species. *Riebeckite* is an amphibole similar in composition to arfvedsonite and a rock-forming mineral of similar occurrence. *Crocidolite*, a blue asbestiform variety of riebeckite, is mined for asbestos in South Africa, Brazil, and Australia.

Holmquistite and *glaucophane* are other sodium-rich members of the amphibole family.

HORNBLENDE

Crystallography. Monoclinic; prismatic. Crystals prismatic, usually terminated by {011}. The vertical prism zone shows, in addition to the prism faces, usually {010}, and more rarely {100}. May be columnar or fibrous; coarse to fine grained.

Physical properties. Perfect {110} cleavage, at angles of 56° and 124°. **H** 5–6. **G** 3.2. Luster vitreous; fibrous varieties often silky. Color various shades of dark green to black. Translucent; will transmit light on thin edges.

Composition. What passes under the name of hornblende is in reality a complex series that varies with respect to the ratios of

Ca : Na, Mg : Fe″, Al : Fe‴, Al : Si, and OH : F. A formula for common hornblende is: $Ca_2Na(Mg,Fe'')_4(Al,Fe''',Ti)(Al,Si)_8O_{22}$-$(O,OH)_2$. The presence of aluminum in hornblende is the principal chemical difference between it and tremolite.

Tests. Fusible at 4. Yields water in the closed tube.

Diagnostic features. Crystal form and cleavage angle serve to distinguish hornblende from dark pyroxenes. Usually distinguished from other amphiboles by its dark color.

Occurrence. Hornblende is an important and widely distributed rock-forming mineral, occurring in both igneous and metamorphic rocks; it is particularly characteristic of metamorphic rocks. It characteristically alters from pyroxene both during the late magmatic stages of crystallization of igneous rocks and during metamorphism. The latter type is frequently called *uralitic hornblende* or *uralite*. Hornblende is the chief constituent of the rock, *amphibolite*.

Name. From an old German word for any dark prismatic mineral occurring in ores but containing no recoverable metal.

Similar species. Because of the variation in the hornblende series, many names have been proposed for members on the basis of chemical composition and physical and optical properties. The most common names on the basis of chemical composition are: *edenite, pargasite, hastingsite, kaersutite.*

Phyllosilicates

As the derivation of the name of this important group implies (Greek: *phyllon*, leaf), all its many members have platy or flaky habit and one prominent cleavage. They are generally soft and of relatively low specific gravity and may show flexibility and even elasticity of the cleavage lamellae. All these characterizing peculiarities arise from the dominance in the structure of the indefinitely extended silicon-oxygen sheet. In this sheet, shown in Fig. 582 (packing model) and schematically in Fig. 583, three of the four oxygens in each SiO_4 tetrahedron are shared with neighboring tetrahedra, leading to a ratio of Si : O = 2 : 5. This structural unit is sometimes called the "siloxane sheet."

Most of the minerals of this class are hydroxyl bearing, and the structural peculiarities associated with the hydroxyl ion are of great importance in determining their properties. All the common phyllosilicates may be placed in one or the other of two clans, depending on the mode of coordination of the hydroxyl groups. One of these clans has as an integral part of its structure sheets of OH ions coordinated by magnesium ions, forming the *brucite*, $Mg_3(OH)_6$, structure. The

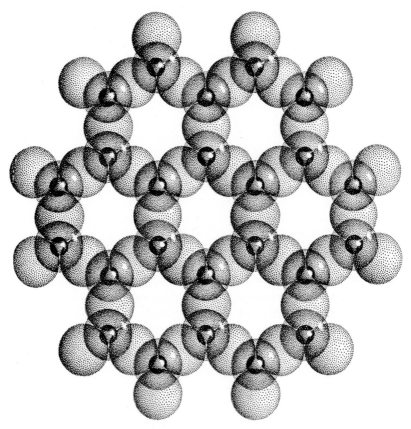

Fig. 582. Model of Si_2O_5 (Sheet Structure).

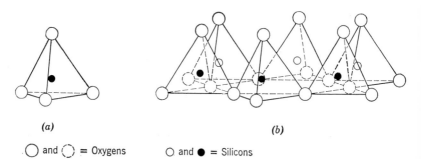

(a)   *(b)*

◯ and ◌ = Oxygens   ◯ and ● = Silicons

Fig. 583. Diagrammatic Sketch Showing (a) Single SiO_4 Tetrahedron and (b) Sheet Structure of Tetrahedra Arranged in a Hexagonal Network. (From Ralph E. Grim, *Clay Mineralogy*, McGraw-Hill Book Co., 1953.)

brucite sheet (Fig. 584) consists of two layers of hydroxyl ions in hexagonal closest packing with magnesium ions occupying the interstices. The radius ratio of magnesium to hydroxyl is such that 6-fold

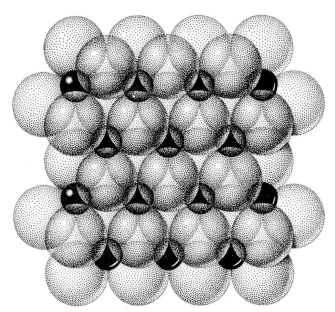

Fig. 584. Brucite Sheet. Large spheres hydroxyl, small spheres magnesium.

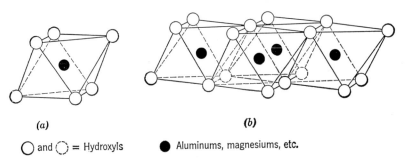

(a)   *(b)*

◯ and ⬡ = Hydroxyls   ● Aluminums, magnesiums, etc.

Fig. 585. Diagrammatic Sketch Showing (*a*) Single Octahedral Unit and (*b*) Sheet of Octahedral Units (after Grim).

coordination of hydroxyl about magnesium has maximum stability. Hence, the hydroxyl ions may be regarded as occupying the apices of a regular octahedron (Fig. 585*a*) with the magnesium ion at its center. The brucite sheet may then be visualized as made up of these octahedra tipped over and placed together so that certain of the (111) faces are coplanar (Fig. 585*b*). Figure 584 reveals that the magnesium ions in the resulting sheet form a pattern of interlocking hexagonal rings such that a magnesium ion falls at the center of each ring of six hydroxyl ions. Hydroxyl ions are shared between adjacent octahedra so that there are three magnesium ions for each octahedron of hydroxyl ions. This configuration is accordingly called the *trioctahedral* sheet and can accommodate divalent ions of such size that they may enter 6-fold coordination with hydroxyl.

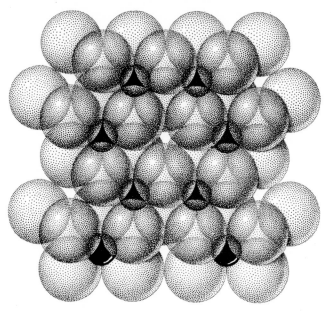

Fig. 586. Gibbsite Sheet. Large spheres hydroxyl, small spheres aluminum. Note that aluminum occupies two-thirds of possible sites.

The other clan is built about similar sheets of hydroxyl ions coordinated by aluminum ions in the *gibbsite*, $Al_2(OH)_6$, structure. Aluminum, like magnesium, forms a stable 6-fold coordination polyhedron with hydroxyl, but, because of the higher charge of the aluminum ion, only two-thirds as many aluminum ions may enter the sheet structure (Fig. 586). Hence, although the hydroxyl ions form double sheets with hexagonal closest packing, not all the interstices may be occupied. The aluminum ions form a pattern of hexagonal rings in which the site at the center of the ring is not occupied. This omission leads to a ratio of two aluminum ions to each octahedron of hydroxyl ions, and the configuration is called the *dioctahedral* sheet. This structure can accommodate only trivalent ions of a size appropriate to octahedral coordination with hydroxyl.

The structures of the common and important members of the phyllosilicate class can all be derived by combination of the Si_2O_5 sheet with either the gibbsite or the brucite sheet.

The simplest derivative structures formed in this way are those of the minerals of the kaolinite group and the antigorite, or serpentine, group. These structures are formed, respectively, by combination of a single gibbsite sheet with a siloxane sheet and of a single brucite

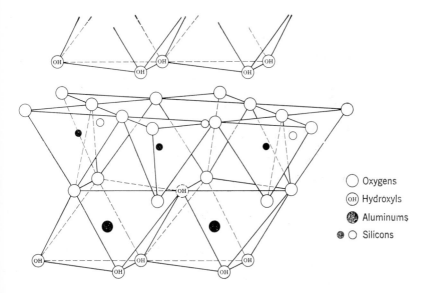

Oxygens
Hydroxyls
Aluminums
Silicons

Fig. 587. Diagrammatic Sketch of the Structure of the Kaolinite Layer (after Grim).

sheet with a siloxane sheet. Both the brucite and gibbsite sheets are electrically neutral, and the minerals gibbsite and brucite are bound together only by the weak van der Waals' bond (Figs. 584 and 586). The Si_2O_5 sheet, however, is not electrically neutral and cannot form a stable structure alone. If the apical oxygens, those not shared in the plane of the sheet, are permitted to enter the hydroxyl sites of the gibbsite or brucite sheet, the space requirements are fulfilled. Moreover, an electrically neutral structure results, since hydroxyl and oxygen have essentially the same ionic radius and the residual unit charge on the apical oxygen equals the hydroxyl charge. This structure, in the dioctahedral clan, is the kaolinite sheet; and in the trioctahedral clan, the antigorite sheet (Figs. 587 and 588). From the first of these structural units the kaolinite group of clay minerals is built up, whereas from the second is built the group of the serpentines. Following the nomenclature of P. Niggli, we may call the siloxane sheet a "*t*" sheet, since the coordination is tetrahedral, and brucite or gibbsite sheets "*o*" sheets since the coordination is octahedral. Hence, their union builds a "*t–o*" sheet, and we may allude to the basic structural unit of either the kaolinite or serpentine groups as a "*t–o*" sheet. If

Fig. 588. Kaolinite, $Al_2Si_2O_5(OH)_4$, Packing Model. O white, (OH) gray, Al black; *c* axis vertical.

we recall that the apical oxygens of a "*t*" sheet replace two hydroxyls of a gibbsite or brucite sheet, it is easy to remember that the formulas resulting in each case are

Dioctahedral

$$\underset{\text{``o''}}{Al_2(OH)_6} - \underset{\text{``t''}}{(OH)_2 + Si_2O_5} \rightarrow \underset{\text{``t–o''}}{Al_2(Si_2O_5)(OH)_4} \qquad \text{Kaolinite}$$

Trioctahedral

$$Mg_3(OH)_6 - (OH)_2 + Si_2O_5 \rightarrow Mg_3(Si_2O_5)(OH)_4 \qquad \text{Antigorite}$$

In exactly similar fashion, we may derive more complex members of the phyllosilicate family tree. Let us substitute the apical oxygens of an Si_2O_5 sheet for two out of the six hydroxyls of a gibbsite or brucite sheet on one side and then do the same on the other side of the same sheet. Now we have a triple sheet made up of an Si_2O_5 "*t*" sheet joined to an "*o*" sheet which in turn is joined to another inverted Si_2O_5 "*t*" sheet. Since each siloxane sheet replaces two out of the six hydroxyls per octahedron of the brucite or gibbsite sheet, two remain, and the formulas of the resulting triple sheets must be

Dioctahedral

$$\underset{\text{``}t\text{''}}{\text{Si}_2\text{O}_5} + \underset{\text{``}o\text{''}}{\text{Al}_2(\text{OH})_6} - \underset{\text{``}t\text{''}}{(\text{OH})_4 + \text{Si}_2\text{O}_5} \rightarrow \underset{\text{``}t\text{-}o\text{-}t\text{''}}{\text{Al}_2(\text{Si}_4\text{O}_{10})(\text{OH})_2} \quad \text{Pyrophyllite}$$

Trioctahedral

$$\text{Si}_2\text{O}_5 + \text{Mg}_3(\text{OH})_6 - (\text{OH})_4 + \text{Si}_2\text{O}_5 \rightarrow \text{Mg}_3(\text{Si}_4\text{O}_{10})(\text{OH})_2 \quad \text{Talc}$$

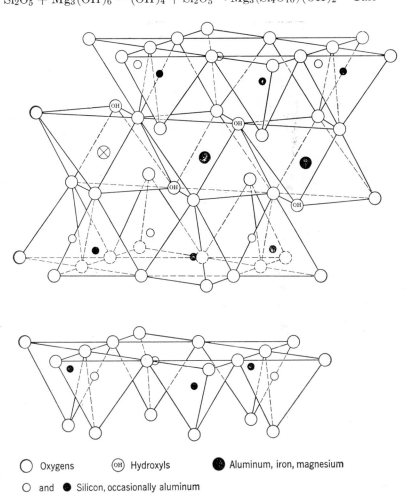

○ Oxygens ⊙ Hydroxyls ● Aluminum, iron, magnesium

○ and ● Silicon, occasionally aluminum

Fig. 589. Diagrammatic Sketch of the *"t-o-t"* Layer (after Grim).

These structural units, which we call *"t-o-t"* sheets, are electrically neutral and form stable structures in which the sheets are joined only by the van der Waals' bond (Figs. 589 and 590). Since this is a very weak bond, we may expect such structures to have excellent cleavage, easy gliding, and a greasy feel. These expectations are borne out, in the minerals talc and pyrophyllite.

If we carry the process of evolution a step farther, we may substitute aluminum ions for some of the silicon in the tetrahedral sites in the Si_2O_5 sheets. Since aluminum is trivalent, whereas silicon is tetrava-

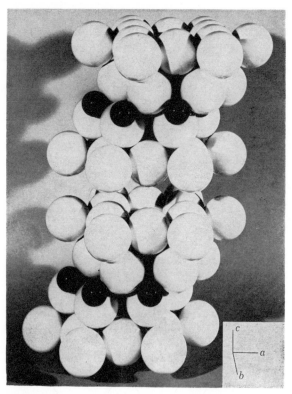

Fig. 590. Talc, $Mg_3Si_4O_{10}(OH)_2$, Packing Model. O white, Mg black. (OH) not visible. c axis vertical. The model shows the wide spacing between two closely packed "t–o–t" sheets.

lent, each substitution of this kind causes a free electrical charge to appear on the surface of the sheet. If aluminum substitutes for every fourth silicon, a charge of sufficient magnitude is produced to bind univalent cations in regular 12-fold coordination between the "t–o–t" sheets. By virtue of these sheet-cation-sheet bonds, the layers are more firmly held together, the ease of gliding is diminished, the hardness is increased, and slippery feel is lost. The resulting mineral structures are those of the true micas (Figs. 591 and 592). In the diocta-

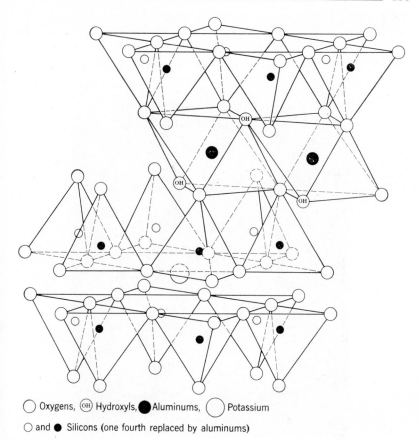

○ Oxygens, (OH) Hydroxyls, ● Aluminums, ◯ Potassium

○ and ● Silicons (one fourth replaced by aluminums)

Fig. 591. Diagrammatic Sketch of the Muscovite Structure (after Grim).

hedral line of descent, the cation is commonly potassium (muscovite) or sodium (paragonite); in the trioctahedral branch of the family it is potassium in both phlogopite and biotite. It is easy to remember the formulas of the micas if it is recalled that *one* of the aluminums belongs in the tetrahedral sites and the formulas written accordingly. Thus,

Dioctahedral	$KAl_2(AlSi_3O_{10})(OH)_2$	Muscovite
Trioctahedral	$KMg_3(AlSi_3O_{10})(OH)_2$	Phlogopite

If half the silicon ions in tetrahedral sites in Si_2O_5 layers are replaced by aluminum, two charges per "t–o–t" sheet become available for binding an interlayer cation. Such ions as calcium, magnesium, and ferrous iron may enter the structure of the mica held between the triple-sheet layers by ionic bonds. In these structures the interlayer binding is so strong that the quality of the cleavage is diminished, the hardness is increased, the flexibility of the layers is

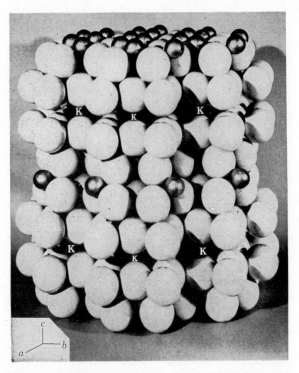

Fig. 592. Muscovite, $KAl_2AlSi_3O_{10}(OH)_2$ (Packing Model). Al in 6-fold co-ordination (metallic), Al in 4-fold coordination not seen. O is white. One complete *"t–o–t"* sheet constitutes the central part of the model, joined by large K ions to portions of adjacent *"t–o–t"* sheets above and below. Compare Fig. 590 (talc), Fig. 588 (kaolinite) and Fig. 594 (chlorite).

almost wholly lost, and the density is increased. The resulting minerals are the *brittle micas*, typified by

Dioctahedral	$CaAl_2(Al_2Si_2O_{10})(OH)_2$	Margarite
Trioctahedral	$CaMg_3(Al_2Si_2O_{10})(OH)_2$	Xanthophyllite

There is little solid solution between members of the dioctahedral and trioctahedral series, although there may be extensive and substantially complete ionic substitution of ferrous iron for magnesium, of ferric iron for aluminum, of calcium for sodium in appropriate sites. Barium may replace potassium, chromium may substitute for alumi-

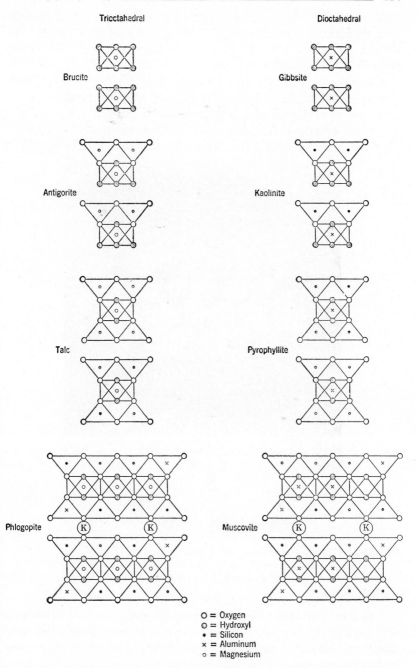

Fig. 593. Family Tree of the Phyllosilicates. (Schematic)

num, and fluorine may replace hydroxyl to a limited extent. Manganese, titanium, and cesium are rarer constituents of some micas. The lithium micas are structurally distinct from muscovite and biotite because of the small lithium ion.

A number of branches may be added to our phyllosilicate family tree (Fig. 593). The important family of *chlorites* may be simply described as having the triple-layered talc structure interlayered with a simple brucite sheet (Fig. 594). This leads to the formula $Mg_3Si_4O_{10}(OH)_2 \cdot Mg_3(OH)_6$. However, in most chlorites aluminum

Fig. 594. Chlorite, $Mg_3Si_4O_{10}(OH)_2 \cdot Mg_3(OH)_6$. Packing Model. O white, (OH) large black, Mg small black; c axis vertical. The model shows "*t–o–t*" sheets alternating with "*o*" sheets. Fe″, Fe‴ and Al may substitute for Mg and Al for Si.

and ferrous and ferric iron substitute for magnesium in octahedral sites both in the talc layers and in the brucite sheets, and aluminum substitutes for silicon in the tetrahedral sites. The formula may now be generalized as:

$$(Mg,Fe'',Fe''',Al)_3(Al,Si)_4O_{10}(OH)_2 \cdot (Mg,Fe'',Fe''',Al)_3(OH)_6$$

The various members of the group differ from one another in amounts of substitution and the manner in which the layers are arranged one over the other.

The important group of the *montmorillonites* may be derived from the pyrophyllite structure by the insertion of sheets of molecular water containing free cations between pyrophyllite *"t–o–t"* triple layers. The essentially uncharged pyrophyllite sheets may be expanded in this way to unusually large cell dimensions, and the minerals of this group accordingly show unrivalled capacity for swelling when wetted. The *vermiculites* are similarly derived from the talc structure by interlamination of sheets of molecular water.

If occasional random substitution of aluminum for silicon in the tetrahedral sites of pyrophyllite sheets takes place, there may not be enough of an aggregate charge on the triple layers to produce an ordered mica structure with all possible interlayer cation sites filled. Locally, however, occasional cation sites may be occupied, leading to properties intermediate between those of clays and micas. Introduction of some molecular water may further complicate this picture. Minerals of this type, intermediate between the montmorillonite clays and the true micas, are referred to the *illite* or *hydromica* group.

The great importance of the phyllosilicates lies in part in the fact that the products of rock weathering and hence the constituents of soils are mostly of this structural type. The release and retention of plant foods, the stockpiling of water in the soil from wet to dry seasons, and the accessibility of the soil to atmospheric gases and organisms depend in large part on the properties of the sheet silicates.

Geologically, the phyllosilicates are of great significance. The micas

Phyllosilicates

Apophyllite	$KCa_4(Si_4O_{10})_2F \cdot 8H_2O$
Kaolinite	$Al_4(Si_4O_{10})(OH)_8$
Serpentine	$Mg_6(Si_4O_{10})(OH)_8$
Garnierite	
Pyrophyllite	$Al_2(Si_4O_{10})(OH)_2$
Talc	$Mg_3(Si_4O_{10})(OH)_2$
Muscovite	$KAl_2(AlSi_3O_{10})(OH)_2$
Phlogopite	$KMg_3(AlSi_3O_{10})(OH)_2$
Biotite	$K(Mg,Fe)_3(AlSi_3O_{10})(OH)_2$
Lepidolite	$K_2Li_3Al_3(AlSi_3O_{10})_2(O,OH,F)_4$
Margarite	$CaAl_2(Al_2Si_2O_{10})(OH)_2$
Chlorite	$(Mg,Fe'',Fe''',Al)_3(Al,Si)_4O_{10}(OH)_2 \cdot (Mg,Fe'',Fe''',Al)_3(OH)_6$
Sepiolite	$Mg_4(Si_6O_{15})(OH)_2 \cdot 6H_2O$

are the chief minerals of the schists and are widespread in igneous rocks. They form at lower temperatures than amphiboles or pyroxenes and frequently are formed as replacements of earlier minerals as a result of hydrothermal alteration.

Apophyllite—$KCa_4(Si_4O_{10})_2F \cdot 8H_2O$

Crystallography. Tetragonal; ditetragonal-dipyramidal. Usually in crystals showing a combination of {010}, {111}, and {001} (Figs. 595 and 596). Small faces of a ditetragonal prism are occasionally observed (Fig. 597). Crystals may resemble an isometric combination of cube and octahedron, but are shown to be tetragonal by difference in luster between faces of prism and base.

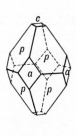

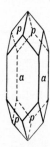

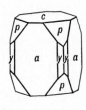

| Fig. 595. | Fig. 596. | Fig. 597. |

Apophyllite.

Physical properties. Perfect {001} cleavage. **H** $4\frac{1}{2}$–5. **G** 2.3–2.4. Luster of base pearly, other faces vitreous. Usually colorless, white, or grayish; may show pale shades of green, yellow, rose. Transparent to translucent.

Composition. A hydrous potassium calcium fluosilicate, KCa_4 $(Si_4O_{10})_2F \cdot 8H_2O$.

Test. Fusible at 2, with swelling, forms a white vesicular enamel. Colors the flame pale violet (potassium). Yields much water in the closed tube. Decomposed by hydrochloric acid with separation of silica but without the formation of a jelly. Solution gives little or no precipitate with ammonia but gives an abundant white precipitate with ammonium oxalate or ammonium carbonate (calcium).

Diagnostic features. Recognized usually by its crystals, color, luster, and basal cleavage.

Occurrence. Apophyllite occurs commonly as a secondary mineral lining cavities in basalt and related rocks. Associated with various zeolites, calcite, datolite, and pectolite.

It is found in fine crystals at Andreasberg, Harz Mountains; Aussig, Bohemia; on the Seiser Alpe in Trentino, Italy; near Bombay, India; Faeroe Islands; Iceland; Greenland; and Guanajuato, Mexico. In the United States at Bergen Hill and Paterson, New Jersey; and Lake Superior copper district. Found in fine crystals in Nova Scotia.

Name. Apophyllite is named from two Greek words meaning *from* and *a leaf*, because of its tendency to exfoliate when ignited.

CLAY MINERALS[1]

Clay is a rock term, and like most rocks it is made up of a number of different minerals in varying proportions. Clay also carries the implication of small particle size. Usually the term clay is used in reference to fine-grained, earthy material which becomes plastic when mixed with a small amount of water. With the use of x-ray techniques, clays have been shown to be made up dominantly of a group of crystalline substances known as the *clay minerals*. They are all essentially hydrous aluminum silicates. In some, magnesium or iron substitute in part for aluminum, and alkalies or alkaline earths may be present as essential constituents. Although a clay may be made up of a single clay mineral, there are usually several mixed with other minerals such as feldspar, quartz, carbonates, and micas.

KAOLINITE—$Al_4(Si_4O_{10})(OH)_8$

Crystallography. Monoclinic; prismatic. In very minute, thin, rhombic or hexagonal-shaped plates. Usually in claylike masses, either compact or friable.

Physical properties. Perfect {001} cleavage. **H** 2–2½. **G** 2.6–2.63. Luster usually dull earthy; crystal plates pearly. Color white. Often variously colored by impurities. Usually unctuous and plastic.

Composition. A hydrous aluminum silicate, $Al_4(Si_4O_{10})(OH)_8$. Al_2O_3 39.5, SiO_2 46.5, H_2O 14.0 per cent.

Tests. Infusible. Insoluble. Assumes a blue color when moistened with cobalt nitrate and ignited (aluminum). Water in the closed tube.

Diagnostic features. Recognized usually by its claylike character, but without optical tests is impossible to distinguish from the other

[1] For a discussion of the clay minerals, their mineralogy, chemistry, occurrence, and origin, see Ralph E. Grim, *Clay Mineralogy*, McGraw-Hill Book Co., New York, 1953.

clay minerals of similar composition which collectively make up *kaolin*.

Occurrence. Kaolinite is of widespread occurrence. The chief constituent of kaolin or clay. Always a mineral of supergene origin, being derived by the alteration of aluminum silicates, particularly feldspar. It is found mixed with feldspar in rocks that are undergoing alteration; in places it forms entire deposits where such alteration has been carried to completion. As one of the common products of the decomposition of rocks it is found in soils and being transported by water is deposited, mixed with quartz and other materials, in lakes, etc., in the form of beds of clay.

Use. Clay is one of the most important of the natural industrial substances, and many and varied products are made from it. These include common brick, paving brick, drain tile, sewer pipe. The commercial users of clay recognize many different kinds having slightly different properties, each of which is best suited for a particular purpose. High-grade clay which goes under the name of *china clay* or *kaolin* has many uses in addition to the manufacture of china and pottery. Its largest is as a filler in paper, but it is also used in the rubber industry and in the manufacture of refractories.

The chief value of clay for ceramic products lies in the fact that when wet it can be easily molded into any desired shape, and then, when it is heated, part of the combined water is driven off, producing a hard, durable substance.

Name. Kaolinite is derived from *kaolin*, which is a corruption of the Chinese *kauling*, meaning *high ridge*, the name of a hill near Jauchu Fa, where the material is obtained.

Similar species. *Dickite* and *nacrite* are similar to kaolinite in structure and chemical composition but are less important constituents of clay deposits. *Anauxite* is also assigned to the kaolinite group but has a higher silicon to aluminum ratio than kaolinite. *Halloysite* has two forms: one with kaolinite composition, $Al_4(Si_4O_{10})(OH)_8$, the other with composition $Al_4(Si_4O_{10})(OH)_8 \cdot 4H_2O$. The second type dehydrates to the first with loss of interlayered water molecules.

The *montmorillonite* group (see page 459) comprises a number of clay minerals composed of "*t–o–t*" silicate layers of both dioctahedral and trioctahedral type. The outstanding characteristic of members of this group is their capacity of absorbing water molecules between the sheets producing marked expansion of the structure. The dioctahedral members are *montmorillonite, beidellite,* and *nontronite;* the trioctahedral members are *hectorite* and *saponite*. Montmorillonite is the dominant clay mineral in *bentonite*, altered volcanic ash. Bentonite has the unusual property of expanding several times its original volume when placed in water.

Illite is a general term for the micalike clay minerals. The illites differ from the micas in having less substitution of aluminum for silicon, in containing more water, and in having potassium partly replaced by calcium and magnesium. Illite is the chief constituent in many shales.

Serpentine—$Mg_6(Si_4O_{10})(OH)_8$

Crystallography. Monoclinic; prismatic. Crystals, except as pseudomorphs, unknown. Serpentine occurs in two distinct habits: (1) a platy variety, known as *antigorite*, which conforms in its properties to those of the phyllosilicates, and (2) a fibrous variety, *chrysotile* (Fig. 598). It has been postulated that the fibers of chrysotile result from the layered silicate structure being curved to form cylindrical tubes.

Physical properties. H 2–5, usually 4. G 2.2 in fibrous varieties to 2.65 in massive varieties. Luster greasy, waxlike in the massive varieties, silky when fibrous. Color often variegated, showing mottling in lighter and darker shades of green. Translucent.

Composition. A hydrous magnesium silicate, $Mg_6(Si_4O_{10})(OH)_8$. MgO 43.0, SiO_2 44.1, H_2O 12.9 per cent. Ferrous iron and nickel may be present in small amount.

Tests. Infusible. Decomposed by hydrochloric acid with the separation of silica but without the formation of a jelly. Filtered solution, after having any iron precipitated by ammonium hydroxide, gives a precipitate of ammonium-magnesium phosphate with sodium phosphate. Water in the closed tube.

Diagnostic features. Recognized by its variegated green color and its greasy luster or by its fibrous nature. Distinguished from fibrous amphibole by the presence of a large amount of water.

Occurrence. Serpentine is a common mineral and widely distributed; usually as an alteration product of some magnesium silicate, especially olivine, pyroxene, and amphibole. Frequently associated with magnesite, chromite, and magnetite. Found in both igneous and metamorphic rocks, frequently in disseminated particles, in places in such quantity as to make up practically the entire rock mass. Serpentine, as a rock name, is applied to such rock masses made up mostly of the variety antigorite. Large deposits of the fibrous variety, chrysotile, are located in the province of Quebec, Canada; in the Ural Mountains, U.S.S.R.; and in South Africa. In the United States chrysotile is found in Vermont; New York; New Jersey; and in

Fig. 598. Veins of Chrysotile Asbestos in Serpentine, Thetford, Quebec.

Arizona near Globe from the Sierra Ancha, and in the Grand Canyon.

Use. The variety *chrysotile* is the chief source of asbestos. Fibrous amphibole is also used for the same purposes. The uses of asbestos depend upon its fibrous, flexible nature, which allows it to be made into felt and woven into cloth and other fabrics, and upon its incombustibility and slow conductivity of heat. Asbestos products, therefore, are used for fireproofing and as an insulation material against heat and electricity. Massive serpentine, which is translucent and of a light to dark green color, is often used as an ornamental stone and may be valuable as building material. Mixed with white marble and showing beautiful variegated coloring, is called *verd antique* marble.

Name. The name refers to the green serpent-like cloudings of the massive variety.

Garnierite—$(Ni,Mg)SiO_3 \cdot nH_2O$

Crystallography. Apparently amorphous. Found as incrustations and earthy masses.

Physical properties. **H** 2–3. **G** 2.2–2.8. Luster earthy and dull. Color apple-green to white.

Composition. A hydrous nickel-magnesium silicate, $(Ni,Mg)SiO_3 \cdot nH_2O$.

Tests. Infusible, but becomes magnetic on heating. Difficultly decomposed by hydrochloric acid, giving separated silica. In the oxidizing flame colors the borax bead brown. In the closed tube blackens and gives water.

Diagnostic features. Characterized by its apple-green color, earthy luster, and lack of crystal structure.

Occurrence. Garnierite is a mineral of secondary origin associated with serpentine, and probably an alteration product of nickel-bearing peridotites. Found in considerable amount, associated with serpentine and chromite, near Noumea, New Caledonia. Also in the Transvaal, U.S.S.R., South Africa, and Madagascar. In the United States found at Riddle, Oregon, and Webster, North Carolina.

Use. An ore of nickel.

Name. In honor of Jules Garnier, discoverer of the mineral.

Pyrophyllite—$Al_2(Si_4O_{10})(OH)_2$

Crystallography. Monoclinic; prismatic. Not observed in distinct crystals. Foliated, in some cases in radiating lamellar aggregates. Also granular to compact. Identical with talc in appearance.

Physical properties. Perfect {001} cleavage. Folia somewhat flexible but not elastic. **H** 1–2 (will make a mark on cloth). **G** 2.8–2.9. Luster pearly to greasy. Color white, apple-green, gray, brown. Translucent, will transmit light on thin edges.

Composition. Hydrous aluminum silicate, $Al_2(Si_4O_{10})(OH)_2$. Al_2O_3 28.3, SiO_2 66.7, H_2O 5.0 per cent.

Tests. Infusible, but, on heating, radiated varieties exfoliate in a fanlike manner. At high temperature yields water in the closed tube.

Diagnostic features. Characterized chiefly by its micaceous habit and cleavage, its softness and greasy feel. Distinguished from talc by moistening a small fragment with cobalt nitrate and igniting, when it assumes a blue color (aluminum). Talc under the same conditions becomes pale violet.

Occurrence. Pyrophyllite is a comparatively rare mineral. Found in metamorphic rocks; frequently with kyanite. Occurs in considerable amount in Guilford and Orange counties, North Carolina.

Use. Quarried in North Carolina and used for the same purposes as talc. (See page 466.) It does not command as high a price as the best grades of talc, however. A considerable part of the so-called *agalmatolite*, from which the Chinese carve small images, is this species.

Name. From the Greek meaning *fire* and *a leaf*, since it exfoliates on heating.

TALC—Mg$_3$(Si$_4$O$_{10}$)(OH)$_2$
Steatite. Soapstone

Crystallography. Monoclinic; prismatic. Crystals rare. Usually tabular with rhombic or hexagonal outline. Foliated massive; in some cases in radiating foliated groups. Also compact.

Physical properties. Perfect {001} cleavage. Thin folia somewhat flexible but not elastic. Sectile. **H** 1 (will make a mark on cloth). **G** 2.7–2.8. Luster pearly to greasy. Color apple-green, gray, white, or silver-white; in soapstone often dark gray or green. Translucent. Greasy feel.

Composition. A hydrous magnesium silicate, Mg$_3$(Si$_4$O$_{10}$)(OH)$_2$. MgO 31.7, SiO$_2$ 63.5, H$_2$O 4.8 per cent. Small amounts of nickel may be present.

Tests. Difficultly fusible (5). Unattacked by acids. Yields water in the closed tube when heated intensely. Moistened with cobalt nitrate and ignited assumes a pale violet color.

Diagnostic features. Characterized by its micaceous habit and cleavage, by its softness and greasy feel. To be distinguished from pyrophyllite by moistening a fragment with cobalt nitrate and heating intensely; talc will assume a pale violet color, pyrophyllite a blue color.

Occurrence. Talc is a mineral of secondary origin formed by the alteration of magnesium silicates, such as olivine, pyroxenes, and amphiboles, and may be found as pseudomorphs after these minerals. Found in igneous rocks, because of the alteration of such silicates, especially in peridotites and pyroxenites. Most characteristically found, however, in metamorphic rocks, where, in the granular to cryptocrystalline form known as *soapstone*, it may make up nearly the entire rock mass. It may also occur as a prominent constituent in the schistose rocks, as in talc schist.

In the United States, talc or soapstone quarries are located chiefly along the line of the Appalachian Mountains, the mineral being produced in Vermont, Massachusetts, Rhode Island, New York, New Jersey, Pennsylvania, Maryland, Virginia, North Carolina, and Georgia. Important deposits are located in St. Lawrence County, New York, where the talc occurs in the form of beds of schist interstratified with limestones. It is associated here with tremolite and enstatite, from masses of which it has evidently been derived. Large deposits of soapstone occur in Virginia in a narrow belt running from Nelson County.

Use. As slabs of the rock soapstone, talc is used for laboratory table tops, electric switchboards, and sanitary appliances. Most of the talc and soapstone produced is powdered as an ingredient in paint, ceramics, rubber, insecticides, roofing, paper, toilet preparations, foundry facings, etc.

Name. The name talc is of ancient and doubtful origin, probably derived from the Arabic, *talk*.

MICA GROUP

The micas crystallize in the monoclinic system but with inclination of the *a* axis practically 90°, so that their monoclinic symmetry is not clearly seen. The crystals are usually tabular with prominent basal planes and have either a diamond-shaped or hexagonal outline with angles of approximately 60° and 120°. Crystals, as a rule, therefore, appear to be either orthorhombic or hexagonal. They are characterized by a highly perfect {001} cleavage. A blow with a somewhat dull-pointed instrument on a cleavage plate develops in all the species a six-rayed *percussion figure* (Fig. 599), two lines of which are nearly parallel to the prismatic edges, and the third, which is most strongly developed, is parallel to the plane of symmetry {010}.

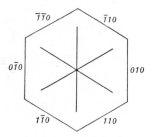

Fig. 599. Percussion Figure in Mica.

There is limited ionic substitution between the different members. Two members of the group, however, frequently crystallize together in parallel position in the same crystal plate with the cleavage extending through both.

MUSCOVITE—$KAl_2(AlSi_3O_{10})(OH)_2$

White Mica. Common Mica. Potash Mica

Crystallography. Monoclinic; prismatic. The β angle is nearly 90°. Distinct crystals comparatively rare. Occurs in tabular crystals with prominent base. The presence of prism faces {110} having angles of nearly 60° with each other gives some plates a diamond-shaped outline, making them simulate orthorhombic symmetry (Fig. 600). If the side pinacoid faces are also present, the crystals have hexagonal outline with apparently hexagonal symmetry. The prism faces are roughened by horizontal striations and frequently taper. Foliated in large to small sheets; in scales which are in some cases aggregated into plumose or globular forms. Also cryptocrystalline and compact massive.

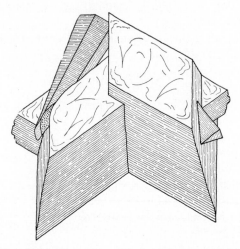

Fig. 600. Muscovite. Diamond-shape crystals.

Physical properties. Extremely perfect {001} cleavage allowing the mineral to be split into excessively thin sheets. Folia very flexible and elastic. **H** $2-2\frac{1}{2}$. **G** 2.76–3.1. Luster vitreous to silky or pearly. Transparent and colorless in thin sheets. In thicker blocks translucent, with light shades of yellow, brown, green, red. Some crystals allow more light to pass in a direction perpendicular to the [001] zone than in a direction perpendicular to the base.

Composition. Essentially $KAl_2(AlSi_3O_{10})(OH)_2$. Frequently contains small amounts of ferrous and ferric iron, magnesium, calcium, sodium, lithium, fluorine, titanium.

Tests. Fusible at 5. Not decomposed by acids. Water in the closed tube.

Diagnostic features. Characterized by its highly perfect cleavage and light color. Distinguished from phlogopite by not being decomposed in sulfuric acid and from lepidolite by not giving a crimson flame.

Occurrence. Muscovite is a widespread and very common rock-forming mineral. Characteristic of deep-seated siliceous igneous rocks as granite and syenite. Especially characteristic of pegmatite dikes, and found lining cavities in granites, where it has evidently been formed by the action of mineralizing vapors during the last stages of the formation of the rock. Also very common in metamorphic rocks, as gneiss and schist, forming the chief constituent in certain mica schists. In some schistose rocks it occurs in the form of fibrous aggregates of minute scales which have a silky luster but which do not show plainly the true nature of the mineral. This variety, known as *sericite*, is usually the product of alteration of feldspar. Sericite also forms an alteration of the wall rock of ore veins. Muscovite also originates as the alteration product of several other minerals, as topaz, kyanite, spodumene, andalusite, scapolite. *Pinite* is a name given to the micaceous alteration product of various minerals, which corresponds in composition more or less closely to muscovite.

In granite pegmatites, muscovite occurs associated with quartz and feldspar, with tourmaline, beryl, garnet, apatite, and fluorite. It is found often in these veins in large crystals, called books, which in some localities are several feet across.

Several notable localities for muscovite are found in the Alps; also Mourne Mountains, Ireland; Cornwall, England; Norway; and Sweden. Large and important deposits occur in India. Muscovite is found in the United States in commercial deposits chiefly in the Appalachian and Rocky Mountain regions. The most productive pegmatite dikes occur in New Hampshire, in North Carolina, and in the Black Hills of South Dakota. Of less importance are the deposits in Colorado, Alabama, and Virginia. Muscovite has been mined in Maine and Connecticut. Crystals measuring 7 to 9 feet across have been mined in Mattawan Township, Ontario, Canada.

Use. Used chiefly as an insulating material in the manufacture of electrical apparatus. Many of the small parts used for electrical insulation are built up of thin sheets of mica cemented together. They may thus be pressed into shape before the cement hardens. Most of the mica used for this purpose in the United States is imported from India. Used as a transparent material, *isinglass*, for stove doors, lanterns, etc. Scrap mica, or the waste material in the manufacture of sheet mica, is used in many ways, as in the manufacture of wall papers to give them a shiny luster; as a lubricant when mixed with oils; as a nonconductor of heat; and as a fireproofing material.

Name. *Muscovite* was so called from the popular name of the mineral, *Muscovy-glass*, because of its use as a substitute for glass in Old Russia (Muscovy). *Mica* was probably derived from the Latin *micare*, meaning *to shine*.

Similar species. *Paragonite*, $NaAl_2(AlSi_3O_{10})(OH)_2$, occurs with and is physically indistinguishable from muscovite. There is limited substitution of potassium for sodium in paragonite.

Phlogopite—$KMg_3(AlSi_3O_{10})(OH)_2$

Crystallography. Monoclinic; prismatic. Usually in six-sided plates or in tapering prismatic crystals. Crystals frequently large and coarse. Found also in foliated masses.

Physical properties. Perfect {001} cleavage. Folia flexible and elastic. **H** $2\frac{1}{2}$-3. **G** 2.86. Luster vitreous to pearly. Color yellowish brown, green, white, often with copperlike reflections from the cleavage surface. Transparent in thin sheets. When viewed in transmitted light, some phlogopite shows a starlike effect, known as asterism, because of tiny oriented inclusions of rutile.

Composition. A hydrous potassium magnesium aluminum silicate, $KMg_3(AlSi_3O_{10})(OH)_2$. Usually contains about 3 per cent of fluorine substituting for hydroxyl and some ferrous iron for magnesium.

Tests. Fusible at $4\frac{1}{2}$-5. Decomposed by boiling concentrated sulfuric acid. Yields water in the closed tube.

Diagnostic features. Characterized by its micaceous cleavage and yellowish brown color. Distinguished from muscovite by its decomposition in sulfuric acid and from biotite by its lighter color. But it is impossible to draw a sharp distinction between biotite and phlogopite.

Occurrence. Phlogopite occurs as a product of metamorphism in crystalline magnesium limestones or dolomitic marbles and is also found in serpentine. Rarely found in igneous rocks. Notable localities are in Finland; Sweden; Campolungo, Switzerland; Ceylon; and Madagascar. In the United States found chiefly in Jefferson and St. Lawrence counties, New York. Found abundantly in Canada in Ontario at North and South Burgess, and in various other localities in Ontario and Quebec.

Use. Same as for muscovite; chiefly as electrical insulator.

Name. Named from a Greek word meaning *firelike*, in allusion to its color.

BIOTITE—$K(Mg,Fe)_3(AlSi_3O_{10})(OH)_2$

Crystallography. Monoclinic; prismatic. In tabular or short prismatic crystals with prominent basal planes. Crystals rare, frequently pseudorhombohedral. Usually in irregular foliated masses; often in disseminated scales or in scaly aggregates.

Physical properties. Perfect {001} cleavage. Folia flexible and elastic. **H** $2\frac{1}{2}$-3. **G** 2.8-3.2. Luster splendent. Color usually dark green, brown to black. More rarely light yellow. Thin sheets usually have a smoky color (differing from the almost colorless muscovite).

Composition. A potassium magnesium-iron-aluminum silicate, essentially $K(Mg,Fe)_3(AlSi_3O_{10})(OH)_2$.

Tests. Difficultly fusible at 5. Unattacked by hydrochloric acid. Decomposed by boiling concentrated sulfuric acid, giving a milky solution. Gives water in the closed tube.

Diagnostic features. Characterized by its micaceous cleavage and dark color.

Occurrence. Biotite is an important and widely distributed rock-forming mineral. Occurs in igneous rocks, especially those in which feldspar is prominent, such as granite and syenite, but occurs in a greater variety of rocks than muscovite. In some cases found in pegmatite dikes in large sheets. Found also in many felsite lavas and porphyries. Less common in the ferromagnesian rocks. Is also present in some gneisses and schists often associated with muscovite. Occurs in fine crystals in blocks included in the lavas of Vesuvius.

Name. In honor of the French physicist, J. B. Biot.

Similar species. *Glauconite*, commonly found in green pellets in sedimentary deposits, is similar in composition to biotite.

Vermiculite forms as an alteration of biotite. The structure is made up of mica sheets interlayered with water molecules. On heating it loses water and expands into wormlike forms. Vermiculite is mined at Libby, Montana, and Macon, North Carolina. In the expanded form it is used extensively in heat and sound insulating.

LEPIDOLITE—$K_2Li_3Al_3(AlSi_3O_{10})_2(O,OH,F)_4$

Lithia Mica

Crystallography. Monoclinic; prismatic. Crystals usually in small plates or prisms with hexagonal outline. Commonly in coarse- to fine-grained scaly aggregates.

Physical properties. Perfect {001} cleavage. **H** $2\frac{1}{2}$–4. **G** 2.8–3.0. Luster pearly. Color pink and lilac to grayish white. Translucent.

Composition. A fluosilicate of potassium, lithium, aluminum, $K_2Li_3Al_3(AlSi_3O_{10})_2(O,OH,F)_4$.

Tests. Fusible at 2, giving a crimson flame (lithium). Insoluble in acids. Gives acid water in the closed tube.

Diagnostic features. Characterized chiefly by its micaceous cleavage and usually by its lilac to pink color. Muscovite may be pink, or lepidolite white, and therefore a flame test should be made to distinguish the two.

Occurrence. Lepidolite is a comparatively rare mineral, found in pegmatite dikes, usually associated with other lithium-bearing minerals such as pink and green tourmaline, amblygonite, and spodumene. Often intergrown with muscovite in parallel position. Notable foreign localities for its occurrence are the Ural Mountains, U.S.S.R.; Isle of Elba; Rožna, Moravia; and Madagascar. In the United States is found in western Maine at Hebron, Auburn, Norway, Paris, Rumford; near Middletown, Connecticut; Pala, San Diego County, California; and Black Hills, South Dakota.

Use. A source of lithium. Used in the manufacture of heat-resistant glass.

Name. Derived from a Greek word meaning *scale*.

Margarite—$CaAl_2(Al_2Si_2O_{10})(OH)_2$

Crystallography. Monoclinic; prismatic. Seldom in distinct crystals. Usually in foliated aggregates with micaceous habit.

Physical properties. Perfect {001} cleavage. **H** $3\frac{1}{2}$–5 (harder than the true micas). **G** 3.0–3.1. Luster vitreous to pearly. Color pink, white, and gray. Translucent. Folia somewhat brittle. Because of this brittleness margarite is known as a *brittle mica*.

Composition. Essentially a hydrous calcium aluminum silicate, $CaAl_2(Al_2Si_2O_{10})(OH)_2$. CaO 14.0, Al_2O_3 51.3, SiO_2 30.2, H_2O 4.5 per cent.

Tests. Fuses at 4–$4\frac{1}{2}$, turning white. Slowly and incompletely decomposed by boiling hydrochloric acid.

Diagnostic features. Characterized by its micaceous cleavage, brittleness, and association with corundum.

Occurrence. Margarite occurs usually with corundum and apparently as one of its alteration products. It is found in this way with the emery deposits of Asia Minor and on the islands Naxos and Nicaria, of the Grecian Archipelago. In the United States associated with emery at Chester, Massachusetts; Chester County, Pennsylvania; and with corundum deposits in North Carolina.

Name. From the Greek meaning *pearl*.

Similar species. Several minerals similar to margarite in structure and physical and chemical properties are included under the general heading of *brittle micas*. Aside from margarite, the most important members of the group are *ottrelite* and *chloritoid*, found in metamorphosed sedimentary rocks.

CHLORITE GROUP

A number of minerals are included in the chlorite group all of which have similar chemical, crystallographic, and physical properties.

Without quantitative chemical analyses or careful study of the optical properties, it is extremely difficult to distinguish between the members. The following is a composite description of the principal members of the group: *clinochlore, penninite,* and *prochlorite.*

CHLORITE—$Mg_3(Si_4O_{10})(OH)_2 \cdot Mg_3(OH)_6$

Crystallography. Monoclinic; prismatic. In pseudohexagonal tabular crystals, with prominent basal planes. Similar in habit to the crystals of the mica group, but distinct crystals rare. Usually foliated massive or in aggregates of minute scales; also in finely disseminated particles.

Physical properties. Perfect {001} cleavage. Folia flexible but not elastic. **H** $2-2\frac{1}{2}$. **G** 2.6–2.9. Luster vitreous to pearly. Color green of various shades. Rarely pale green, yellow, white, rose-red. Transparent to translucent.

Composition. Hydrous magnesium aluminum silicate, $Mg_3(Si_4O_{10})(OH)_2 \cdot Mg_3(OH)_6$ essentially. Aluminum and ferrous and ferric iron substitute for magnesium, and aluminum for silicon (see page 458). The different members vary in amounts of substitution. The composition of *clinochlore* may be written as $(Mg,Al)_3(AlSi_3O_{10})(OH)_2 \cdot Mg_3(OH)_6$.

Tests. Difficultly fusible ($5-5\frac{1}{2}$). Unattacked by hydrochloric acid. Decomposed by boiling concentrated sulfuric acid, giving a milky solution. Water in the closed tube at high temperature.

Diagnostic features. Characterized by its green color, micaceous habit and cleavage, and by the fact that the folia are not elastic.

Occurrence. Chlorite is a common and widespread mineral, usually of secondary origin. It results from the alteration of silicates containing aluminum, ferrous iron, and magnesium, such as pyroxenes, amphiboles, biotite, garnet, idocrase. To be found where rocks containing such minerals have undergone metamorphic change. Some schists are composed almost entirely of chlorite. The green color of many igneous rocks is due to the chlorite into which the ferromagnesian silicates have altered. The green color of many schists and slates is due to finely disseminated particles of the mineral. Some chlorite is deposited from hydrothermal solutions.

Name. Chlorite is derived from a Greek word meaning *green,* in allusion to the common color of the mineral.

Sepiolite—$Mg_4(Si_6O_{15})(OH)_2 \cdot 6H_2O$

Meerschaum

Crystallography. Crystal system uncertain, probably monoclinic. Microscopically is seen to be a mixture of fine fibrous material and an amorphous substance of apparently the same composition. Fine textured and compact.

Physical properties. H $2-2\frac{1}{2}$. G 2.0. Conchoidal fracture. When dry floats on water because of porosity. Luster earthy. Color grayish white, white, or with yellowish or reddish tinge. Smooth feel. Translucent.

Composition. Hydrous magnesium silicate, $Mg_4(Si_6O_{15})(OH)_2 \cdot 6H_2O$. MgO 27.1, SiO_2 60.8, H_2O 12.1 per cent.

Tests. Fusible at $5-5\frac{1}{2}$. Yields much water in the closed tube at high temperature and gives a burnt odor.

Diagnostic features. Characterized by its smooth feel, compact nature, and low specific gravity.

Occurrence. Sepiolite is found as a secondary mineral in nodular masses associated with serpentine; also with magnesite and opal. Occurs in Asia Minor in stratified earthy or alluvial deposits near Eski-Shehr. Also found in Greece, Czechoslovakia, Spain, and Morocco. In the United States has been found in Pennsylvania, Utah, New Mexico, and California.

Use. Chief use is in the manufacture of meerschaum pipes.

Name. From the Greek word meaning *cuttlefish*, the bone of which is light and porous.

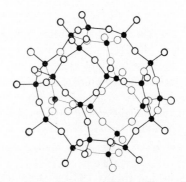

Fig. 601. Three-Dimensional Linkage. (From Harry Berman, "Constitution and Classification of the Natural Silicates," *Am. Min.*, 1937.)

Tectosilicates

Nearly three-quarters of the rocky crust of the earth is made up of minerals built about a three-dimensional framework of linked SiO_4 tetrahedra. These minerals belong to the *tectosilicate* class in which all the oxygen ions in each SiO_4 tetrahedron are shared with neighboring tetrahedra. This results in a stable, strongly bonded structure in which the ratio of Si : O is 1 : 2 (Fig. 601).

Tectosilicates

SiO$_2$ GROUP	
Quartz	SiO$_2$
Tridymite	SiO$_2$
Cristobalite	SiO$_2$
Opal	SiO$_2 \cdot n$H$_2$O
FELDSPAR GROUP	
K-Feldspar Series	
Microcline	K(AlSi$_3$O$_8$)
Orthoclase	K(AlSi$_3$O$_8$)
Na-Ca Feldspar Series	
Albite	Na(AlSi$_3$O$_8$)
Anorthite	Ca(Al$_2$Si$_2$O$_8$)
Danburite	Ca(B$_2$Si$_2$O$_8$)
FELDSPATHOID FAMILY	
Leucite	K(AlSi$_2$O$_6$)
Nepheline	(Na,K)(AlSiO$_4$)
Sodalite	Na$_4$(AlSiO$_4$)$_3$Cl
Lazurite	(Na,Ca)$_4$(AlSiO$_4$)$_3$(SO$_4$,S,Cl)
Petalite	Li(AlSi$_4$O$_{10}$)
SCAPOLITE GROUP	
Marialite	Na$_4$(AlSi$_3$O$_8$)$_3$(Cl)
Meionite	Ca$_4$(Al$_2$Si$_2$O$_8$)$_3$(CO$_3$)
ZEOLITE FAMILY	
Analcime	Na(AlSi$_2$O$_6$)·H$_2$O
Natrolite	Na$_2$(Al$_2$Si$_3$O$_{10}$)·2H$_2$O
Chabazite	(Ca,Na)$_2$(Al$_2$Si$_4$O$_{12}$)·6H$_2$O
Heulandite	Ca(Al$_2$Si$_7$O$_{18}$)·6H$_2$O
Stilbite	Ca(Al$_2$Si$_7$O$_{18}$)·7H$_2$O

SiO$_2$ GROUP

In its simplest form the SiO$_2$ framework is electrically neutral and does not contain other structural units. There are, however, at least eight different ways in which the linked tetrahedra may share all oxygens and at the same time build a continuous, electrically neutral, three-dimensional network. These eight modes of geometrical arrangement correspond to the eight known polymorphs of SiO$_2$, two of which are known only as synthetic substances. Each of these polymorphs has its characteristic external morphology, cell dimensions, and lattice energy. Which polymorph is stable is determined chiefly by energy considerations; the higher-temperature forms possessing the more expanded structures with greater lattice energy.

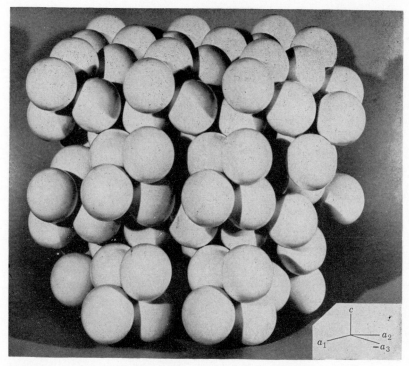

Fig. 602. Low-Temperature Quartz, SiO_2, Packing Model. The tetrahedral SiO_4 groups are arranged spirally about the c-axis with trigonal symmetry. Three groups form a unit cell.

The SiO_2 polymorphs fall into three structural categories: *quartz*, with the lowest symmetry and most compact lattice; *tridymite*, with higher symmetry and more open structure; and *cristobalite*, with the highest symmetry and the most expanded lattice. Each of these structural types may be transformed into the other only by breaking silicon-oxygen bonds and rearranging the tetrahedra into a new pattern. The transformation of one type into another is accordingly a sluggish process, and all may exist metastably in the presence of the others. Each structure type has, however, high- and low-temperature modifications which differ from each other only in the length or direction of the bonds joining the silicon and oxygen ions. (See Figs. 602 and 603.) Hence, these transformations take place quickly and reversibly at a fairly constant and sharply defined temperature of inversion and may be repeated over and over again without physical disintegration of the crystal. The table, page **477**, summarizes some of the principal facts about the polymorphs of SiO_2.

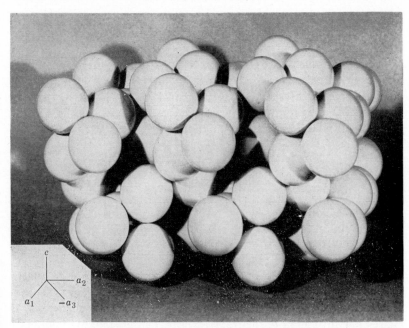

Fig. 603. High-Temperature Quartz, SiO_2, Packing Model. c-axis vertical. As in low-temperature quartz, the SiO_4 tetrahedra are arranged in three layers but are shifted in such a way as to convert the 3-fold axis to a 6-fold axis.

Polymorphs of SiO_2

Name	Symmetry	Cell Dimensions	V/Z	Z
Quartz (α)	32	$a_0 = 4.9130, c_0 = 5.405$	7.65	3
High-quartz (β)	622	$a_0 = 4.999, c_0 = 5.457$	7.88	3
Tridymite	$2/m\,2/m\,2/m$	$a_0 = 9.90, b_0 = 17.1, c_0 = 16.3$	?	64
High-tridymite	$6/m\,2/m\,2/m$	$a_0 = 5.04, c_0 = 8.24$	8.99	4
Cristobalite	422	$a_0 = 4.97, c_0 = 6.93$	?	4
High-cristobalite	$4/m\,\bar{3}\,2/m$	$a_0 = 7.13$	12.71	4
Coesite	$2/m$	$a_0 = 7.23, b_0 = 12.52$		
		$c_0 = 7.23, \beta = 120°$	4.90	16
Fibrous SiO_2	$2/m\,2/m\,2/m$	$a_0 = 4.72, b_0 = 5.16, c_0 = 8.36$		4
Lechatelierite	Glassy, amorphous			

Comparison of the cell volume per formula (V/Z) of the high-temperature forms of quartz, tridymite, and cristobalite shows the increase in specific cell volume in the high-temperature forms. The low-temperature form of each type has, in general, a smaller specific cell volume and lower symmetry than the higher-temperature form, but the change in cell volume and symmetry is less than in the transformation from one of the principal types to the other.

The effect of increased pressure is to raise all inversion temperatures and for any temperature to favor the crystallization of the polymorph most economical of space. *Coesite,* which is known as a synthetic substance only, is formed at very high pressures and has the smallest specific cell volume of the polymorphs.

High-Temperature Polymorph	Crystallizes as the Stable Form Above 1 atm. P	Inverts to the Low-Temperature Form at 1 atm. P
High-cristobalite	1470°	163–275°(?)
High-tridymite	870°	117–163°(?)
High-quartz	573°	573°

Inversions from cristobalite to tridymite, or from tridymite to quartz, are slow, and the temperature of inversion varies widely, depending chiefly on the direction and rate of temperature change. The high → low inversions of quartz, tridymite, and cristobalite take place almost instantaneously, with the release of a fairly constant amount of energy. The inversions are reversible with the low → high reactions taking place at temperatures near those of the high → low reactions with absorption of energy.

QUARTZ—SiO$_2$

Crystallography. α-Quartz, hexagonal–*R;* trigonal, trapezohedral. β-Quartz, hexagonal-trapezohedral. Crystals commonly prismatic, with prism faces horizontally striated. Terminated usually by a combination of positive and negative rhombohedrons, which often are so equally developed as to give the effect of a hexagonal dipyramid (Fig. 604). In some crystals one rhombohedron predominates or occurs alone (Fig. 605). The prism faces may be wanting, and the combination of the two rhombohedrons gives what appears to be a doubly terminated hexagonal dipyramid (known as a quartzoid) (Fig. 606). Some crystals are malformed, but the recognition of the prism faces by their horizontal striations will assist in the orientation of the crystal. The trigonal trapezohedral faces x are occasionally observed and reveal the true symmetry. These x faces are small truncations between a prism face and a face of an adjoining rhombohedron. They occur at the upper right of the prism faces in right-hand quartz and to the upper left in left-hand quartz. The right- and left-hand trigonal trapezohedrons are enantiomorphous forms and reflect the internal structure (Figs. 607 and 608). The arrangement of the SiO_4 tetrahedra either in the form of a right- or left-hand screw determines the "hand" of the quartz. In the absence of x faces, this can be recognized by observing whether plane polarized light passing parallel to the c axis is rotated to the left or right.

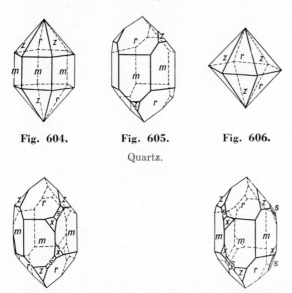

Fig. 604.   Fig. 605.   Fig. 606.

Quartz.

Fig. 607. Right-Hand Quartz.   Fig. 608. Left-Hand Quartz.

Crystals are often elongated in tapering and sharply pointed forms, owing to an oscillatory combination between the faces of the different rhombohedrons and those of the prism (Fig. 609). Some crystals are twisted and bent. Crystals showing the higher symmetry of β-quartz are rare.

Crystals are usually twinned (see page 109). The twins are usually so intimately intergrown that they can be determined only by the irregular position of the trapezohedral faces, by etching the crystal, or by observing them parallel to the c axis in polarized light. The size of crystals varies from individuals weighing a ton to finely crystalline coatings, forming "drusy" surfaces. Also common in massive forms of great variety. From coarse- to fine-grained crystalline to flintlike or cryptocrystalline, giving rise to many variety names (see below). May form in concretionary masses.

Physical properties. H 7. G 2.65. Fracture conchoidal. Luster vitreous, in some specimens greasy, splendent. Usually colorless or white, but frequently colored by various impurities and may then be any color. The color gives rise to several varieties (see page 481). Transparent to translucent. Possesses strong piezoelectric and pyroelectric properties.

Courtesy of Ward's Natural Science Establishment, Inc.

Fig. 609. Quartz Crystals, Hot Springs, Arkansas.

Composition. SiO_2. Si 46.7, O 53.3 per cent. Of all the minerals, quartz is most nearly a pure chemical compound and has constant physical properties. However, spectrographic analyses show that even its most perfect crystals have traces of lithium, sodium, potassium, aluminum, ferric iron, divalent manganese, and titanium. With precise measurements, the physical properties can be observed to vary with these minor impurities.

Tests. Infusible. Insoluble. Yields a clear glass when the finely powdered mineral is fused with an equal volume of sodium carbonate. Soluble in hydrofluoric acid.

Diagnostic features. Characterized by its glassy luster, conchoidal fracture, and crystal form. Distinguished from calcite by its high hardness, and from white varieties of beryl by its inferior hardness.

Varieties. A great many different forms of quartz exist, to which varietal names have been given. The more important varieties, with a brief description of each, follow.

Coarsely crystalline varieties

1. *Rock Crystal.* Colorless quartz, commonly in distinct crystals.
2. *Amethyst.* Quartz colored purple or violet, often in crystals. The impurity causing the color is apparently small amounts of ferric iron.
3. *Rose Quartz.* Coarsely crystalline but usually without crystal form, color a rose-red or pink. Often fades on exposure to light. Small amounts of titanium appear to be the coloring agent.
4. *Smoky Quartz; Cairngorm Stone.* Frequently in crystal of a smoky yellow to brown and almost black color. Named *cairngorm* from the locality of Cairngorm in Scotland. Spectographic analyses of smoky quartz show no dominant impurity and are similar to those of colorless quartz. The dark color results from exposure to radiation from radioactive material.
5. *Citrine.* Light yellow in color.
6. *Milky Quartz.* Milky white in color owing to minute fluid inclusions. In some cases with greasy luster.
7. *Cat's-eye.* A stone which, when cut in a round shape (*en cabochon*), exhibits an opalescent or chatoyant effect, as it is termed, is called a cat's-eye. Quartz, among other minerals, at times gives this effect, which is due either to fibrous inclusions, or to the fibrous nature of the quartz itself. *Tiger's-eye* is a yellow fibrous quartz from South Africa, which is pseudomorphic after the fibrous mineral crocidolite.
8. *With Inclusions.* Many other minerals occur as inclusions in quartz and thus give rise to variety names. *Rutilated quartz* has fine needles of rutile penetrating it. Tourmaline and other minerals are found in quartz in the same way. *Aventurine* is quartz including brilliant scales of hematite or mica. Liquids and gases may occur as inclusions; both liquid and gaseous carbon dioxide exist in some quartz.

Cryptocrystalline varieties

The cryptocrystalline varieties of quartz may be divided into two general classes, namely, *fibrous* and *granular*, which usually cannot be told apart without microscopic aid.

Fig. 610.   Agate Cut and Polished, Brazil.

A. FIBROUS VARIETIES

Chalcedony is the general name applied to fibrous varieties. It is more specifically thought of as a brown to gray, translucent variety, with a waxy luster, often mammillary and in other imitative shapes. Chalcedony has been deposited from aqueous solutions and is frequently found lining or filling cavities in rocks.   Color and banding give rise to the following varieties:

1. *Carnelian.*   A red chalcedony.
2. *Sard.*   Carnelian grades into *sard*, a brown chalcedony.
3. *Chrysoprase.*   An apple-green chalcedony colored by nickel oxide.
4. *Agate.*   A variegated variety with alternating layers of chalcedony and opal, or granular cryptocrystalline quartz.   The different colors are usually in delicate, fine parallel bands which are commonly curved, in some specimens concentric (Fig. 610).   Most agate used for commercial purposes is colored by artificial means.   Some agates have the different colors not arranged in bands but irregularly distributed. *Moss agate* is a variety in which the variation in color is due to visible impurities, often manganese oxide in mosslike patterns.

Wood that has been petrified by replacement by clouded agate is known as *silicified* or *agatized wood*.

5. *Heliotrope* or *Bloodstone.*   A green chalcedony with small red spots of jasper in it.

6. *Onyx.* Like agate, is a layered chalcedony, with layers arranged in parallel planes. *Sardonyx* is an onyx with sard alternating with white or black layers.

B. GRANULAR VARIETIES

1. *Flint.* Something like chalcedony in appearance, but dull, often dark, in color. It usually occurs in nodules in chalk and breaks with a prominent conchoidal fracture, giving sharp edges. Used for various implements by early man.

2. *Chert.* A compact massive rock similar in most properties to flint, but usually light in color.

3. *Jasper.* A granular cryptocrystalline quartz, usually colored red from hematite inclusions.

4. *Prase.* Dull green in color; otherwise similar to jasper, and occurs with it.

Occurrence. Quartz occurs as an important constituent of those igneous rocks which have an excess of silica, such as granite, rhyolite, and pegmatite. It is extremely resistant to both mechanical and chemical attack, and thus the breakdown of igneous rocks containing it yields quartz grains which may accumulate and form the sedimentary rock, sandstone. Also occurs in metamorphic rocks, as gneisses and schists, and it forms practically the only mineral of quartzites. Deposited often from solution and is the most common vein and gangue mineral. Forms as flint deposited with chalk on the sea floor in nodular masses. Solutions carrying silica may replace beds of limestone with a granular cryptocrystalline quartz known as *chert*, or discontinuous beds of chert may form contemporaneously with the limestone. In rocks quartz is associated chiefly with feldspar and muscovite; in veins with practically the entire range of vein minerals. Quartz occurs in large amounts as sand in stream beds and upon the seashore, and as a constituent of soils.

Rock crystal is found widely distributed, some of the more notable localities being: the Alps; Minas Geraes, Brazil; the island of Madagascar; and Japan. The best quartz crystals from the United States are found at Hot Springs, Arkansas, and Little Falls and Ellenville, New York. Important occurrences of amethyst are in the Ural Mountains; Czechoslovakia; Tyrol; and Brazil. Found at Thunder Bay on the north shore of Lake Superior. In the United States found in Delaware and Chester counties, Pennsylvania; Black Hills, South Dakota; and Wyoming. Smoky quartz is found in large and fine crystals in Switzerland; and in the United States at Pikes Peak, Colorado; Alexander County, North Carolina; and Auburn, Maine.

The chief source of agates at present is a district in southern Brazil and northern Uruguay. Most of these agates are cut at Oberstein, Germany, itself a famous agate locality. In the United States agate is found in numerous places, notably in Oregon and Wyoming. The chalk cliffs of Dover, England, are famous for the flint nodules that weather from them. Similar nodules are found on the French coast of the English channel and on islands off the coast of Denmark. Massive quartz, occurring in veins or with feldspar in pegmatite dikes, is mined in Connecticut, New York, Maryland, and Wisconsin for its various commercial uses.

Use. Quartz has many and varied uses. It is widely used in its various colored forms as gem stones or ornamental material, as amethyst, rose quartz, cairngorm, tiger's-eye, aventurine, carnelian, agate, and onyx. As sand, quartz is used in mortar, in concrete, as a flux, as an abrasive, and in the manufacture of glass and silica brick. In powdered form it is used in porcelain, paints, sandpaper, scouring soaps, and as a wood filler. In the form of quartzite and sandstone it is used as a building stone and for paving purposes.

Quartz is used in optical and scientific apparatus. It is made into lenses and prisms for optical equipment because of its transparency in both the infrared and ultraviolet portions of the spectrum. The *optical activity* of quartz (the ability to rotate the plane of polarization of light) is utilized in the manufacture of an instrument to produce monochromatic light of differing wave lengths. Quartz wedges, cut from transparent crystals, are used as an accessory to the polarizing microscope. Because of its piezoelectric property, quartz has specalized uses. It is cut into small oriented plates and used as radio oscillators to permit both transmission and reception on a fixed frequency. This property also renders it useful in the measurement of instantaneous high pressures such as result from firing a gun or atomic explosion.

Name. The name quartz is a German word of ancient derivation.

Similar species. *Lechatelierite*, SiO_2 is fused silica or silica glass. Found in fulgurites, tubes of fused sand formed by lightning, and in cavities in some lavas. Lechatelierite is also found at Meteor Crater, Arizona. Here sandstone has been fused by the heat generated by the impact of a falling meteorite.

Tridymite—SiO_2

Crystallography. Orthorhombic but pseudohexagonal, paramorphic after high-temperature hexagonal tridymite. Crystals are small and commonly twinned.

Physical properties. H 7. **G** 2.26. Luster vitreous. Colorless to white. Transparent to translucent. Stable only between 870 and 1470° C.

Composition. SiO_2, like quartz.

Tests. Infusible. Soluble in boiling sodium carbonate. More soluble than quartz in hydrofluoric acid.

Diagnostic features. It is impossible to identify tridymite by macroscopic means, but under the microscope its crystalline outline and refractive index distinguish it from the other silica minerals.

Occurrence. Tridymite is present on a large scale in certain siliceous volcanic rocks and for this reason may be considered an abundant mineral. Usually associated with cristobalite. It is found in large amounts in the lavas of the San Juan district of Colorado.

Name. From the Greek meaning *threefold,* in allusion to its common occurrence in trillings.

Cristobalite—SiO_2

Crystallography. Tetragonal (?); pseudoisometric. High-temperature cristobalite is isometric and frequently forms in small octahedral crystals. The outward appearance is retained when inversion to the low-temperature form takes place.

Physical properties. H 7. **G** 2.30. Luster vitreous. Colorless. Translucent. Stable only above 1470° C.

Composition. SiO_2, like quartz.

Tests. Infusible, but when heated to 200° C inverts to the high-temperature isometric form and becomes nearly transparent; on cooling, again inverts and assumes its initial white, translucent appearance.

Diagnostic features. The occurrence in small lava cavities in spherical aggregates and its behavior when heated are characteristic, but like tridymite it cannot be determined with certainty without optical determinations made with the microscope.

Occurrence. Cristobalite is present in many siliceous volcanic rocks, both as the lining of cavities and as an important constituent in the fine-grained ground mass. It is, therefore, an abundant mineral. Associated with tridymite in the lavas of the San Juan district, Colorado.

Name. From the Cerro San Cristobal near Pachuca, Mexico.

OPAL—$SiO_2 \cdot nH_2O$

Crystallography. Amorphous. Massive; often botryoidal, stalactitic.

Physical properties. Conchoidal fracture. **H** 5–6. **G** 1.9–2.2. Luster vitreous; often somewhat resinous. Colorless, white, pale shades of yellow, red, brown, green, gray, and blue. With darker colors, which are due to various impurities. Often has a milky or "opalescent" effect and may show a fine play of colors. Transparent to translucent.

Composition. Silicon dioxide, like quartz, with a varying amount of water, $SiO_2 \cdot nH_2O$. A mineraloid.

Tests. Infusible. Insoluble. Reacts like quartz. Gives water upon intense ignition in the closed tube.

Diagnostic features. Distinguished from cryptocrystalline varieties of quartz by lesser hardness and specific gravity and by the presence of water.

Varieties. *Precious Opal.* White, milky blue, yellow. In some specimens dark, as in so-called *black opal.* Translucent, with an internal play of colors. This phenomenon is said to be due to thin curved laminae which refract the light differently from the mass of the material, and so serve to break it up into the various prismatic colors. *Fire opal* is a variety with intense orange to red reflections.

Common Opal. Milk-white, yellow, green, red, etc., without internal reflections.

Hyalite. Clear and colorless opal with a globular or botryoidal surface.

Geyserite or *Siliceous Sinter.* Opal deposited by hot springs and geysers. Found about the geysers in Yellowstone National Park.

Wood Opal. Fossil wood with opal as the petrifying material.

Diatomite. Fine-grained deposits, resembling chalk in appearance. Formed by sinking from near the surface and the accumulation on the sea floor of the siliceous tests of diatoms. Also known as *diatomaceous earth* or *infusorial earth.*

Occurrence. Opal is found lining and filling cavities in igneous and sedimentary rocks, where it has evidently been deposited through the agency of hot waters. It may also replace wood buried by volcanic tuff. Deposited from hot springs and occurs in sedimentary beds as the result of the accumulation of siliceous skeletons of minute sea animals. In its ordinary variety it is of widespread occurrence.

Precious opals are found at Caernowitza, Hungary; in Queretara and other states in Mexico; in Honduras; and various localities in Australia, the chief district being White Cliffs, New South Wales. Black opal has been found in the United States in Nevada and Idaho. Diatomaceous earth is mined in several western states, chiefly in California.

Use. As a gem, opal is usually cut in round shapes, *en cabochon.* Stones of large size and exceptional quality are very highly prized. Diatomaceous earth is used extensively as an abrasive, filler, filtration powder, and in insulation products.

Name. The name opal originated in the Sanskrit, *upala,* meaning stone or precious stone.

FELDSPAR GROUP

The feldspars form one of the most important of mineral groups. They are silicates of aluminum with potassium, sodium, and calcium, and rarely barium. They may belong to either the monoclinic or the triclinic systems, but the crystals of the different systems resemble each other closely in angles and crystal habit. They all show good cleavages in two directions which make an angle of 90°, or close to 90°, with each other. Hardness is about 6, and specific gravity ranges from 2.55 to 2.76.

The aluminosilicate framework. In all tectosilicates other than the SiO_2 minerals, aluminum is present in 4-fold coordination forming aluminum-oxygen tetrahedra almost identical in size and shape to the silicon-oxygen tetrahedra. These AlO_4 tetrahedra link with SiO_4 tetrahedra by sharing oxygen ions to form a three-dimensional framework. However, because aluminum is trivalent the AlO_4 tetrahedron has an aggregate charge of -5 rather than the -4 of SiO_4. This excess negative charge permits the introduction into the structure of one monovalent cation per AlO_4 tetrahedron. Introduction of a divalent cation calls for two AlO_4 tetrahedra, and so on. This introduction of aluminum in 4-fold coordination cannot be regarded as "solid solution" or "ionic proxying" of aluminum for silicon. In such minerals as orthoclase, $KAlSi_3O_8$, aluminum is not a vicarious constituent whose percentage varies from sample to sample and which may be wholly replaced by silicon. It is an essential constituent, present in stoichiometric amount, and is not replaceable by silicon without breakdown of the structure. However, where a monovalent cation is replaced by a divalent cation, as, for example, sodium by calcium in the plagioclase feldspars, the amount of aluminum in 4-fold coordination varies in proportion to the relative amounts of calcium and sodium so as to maintain electrical neutrality; the more calcium, the greater the amount of aluminum. Here the variation in amount of aluminum may be properly regarded as part of a process of coupled ionic substitution. In order to express such relationships quantitatively, a general formula for the plagioclase feldspars may be written as

$$Na_{1-x}Ca_xAl(Si_{3-x}Al_x)O_8$$

where x may have all the values between 0 and 1.

This formula shows that the number of ions of calcium that substitute for sodium is equaled by the number of aluminum ions substituting for silicon in 4-fold coordination in the silicon-oxygen framework. The total number of sodium and calcium ions must equal 1, and the total number of silicon and aluminum ions must equal 3. One tetrahedron out of every four must be an AlO_4 tetrahedron, even if all the cation sites are occupied by sodium, so one aluminum appears in the formula irrespective of the changes in the proportion of the other cations. If the writing of a formula containing parts of atoms seems unnatural, multiply all the quantities by 100. For instance, if the proportion of atoms of Na : Ca is such that twelve calcium are present out of every 100 Ca + Na, the composition may be written as:

$$Na_{88}Ca_{12}Al_{100}Si_{288}Al_{12}O_{800} \quad \text{or} \quad Na_{0.88}Ca_{0.12}AlSi_{2.88}Al_{0.12}O_8$$

Note that the aluminum atoms which balance the calcium atoms are written separately from those that are invariably present.

Structure. The feldspars are the most important of the aluminosilicate minerals that result from the partial substitution of aluminum for silicon in the tectosilicate framework. They may be considered to form three major chemical groups; the potassium feldspars, the sodium-calcium feldspars, and the barium feldspars. All have essentially the same structure, consisting of warped chains of four-membered rings extending in the direction of the a axis and joined together by ionic bonds through the potassium, sodium, calcium, or barium ions. The square, blocky outline of the chains, imparted by the four-membered rings, finds its outward expression in the right-angled cleavage and pseudotetragonal habit characteristic of the feldspars. The mono- or divalent cations are surrounded by ten oxygens, but these cannot be regarded as occupying the apices of a regular polyhedron.

Composition. Potassium, sodium, calcium, barium, and to a lesser extent iron, lead, rubidium, and cesium may all occupy the single type of cation site, and ionic substitution to some degree exists between all. However, the common feldspars may be considered to be solid solutions of the three components

orthoclase	$KAlSi_3O_8$
albite	$NaAlSi_3O_8$
anorthite	$CaAl_2Si_2O_8$

Celsian, $BaAl_2Si_2O_8$, is of minor importance. Albite and anorthite form a continuous solid-solution series at all temperatures; anorthite and orthoclase display very limited solid solution, whereas albite and orthoclase form a continuous series at high temperatures, becoming discontinuous at lower temperatures. These relationships are ex-

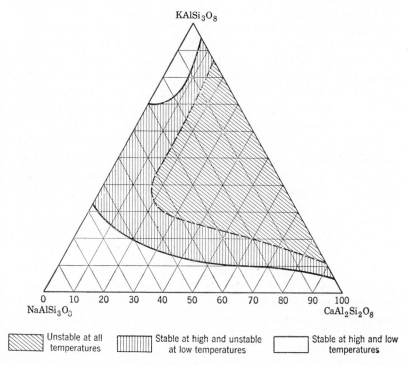

$KAlSi_3O_8$

0 10 20 30 40 50 60 70 80 90 100
$NaAlSi_3O_8$ $CaAl_2Si_2O_8$

Unstable at all temperatures   Stable at high and unstable at low temperatures   Stable at high and low temperatures

Fig. 611. Variation in Composition of Feldspars. [After H. L. Alling, *Jour. Geol.*, XXIX, 1921 (modified).]

pressed in the diagram of Fig. 611. Any composition on the triangle of Fig. 611 may be expressed by giving the percentages of three components, often abbreviated Ab, An, and Or; as $Ab_{95}An_2Or_3$ (a nearly pure albite), or $Ab_{20}An_2Or_{78}$ (a soda-rich orthoclase).

Exsolution, perthite. If feldspar compositions in the vicinity of $Ab_{50}An_0Or_{50}$ are considered, it will be seen that these are homogeneous solid solutions at elevated temperature, in which potassium and sodium are distributed in a statistically random way among the cation sites. When the temperature decreases, the size requirements of the lattice become more stringent, and strong ordering forces operate to separate potassium and sodium into regions having the lattice configuration proper to each. This separation generally results in thin layers of potassium-saturated albite in a host crystal of orthoclase containing some sodium still in solid solution. The layers of albite tend to form roughly parallel to (100), perpendicular to the direction of maximum contraction of the feldspar on cooling. The growing regions of albite thus take advantage of the zones of weakness induced in the feldspar crystal by differential contraction during cooling. This process of separation is called *exsolution*, and the resulting intergrowth is called *perthite*. Perthitelike intergrowths may also arise from later replacement of one feldspar by another. When the lamellae are so finely dispersed that they can be resolved only with a microscope, the intergrowth is called *microperthite*. More rarely, the host crystal has the lattice of the sodium-calcium feldspar, and the lamellae are of orthoclase. This is called *antiperthite*.

Polymorphism. All three of the principal types of feldspar have both high- and low-temperature modifications. In the high-temperature forms the tetrahedrally coordinated aluminum is randomly distributed, whereas in the low-temperature forms aluminum and silicon have an ordered relationship. Thus, $CaAl_2Si_2O_8$ occurs not only as anorthite, in which the aluminum ions occupy definite sites but also as high-anorthite, in which aluminum and silicon are statistically distributed. Orthorhombic and hexagonal polymorphs of $CaAl_2Si_2O_8$ have been synthesized as well. Likewise, albite has a high-temperature form. Potassium feldspar comprises the ordered low-temperature *microcline*, and the partly ordered *orthoclase*, and the disordered high-temperature form, *sanidine*. Microcline is particularly characteristic of deep-seated rocks and pegmatites, orthoclase of porphyries and hydrothermal veins, and sanidine of extrusive lavas.

Although albite and anorthite differ slightly in structure, the latter having a double cell with twice the c_0 dimension of albite, the discontinuities in the solid-solution series between them are minor, and most properties, such as specific gravity, show linear change with chemical composition. Thus determination of a suitable property with sufficient precision permits a close approximation of the chemical composition (see Fig. 625).

ORTHOCLASE—$K(AlSi_3O_8)$

Crystallography. Monoclinic; prismatic. Crystals are usually prismatic in habit and elongated parallel to the a axis, or elongated parallel to the c axis and flattened parallel to the side pinacoid, and have, as prominent forms, {010}, {001}, and {110}, often with smaller second- and fourth-order prisms (Figs. 614–616). Frequently twinned

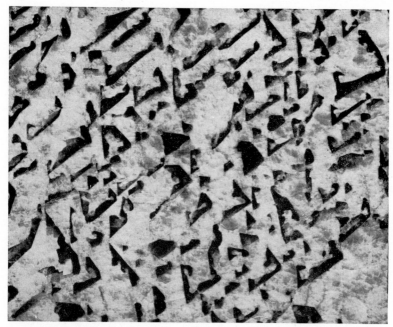

Fig. 612. Graphic Granite, Hybla, Ontario. Quartz dark, feldspar light.

Fig. 613. Phenocrysts of Orthoclase in Lava.

according to the following laws: *Carlsbad* a penetration twin with *c* axis as twin axis (Fig. 618); *Baveno* with {021} as twin and composition plane (Fig. 620); *Manebach* with {001} as twin and composition plane (Fig. 619). Commonly in crystals or in coarsely cleavable to granular masses; more rarely fine-grained, massive, and crypto-crystalline. Most abundantly in rocks as formless grains.

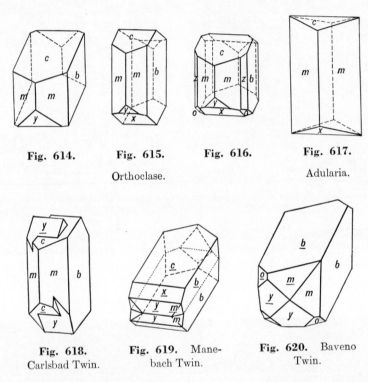

Fig. 614.   Fig. 615.   Fig. 616.   Fig. 617.

Orthoclase.   Adularia.

Fig. 618.   Fig. 619. Mane-   Fig. 620. Baveno
Carlsbad Twin.   bach Twin.   Twin.

Physical properties. Two prominent cleavages making an angle of 90° with each other; one {001}, perfect; the other {010}, good. Prismatic cleavage {110} frequently observed. **H** 6. **G** 2.57. Luster vitreous. Colorless, white, gray, flesh-red. Streak white. *Adularia* is a colorless and translucent to transparent variety. It is usually in pseudo-orthorhombic crystals (Fig. 617). Some adularia shows an opalescent play of colors and is called *moonstone. Sanidine* is a glassy, often transparent, variety found as phenocrysts in some igneous rocks.

Composition. Potassium aluminum silicate, $K(AlSi_3O_8)$. K_2O 16.9, Al_2O_3 18.4, SiO_2 64.7 per cent. Orthoclase and microcline (page 493) are together known as *potash feldspar.* Sodium may replace potassium, and in the variety *sanidine* as much as 50 per cent of the potassium is replaced. In *hyalophane,* $(K,Ba)(Al,Si)_2Si_2O_8$, barium replaces part of the potassium. Celsian, $Ba(Al_2Si_2O_8)$ is a rare barium feldspar.

Tests. Difficultly fusible (5). Insoluble in acids. When mixed with powdered gypsum and heated on platinum wire gives the violet flame of potassium.

Diagnostic features. Is usually recognized by its color, hardness, and cleavage. Distinguished from the other feldspars by its right-angle cleavage and the lack of twin striations on the best cleavage surface.

Alteration. When acted upon by waters carrying carbon dioxide, orthoclase alters, forming a soluble carbonate of potassium and leaving as a residue a mixture either of a clay mineral and silica or of muscovite and silica.

Occurrence. Orthoclase is one of the most common of minerals. It is formed during the crystallization of igneous rocks, and by hydrothermal agencies in pegmatite dikes and in druses in rocks. More rarely by crystallization from aqueous solutions at low temperatures in veins. Widely distributed as a prominent rock constituent, occurring in many types of igneous rocks, especially in granites, syenites, and nepheline syenites; in sedimentary rocks is present in arkose and in certain sandstones and conglomerates; in metamorphic rocks in gneisses. Also in large crystals and cleavable masses in pegmatite dikes, associated chiefly with quartz, muscovite, and albite.

Use. Orthoclase is used chiefly in the manufacture of porcelain. It is ground very fine and mixed with kaolin or clay, and quartz. When heated to high temperature the feldspar fuses and acts as a cement to bind the material together. Fused feldspar also furnishes the major part of the glaze on porcelain ware. A small amount of feldspar is used in the manufacture of glass to contribute alumina to the batch.

Name. The name *orthoclase* refers to the right-angle cleavage possessed by the mineral. *Feldspar* is derived from the German word *feld*, field.

MICROCLINE—$K(AlSi_3O_8)$

Crystallography. Triclinic; pinacoidal. Axial lengths and angles only slightly different from those of orthoclase. Microcline crystals may be twinned according to the same laws as orthoclase; Carlsbad twins are common, but Baveno and Manebach twins are rare. It is also twinned according to the *albite law* with the side pinacoid the twin plane, and the *pericline law* with the b crystallographic axis the twin axis. These two types of twinning are characteristic of the triclinic feldspars. A thin section of microcline under the microscope in polarized light usually shows a characteristic grating structure, caused by the crossing at nearly right angles of the twin lamellae formed according to the albite and pericline laws. Orthoclase, being monoclinic, could not show such twinning. Microcline is found in cleavable masses, in crystals, and as a rock constituent in irregular grains. Microcline probably forms the largest known crystals. In Karelia, U.S.S.R., masses weighing over 2000 tons showed the continuity of a single crystal.

In pegmatites microcline may be intimately intergrown with quartz, forming *graphic granite* (Fig. 612). Large pegmatite dikes of this character from which feldspar is quarried in considerable amounts occur in North Carolina, South Dakota, Colorado, Virginia, Wyoming, Maine, and Connecticut.

Microcline frequently has irregular and discontinuous bands crossing the basal and side pinacoids. These bands are composed of albite, and the intergrowth as a whole is called *perthite*, or, if very fine, *microperthite*. (See page 490.)

Physical properties. Cleavage {001} and {010}, with angle of 89° 30′ (orthoclase has a 90° angle). Poor {110} cleavage. **H** 6. **G** 2.54–2.57. Luster vitreous. Color white to pale yellow, more rarely red. Green microcline is known as *Amazon stone*. Translucent to transparent.

Composition. Like orthoclase, $K(AlSi_3O_8)$. Sodium may replace potassium, giving rise to *soda-microcline*, and if sodium exceeds potassium the mineral is known as *anorthoclase*.

Tests. Same as for orthoclase.

Diagnostic features. Distinguished from orthoclase only by determining the presence of triclinic twinning, which can rarely be determined without the aid of the microscope. If a feldspar is a deep green it is microcline.

Occurrence. Same as for orthoclase, and often associated with it. Much that passes as orthoclase is in reality microcline. *Amazon stone*, microcline with a green color, is found in the Ural Mountains and in various places in Norway and Madagascar. In the United States it is found at Pikes Peak, Colorado, and Amelia Court House, Virginia.

Use. Same as for orthoclase. Amazon stone is polished and used as an ornamental material.

Name. *Microcline* is derived from two Greek words meaning *little* and *inclined*, referring to the slight variation of the cleavage angle from 90°.

Plagioclase Feldspar Series

The plagioclase feldspars, also called the soda-lime feldspars, form a complete solid-solution series from pure albite, $NaAlSi_3O_8$, to pure anorthite, $CaAl_2Si_2O_8$. Calcium substitutes for sodium, with a concomitant substitution of aluminum for silicon, in all proportions. The series is divided into the following six wholly arbitrary divisions, according to the relative amounts of albite and anorthite:

	Per Cent Albite	Per Cent Anorthite
Albite $NaAlSi_3O_8$	100–90	0–10
Oligoclase	90–70	10–30
Andesine	70–50	30–50
Labradorite	50–30	50–70
Bytownite	30–10	70–90
Anorthite $CaAl_2Si_2O_8$	10–0	90–100

Although species names are given to the above arbitrary divisions, most of the properties vary in a uniform manner with the change in chemical composition. For this reason the series can be more easily understood if one comprehensive description is given, rather than six individual descriptions, and the dissimilarities between members indicated. The distinction between the high- and low-temperature modifications can be made only by x-ray or optical means.

ALBITE—ANORTHITE

Crystallography. Triclinic; pinacoidal. Crystals commonly tabular parallel to {010} (Fig. 621); occasionally elongated parallel to

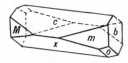

Fig. 621.   **Fig. 622.**

Albite.

the b crystal axis (Fig. 622). In anorthite crystals may be prismatic elongated parallel to the c crystal axis.

Crystals are frequently twinned according to the various laws governing the twins of orthoclase, i.e., Carlsbad, Baveno, and Manebach.

In addition, they are nearly always twinned according to one or both of two laws known as the *albite* and *pericline laws*. The twinning plane in the albite law is {010}. The angle between the basal plane and this twinning plane is about 94°. (See page 111.) Albite twinning is commonly polysynthetic and gives rise to thin lamellae, each one in twin position in respect to those on either side (see Fig. 623). Consequently a basal plane or basal cleavage of such a twinned crystal will be crossed by parallel groovings or striations (Fig. 624). Often these striations are so fine as not to be visible to the unaided eye, but on some specimens they are coarse and easily seen. The

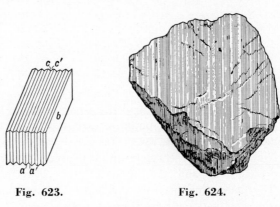

Fig. 623.   **Fig. 624.**

Albite Twinning.

presence of the striation lines upon the basal cleavage (the better cleavage surface of a feldspar) is one of the best proofs that it belongs to the plagioclase series. In the pericline law the twinning axis is the *b* crystallographic axis, and when this results in polysynthetic twins the consequent striations are to be seen on the side pinacoid.

Distinct crystals are rare. Usually in twinned, cleavable masses; as irregular grains in igneous rocks.

Physical properties. Cleavage {001} perfect, and good parallel to {010}. Cleavage poor parallel to {110} and {1$\bar{1}$0}. The angle between the {001} and {010} cleavages varies between 93° 34′ in albite and 94° 12′ in anorthite. **H** 6. **G** 2.62 in albite to 2.76 in anorthite (Fig. 625). Colorless, white, gray; less frequently greenish, yellowish, flesh-red. Certain of the species have characteristic colors. Luster vitreous to pearly. Transparent to translucent. A beautiful play of colors is frequently seen, especially in labradorite and andesine.

Composition. Sodium and calcium aluminum silicates. A complete solid-solution series extends from albite, $NaAlSi_3O_8$, to anorthite,

$CaAl_2Si_2O_8$. Considerable potassium may be present toward the albite end of the series.

Tests. Fusible at $4\text{-}4\frac{1}{2}$ to a colorless glass. Albite is insoluble, but anorthite is decomposed by hydrochloric acid. Between these extremes the intermediate members show a greater solubility the greater the amount of calcium. A strong sodium flame is given by members rich in soda.

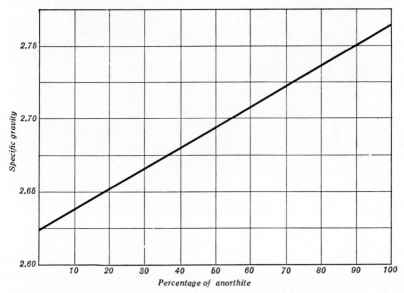

Fig. 625. Specific Gravity of the Plagioclase Feldspars.

Diagnostic features. The plagioclase feldspars can be distinguished from other feldspars by detecting the presence on the basal cleavage of striations caused by albite twinning. They may be placed accurately in their proper places in the series only by optical tests or quantitative chemical analyses, but they can be roughly distinguished from one another by specific gravity.

Occurrence. The plagioclase feldspars, as rock-forming minerals, are even more widely distributed and more abundant than the potash feldspars. They are found in igneous, metamorphic, and, more rarely, sedimentary rocks. Albite is included with orthoclase and microcline in what are known as the *alkali* feldspars, all of which have a similar occurrence. They are usually found together in granites, syenites, rhyolites, and trachytes.

The classification of igneous rocks is based largely on the kind and

Fig. 626. Microcline and Smoky Quartz, Crystal Peak, Colorado.

amount of feldspar present (see page 515). As a rule, the greater the percentage of silica in a rock the fewer the dark minerals, the greater amount of potash feldspar, and the more sodic the plagioclase; and, conversely, the lower the percentage of silica the greater the percentage of dark minerals and the more calcic the plagioclase.

Albite. In addition to its occurrence as a constituent of igneous rocks, albite is present in pegmatite dikes and may be found in crystals and replacing earlier orthoclase. *Cleavelandite* is a platy variety of albite found in some pegmatites. Notable localities for crystals of albite are in Switzerland and the Tyrol. In the United States at Paris, Maine; Chesterfield, Massachusetts; Haddam and Branchville, Connecticut; and Amelia Court House, Virginia. Some albite shows an opalescent play of colors and is known as *moonstone.* The name albite is derived from the Latin *albus,* meaning *white,* in allusion to the color.

Oligoclase. Found in various localities in Norway, notably at Tvedestrand, where it contains inclusions of hematite, which give the mineral a golden shimmer and sparkle. Such feldspar is called *aventurine* oligoclase, or *sunstone.* The name is derived from two Greek words meaning *little* and *fracture,* since it was believed to have less perfect cleavage than albite.

Andesine. Rarely found except as grains in igneous rocks. Named from the Andes Mountains where it is the chief feldspar in the andesite lavas.

Labradorite. Widespread as a rock mineral, and in large masses of rocks known as anorthosite is the only important constituent. Found on the coast of Labrador in large cleavable masses which show a fine iridescent play of colors. The name is derived from this locality.

Bytownite. Rarely found except as grains in igneous rocks. Named from Bytown, Canada (now the city of Ottawa).

Anorthite. Rarer than the more sodic plagioclase. Found in rocks rich in dark minerals and in druses of ejected volcanic blocks and in granular limestones of contact metamorphic deposits. Name derived from the Greek word meaning *oblique,* because its crystals are triclinic.

Use. Plagioclase feldspars are less widely used than potash feldspars. Albite, or *soda spar,* as it is called commercially, is used in ceramics in a manner similar to orthoclase. Labradorite that shows a play of colors is polished and used as an ornamental stone. Those varieties which show opalescence are cut and sold under the name of *moonstone* or *sunstone.*

Name. The name plagioclase is derived from the Greek meaning *oblique,* in allusion to the oblique angle between the cleavages. (See under "Occurrence" for names of specific species.)

Danburite—$Ca(B_2Si_2O_8)$

Crystallography. Orthorhombic; dipyramidal. Prismatic crystals, closely related to those of topaz in habit. Commonly in crystals.

Physical properties. H 7. G 2.97–3.02. Luster vitreous. Colorless or pale yellow. Transparent to translucent.

Composition. Calcium borosilicate, $Ca(B_2Si_2O_8)$. CaO **22.8**, B_2O_3 28.4, SiO_2 48.8 per cent.

Tests. Fusible at $3\frac{1}{2}$–4 to a colorless glass, giving a green flame. Insoluble in acids, but when previously ignited gelatinizes in hydrochloric acid.

Diagnostic features. Characterized by its crystal form and high hardness. Distinguished from topaz by the test for boron.

Occurrence. Found in crystals in eastern Switzerland, Madagascar, and Japan. In the United States at Danbury, Connecticut, and Russell, New York; also found in small crystals in a salt dome in Louisiana.

Name. From the locality, Danbury, Connecticut.

FELDSPATHOID GROUP

The feldspathoids are chemically similar to the feldspars, in that they are aluminosilicates of chiefly potassium, sodium, and calcium but with minor amounts of other ions. The chief chemical difference between feldspathoids and feldspars lies in the silica content. The feldspathoids contain about two-thirds as much silica as alkali feldspars, and hence tend to form from solutions rich in alkalis (sodium and potassium) and poor in silica. Their structures are aluminosilicate frameworks in whose interstices the cations are bound and which occasionally play host to unusual anions as well. Thus, in sodalite, chlorine is an essential constituent and in cancrinite the carbonate ion, whereas noselite contains sulfate, and lazurite sulfate, sulfide, and chlorine ions. The formulas of these minerals may be thought of as three formula weights of nepheline ($NaAlSiO_4$) to one formula weight of $NaCl$ for sodalite, one formula weight of Na_2SO_4 for noselite, etc. The structures, of course, show no such simple relation, and the strange anions are simply held in open spaces in the rather spacious aluminosilicate framework.

LEUCITE—$K(AlSi_2O_6)$

Crystallography. Pseudoisometric. Trapezohedral habit (Fig. 627). Other forms rare. Strictly isometric only at temperatures above 500° C. On cooling below this temperature it undergoes an internal atomic rearrangement to that of some other crystal system, probably tetragonal, but the external form does not change. It is formed in lavas at high temperatures and is then isometric in internal structure as well as outward form. Usually in distinct crystals, also in disseminated grains.

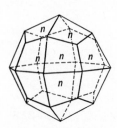

Fig. 627. Leucite.

Physical properties. H $5\frac{1}{2}$–6. G 2.45–2.50. Luster vitreous to dull. Color white to gray. Translucent.

Composition. Potassium aluminum silicate, $K(AlSi_2O_6)$. K_2O 21.5, Al_2O_3 23.5, SiO_2 55.0 per cent.

Tests. Infusible. Decomposed by hydrochloric acid with the separation of silica but without the formation of a jelly. When mixed with powdered gypsum and fused gives violet potassium flame.

Diagnostic features. Characterized by its trapezohedral form and infusibility. It is softer than garnet and harder than analcime; analcime, moreover, is fusible and yields water. Leucite, a rock-forming mineral, is usually imbedded in a fine-grained matrix, whereas anal-cime is usually in cavities in free-growing crystals.

Occurrence. Leucite is a rather rare mineral, occurring only in igneous rocks, usually in the recent lavas; rarely observed in deep-seated rocks. Found in rocks in which the amount of silica in the magma was insufficient to combine with the potassium to form feldspar. Is not observed, therefore, in rocks that contain quartz. Chiefly found in the rocks of central Italy, notably as phenocrysts in the lavas of Vesuvius. In the United States found in rocks of the Leucite Hills, Wyoming, and in certain of the rocks in the Highwood Mountains and Bear Paw Mountains, Montana. Pseudomorphs of a mixture of nepheline, orthoclase, and analcime after leucite, *pseudoleucite*, are found in syenites of Arkansas, Montana, and Brazil.

Name. From a Greek word meaning *white*.

Similar species. *Pollucite*, $Cs_4Al_4Si_9O_{26}\cdot H_2O$, is a rare isometric mineral usually occurring in pegmatites.

NEPHELINE—(Na,K) (AlSiO₄)

Crystallography. Hexagonal; pyramidal. Rarely in small pris-matic crystals with basal plane; in some cases shows pyramidal planes. Almost invariably massive, compact, and in imbedded grains. Massive variety often called *eleolite* because of its greasy luster.

Physical properties. Distinct cleavage parallel to $\{10\bar{1}0\}$. **H** $5\frac{1}{2}$–6. **G** 2.55–2.65. Luster vitreous in the clear crystals to greasy in the massive variety. Colorless, white, or yellowish. In the massive variety gray, greenish, and reddish. Transparent to translucent.

Composition. Sodium-potassium aluminum silicate, (Na,K) (AlSiO₄). The amount of potassium present is usually low. The percentages of oxides in the artificial compound $NaAlSiO_4$ are: Na_2O 21.8, Al_2O_3 35.9, SiO_2 42.3. *Kaliophilite*, $K(AlSiO_4)$, forms a solid solution series with nepheline.

Tests. Fusible at 4 to a colorless glass giving a strong yellow flame of sodium. Readily soluble in hydrochloric acid and on evaporation yields a silica jelly.

Diagnostic features. Characterized in massive varieties by its greasy luster. Distinguished from quartz by inferior hardness and from feldspar by gelatinizing in acid.

Alteration. Easily alters to various other minerals, such as zeolites, sodalite, muscovite, kaolin.

Occurrence. Nepheline is rarely found except in igneous rocks. It occurs in some recent lavas as glassy crystals, such as are found in the lavas of Vesuvius. The massive or coarsely crystalline variety is found in the older rocks and is called *eleolite*. Phonolite, nepheline syenite, and nepheline basalt are important rocks in which nepheline is an essential constituent. It is found only in rocks whose magmas contained insufficient silica to combine with soda to form feldspar. Only in exceptional circumstances, therefore, is it found in rocks that contain quartz. The largest known mass of nepheline rocks is found on the Kola Peninsula, U.S.S.R. Locally in these rocks nepheline is associated with apatite. Extensive masses of nepheline rocks are found in Norway and South Africa. In crystals in the lavas of Vesuvius. In the United States nepheline, both massive and in crystals, is found at Litchfield, Maine, associated with cancrinite. Found near Magnet Cove, Arkansas, and Beemerville, New Jersey. Common in the syenites of the Bancroft region of Ontario, Canada, where there are pegmatites with rather large masses of nearly pure nepheline.

Use. Iron-free nepheline, because of its high alumina content, has been used in place of feldspar in the glass industry. Most of the commercial nepheline comes from Ontario. Nepheline produced as a by-product of apatite mining on the Kola Peninsula is used by the Russians in several industries including ceramics, leather, textile, wood, rubber, and oil.

Name. *Nepheline* is derived from a Greek word meaning a *cloud*, because when immersed in acid the mineral becomes cloudy. *Eleolite* is derived from the Greek word for *oil*, in allusion to its greasy luster.

Similar species. *Cancrinite,* a hydrous silicate of sodium, calcium, and aluminum, is a rare mineral similar to nepheline in occurrence and associations.

SODALITE—$Na_4(AlSiO_4)_3Cl$

Crystallography. Isometric; hextetrahedral. Crystals rare, usually dodecahedrons. Commonly massive, in imbedded grains.

Physical properties. Dodecahedral {011} cleavage. **H** $5\frac{1}{2}$–6. **G** 2.15–2.3. Luster vitreous. Color usually blue, also white, gray, green. Transparent to translucent.

Composition. Sodium aluminum silicate with chlorine, $Na_4(AlSiO_4)_3Cl$. Na_2O 25.6, Al_2O_3 31.6, SiO_2 37.2, Cl 7.3 per cent.

Tests. Fusible at $3\frac{1}{2}$–4, to a colorless glass, giving a strong yellow flame (sodium). Soluble in hydrochloric acid and gives gelatinous silica upon evaporation. Nitric acid solution with silver nitrate gives white precipitate of silver chloride. In a salt of phosphorus bead with copper oxide gives azure-blue copper chloride flame.

Diagnostic features. Distinguished in most instances by its blue color, and told from lazurite by the different occurrence and absence of associated pyrite. If color is not blue, a positive test for chlorine is the only way to distinguish it from analcime, leucite, and hauynite.

Occurrence. Sodalite is a comparatively rare rock-forming mineral associated with nepheline, cancrinite, and other feldspathoids in nepheline syenites, trachytes, phonolites, etc. Found in transparent crystals in the lavas of Vesuvius. The massive blue variety is found at Litchfield, Maine; in Ontario and Quebec; and near Kicking Horse Pass, British Columbia.

Name. Named in allusion to its sodium content.

Similar species. Other feldspathoids, but rare in their occurrence, are *hauynite*, $(Na,Ca)_{6-8}Al_6Si_6O_{24}\cdot(SO_4)_{1-2}$, and *noselite*, $Na_4Al_3Si_3O_{12}\cdot SO_4$.

LAZURITE— $(Na,Ca)_4(AlSiO_4)_3(SO_4,S,Cl)$

Lapis Lazuli

Crystallography. Isometric. Crystals rare, usually dodecahedral. Commonly massive, compact.

Physical properties. Imperfect dodecahedral {011} cleavage. H 5-5½. G 2.4–2.45. Luster vitreous. Color deep azure-blue, greenish blue. Translucent.

Composition. $(Na,Ca)_4(AlSiO_4)_3(SO_4,S,Cl)$ essentially, but with considerable variation in amounts of SO_4, S, and Cl. Small amounts of rubidium, cesium, strontium, and barium may substitute for sodium.

Tests. Fusible at 3½, giving strong yellow flame (sodium). Soluble in hydrochloric acid with slight evolution of hydrogren sulfide gas.

Diagnostic features. Characterized by its blue color and the presence of associated pyrite.

Occurrence. Lazurite is a rare mineral, occurring usually in crystalline limestones as a product of contact metamorphism. *Lapis lazuli* is usually a mixture of lazurite with small amounts of calcite, pyroxene, and other silicates, and commonly contains small disseminated particles of pyrite. The best quality of lapis lazuli comes from northeastern Afghanistan. Also found at Lake Baikal, Siberia, and in Chile.

Use. Lapis lazuli is highly prized as an ornamental stone, for carvings, etc. As a powder it was formerly used as the paint pigment *ultramarine*. Now ultramarine is produced artificially.

Name. Lazurite is an obsolete synonym for azurite, and hence the mineral is named because of its color resemblance to azurite.

Petalite—Li$(AlSi_4O_{10})$

Crystallography. Monoclinic; domatic. Crystals rare, flattened on {010} or elongated on [100]. Usually massive or in foliated cleavable masses.

Physical properties. Cleavage {001} perfect, {201} good. Fracture imperfectly conchoidal. Brittle. **H** 6–6½. **G** 2.4. Luster vitreous, pearly on {001}. Colorless, white, gray. Transparent to translucent.

Composition. Lithium aluminum silicate, Li$(AlSi_4O_{10})$. LiO 4.9, Al_2O_3 16.7, SiO_2 78.4 per cent.

Tests. Fusible at 5 giving the red lithium flame. When gently heated emits a blue phosphorescent light. Insoluble in acids.

Diagnostic features. Characterized by its platy habit. Distinguished from spodumene by its cleavage and lesser specific gravity.

Occurrence. Petalite is found in pegmatites where it is associated with quartz and lithium-bearing minerals such as spodumene, tourmaline, and lepidolite. Until the middle of the twentieth century, it was considered a rather rare mineral having been reported from Utö, Sweden; Peru, Maine; and with scapolite at Bolton, Massachusetts. Recent discoveries of petalite in Southern Rhodesia and South-West Africa make it an abundant mineral. At these localities, associated with lepidolite and eucryptite, it is mined extensively.

Use. An important ore of lithium. (See spodumene, page 437.)

Name. From the Greek, *leaf*, alluding to the cleavage.

Scapolite Group

The *scapolites* are metamorphic minerals with formulas suggestive of the feldspars and with structures consisting of endless chains of aluminosilicate framework parallel to the *c* axis. The crystals are tetragonal prisms elongate parallel to the chains. The structure is rather open, and accommodates large anions such as chlorine, sulfate, and carbonate in much the same way that these ions are housed in the feldspathoids. There is a solid-solution series in the scapolites between the sodium member, *marialite,* and the calcium member, *meionite.* The formula for marialite may best be recalled by considering it to consist of three formula weights of albite, 3$(NaAlSi_3O_8)$ plus one formula weight of NaCl; and meionite as three formula weights of anorthite, 3$(CaAl_2Si_2O_8)$ plus one formula weight of $CaCO_3$ or $CaSO_4$. There is complete ionic substitution of calcium for sodium with charge compensation effected as in the feldspars by concomitant substitution of aluminum for silicon in the chains. There is also complete substitution of carbonate, sulfate, and chlorine for each other. Therefore, most scapolite to which the name *wernerite* is given is intermediate in composition between the end members marialite and meionite.

SCAPOLITE

Wernerite

Crystallography. Tetragonal; dipyramidal. Crystals usually prismatic. Prominent forms are prisms of the first and second orders, and dipyramid of first order (Fig. 628). Rarely shows the faces of the tetragonal dipyramid (Fig. 629). Crystals are usually coarse, or with faint fibrous appearance.

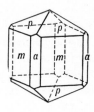

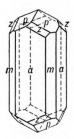

Fig. 628.   **Fig. 629.**

Scapolite.

Physical properties. Imperfect prismatic cleavage, both {100} and {110}. **H** 5–6. **G** 2.65–2.74. Luster vitreous when fresh and unaltered. Color white, gray, pale green; more rarely bluish or reddish. Transparent to translucent.

Composition. Scapolite is of varied composition since the name is used to designate all intermediate members of a series, the end members of which are: *marialite*, $(Na,Ca)_4Al_3(Al,Si)_3Si_6O_{24}(Cl,CO_3,SO_4)$; and *meionite*, $(Ca,Na)_4Al_3(Al,Si)_3Si_6O_{24}(Cl,CO_3SO_4)$.

Tests. Fusible at 3 with intumescence to a white blebby glass and colors the flame yellow. Imperfectly decomposed by hydrochloric acid, yielding separated silica but without the formation of a jelly.

Diagnostic features. Characterized by its crystals with square cross section and four cleavage directions at $45°$. When massive resembles feldspar but has a characteristic fibrous appearance on the cleavage surfaces. It is also more readily fusible. Its fusibility with intumescence distinguishes it from pyroxene.

Alteration. Easily altered to various other minerals such as mica, epidote, talc, kaolin.

Occurrence. Scapolite occurs in the crystalline schists, gneisses, and amphibolites, and in many cases has probably been derived by alteration from plagioclase feldspars. It also characteristically occurs in crystalline limestones formed through the contact metamorphic action of an intruded igneous rock. Associated with diopside, amphibole, garnet, apatite, sphene, and zircon.

Crystals of gem quality with a yellow color occur in Madagascar. In the United States found in various places in Massachusetts, notably at Bolton; Orange, Lewis, and St. Lawrence counties, New York. Also found at various points in Ontario, Canada.

Name. From the Greek meaning *a shaft*, in allusion to the prismatic habit of the crystals.

ZEOLITE FAMILY

The zeolites form a large family of hydrous silicates which show close similarities in composition and in their associations and mode of occurrence. They are silicates of aluminum with sodium and calcium as the important bases. They average between $3\frac{1}{2}$ and $5\frac{1}{2}$ in hardness and between 2.0 and 2.4 in specific gravity. Many of them fuse readily with marked intumescence, hence the name *zeolite*, from two Greek words meaning *to boil* and *stone*. They are secondary minerals found characteristically in cavities and veins in basic igneous rocks.

All the zeolites are aluminosilicates whose gross compositions somewhat resemble those of the feldspars, and, like the feldspars, are built about chains made up of 4-fold rings of SiO_4 and AlO_4 tetrahedra. The chains, bound by the interstitial cations, sodium, potassium, calcium, and barium, form an open structure with wide channelways in which water and other molecules may be readily housed. Much of the interest in zeolites derives from the presence of these spacious channels. When a zeolite is heated, the water in the channelways is given off easily and continuously as the temperature rises, leaving the structure intact. This is in sharp contrast to other hydrated compounds, as gypsum, in which the water molecules play a structural role and complete dehydration produces structural collapse. After essentially complete dehydration of a zeolite, the channels may be filled again with water or with ammonia, mercury vapor, iodine vapor, or a variety of substances. This process is selective and depends on the particular zeolite structure and the size of the molecules, and, hence, zeolites are used as "molecular sieves."

Zeolites have a further useful property that derives from their structure. Water may pass easily through the channelways, and, in the process, ions in solution may be exchanged for ions in the structure. This process is called "base exchange" or "cation exchange," and by its agency zeolites or synthetic compounds with zeolitic structure are used for water softening. The zeolite used has a composition about $Na_2Al_2Si_3O_{10} \cdot 2H_2O$ (like natrolite). "Hard" water, that is, water containing many calcium ions in solution, is passed through a tank filled with zeolite grains. The calcium ions replace the sodium ions in the zeolite, forming $CaAl_2Si_3O_{10} \cdot 2H_2O$, contributing sodium ions to the solution. Water containing sodium does not form scum and is said to be "soft." When the zeolite in the tank has become saturated with calcium, a strong NaCl brine is passed through the tank. The high concentration of sodium ion forces the reaction to go in the reverse direction, and the $Na_2Al_2Si_3O_{10} \cdot 2H_2O$ is reconstituted, calcium going into solution. By base exchange many ions, including silver, may be substituted for the alkali-metal cation in the zeolite structure.

ANALCIME—$Na(AlSi_2O_6)H_2O$

Analcite

Crystallography. Isometric; hexoctahedral. Usually in trapezohedrons (Fig. 630). Cubes with trapezohedral truncations also known (Fig. 631). Usually in crystals, also massive granular.

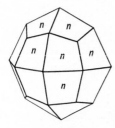

Fig. 630.   Fig. 631.

Analcime.

Physical properties. H 5–5$\frac{1}{2}$. G 2.27. Luster vitreous. Colorless or white. Transparent to translucent.

Composition. Hydrous sodium aluminum silicate, $Na(AlSi_2O_6) \cdot H_2O$. The percentages of oxides are: Na_2O 14.1, Al_2O_3 23.2, SiO_2 54.5, H_2O 8.2.

Tests. Fusible at 3$\frac{1}{2}$, becoming first a milky white and then a clear glass. Colors the flame yellow (sodium). Gives water in the closed tube.

Diagnostic features. Usually recognized by its free-growing crystals and its vitreous luster. Crystals resemble garnet and leucite in form. Distinguished from garnet by inferior hardness and by giving water in the closed tube; from leucite by ease of fusibility, presence of water, and occurrence. (Leucite is always imbedded in rock matrix.)

Occurrence. Analcime is commonly a secondary mineral formed by the action of hot circulating waters and is thus found deposited in the cavities of igneous and especially volcanic rocks. Associated with calcite, and various zeolites and related minerals. Also as an original constituent of igneous rocks as in the analcime basalts. Fine crystals are found in the Cyclopean Islands near Sicily; in the Val di Fassa and on the Seiser Alpe, Trentino, Italy; in Victoria, Australia; and Kerguelen Island in the Indian Ocean. In the United States found at Bergen Hill, New Jersey; in the Lake Superior copper district; and at Table Mountain, near Golden, Colorado. Also found at Cape Blomidon, Nova Scotia.

Name. Derived from a Greek word meaning *weak*, in allusion to its weak electric property when heated or rubbed.

Similar species. *Laumontite* is a monoclinic, and *thomsonite* an orthorhombic zeolite associated with other zeolites but much rarer in occurrence.

NATROLITE—$Na_2(Al_2Si_3O_{10}) \cdot 2H_2O$

Crystallography. Monoclinic; sphenoidal. Pseudo-orthorhombic, prismatic, often acicular. Prism zone vertically striated. Some specimens terminated by low fourth-order prism. In some cases in cruciform twins. Usually in radiating crystal groups; also fibrous, massive, granular, or compact.

Physical properties. Perfect prismatic {110} cleavage. **H** 5–5½. **G** 2.25. Luster vitreous. Colorless or white. In some cases tinted yellow to red. Transparent to translucent.

Composition. A hydrous sodium aluminum silicate, $Na_2(Al_2Si_3O_{10}) \cdot 2H_2O$. The percentages of oxides are: Na_2O 16.3, Al_2O_3 26.8, SiO_2 47.4, H_2O 9.5. Potassium may replace sodium with the ratio Na : K = 15 : 1.

Tests. Fusible at 2½ to a clear, transparent glass, giving a yellow (sodium) flame. Water in the closed tube. Soluble in hydrochloric acid and gelatinizes upon evaporation.

Diagnostic features. Recognized chiefly by its radiating crystals. Distinguished from aragonite by its easy fusibility and water in the closed tube.

Occurrence. Natrolite is a mineral of secondary origin, found lining cavities in basalt. Associated with other zeolites and calcite. Notable localities for its occurrence are Aussig and Salesel, Bohemia; Puy-de-Dôme, France; and Val di Fassa, Trentino, Italy. In the United States found at Bergen Hill, New Jersey. Also found in various places in Nova Scotia.

Name. From the Latin *natrium*, meaning *sodium*, in allusion to its composition.

Similar species. *Scolecite* (monoclinic), $Ca(Al_2Si_3O_{10}) \cdot 3H_2O$, is a zeolite similar to natrolite.

CHABAZITE—$(Ca,Na)_2(Al_2Si_4O_{12}) \cdot 6H_2O$

Crystallography. Hexagonal–R; scalenohedral. Usually in crystals. The common form is the simple rhombohedron $\{10\bar{1}1\}$, having nearly cubic angles. May show several different rhombohedrons (Fig. 632). Often in penetration twins.

Physical properties. Poor rhombohedral $\{10\bar{1}1\}$ cleavage. **H** 4–5. **G** 2.05–2.15. Luster vitreous. Color white, yellow, pink, red. Transparent to translucent.

Composition. Essentially a hydrous calcium-sodium aluminum silicate. $(Ca,Na)_2(Al_2Si_4O_{12}) \cdot 6H_2O$. Potassium is usually present.

Tests. Fuses with swelling at 3 to a blebby glass. Decomposed by hydrochloric acid with the separation of silica

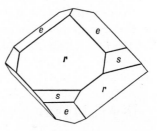

Fig. 632. Chabazite.

but without the formation of a jelly. Solution after filtering off silica gives precipitate of aluminum hydroxide with ammonia, and in filtrate ammonium carbonate gives white precipitate of calcium carbonate. Gives much water in the closed tube.

Diagnostic features. Recognized usually by its rhombohedral crystals, and distinguished from calcite by its poorer cleavage and lack of effervescence in hydrochloric acid.

Occurrence. Chabazite is a mineral of secondary origin found usually with other zeolites, lining cavities in basalt. Notable localities for its occurrence are the Faeroe Islands; the Giant's Causeway, Ireland; Aussig, Bohemia; Seiser Alpe, Trentino, Italy; and Oberstein, Germany. In the United States found at West Paterson, New Jersey, and Goble Station, Oregon. Also found in Nova Scotia and there known as *acadialite*.

Name. Chabazite is derived from a Greek word which was an ancient name for *a stone*.

Similar species. *Gmelinite* is closely related chemically to chabazite but rarer in occurrence.

HEULANDITE—Ca(Al$_2$Si$_7$O$_{18}$)·6H$_2$O

Crystallography. Monoclinic; prismatic, but crystals often simulate orthorhombic symmetry (Fig. 633). Side pinacoid prominent, often having a diamond shape.

Physical properties. Perfect cleavage parallel to the side pinacoid {010}. **H** 3½–4. **G** 2.18–2.2. Luster vitreous, pearly on the side pinacoid. Colorless, white, yellow, red. Transparent to translucent.

Composition. Essentially a hydrous calcium aluminum silicate, Ca(Al$_2$Si$_7$O$_{18}$)·6H$_2$O. Sodium and potassium substitute for calcium.

Tests. Fusible at 3 with intumescence to a white glass. Water in the closed tube.

Diagnostic features. Characterized by its crystal form and one direction of perfect cleavage with pearly luster.

Occurrence. Heulandite is a mineral of secondary origin found usually in cavities of basic igneous rocks associated with other zeolites and calcite. Found in notable quality in Iceland; the Faeroe Islands; Andreasberg, Harz Mountains; Tyrol, Austria; and India, near Bombay. In the United States found at West Paterson, New Jersey. Also found in Nova Scotia.

Name. In honor of the English mineral collector, H. Heuland.

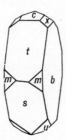

Fig. 633. Heulandite.   **Fig. 634.** Stilbite.

STILBITE—Ca(Al$_2$Si$_7$O$_{18}$)·7H$_2$O

Crystallography. Monoclinic; prismatic. Uniformly in cruciform (pseudo-orthorhombic) twins. Commonly tabular parallel to the side pinacoid. Crystals usually in distinct individuals or in sheaflike aggregates (Fig. 634).

Physical properties.   Perfect cleavage parallel to {010}.   **H** $3\frac{1}{2}$–4. **G** 2.1–2.2.   Luster vitreous; pearly on side pinacoid.   Color white, more rarely yellow, brown, red.   Translucent.

Composition.   Essentially a hydrous calcium aluminum silicate, $Ca(Al_2Si_7O_{18})\cdot7H_2O$.   Sodium and potassium are usually present in small amounts.

Tests.   Fuses with intumescence at 3 to a white enamel.   Decomposed by hydrochloric acid with separation of silica but without the formation of a jelly.   Water in the closed tube.

Diagnostic features.   Characterized chiefly by its cleavage, pearly luster on the cleavage face, and common sheaflike groups of crystals.

Occurrence.   Stilbite is a mineral of secondary origin found in cavities in basalts and related rocks.   Associated with other zeolites and calcite.   Notable localities for its occurrence are Poonah, India; Isle of Skye; Faeroe Islands; Kilpatrick, Scotland; and Iceland.   In the United States found in northeastern New Jersey.   Also found in Nova Scotia.

Name.   Derived from a Greek word meaning *luster*, in allusion to the pearly luster

Similar species.   *Phillipsite* and *harmotome* are monoclinic zeolites in the stilbite group with complex and variable composition.

OCCURRENCE AND ASSOCIATION OF MINERALS

Although minerals have many modes of occurrence, and an almost endless variety of associations, there are, nevertheless, certain ways in which their occurrence is common and characteristic. An understanding of the conditions under which a particular mineral is usually formed, together with a knowledge of the other minerals that are characteristically associated with it, is of the greatest value in the identification of the mineral. On the following pages is given, therefore, a brief discussion of the more important modes of mineral occurrence, and of the more common associations.

ROCKS AND ROCK-FORMING MINERALS

Since minerals occur most commonly and abundantly as rock constituents a short description of the more important rock types and of the common rock-forming minerals will be given first. Only the barest outline of the subject can be presented here; for more detailed information the reader is referred to one of the textbooks which treat more particularly of petrology.

Rocks are divided into the three main divisions:

I. Igneous.   II. Sedimentary.   III. Metamorphic.

I. IGNEOUS ROCKS

Igneous rocks, as the name indicates, are those that have been formed by the cooling and consequent solidification of a once hot and fluid mass of rock material, known as a rock magma. A magma is a solution containing the chemical constituents which, when cooled sufficiently, crystallize to form the various minerals that make up the resulting rock. The elements that form the chief constituents of the magmas of igneous rocks, named in the order of their abundance, are oxygen, silicon, aluminum, iron, calcium, magnesium, sodium, and potassium. When a magma cools, each mineral crystallizes out as its point of supersaturation is reached. Some minerals crystallize from the fluid mass earlier than others, and thus, in most igneous rocks, a more or less definite order of crystallization of the various mineral constituents can be determined. In general, the dark minerals and those containing the smaller amounts of silica crystallize first, and minerals rich in silica last. Among the more common rock-forming minerals the usual order of crystallization is: the accessory minerals such as zircon, rutile, hematite, ilmenite, magnetite; then the ferromagnesian minerals, like pyroxenes and amphiboles; next the plagioclase feldspars; and then orthoclase and quartz.

The mineral assemblage found in any igneous rock depends chiefly upon the chemical composition of the original magma. If the magma had a high percentage of silica, the resulting rock would contain the silica-rich minerals and quartz. It would usually be light in color. If, on the other hand, the magma had a low percentage of silica, the resulting rock would contain minerals poor in silica and no quartz. It would, in general, be dark in color.

In addition to the wide variation in chemical and mineral composition shown by igneous rocks there is also a variation in the size of the crystals that make up the rock. This is determined chiefly by the rate at which the magma cooled. If a rock has been formed from a magma buried at a considerable depth in the crust of the earth it must have cooled very slowly and taken a long period of time for its gradual crystallization and solidification. Under these conditions the mineral particles would have had the opportunity, because of the slowness of crystallization, to grow to considerable size. A rock having such a deep-seated origin has, therefore, a coarse texture, and its constituent minerals can usually be recognized and differentiated by the unaided eye. Such rocks are commonly termed *plutonic*.

On the other hand, if the magma has been extruded as lava upon the surface of the earth, its subsequent cooling and solidification go on rapidly. Under these conditions the mineral particles not already formed have little chance to grow and the resulting rock is fine grained. In some cases the cooling has been too rapid to allow the separation of any minerals, and the resulting rock is a glass. Ordinarily the mineral constituents of fine-grained rocks can be definitely recognized only by a microscopic examination of a thin section of the rock. Such igneous rocks are known as *volcanic* or *extrusive* rocks.

Magma intruded as dikes and sills close to the earth's surface forms a group of rocks known as *hypabyssal*. The texture of these rocks is usually finer than that of the plutonic but coarser than that of the volcanic.

Porphyry and Porphyritic Texture

Some igneous rocks show distinct crystals of some minerals which lie imbedded in a much finer-grained matrix. These larger crystals are known as *phenocrysts,* and the finer-grained material as the *groundmass*. (See Fig. 613, page 492.) Such rocks are known as *porphyries*. The phenocrysts may vary in size from crystals an inch or more across down to very small individuals. The groundmass may also be composed of fairly coarse-grained material, or its grains may be microscopic. It is the difference in size between the phenocrysts and the particles of the groundmass that is the distinguishing feature of a porphyry. The porphyritic texture develops when some of the crystals grow to considerable size before the main mass of the magma consolidates into the finer and uniform-grained material. Any one of the types of igneous rocks described below may have a porphyritic variety, such as *granite porphyry, diorite porphyry, rhyolite porphyry*. Porphyritic varieties occur more frequently in volcanic rocks, especially in the more siliceous types.

An igneous rock, because of the mode of its formation, consists of crystalline particles which may be said to interlock with each other, and each mineral particle is intimately and firmly imbedded in the surrounding particles. This texture will enable one ordinarily to distinguish between an igneous and a sedimentary rock, sedimentary rock being composed of grains which do not interlock with each other but stand out, more or less, by themselves. A sedimentary rock is not so firm and coherent as an igneous rock. Further, the texture of most igneous rocks is the same in all directions, giving rise to a fairly uniform and homogeneous mass. This characteristic will enable one to distinguish an igneous from a metamorphic rock, since the metamorphic rock commonly shows a layered structure, with a more or less definite parallel arrangement of its minerals.

Because of the almost infinite variation possible in the chemical composition of magmas and because of the various conditions under which they may form, igneous rocks show a wide variation in character; and there is a complete gradation from one rock type into another, so that the names of igneous rocks, and the boundaries between types, are largely arbitrary.

Classification of the Igneous Rocks

Many schemes have been proposed for the classification of igneous rocks, but the most practical for the elementary student are based on the mineral content. It can be said in general that three criteria are to be considered in classifying a rock. (1) The relative amount of silica present. Quartz indicates an excess of silica; feldspathoids indicate a deficiency of silica. (2) The kinds of feldspar present and the relative amount of each kind. (3) The texture, or size of the grains. Is the rock coarse or fine grained; that is, is it plutonic or volcanic?

It is obvious that the exact determination of the kind of feldspar or a correct estimate of the amount of each kind is impossible in the field or in the hand specimen. It is also impossible in many fine-grained rocks to recognize individual minerals. Such precise work must be left for the laboratory and carried out by the microscopic examination of thin sections of rocks. Nevertheless, it is important that the basis for the general classification be understood in order that a simplified field classification may have more meaning.

Three major divisions may be made on the basis of the silica content.[1] (1) Quartz present in amounts greater than 5 per cent. (2) Less than 5 per cent quartz or 5 per cent feldspathoids. (3) Feldspathoids in amounts greater than 5 per cent. The above divisions made on the basis of silica content are further divided according to the kind and amount (or the absence) of feldspar. Most of the rocks thus classified have a coarse- and fine-grained variety, which receive different names. The table on page 518 gives the principal rock

---

[1] Feldspathoids are minerals which take the place of all, or part, of the feldspar in rocks low in silica. A magma may have just the exact amount of silica to combine with the alkalis, calcium, and aluminum and form feldspar on complete crystallization of the rock. If silica is in excess of this amount, quartz will form; if there is a deficiency, feldspathoids will form.

types according to such a classification. It should be remembered that, although these rock names are the most important, more than 600 have been proposed to indicate specific types.

Plutonic Rocks

Brief descriptions of the more important rock types listed in the accompanying table are given below.

Granite–granodiorite. Granite is a granular rock of light color and even texture consisting chiefly of feldspar and quartz. Usually both potash feldspar and oligoclase are present; potash feldspar may be flesh-colored or red, whereas oligoclase is commonly white and can be recognized by the presence of albite twinning striations. The quartz can be recognized by its glassy luster and lack of cleavage. Granites usually carry a small amount (about 10 per cent) of mica or hornblende. The mica is commonly biotite, but muscovite may also be present. The minor accessory minerals are zircon, sphene, apatite, magnetite, ilmenite.

A complete series of rocks exists, which grades from a granite whose feldspar is almost entirely potash varieties to granodiorite whose feldspar is mostly plagioclase with only slightly more than 5 per cent potash feldspar. The boundary between the two types is arbitrarily set. Granites are those rocks in which potash feldspar exceeds plagioclase; granodiorites are those in which plagioclase exceeds potash feldspar. In most instances it so happens that as the plagioclase increases in amount the percentage of dark minerals also increases, and thus, in general, granodiorites are darker than granites. However, in the field or in a hand specimen, it is usually impossible to distinguish between the two rock types with certainty.

Syenite–monzonite. A syenite is a granular rock of light color and even texture composed essentially of potash feldspar and oligoclase, with lesser amounts of hornblende, biotite, and pyroxene. It thus resembles a granite in appearance but differs from granite in that it contains less than 5 per cent quartz. Accessory minerals are apatite, sphene, zircon, and magnetite.

A series exists between syenite and monzonite, and if plagioclase feldspar exceeds potash feldspar the rock is called a monzonite. Monzonites are usually darker than syenites, for an increase in dark minerals frequently accompanies an increase in plagioclase. However, without microscopic aid it is rarely possible to distinguish between the two types.

Nepheline is present in some syenites; if the amount exceeds 5 per cent, the rock is called a *nepheline syenite*. The nepheline has a greasy luster and may be mistaken for quartz, but can be distinguished by its hardness ($5\frac{1}{2}$–6). Some nepheline syenites may contain sodalite; others, corundum.

Syenites in which leucite is present in amounts greater than 5 per cent are called *leucite syenites*. The leucite can be recognized by its trapezohedral form. Such rocks are extremely rare.

Tonalite. A tonalite or *quartz diorite* is composed essentially of plagioclase feldspar and quartz with only minor amounts of potash feldspar (less than 5 per cent). The plagioclase is oligoclase or andesine. Dark minerals, especially biotite and hornblende, are plentiful; pyroxene is more rarely present. Apatite, sphene, magnetite are common accessory minerals. Although not essential to the classification, dark minerals are usually abundant, and thus, in general, tonalites are darker in color than granites and granodiorites.

As the plagioclase becomes richer in lime, tonalite grades into the rather uncommon rock *quartz gabbro*. With a lessening of the amount of quartz, it grades into *diorite*.

Diorite–gabbro. A diorite is a granular rock characterized by plagioclase feldspar (oligoclase to andesine) but lacking quartz and potash feldspar in appreciable amounts. Hornblende is the principal dark mineral, but biotite is usually present. Pyroxenes are rare. Magnetite, ilmenite, apatite, and, less commonly, sphene and zircon are accessory minerals. Normally dark minerals are present in sufficient amount to give the rock a dark appearance.

If the plagioclase is more calcic in composition than andesine (labradorite to anorthite) the rock is called a gabbro. Although the distinction is made on this criterion alone, it so happens that rocks carrying labradorite or more calcic plagioclase usually have pyroxene as the chief dark constituent, whereas the diorites with more sodic feldspar usually have amphiboles as dark minerals. Olivine is also present in most gabbros.

The name *norite* is given to a gabbro in which the pyroxene is essentially hypersthene; it is usually impossible to make this distinction without microscopic aid. A type of gabbro known as *anorthosite* is composed almost entirely of feldspar and may therefore be light in color.

If amounts of nepheline in diorites and gabbros exceed 5 per cent the rocks are called respectively nepheline diorite and nepheline gabbro. These rocks are rare and unimportant.

The term *diabase* is sometimes used to indicate a fine-grained gabbro

Simplified Classification of the Igneous Rocks

Feldspar	Quartz > 5 per cent		No Quartz; No Feldspathoids		Nepheline or Leucite > 5 per cent	
	Coarse	Fine	Coarse	Fine	Coarse	Fine
*Potash feldspar > plagioclase	Granite	Rhyolite	Syenite	Trachyte	Nepheline syenite / Leucite syenite	Phonolite / Leucite phonolite
Plagioclase > potash feldspar	Granodiorite	Quartz latite	Monzonite	Latite	Nepheline monzonite	
Plagioclase (oligoclase or andesine)	Tonalite	Dacite	Diorite	Andesite	Nepheline diorite	
Plagioclase (labradorite to anorthite)	Quartz gabbro		Gabbro	Basalt	Nepheline gabbro	Tephrite (−olivine) / Basanite (+olivine)
No feldspar			Peridotite (olivine dominant) / Pyroxenite (pyroxene dominant) / Hornblendite (hornblende dominant)		Ijolite	Nephelinite (−olivine) / Nepheline basalt (+olivine)

* Under potash feldspar are included orthoclase, microcline, anorthoclase, microperthite.

characterized by a certain texture. This "diabasic" texture is shown microscopically to have augite filling the interstices of tabular plagioclase crystals.

Peridotite. A peridotite is a granular rock composed of dark minerals; feldspar is negligible (less than 5 per cent). The dark minerals are chiefly pyroxene and olivine in varying proportions, but hornblende may be present. If the rock is composed almost wholly of pyroxene it is called a *pyroxenite;* if it is composed almost wholly of olivine it is called a *dunite.* The name *hornblendite* is given to a rare type of rock composed almost wholly of hornblende. Magnetite, chromite, ilmenite, and garnet are frequently associated with peridotites. Platinum is associated with chromite in some peridotites, usually dunites, whereas diamond is found in a variety of peridotite known as *kimberlite.*

The olivine in peridotites is usually altered in whole or in part to the mineral serpentine. If the entire rock is thus altered the name *serpentine* is given to it.

Volcanic Rocks

Because of their fine-grained texture it is much more difficult to distinguish between the different types of volcanic rocks than between their plutonic equivalents. In the field only an approximate classification, depending chiefly upon whether the rock is light or dark in color, can be made. The term *felsite* is thus used to include the dense, fine-grained rocks of all colors except dark gray, dark green, or black. Felsite thus embraces the following types described below: rhyolite, trachyte, quartz latite, latite, dacite, and andesite. The experienced petrographer may be able, by the aid of a hand lens, to discern differences in texture or mineral composition which enable him to classify these rocks fairly accurately, but to the untrained observer they all appear much the same.

Fine-grained rocks that are a very dark green or black are called *traps.* This term is applied to dark, fine-grained rocks of indefinite mineral composition irrespective of whether they have been intruded as dikes or extruded as lava. It so happens that most rocks thus classified as traps in the field or hand specimen are basalts and satisfy the more rigorous classification based on microscopic examination.

Rhyolite is a dense fine-grained rock, the volcanic equivalent of a granite. It is thus composed essentially of alkali feldspar and quartz, but much of the silica may be present as tridymite or cristobalite. Phenocrysts of quartz, orthoclase (frequently sanidine), and oligoclase are common. Dark minerals are never abundant, but dark brown biotite is most common. Augite and hornblende are found in some rhyolites.

Rhyolites may be very uniform in appearance or may show a flow structure, giving a banded or streaked appearance to the rock. The groundmass may be partly or wholly glassy. Where the rock is completely glassy and of a compact nature it is known as *obsidian* and is usually black. Similar glassy rocks of a brown, pitchy appearance are called *pitchstones*. *Pumice* is rhyolite glass in which expanding gas bubbles have distended the magma to form a highly vesicular material. In pumice, therefore, cavities are so numerous as to make up the bulk of the rock and give it an apparent low specific gravity.

Trachyte is the volcanic equivalent of syenite. It is thus composed chiefly of alkali feldspar with some dark minerals but lacks quartz. Small amounts of tridymite and cristobalite are often found in gas cavities. Phenocrysts of sanidine are frequently present and characteristically show Carlsbad twinning; phenocrysts of oligoclase, biotite, hornblende, and pyroxene are less common. Olivine may be present.

Banding or streaking, due to flow, is common in the trachytes. Unlike the rhyolites, glass is seldom found in the groundmass, and there are thus few glassy or vesicular types. As a result of flow the tabular feldspar frequently shows a subparallel orientation which is so common in trachytes that it is called *trachytic texture*.

Phonolite is the volcanic equivalent of nepheline syenite and is thus poorer in silica than trachyte. This is expressed mineralogically by the presence of feldspathoids. Orthoclase (sanidine) is the common feldspar; albite is rarely present. Nepheline occurs in the groundmass as minute hexagonal crystals and can be observed only by microscopic aid. Sodalite and other feldspathoids may be present, usually altered to zeolites. When leucite is present it is in well-formed crystals which range from microscopic sizes to half an inch in diameter. When leucite is present the rock is known as a *leucite phonolite*. Aegirite is the common dark mineral and normally occurs as phenocrysts, but biotite may be abundant in the leucite-rich rocks. The phonolites are completely crystalline, and there are thus no glassy varieties.

Latite and **quartz latite** are respectively the volcanic equivalents of monzonite and granodiorite. They, therefore, contain plagioclase in excess of potash feldspar. The dark minerals are chiefly biotite and hornblende. The distinction between them rests on the amount of quartz present; quartz latites would contain more, latites less, than 5 per cent quartz. Both of these rocks are relatively unimportant.

Dacite is the dense volcanic equivalent of tonalite or quartz diorite. It contains plagioclase feldspar and quartz, both of which may occur as phenocrysts. The dark mineral is usually hornblende, but biotite is found in some varieties. Some glass may be present in the groundmass, but glassy equivalents of dacites are rare.

Andesite is the volcanic equivalent of diorite and thus is composed chiefly of oligoclase or andesine feldspar. Orthoclase and quartz are absent or present in amounts of less than 5 per cent. Hornblende, biotite, augite, or hypersthene may be present, frequently as phenocrysts. Andesites are usually named according to the dark mineral present, as *hornblende andesite, hypersthene andesite,* etc. In some andesites the groundmass is partly glassy and in rarer types completely so.

Andesites are abundant in certain localities, notably in the Andes Mountains of South America, from which locality the rock receives its name.

Basalt is a dark-colored, fine-grained rock, the volcanic equivalent of gabbro. Labradorite feldspar is the chief constituent of the groundmass, whereas more calcic plagioclase (bytownite to anorthite) may be present as phenocrysts. Augite and olivine are usually present; the augite is frequently found both as phenocrysts and in the groundmass, but olivine, as a rule, is only in phenocrysts. Brown hornblende and brown biotite are present in some basalts.

The groundmass of some basalts contains small amounts of interstitial glass and in rare instances is wholly glassy. Gas cavities near the top of basalt flows may be abundant enough to make the rock vesicular.

The presence of nepheline or leucite in basalt gives rise to the rare rock types *tephrite* and *leucite tephrite.*

Basalts are the most abundant of the volcanic rocks and form extensive lava flows in many regions; the most noted are the Columbia River flows in western United States and the Deccan "traps" of western India. Many of the great volcanos, such as form the Hawaiian Islands, are built up of basaltic material. In addition to forming extrusive rock masses, basalt is widely found forming many small dikes and other intrusives.

Fragmental Igneous Rocks

During periods of igneous activity volcanos eject much fragmental material which accumulates and forms the *fragmental igneous rocks,* or *pyroclastic rocks.* The ejectamenta vary greatly in size. Rock composed of finer particles of *volcanic ash* and *volcanic dust* is called *tuff;* that composed of coarser *volcanic bombs* is called *agglomerate,* or *volcanic breccia.* Such rocks are frequently waterlaid and bedded, and thus form a transition between the igneous and sedimentary rocks.

The Igneous Rock-Forming Minerals

Many minerals are found in the igneous rocks, but those that can be called rock-forming minerals are comparatively few. The following list is divided into two parts: (1) the common rock-forming minerals of igneous rocks; (2) the accessory minerals of igneous rocks.

Common Rock-Forming Minerals of Igneous Rocks

1. Quartz.
2. Feldspars.
    Orthoclase.
    Microcline.
    Plagioclase.
3. Nepheline.
4. Sodalite.
5. Leucite.
6. Micas.
    Muscovite.
    Biotite.
    Phlogopite.
7. Pyroxenes.
    Augite.
    Aegirite.
    Hypersthene.
8. Amphiboles.
    Hornblende.
    Arfredsonite.
    Riebeckite.
9. Olivine.

Common Accessory Minerals of Igneous Rocks

1. Zircon
2. Sphene.
3. Magnetite.
4. Illmenite.
5. Hematite.
6. Apatite.
7. Pyrite.
8. Rutile
9. Corundum.
10. Garnet.

Pegmatites

Pegmatites are extremely coarse-grained igneous bodies closely related genetically and in space to large masses of plutonic rocks. They are commonly found as veins or dikes traversing the granular igneous rock or extending out from it into the surrounding country rock. Granites more frequently than any other rock have pegmatites genetically associated with them; consequently, unless modified by other terms, pegmatite refers to *granite pegmatite*. The minerals in most pegmatites, therefore, are the common minerals found in granite —quartz, feldspar, mica—but of extremely large size. Crystals of these minerals measuring a foot across are common, and in some localities they reach gigantic sizes. Probably the largest crystals ever found were of feldspar in pegmatites in Karelia, U.S.S.R., where material weighing thousands of tons was mined from single crystals. Quartz crystals weighing thousands of pounds and mica crystals over 10 feet across have been found. One of the characteristics of pegmatites is the simultaneous and interpenetrating crystallization of quartz and feldspar (usually microcline) to form *graphic granite*. (See Fig. 612, page 492.)

Although most pegmatites are composed entirely of the minerals found abundantly in granite, those of greatest interest contain other, and rarer, minerals. In these pegmatites there has apparently been a definite sequence in deposition. The earliest minerals are microcline and quartz, with smaller amounts of garnet and black tourmaline. These are followed, and partly replaced, by albite, lepidolite, gem tourmaline, beryl, spodumene, amblygonite, topaz, apatite, and fluorite. A host of rarer minerals such as triphylite, columbite, monazite, molybdenite, and uranium minerals may be present. In places some of the above minerals are abundant and form large crystals that are mined for their rare constituent elements. Thus spodumene crystals over 40 feet long have been found in the Black Hills of South Dakota, and beryl crystals from Albany, Maine, have measured as much as 27 feet long and 6 feet in diameter.

The formation of pegmatite dikes is believed to be directly connected with the crystallization of the larger mass of associated plutonic rock. The process of crystallization brings about a concentration of the volatile constituents in the remaining liquid portion of the magma. The presence of these volatiles (water, boron, fluorine, chlorine, and phosphorus) decreases the viscosity and thus facilitates crystallization. Such an end product of consolidation is also enriched in the rare elements originally disseminated through the magma. When this residual liquid is injected into the cooler surrounding rock, it crystallizes from the borders inward frequently giving a zonal distribution of minerals with massive quartz at the center.

Nepheline syenite pegmatites have been found in a number of localities. They are commonly rich in unusual constituents and contain numerous zirconium, titanium, and rare-earth minerals.

II. SEDIMENTARY ROCKS

Sedimentary rocks are secondary in their origin; the materials of which they are composed have been derived from the weathering of some previously existing rock mass. They are deposited in areas of accumulation by the action of water or, less frequently, by glacial or wind action. Weathering includes both chemical decomposition and mechanical disintegration, and thus the end products consist of clay minerals, various soluble salts, and grains of inert minerals such as quartz, zircon, rutile, and magnetite. The sedimentary rocks may be divided into two classes, depending upon whether their origin has been mechanical or chemical in its nature. Sedimentary rocks of mechanical origin are composed of particles of clay minerals, or grains of minerals which have resisted chemical attack. These materials have been mechanically transported by streams into a body of water, where they have been deposited in layers. Sedimentary rocks of chemical origin have had the materials of which they are composed dissolved by waters circulating through the rocks and brought ultimately by these waters into the sea or a lake, where, through some chemical or organic process, they are precipitated.

All sedimentary rocks are, in general, characterized by a parallel arrangement of their constituent particles forming layers or beds which are distinguished from each other by differences in thickness, size of grain, or color. In all the coarser-grained sedimentary rocks there is some material which acts as a cement and surrounds the individual mineral particles, binding them together. This cement is usually silica, calcium carbonate, or iron oxide.

Mechanical Sedimentary Rocks

Conglomerate. Conglomerates may be considered consolidated gravels. They are composed of coarse pebbles, usually rounded by stream transportation. The individual pebbles may be composed of quartz entirely, or may be rock fragments that have not been decomposed. Fine conglomerates grade into coarse sandstones.

Sandstone. Beds of sand that have been consolidated into rock masses are called sandstones. The constituent grains are usually rounded and waterworn but may be more or less angular. The cement which binds the sand grains together may be silica, a carbonate (usually calcite), an iron oxide (hematite or goethite), or fine-grained argillaceous material. The color of the rock depends in large measure upon the character of the cement. The rocks which have silica or calcite as their binding material are light in color, usually pale yellow, buff, white to gray; those that contain an iron oxide are red to reddish brown. It is to be noted that when a sandstone breaks it is usually the cement that is fractured, the individual grains remaining unbroken, so that the fresh surfaces of the rock have a granular appearance and feeling. The chief mineral of sandstones is quartz; if the rock contains notable amounts of feldspar it is termed *arkose*. In the finer-grained sandstones there may be considerable clayey material; such rocks grade into the shales.

Shale. The shales are very fine-grained sedimentary rocks which have been formed by the consolidation of beds of mud, clay, or silt. They usually have a thinly laminated structure. Their color is commonly some tone of gray, although they may be white, yellow, brown, red, or green to black. They are composed chiefly of the clay minerals with quartz and mica but are too fine grained to permit the recognition of their mineral constituents by the eye alone. By the introduction of quartz and an increase in the size of grain they grade into the sandstones, and with the presence of calcite they grade into the limestones.

Chemical Sedimentary Rocks

The sedimentary rocks that are formed by chemical processes are here divided into three groups: (1) those produced by direct precipitation from an aqueous solution; (2) those in which organisms have been the active agent in extracting the rock-forming materials from solution; (3) those in which the final rock is the result of a partial or complete replacement of an earlier-formed sedimentary rock.

1. **Precipitation.** When a saline solution evaporates, the dissolved salts are precipitated in a definite order, the least soluble first, the most soluble last. There are thus several types of sedimentary rocks which have formed through precipitation from evaporating sea water and are called *evaporites*. Gypsum, anhydrite, and rock salt are the most important.

Gypsum is the first mineral to precipitate in large amounts on the evaporation of sea water, and under appropriate conditions thick beds of gypsum may be built up. As a rock, gypsum is usually fine grained but in places shows a fibrous or platy habit. Because of its method of formation, gypsum is frequently associated with other saline deposits and with limestone and shale.

Anhydrite follows gypsum in the sequence of the precipitation of salts from sea water. It thus is found in beds similar to gypsum and associated with it and saline deposits. Anhydrite may alter to gypsum.

Rock Salt. Granular aggregates of the mineral halite commonly occur in beds of considerable thickness and in this form are known as *rock salt*. Halite follows gypsum and anhydrite in the sequence of precipitation from an evaporating sea water, and thus commonly overlies beds of these minerals. In some deposits the more soluble salts such as sylvite, carnallite, and polyhalite are associated with halite; the deposit may then become a source of potash.

Oölitic Limestone. This variety of limestone, composed of small spherical concretions resembling fish roe, is believed to have been chemically precipitated. Each tiny concretion has a nucleus of a sand grain, shell fragment, or some foreign particle around which deposition has taken place. Oölitic sand which is forming at the present time on the floor of the Great Salt Lake would on consolidation, produce an oölitic limestone.

Travertine is a calcareous material deposited from spring waters under atmospheric conditions. If the deposit is porous it is known as *calcareous tufa.* Such deposits are prevalent in limestone regions where circulating ground water containing carbon dioxide has taken considerable calcium carbonate in solution. When the ground water reaches the surface as springs some of the carbon dioxide is given off, resulting in the precipitation of some of the calcium carbonate. In this way travertine deposits are built up.

Siliceous Sinter. In certain volcanic regions hot springs deposit an opaline material known as *siliceous sinter* or *geyserite.* The deposit is apparently due both to evaporation and to secretion of silica by algae.

2. Organic precipitation. *Limestone.* Many organisms living in the sea utilize calcium carbonate from the water to build up hard, protective shells. On the death of the organisms the hard calcareous parts accumulate on the sea floor. When marine life is abundant great thicknesses of shells and other hard parts may build up, which, when consolidated, produce limestone. There are several varieties of limestone, depending on the type of fossil from which it is made, or on the texture. *Chalk* is a variety of porous, fine-grained limestone composed for the most part of foraminiferal shells. *Coquina* is a limestone, found on the coast of Florida, consisting of shells and shell fragments only partially consolidated. *Lithographic limestone* is an extremely fine-grained rock from Solenhofen, Bavaria.

Limestones are made up dominantly of calcite but may contain small amounts of other minerals. If impurities of clay are abundant, limestone grades toward shale and would be called an *argillaceous limestone.* When dolomite becomes an important constituent of a limestone the rock grades toward the rock known as *dolomite.*

Limestone is a common type of sedimentary rock and in many regions is not only of great areal extent but of great vertical thickness as well.

Diatomite. Diatoms are minute one-celled organisms which live in both fresh and sea water and have the power of secreting tests of opaline material. When the organisms die their tiny shells accumulate to build up a chalklike deposit of diatomaceous earth.

3. **Replacement.** Some sedimentary rocks, particularly limestones, have, after their formation, been replaced in whole or in part through reaction with elements in sea water or in circulating ground waters. The rocks resulting from such reactions are considered here.

Dolomite. The rock *dolomite* resembles limestone so closely in all its physical properties that it is usually impossible to distinguish between them without a chemical test. Moreover, dolomite as a rock name is not restricted to a material of the composition of the mineral dolomite but may have admixed calcite. Dolomites have formed not as original rocks but by the alteration of a pure limestone in which part of the calcium is replaced by magnesium. This process of *dolomitization* is believed to have been brought about either by the action of sea water shortly after original deposition, or by the action of circulating ground water after the rock has been consolidated and raised above sea level.

Magnesite. As a sedimentary rock *magnesite* is much more restricted in its distribution than dolomite. It has been formed by the almost complete replacement by magnesium of the calcium of an original limestone. Such magnesite rocks are found in Austria; in the Ural Mountains, U.S.S.R.; and in Stevens County, Washington.

III. METAMORPHIC ROCKS

Metamorphic rocks are those which have undergone some chemical or physical change subsequent to their original formation. In general, metamorphic rocks are divided into two groups: (1) those formed by regional metamorphism, (2) those formed by contact metamorphism.

Regional Metamorphic Rocks

Various geologic agencies acting over wide areas bring about changes in great masses of rocks. The metamorphosis is brought about by means of high temperature and high pressure aided by the action of water and other chemical agents. The changes involve the formation of new minerals, the adding or subtracting of chemical constituents, and a physical readjustment of the mineral particles to conform to the new condition. The original rock from which a metamorphic rock has been derived may be either igneous or sedimentary, but the process of metamorphism may completely alter the original features. As rocks become involved in movements of the earth's crust, they are subjected to extreme pressures accompanied usually by high temperatures. The result will frequently be to transform the existing minerals into others, more stable under the new conditions. The physical structure of the rock will also ordinarily be changed during the process. Because of the pressure to which the rock is subjected, the mineral particles will be more or less broken and flattened or will recrystallize to form in parallel layers. This banded or laminated character given by the parallel arrangement of minerals is the most striking peculiarity of a metamorphic rock. Because of this structure a metamorphic rock can usually be distinguished from an igneous rock. Further, most metamorphic rocks have a texture of interlocking crystals which distinguishes them from sedimentary rocks. There are, of course, all gradations from a typical metamorphic rock into an unaltered sedimentary rock on the one hand and into an unaltered igneous rock on the other. The resulting metamorphic rock depends not only upon the bulk composition of the original rock but also upon the temperature and pressure at which the metamorphism took place. As the intensity of metamorphism changes with increased temperature and pressure there are corresponding mineralogical changes by means of which metamorphic rocks have been grouped into broad zones. These zones for an argillaceous rock and the principal minerals in them are listed below in order of increasing intensity.

Zone	Minerals
Chlorite	Muscovite, chlorite, quartz
Biotite	Biotite, muscovite, chlorite, quartz
Garnet	Garnet (almandite), muscovite, biotite, quartz
Staurolite	Staurolite, garnet, biotite, muscovite, quartz
Kyanite	Kyanite, garnet, biotite, muscovite, quartz
Sillimanite	Sillimanite, quartz, garnet, muscovite, biotite, oligoclase, orthoclase

The most common types of metamorphic rocks are briefly described below.

Gneiss. When the word gneiss is used alone it refers to a coarsely foliated metamorphic rock. The banding is caused by the segregation of quartz and feldspar into layers alternating with layers of dark minerals. Since the metamorphism of many igneous or sedimentary rocks may result in a gneiss, there are many varieties, with varied mineral associations. Thus such names as *granite gneiss, diorite gneiss, syenite gneiss* are used to indicate the composition; *biotite gneiss* or *hornblende gneiss* would be used to indicate rocks unusually rich in a given mineral. Granite gneisses, that is, rocks derived from the metamorphism of granites, are common, especially in regions in which rocks of Archean age are found.

Schist. Schists are metamorphic rocks which are distinguished from gneisses by the absence of coarse banding and the presence of lamination or "schistosity" along which the rock may be easily broken. There are several varieties, the most important of which is *mica schist*, composed essentially of quartz and a mica, usually either muscovite or biotite. The mica is the prominent mineral, occurring in irregular leaves and in foliated masses. The mica plates all lie with their cleavage planes parallel to each other and give to the rock a striking laminated appearance. The mica schists frequently carry characteristic accessory minerals, such are garnet, staurolite, kyanite, sillimanite, andalusite, epidote, and hornblende; thus the rock may be called *garnet schist, staurolite schist*, etc. Mica schists may have been derived from either an igneous or a sedimentary rock. Next to the gneisses the mica schists are the most common metamorphic rocks.

There are various other kinds of schistose rocks, which are chiefly derived by the metamorphism of the igneous rocks rich in ferromagnesian minerals. The most important types are *talc schist, chlorite schist*, and *amphibolite* or *hornblende schist*. They are characterized, as their names indicate, by the preponderance of some metamorphic ferromagnesian mineral.

Quartzite. As its name indicates, a quartzite is a rock composed essentially of quartz. It has been derived from a sandstone by intense metamorphism. It is a common and widely distributed rock in which solution and redeposition of silica have yielded a compact rock of interlocking quartz grains. It is distinguished from a sandstone by noting the fracture, which in a quartzite passes through the grains but in a sandstone passes around them.

Slate. Slates are exceedingly fine-grained rocks which have a remarkable property known as *slaty cleavage* that permits them to be split into thin, broad sheets. Their color is commonly gray to black but may be green, yellow, brown, and red. Slates are usually the result of the metamorphism of shales. Their characteristic slaty cleavage may or may not be parallel to the bedding planes of the original shales. Slate is rather common in occurrence.

Marble. A marble is a metamorphosed limestone. It is a crystalline rock composed of grains of calcite, or more rarely dolomite. The individual grains may be so small that they cannot be distinguished by the eye, and again they may be coarse and show clearly the characteristic calcite cleavage. Like limestone, a marble is characterized by its softness and its effervescence with acids. When pure, marble is white in color, but it may show a wide range of color, due to various impurities that it contains. It is a rock which is found in many localities and may be in thick and extensive beds. Commercially *marble* is used to indicate any lime carbonate rock capable of taking a polish and thus includes some limestones.

Serpentine. Serpentine, as a rock, is composed essentially of the mineral serpentine derived by the metamorphism of a peridotite. Such rocks are compact, of a green to greenish yellow color, and may have a slightly greasy feel. Serpentines may be a source for associated chromite and platinum, as in the Ural Mountains, or a source of nickel from the associated garnierite, as in New Caledonia.

Contact Metamorphism

When a magma is intruded into the earth's crust, it causes through the attendant heat and accompanying solutions a greater or lesser alteration in the surrounding rock. This alteration of the rocks lying next to an igneous intrusion is known as *contact metamorphism* and usually consists in the development of characteristic mineral species. The minerals that are formed under these conditions are called *contact metamorphic minerals* and are found at or near the contact between the rock in which they lie and an igneous rock. Two kinds of contact metamorphism are recognized: (1) *thermal,* due to the heating up of the country rock by the intrusion; (2) *hydrothermal,* where solutions, as well as heat, emanating from the igneous rock have reacted with the country rock and formed contact metamorphic minerals.

Any rock into which an igneous mass is intruded will be affected in a greater or lesser degree, the amount and nature of the change depending chiefly upon the size of the intruded mass and upon the chemical and physical character of the surrounding rock. Sandstones are converted to quartzites, and shales changed to "hornfels," a dense rock containing biotite, andalusite, staurolite, cordierite, garnet, and scapolite. The most striking and important contact metamorphic changes take place when the igneous rock is intruded into limestones. When a pure limestone is subjected to thermal metamorphism, it is recrystallized and converted into a marble but without any development of new species. On the other hand, in an impure limestone the heat caused by the igneous intrusion may serve to develop new and characteristic minerals in the rock. An impure limestone will ordinarily contain, besides the calcium carbonate of the rock, varying amounts of dolomite, quartz, clay, and iron oxide. Under the influence of the heat and pressure these materials will combine with the calcium carbonate to form new minerals. For instance, the calcite and quartz may combine to form wollastonite. The reaction of dolomite with quartz may produce diopside. If clay is present, aluminum will enter into the reaction and such minerals as corundum, spinel, and grossularite garnet may result. If any carbonaceous materials are present, the effect of the thermal metamorphism may convert them into graphite. The common thermal contact metamorphic minerals found in impure limestone are as follows: *graphite, spinel, corundum, wollastonite, tremolite, diopside,* and the lime garnets, *grossularite* and *andradite.*

The greatest changes are produced in a limestone by *hydrothermal contact metamorphism.* In this process, solutions given off by the intruded magma react with the limestone to produce new minerals containing elements not present in the limestone. At the contact with the intrusion the limestone may be completely replaced, farther away only partly replaced, and at a distance the only evidence may be a recrystallization of the limestone. In this type of contact metamorphism, ore minerals are frequently present and the deposit may be of economic importance. Such deposits may grade into hydrothermal vein deposits.

The introduction of material into the hydrothermal contact metamorphic deposits gives rise to a greater abundance and variety of minerals than are formed by pure thermal metamorphism. The most important silicates are *quartz, grossularite* and *andradite* garnet, *diopside, epidote, zoisite, idocrase, wollastonite, tremolite, olivine.* Scapolite, chondrodite, axinite, topaz, tourmaline, and fluorite may be present and contain hydroxyl, fluorine, chlorine, or boron. The sulfide ore minerals found in hydrothermal contact metamorphic deposits include *pyrite, chalcopyrite, bornite, sphalerite, pyrrhotite, molybdenite,* and *arsenopyrite.* The oxides include *magnetite, ilmenite, hematite, spinel,* and *corundum.*

VEINS AND VEIN MINERALS

Many mineral deposits, especially those of economic importance, exist as tabular or lenticular bodies known as *veins.* The veins have been formed by the filling with mineral material of a pre-existing fracture or fissure.

The shape and general physical character of a vein depends upon the type of fissure in which its minerals have been deposited, and the type of fissure in turn depends upon the character of the rock in which it lies and the kind of force which originally caused its formation. In a firm, homogeneous rock, like a granite, a fissure will be fairly regular and clean-cut in character. It is likely to be comparatively narrow in respect to its horizontal and vertical extent and reasonably straight in its course. On the other hand, if a rock that is easily fractured and splintered, like a slate or a schist, is subjected to a breaking stress, a zone of narrow and interlacing fissures is more likely to have formed than one straight crack. In an easily soluble rock like a limestone, a fissure will often be extremely irregular in its shape and size owing to the differential solution of its walls by the waters that have flowed through it.

A typical vein consists of a mineral deposit which has filled a fissure solidly from wall to wall and shows sharply defined boundaries. There are, however, many variations from this type. Frequently irregular openings termed *vugs* may occur along the center of the vein. It is from these vugs that many well-crystallized mineral specimens are obtained. Again, the walls of a vein may not be sharply defined. The mineralizing waters that filled the fissure may have acted upon the wall rocks and partially replaced them with the vein minerals. Consequently, there may be an almost complete gradation from the unaltered rock to the pure vein filling with no sharp line of division between. Some deposits have been largely formed by the deposition of vein minerals in the wall rocks and are known as *replacement deposits*. They are more likely to be found in, but by no means confined to, the soluble rocks like limestones. There is every gradation possible, from a vein formed by filling of an open fissure with sharply defined walls to a replacement deposit with indefinite boundaries.

It is now almost universally believed that the mineral matter in veins has been deposited from aqueous solutions. Some deposits have formed by the method of *lateral secretion* in which ground waters circulating through the rocks have dissolved disseminated mineral matter which is later deposited in veins. However, the deposits of greatest economic importance are believed to have been deposited from hot ascending magmatic solutions which originated from a cooling and crystallizing magma. As such hydrothermal solutions move upward the pressure and temperature become less and deposition of dissolved material results. It has been shown that certain minerals characteristically form under given conditions of temperature and pressure. Lindgren[1] has thus divided the hydrothermal vein deposits into the following three groups, each with characteristic mineral associations.

1. **Hypothermal deposits;** deposited at great depth at high pressure and high temperature ($300\text{–}500°\,C\pm$). Several types of hypothermal veins exist, each with characteristic mineral associations: (*a*) cas-

---

[1] Waldemar Lindgren, *Mineral Deposits*, McGraw-Hill Book Co., New York, 1933.

siterite, wolframite, and molybdenite veins; (b) gold-quartz veins; (c) copper-tourmaline veins; (d) lead-tourmaline veins.

The minerals of greatest importance are, therefore, cassiterite, wolframite and scheelite, molybdenite, native gold, chalcopyrite, and galena. Often associated ore minerals are pyrite, pyrrhotite, arsenopyrite, bismuthinite, and magnetite. Quartz is the predominant gangue mineral but is frequently accompanied by fluorite, tourmaline, topaz, axinite, and other minerals containing volatiles. The chief metals won from hypothermal deposits are tin, tungsten, gold, molybdenum, copper, and lead.

2. **Mesothermal deposits;** formed at intermediate depths at high pressure and temperature $(200-300° C\pm)$. The chief ore minerals are pyrite, chalcopyrite, arsenopyrite, galena, sphalerite, tetrahedrite, and native gold. Quartz is the chief gangue mineral, but carbonates such as calcite, ankerite, siderite, rhodochrosite are also common. The chief metals mined are gold, silver, copper, lead, and zinc.

3. **Epithermal deposits;** formed at slight depth under moderate pressure and temperature $(50-200° C\pm)$. Typical ore minerals of epithermal deposits are native gold, marcasite, pyrite, cinnabar, and stibnite, and the gangue minerals include quartz, opal, chalcedony, calcite, aragonite, fluorite, and barite. The chief metals found in these deposits are gold, silver, and mercury.

Alteration of Vein Minerals

Secondary vein minerals. In many mineral veins, it is obvious that certain minerals belong to the original vein deposit whereas certain others have been formed subsequently. These two classes of minerals are known respectively as *primary* (or *hypogene*) and *secondary* (or *supergene*) *minerals.* The primary vein minerals are those which were originally deposited by the ascending waters in the vein fissure. The primary sulfide minerals found in veins are comparatively few in number, the more important being pyrite, chalcopyrite, galena, and sphalerite. The secondary minerals have been formed from the primary minerals by some chemical reactions. These changes are ordinarily brought about through the influence of oxidizing waters which, coming from the surface of the earth, descend through the upper portions of the vein. Under these conditions, various new minerals are formed, many of them being oxidized compounds. Sphalerite alters to hemimorphite and smithsonite; galena to anglesite and cerussite; copper sulfides to malachite, azurite, cuprite, and native copper. Many other rarer oxidized minerals are found at some localities. Because the descending waters lose their oxygen content within a comparatively short distance of the earth's surface, the secondary minerals are found only in the upper part of a vein.

Secondary enrichment. Together with the formation of supergene minerals, there is frequently a downward migration of the valuable metals in the vein. This is brought about by the solution of the minerals in the uppermost portion of the vein and a subsequent reprecipitation a little farther down. As the surface of the earth is gradually lowered by erosion, the upper part of a vein is continually being worn away; but the metallic content of the uppermost part of the vein may be carried downward by the descending oxidizing waters. In this way, the metallic content of the upper part of many veins may be notably enriched if in a short vertical distance most of the original contents of hundreds, perhaps thousands, of feet of the vein, which have been slowly worn away by the general erosion of the country, are concentrated. Consequently, the zone of the secondary minerals is frequently a zone of secondary enrichment. This is an important fact to be borne in mind since, because of it, the upper portion of a vein may be the richest portion of a deposit. The ore below that depth gradually grades into its original unaltered and unenriched state and may frequently prove too low in value to warrant its being mined. The prevalent idea that the ore of a vein must increase in value with increasing depth is not true in the great majority of veins.

It will be of interest to consider the more important primary vein minerals and the secondary minerals that are commonly formed from them in the process of secondary enrichment.

1. *Iron Minerals.* The common primary vein mineral of iron is pyrite, FeS_2. Marcasite, FeS_2, though not so common in occurrence is also a primary mineral. When oxidized, these minerals yield ordinarily the hydrated oxide limonite, $Fe_2O_3 \cdot nH_2O$. The upper portion of a vein that was originally rich in pyrite will thus be converted into a cellular and rusty mass of limonite. This limonite deposit near the surface is commonly termed *gossan*. The yellow, rusty appearance of the outcrop of many veins enables one frequently to locate them and to trace them across the country.

2. *Copper Minerals.* The most common primary copper mineral is chalcopyrite, $CuFeS_2$, but bornite, Cu_5FeS_4, tetrahedrite, $(Cu,Fe,-Zn,Ag)_{12}Sb_4S_{13}$, and enargite, Cu_3AsS_4, are frequently present. The oxidation of these minerals yields at the surface of a copper deposit limonite, malachite, azurite, cuprite, native copper, chrysocolla, and antlerite. The zone of oxidation usually extends downward to the water table where secondary sulfides appear.

The breakdown of the copper sulfides and associated pyrite produces ferric sulfate and sulfuric acid which react with the copper to form copper sulfate, which is soluble and is carried downward. When the copper sulfate solution reaches a reducing environment it reacts with the sulfides there present, coating them with or replacing them by chalcocite, Cu_2S. Such long-continued action may give rise to massive chalcocite bodies at the water table. Many of the "porphyry" copper deposits of the western United States are commercial because of a slight supergene enrichment of this type.

REFERENCES

Rocks

L. V. Pirsson and A. Knopf, *Rocks and rock minerals*, 3rd ed. John Wiley and Sons, New York, 1947. Description of common rocks from hand specimens with a discussion of origin, occurrence, and use.

H. Williams, F. J. Turner, and C. M. Gilbert, *Petrography*. W. H. Freeman, San Francisco, 1950. Description of rocks based on a study of thin sections.

Ore Minerals

A. M. Bateman, *The formation of mineral deposits*. John Wiley and Sons, 1951. A discussion of the origin of mineral deposits.

Pegmatites

R. H. Jahns, *The study of pegmatites*, Economic Geology, 50th Ann. Vol., pp. 1025–1130, 1952.

7

MINERAL
USES

Minerals are extremely important from an economic point of view, for all the inorganic materials of commerce are either minerals or substances derived from minerals. In this section, some of the more important economic minerals are listed according to their various uses, but one is referred to the paragraph "Use" in the individual descriptions for details. The uses of minerals are grouped under the following headings:

Gem Minerals   Pottery, Glass, Enamel
Ornamental Minerals   Fertilizers
Abrasives   Optical and Scientific
Fluxes   Apparatus
Refractories   Ores of the Metals

GEM MINERALS

The physical properties of minerals that make them valuable as gem stones are color, luster, dispersion, and hardness. The gem value of some minerals may be attributed to but one of these properties, for example, color, in the case of turquoise. On the other hand, diamond, ruby, sapphire, and emerald combine all the properties, and they are thus prized above all other gems and are known as the *precious stones*. In addition to the physical properties mentioned, popular gem stones must be relatively rare, but at the same time abundant enough so that a demand can be created for them.

Diamond, page 240
Corundum, page 290
  Ruby (red)
  Sapphire (blue)
Beryl, page 424
  Emerald (green)
  Aquamarine (blue-green)
  Morganite (pink)
  Golden beryl (yellow)
Spodumene, page 437
  Kunzite (pink)
  Hiddenite (green)
Tourmaline, page 426
  Rubellite (red)
  Brazilian emerald (green)
  Indicolite (dark blue)
Spinel (many colors), page 306
  Ruby spinel (deep red)

Garnet (usually red), page 401
  Demantoid (green)
Topaz (wine, yellow, blue, pink), page 408
Zircon (colorless), page 404
  Hyacinth (yellow, red brown)
Opal, page 485
Olivine, page 400
  Peridot (olive-green)
Turquoise (green to blue), page 380
Quartz, page 478
  Rock crystal (colorless)
  Amethyst (purple to violet)
  Smoky quartz (dark brown to black)
  Rose quartz (rose-pink)
  Citrine (yellow)
Feldspar, page 487
  Moonstone (milky white)
  Amazonstone (green)

Minor gem minerals. Some minerals in addition to those listed are found occasionally in specimens of gem quality. The more important of these are: sphene, benitoite, cassiterite, apatite, kyanite, axinite, cordierite, diopside, euclase, fluorite, idocrase, andalusite, and zoisite.

ORNAMENTAL MINERALS

Many minerals have been used for ornamental purposes, but a considerable number of them have been employed only locally. The ornamental minerals of more general use are:

Calcite, page 334
  Marble
  Onyx marble
  Travertine
Serpentine, page 463
  Verde antique marble
Malachite, page 349
Lazurite, page 503
Feldspar, page 487
  Labradorite
  Larvikite

Rhodonite, page 441
Gypsum, page 366
  Satin spar
  Alabaster
Jade.
  Jadeite, page 438
  Nephrite, page 445
Quartz, page 478
  Agate
  Rose quartz

ABRASIVES

Diamond, page 240
Corundum, page 290
Emery
Opal, page 485
Diatomite

Quartz, page 478
Silica rocks
Novaculite
Flint
Garnet, page 401

FLUXES

Minerals used in smelting operations to render the slag more fluid are fluxes. The chief minerals used for this purpose are: calcite (page 334), fluorite (page 325), and quartz (page 478).

POTTERY, GLASS, ENAMEL

Clay (kaolinite), page 461. Brick, drain tile, sewer pipe, china, pottery
Quartz, page 478. Basis of glass manufacture
Feldspar, page 487. Manufacture of glass. Glaze on pottery, china, tile, etc.
Nepheline, page 501. Manufacture of glass
Fluorite, page 325. Manufacture of glass and enamel coatings.

FERTILIZERS

Many elements are necessary for plant growth, but the most essential are phosphorus, potassium, and nitrogen. These elements are found in certain minerals that are mined on a large scale for fertilizers.

Apatite and phosphate rock, page 373. For phosphorus
Sylvite, page 323. For potassium
Soda niter, page 351. For nitrogen.

OPTICAL AND SCIENTIFIC APPARATUS

Quartz, page 478. Radio oscillators and special prisms and lenses.
Fluorite, page 325. Lenses transparent in ultra-violet and infra-red.
Gypsum, page 366. Gypsum plates, microscope accessory.
Mica (muscovite), page 467. Mica plate, microscope accessory.
Tourmaline, page 426. Pressure gages for high transient pressures.

REFRACTORIES

Magnesite, page 340. Dead-burned magnesite, MgO, for furnace linings.
Dolomite, page 338. Dead-burned, $CaO + MgO$, for furnace linings.

Kyanite, page 407; andalusite, page 406; dumortierite, page 413.
For high-grade porcelain, as spark plugs.
Graphite, page 244. Crucibles for steel manufacture.
Bauxite, page 317. Furnace linings.
Chromite, page 310. Bricks for furnace linings.
Zircon, page 404. Refractory brick.
Asbestos (chrysotile), page 400. Heat-resisting fabrics, insulating
purposes.
Talc, page 466. As slabs of soapstone for table tops, etc.
Clay (kaolinite), page 461. Bricks for furnace linings.
Mica (muscovite), page 467. Electrical insulation purposes.

ORES OF THE METALS

The following lists may include several minerals as ores of a given element. The principal ores are given in bold-face type and the page reference is given for that mineral under which the uses of the metal are considered.

Aluminum	**Bauxite,** page 317, diaspore, gibbsite, boehmite, cryolite.
Antimony	**Stibnite,** page 264, native antimony.
Arsenic	**Arsenopyrite,** page 272, native arsenic, realgar, orpiment.
Bismuth	Native bismuth, page 235, bismuthinite.
Cadmium	Greenockite, page 257.
Chromium	**Chromite,** page 310, crocoite.
Cobalt	Cobaltite, page 270, skutterudite, linnaeite, erythrite.
Copper	**Native copper,** page 229, **chalcocite, bornite, chalcopyrite, tetrahedrite, enargite, antlerite,** covellite, cuprite, atacamite, malachite, azurite, chalcanthite, chrysocolla.
Gold	**Native gold,** page 225, calaverite, petzite, krennerite, sylvanite.
Iron	**Hematite,** page 292, **magnetite, goethite,** limonite, siderite.
Lead	**Galena,** page 250, **cerussite, anglesite,** phosgenite, pyromorphite, mimetite, vanadinite, crocoite, wulfenite.
Magnesium	**Magnesite,** page 340, carnallite, dolomite, brucite.
Manganese	**Pyrolusite,** page 297, **manganite, psilomelane,** franklinite, alabandite, rhodochrosite, rhodonite, braunite.
Mercury	**Cinnabar,** page 262.
Molybdenum	**Molybdenite,** p. 273, wulfenite.
Nickel	**Pentlandite,** p. 260, **garnierite,** niccolite, millerite, gersdorffite, nickel skutterudite, genthite.
Platinum	**Native platinum,** page 231, sperrylite.
Silver	**Native silver,** page 228, **argentite,** stromeyerite, sylvanite, polybasite, stephanite, pyargyrite, proustite, cerargyrite, embolite.
Tin	**Cassiterite,** page 299, stannite.
Titanium	**Ilmenite,** page 295, **rutile,** brookite, octahedrite, sphene.
Tungsten	**Wolframite,** page 385, **scheelite,** ferberite, huebnerite.
Uranium	**Uraninite,** p. 301, **carnotite,** tyuyamunite, torbernite, autunite.

Vanadium   Vanadinite, p. 377, carnotite, roscoelite.

Zinc   **Sphalerite,** p. 252, **smithsonite, hemimorphite,** franklinite, willemite.

REFERENCES

Minerals Yearbook. Published annually by the United States Bureau of Mines, Washington, D. C. A summary of world production of economically valuable metals and minerals.

R. B. Ladoo and W. M. Myers, *Nonmetallic minerals.* McGraw-Hill Book Co., New York, 1951. An account of the occurrence, origin, and beneficiation of the economic nonmetallic minerals.

Alan M. Bateman. *The formation of mineral deposits.* John Wiley and Sons, 1951. A discussion of the origin of the useful minerals.

E. H. Kraus and C. B. Slawson, *Gems and gem materials.* McGraw-Hill Book Co., New York, 1947.

MINERALS FOR A SMALL COLLECTION

LIST OF MINERALS SUITABLE FOR A SMALL MINERAL COLLECTION

For the convenience of those who desire to possess a small but representative mineral collection the following list is given. The names of the more important species are printed in bold-face type, and the names of other desirable but less important minerals in ordinary type. The first group includes 63 names, and the complete list numbers 112.

Gold in quartz	Bauxite	Sodalite
Silver	**Halite**	Scapolite
Copper	Cryolite	Heulandite
Sulfur	**Fluorite**	**Stilbite**
Graphite	**Calcite**	Chabazite
Argentite	**Dolomite**	**Natrolite**
Chalcocite	**Siderite**	**Analcime**
Bornite	Rhodochrosite	**Talc**
Galena	**Smithsonite**	**Serpentine**
Sphalerite	**Aragonite**	**Apophyllite**
Chalcopyrite	Witherite	**Chlorite**
Pyrrhotite	Strontianite	**Prehnite**
Niccolite	**Cerussite**	**Muscovite**
Millerite	**Malachite**	**Biotite**
Cinnabar	**Azurite**	Phlogopite
Realgar	**Borax**	Lepidolite
Orpiment	Kernite	**Amphiboles**
Stibnite	Ulexite	(several varieties)
Pyrite	Colemanite	**Pyroxenes**
Marcasite	**Apatite**	(several varieties)
Arsenopyrite	Pyromorphite	Spodumene
Molybdenite	Amblygonite	Rhodonite
Tetrahedrite	Wavellite	**Tourmaline**
Proustite	Turquoise	**Beryl**
Cuprite	**Barite**	**Hemimorphite**
Zincite	**Celestite**	**Olivine**
Corundum	**Anglesite**	Willemite
Hematite	Anhydrite	**Garnet**
Ilmenite	**Gypsum**	Idocrase
Spinel	Scheelite	**Epidote**
Magnetite	Wulfenite	**Zircon**
Franklinite	**Quartz** (several varieties)	Datolite
Chromite	**Opal**	Topaz
Chrysoberyl	**Orthoclase**	Andalusite
Cassiterite	**Albite**	Kyanite
Rutile	Oligoclase	**Staurolite**
Pyrolusite	Labradorite	Sphene
Goethite	Leucite	Axinite

DETERMINATIVE
MINERALOGY

INTRODUCTION

Determinative tables for minerals are of two kinds: (1) those which rely chiefly upon chemical tests, and (2) those which make use solely of physical tests. Obviously, since the chemical composition of a mineral is its most fundamental property, those tables which emphasize chemical tests are much more satisfactory. Moreover, the tables which depend wholly upon physical tests have distinct limitations beyond which it is impossible to use them; they have, however, the important advantages that their tests are simpler, more readily and quickly performed, and do not require the equipment of a laboratory. For these reasons physical determinative tables probably have a wider use, in spite of their limitations, than those that involve chemical tests.

The limited scope of this book forbids the inclusion of elaborate chemical tables and requires instead the introduction of physical tables of as simple a form as possible. Such tables, however, must be used with a thorough understanding of their nature and their inherent disadvantages. Many of the physical properties of minerals are not entirely fixed in their character. Color, for instance, is frequently an extremely variable property. Hardness, though more definite, may vary to a slight extent and, by a change in the state of aggregation of a mineral, may appear to vary much more widely. Cleavage is a property which may often be obscured by the physical condition of the mineral. Consequently, in making a determination of a mineral by means of its physical properties alone, it is necessary to have a fairly typical specimen and one of sufficient size to enable its properties to be easily observed. Moreover, it often will be impossible by the aid of such tables to differentiate positively between two or three similar species. Frequently, however, the descriptions of these possible minerals given in the section on descriptive mineralogy will enable one to make a definite decision. Moreover, the tables that follow, used in connection with the chemical tests given under the description of the individual minerals, together with the more detailed explanations of the various tests to be found in the section on chemical mineralogy, may serve as a substitute for more elaborate chemical tables.

The determinative tables given below have been made as brief and simple as possible. Only the common species or those which, though rarer in occurrence, are of economic importance have been included. The chances of having a mineral to determine that is not included in these tables are small, but it must be borne in mind that there is such a possibility. The names of the minerals have been printed in three different styles of type, as **CHALCOCITE,** ARGENTITE, and Stephanite, in order to indicate their relative importance and frequency of occurrence. Whenever it was felt that difficulty might be experienced in placing a mineral correctly, it has been included in the two or more possible divisions.

On page 547 will be found a general classification of the tables. The proper division in which to look for a mineral can be determined by means of the tests indicated there. The tables are divided into two main sections on the basis of luster. The first division includes those minerals which have a metallic or submetallic luster. By that is meant those minerals which on their thinnest edges remain opaque and which consequently will give black or dark-colored "streaks" when they are rubbed across a piece of unglazed porcelain, the so-called streak plate. The second division includes minerals with a nonmetallic luster, or those which are transparent upon their thinnest edges, and which therefore give either a colorless or a light-colored streak. It should be noted that the color of the streak cannot always be foretold from the color of the mineral itself. Frequently a dark-colored mineral will be found to give a light-colored streak.

The tables are next subdivided according to hardness. For metallic minerals: (1) minerals of a hardness less than $2\frac{1}{2}$ (soft enough to leave a mark on paper); (2) greater than $2\frac{1}{2}$, less than $5\frac{1}{2}$ (can be scratched by a knife but will not leave a mark on paper); (3) greater than $5\frac{1}{2}$ (cannot be scratched by a knife). For nonmetallic minerals: (1) less than $2\frac{1}{2}$ (can be scratched by the fingernail); (2) $2\frac{1}{2}$–3 (cannot be scratched by the fingernail but can be scratched by a copper coin); (3) 3–$5\frac{1}{2}$ (cannot be scratched by a copper coin but can be scratched by a knife); (4) $5\frac{1}{2}$–7 (cannot be scratched by a knife but can be scratched by quartz); (5) greater than 7 (cannot be scratched by quartz). In applying the tests for hardness, certain precautions should be observed. Before deciding upon the relative hardness of a mineral, it is well to try the test if possible in two ways. For instance, if a mineral is apparently scratched by the knife, make sure on the other hand that the knife cannot be scratched by the mineral. Further, the copper coin and the knife blade used in making the tests should be bright and clean; otherwise the rubbing off of a layer of dirt or tarnish might be mistaken for a scratch. The possession of specimens of the minerals of the Mohs scale, so that the hardness of a mineral can be closely determined, would frequently be of great assistance in the use of the tables. Lastly, it is to be remembered that the physical condition of a mineral may apparently change its hardness. For instance, minerals that may occur in pulverulent or fibrous forms will under these conditions appear to be much softer than when in their more compact form.

The minerals with nonmetallic luster are, in general, further subdivided according to whether or not they show a prominent cleavage. This will frequently be a difficult decision to make. It will require some practice and experience before one can always make the determination rapidly and accurately. Note that the minerals are divided according to whether or not they show a *prominent* cleavage. Minerals in which the cleavage is imperfect or ordinarily obscure are included with those that have no cleavage. It will always be best, if it is possible, actually to try to produce a cleavage upon the specimen rather than to judge from its appearance alone. If a mineral shows a cleavage, the number of the cleavage planes and their relations to each other and to any crystal forms present should be noted. As far as possible, the minerals in which the cleavage may become obscure, because of certain conditions in the state of aggregation, have been included in both divisions.

The minerals that fall in any one of the different divisions of the tables have been arranged according to various methods. In some cases, those that possess similar cleavages have been grouped together; frequently color determines their order, etc. The column farthest to the left will indicate the method of arrangement used in each section.

Most of the different properties listed need no special explanation. A few words, however, may be said concerning the column headed **G.** (specific gravity). For a discussion of specific gravity and the methods for its accurate determination, see page 155. If the specimen to be determined is of sufficient size and is pure, its approximate specific gravity can be determined by simply weighing it in the hand. This, however, will require some experience. Below is given a list of common minerals which show a wide range of specific gravity. By experimenting with specimens of these one can become expert in the approximate determination of the specific gravity of any mineral.

Halite, 2.16	Corundum, 4.02	Cassiterite, 6.95
Gypsum, 2.32	Chalcopyrite, 4.20	Galena, 7.50
Orthoclase, 2.57	Barite, 4.45	Cinnabar, 8.10
Calcite, 2.72	Pyrite, 5.02	Copper, 8.9
Fluorite, 3.18	Chalcocite, 5.75	Silver, 10.5
Topaz, 3.53	Cerussite, 6.55	

It should be emphasized that specimens of minerals should be pure no matter what method is used in determining specific gravity. It is usually better to use a small specimen since it is easier to obtain small than large fragments of pure material.

Following the tables on determinative mineralogy a list of the common minerals is given, arranged according to increasing specific gravity.

DETERMINATIVE TABLES

GENERAL CLASSIFICATION OF THE TABLES

LUSTER — METALLIC OR SUBMETALLIC

I. Hardness: $< 2\frac{1}{2}$. (Will leave a mark on paper.) Page 458.

II. Hardness: $> 2\frac{1}{2}$, $< 5\frac{1}{2}$. (Can be scratched by knife; will not readily leave a mark on paper.) Page 549.

III. Hardness: $> 5\frac{1}{2}$. (Cannot be scratched by knife.) Page 555.

LUSTER — NONMETALLIC

I. Streak definitely colored. Page 557.

II. Streak colorless.

    A. Hardness: $< 2\frac{1}{2}$. (Can be scratched by fingernail.) Page 560.

    B. Hardness: $> 2\frac{1}{2}$, < 3. (Cannot be scratched by fingernail; can be scratched by cent.)

        1. Cleavage prominent. Page 563.

        2. Cleavage not prominent.

            a. A small splinter is fusible in the candle flame. Page 565.

            b. Infusible in candle flame. Page 566.

    C. Hardness: > 3, $< 5\frac{1}{2}$. (Cannot be scratched by cent; can be scratched by knife.)

        1. Cleavage prominent. Page 567.

        2. Cleavage not prominent. Page 571.

    D. Hardness: $> 5\frac{1}{2}$, < 7. (Cannot be scratched by knife; can be scratched by quartz.)

        1. Cleavage prominent. Page 575.

        2. Cleavage not prominent. Page 577.

    E. Hardness: > 7. (Cannot be scratched by quartz.)

        1. Cleavage prominent. Page 581.

        2. Cleavage not prominent. Page 500.

LUSTER: METALLIC OR SUBMETALLIC
I. Hardness: $< 2\frac{1}{2}$. (Will leave a mark on paper.)

Streak	Color	G.	H.	Remarks	Name, Composition, Crystal System
Black	Iron-black	4.7	1–2	Usually splintery or in radiating fibrous aggregates.	PYROLUSITE MnO_2 Tetragonal
	Steel-gray to iron-black	2.3	1–1½	Cleavage perfect basal {0001}. May be in hexagonal-shaped plates. Greasy feel.	GRAPHITE C Hexagonal
Black to greenish black	Blue-black	4.7	1–1½	Cleavage perfect basal {0001}. Micaceous, may be in hexagonal-shaped leaves. Greenish streak on glazed porcelain (graphite, black). Greasy feel.	MOLYBDENITE MoS_2 Hexagonal
Gray-black	Blue-black to lead-gray	7.6	2½	Cleavage perfect cubic {100}. In cubic crystals. Massive granular.	GALENA PbS Isometric
	Blue-black	4.5	2	Cleavage perfect pinacoidal {010}. Bladed with cross striations. Fuses in the candle flame.	STIBNITE Sb_2S_3 Orthorhombic
Bright red	Red to vermilion	8.1	2–2½	Cleavage perfect prismatic {10$\overline{1}$0}. Luster adamantine. Usually granular massive.	CINNABAR HgS Rhombohedral
Red-brown	Red to vermilion	5.2	1+	Earthy. Frequently as pigment in rocks. Crystalline hematite is harder.	HEMATITE Fe_2O_3 Rhombohedral
Yellow-brown	Yellow-brown	3.6 to 4.0	1+	Earthy. Limonite is usually harder.	LIMONITE $FeO(OH) \cdot nH_2O$ Amorphous

Streak	Color	G.	H.	Remarks	Name, Composition, Crystal System
Black. May leave a slight mark on paper	Gray-black	7.3	$2-2\frac{1}{2}$	Usually massive or earthy. Distinguished by being easily sectile, i.e., can be cut with a knife like lead. Bright steel-gray on fresh surfaces; darkens on exposure.	ARGENTITE Ag$_2$S Isometric
	Indigo-blue; may tarnish to blue-black	4.6	$1\frac{1}{2}-2$	Usually in platy masses or in thin 6-sided platy crystals. Moistened with water turns purple.	Covellite CuS Hexagonal

LUSTER: METALLIC OR SUBMETALLIC
II. Hardness: $> 2\frac{1}{2}, < 5\frac{1}{2}$
(Can be scratched by a knife; will not readily leave a mark on paper).

Streak	Color	G.	H.	Remarks	Name, Composition, Crystal System
Black; may have brown tinge	Steel-gray. May tarnish to dead black on exposure	4.7 to 5.0	$3-4\frac{1}{2}$	Massive or in tetrahedral crystals. Often associated with silver ores.	TETRAHEDRITE (Cu,Fe,Zn,Ag)$_{12}$-Sb$_4$S$_{13}$ Isometric
Gray-black		5.7	$2\frac{1}{2}-3$	Somewhat sectile. Usually compact massive. Associated with other copper minerals.	CHALCOCITE Cu$_2$S Orthorhombic
Black. May leave a mark on paper	Steel-gray on fresh surface. Tarnishes to dull gray on exposure	7.3	$2-2\frac{1}{2}$	Easily sectile. Usually massive or earthy. Rarely in cubic crystals.	ARGENTITE Ag$_2$S Pseudoisometric
	Iron-black	4.7	$1-2$	Usually splintery or in radiating fibrous aggregates.	PYROLUSITE MnO$_2$ Tetragonal

LUSTER: METALLIC OR SUBMETALLIC

II. Hardness: $> 2\frac{1}{2}$, $< 5\frac{1}{2}$

(Can be scratched by a knife; will not readily leave a mark on paper.) *(Continued)*

Streak	Color	G.	H.	Remarks	Name, Composition, Crystal System
Black	Steel-gray on fresh surface. Tarnishes to dull gray on exposure	6.2	$2-2\frac{1}{2}$	Fuses easily in candle flame. Usually in small irregular masses, often earthy. A rare mineral.	Stephanite Ag_5SbS_4 Orthorhombic
	Gray-black	4.4	3	Cleavage prismatic {110}. Usually in bladed masses showing cleavage. Associated with other copper minerals.	ENARGITE Cu_3AsS_4 Orthorhombic
		5.5 to 6.0	2–3	Fuses easily in candle flame. Characteristically in fibrous, featherlike masses.	Jamesonite $Pb_4FeSb_6S_{14}$ Monoclinic
		5.8 to 5.9	$2\frac{1}{2}-3$	Fuses easily in candle flame. In stout prismatic crystals; characteristically twinned with re-entrant angles giving a "cogwheel" effect.	Bournonite $PbCuSbS_3$ Orthorhombic
		6.2	$2\frac{1}{2}$	Fuses easily in candle flame. Often in thin 6-sided crystal plates with triangular marking. Also massive and earthy.	Polybasite $Ag_{16}Sb_2S_{11}$ Monoclinic
	Steel-gray	4.4	4	Decrepitates and fuses in candle flame. Irregular massive.	Stannite Cu_2FeSnS_4 Tetragonal
Gray-black. Will mark paper	Lead-gray	4.6	2	Cleavage perfect pinacoidal {010}. Fuses easily in candle flame. Characterized by bladed crystal aggregates with cross striations.	STIBNITE Sb_2S_3 Orthorhombic

Streak	Color	G.	H.	Remarks	Name, Composition, Crystal System
Gray-black. Will mark paper	Lead-gray	6.8	$2\frac{1}{2}$	Cleavage perfect pinacoidal {010}. Fuses easily in candle flame. Resembles stibnite and can be told from it only by test for bismuth.	Bismuthinite Bi_2S_3 Orthorhombic
	Lead-gray	7.5	$2\frac{1}{2}$	Cleavage perfect cubic {100}. In cubic crystals and granular masses. If a fragment is held in the candle flame, it does not fuse but is slowly reduced and small globules of metallic lead collect on the surface.	GALENA PbS Isometric
Gray-black	Tin-white; tarnishes to dark gray	5.7	$3\frac{1}{2}$	Cleavage perfect basal {0001}, rarely seen. Usually occurs in fibrous botryoidal masses. Heated in the candle flame gives off white fumes and yields a strong garlic odor.	Arsenic As Rhombohedral
	Tin-white	8 to 8.2	2	Cleavage pinacoidal {010}. Fuses easily in candle flame. Often as thin coatings and in lath-shaped crystals.	Sylvanite $(Au,Ag)Te_2$ Monoclinic
	Tin-white to brass yellow	9.4	$2\frac{1}{2}$	Fuses easily in candle flame. In irregular masses or in thin deeply striated lath-shaped crystals. Told from sylvanite by its lack of cleavage.	Calaverite $AuTe_2$ Monoclinic
Black	Usually pale copper-red. May be silver-white with pink tone	7.8	$5–5\frac{1}{2}$	Usually massive. May be coated with green nickel bloom. Associated with cobalt and nickel minerals.	NICCOLITE NiAs Hexagonal
	Fresh surface brownish bronze; tarnishes purple	5.1	3	Usually massive. Associated with other copper minerals, chiefly chalcocite and chalcopyrite.	BORNITE Cu_5FeS_4 Isometric

LUSTER: METALLIC OR SUBMETALLIC

II. Hardness: $> 2\frac{1}{2}$, $< 5\frac{1}{2}$

(Can be scratched by a knife; will not readily leave a mark on paper.) *(Continued)*

Streak	Color	G.	H.	Remarks	Name, Composition, Crystal System
Black	Brown-ish bronze	4.6	4	Small fragments magnetic. Usually massive. Often associated with chalcopyrite and pyrite.	**PYRRHOTITE** $Fe_{1-x}S$ Hexagonal
		4.6 to 5.0	$3\frac{1}{2}$–4	Cleavage octahedral. Resembles pyrrhotite with which it usually is associated. Distinguished by cleavage.	Pentlandite $(Fe,Ni)_9S_8$ Isometric
	Brass-yellow	4.1 to 4.3	$3\frac{1}{2}$–4	Usually massive, but may be in sphenoidal crystals resembling tetrahedrons. Associated with other copper minerals and pyrite.	**CHALCOPYRITE** $CuFeS_2$ Tetragonal
	Brass-yellow. Almost greenish when in very slender crystals	5.5	3–$3\frac{1}{2}$	Cleavage rhombohedral $\{10\bar{1}1\}$, rarely seen. Usually in radiating groups of hairlike crystals.	MILLERITE NiS Rhombohedral
Dark brown to black	Steel-gray to iron-black	4.3	4	In radiating fibrous or crystalline masses. Distinct prismatic crystals often grouped in bundles. Frequently associated with pyrolusite.	MANGANITE $MnO(OH)$ Orthorhombic
	Iron-black to brown-ish black	4.6	$5\frac{1}{2}$	Luster pitchy. May be accompanied by yellow or green oxidation products. Usually in granular masses in peridotites.	**CHROMITE** $FeCr_2O_4$ Isometric
	Brown to black	7.0 to 7.5	5–$5\frac{1}{2}$	Cleavage perfect pinacoidal $\{010\}$. With greater amounts of manganese the streak and color are darker.	WOLFRAMITE $(Fe,Mn)WO_4$ Monoclinic

Streak	Color	G.	H.	Remarks	Name, Composition, Crystal System
Black	Indigo-blue; may tarnish to blue-black	4.6	$1\frac{1}{2}$–2	Usually in platy masses or in thin 6-sided platy crystals. Moistened with water turns purple.	Covellite CuS Hexagonal
Usually black. May be brownish	Black	3.7 to 4.7	5–6	Massive botryoidal and stalactitic. Usually associated with pyrolusite.	PSILOMELANE $BaMn''Mn_8'''O_{16}$-$(OH)_4$ Appears amorphous
Light to dark brown	Dark brown to coal-black. More rarely yellow or red	3.9 to 4.1	$3\frac{1}{2}$–4	Cleavage perfect dodecahedral $\{110\}$ (6 directions). Usually cleavable granular; may be in tetrahedral crystals. The darker the specimen the higher the percentage of iron. The streak is always of a lighter color than the specimen.	SPHALERITE ZnS Isometric
Red brown to Indian red	Dark brown to steel-gray to black	4.8 to 5.3	$5\frac{1}{2}$–$6\frac{1}{2}$	Usually harder than knife. Massive, radiating, reniform, micaceous.	HEMATITE Fe_2O_3 Rhombohedral
	Deep red to black	5.85	$2\frac{1}{2}$	Cleavage rhombohedral $\{10\bar{1}1\}$. Easily fusible in candle flame. Dark "ruby silver" and shows dark ruby-red color in thin splinters. Associated with other silver minerals.	Pyrargyrite Ag_3SbS_3 Rhombohedral
	Red-brown to deep red. Ruby-red if transparent	6.0	$3\frac{1}{2}$–4	Massive or in cubes or octahedrons. May be in very slender crystals (chalcotrichite). Associated with other oxidized copper minerals as malachite, azurite, native copper.	CUPRITE Cu_2O Isometric
Bright red	Ruby-red	5.55	2–$2\frac{1}{2}$	Cleavage rhombohedral $\{10\bar{1}1\}$. Easily fusible in candle flame. Light "ruby silver." Associated with pyrargyrite.	Proustite Ag_3AsS_3 Rhombohedral
Yellow brown. Yellow ocher	Dark brown to black	3.6 to 4.0	5–$5\frac{1}{2}$	Vitreous luster. Usually contains about 15% water while goethite contains 10%.	LIMONITE $FeO(OH)\cdot nH_2O$ Amorphous

LUSTER: METALLIC OR SUBMETALLIC
II. Hardness: $> 2\frac{1}{2}$, $< 5\frac{1}{2}$
(Can be scratched by a knife; will not readily leave a mark on paper.) *(Continued)*

Streak	Color	G.	H.	Remarks	Name, Composition, Crystal System
Yellow brown. Yellow ocher	Dark brown to black	4.37	5–5½	Cleavage pinacoidal {010}. In radiating fibers, mammillary and stalactitic forms. Rarely in crystals. Definitely distinguished from limonite by presence of cleavage or crystal form.	**GOETHITE** HFeO₂ Orthorhombic
Dark red. (Some varieties mark paper.)	Dark red to vermilion	8.10	2½	Cleavage prismatic {10$\bar{1}$1}. Usually granular or earthy. Commonly impure and of a dark red or brown color. When pure, translucent or transparent and bright red.	**CINNABAR** HgS Rhombohedral
Copper-red, shiny	Copper-red on fresh surface; tarnishes black	8.9	2½–3	Malleable. Usually in irregular grains. May be in branching crystal group or in rude isometric crystals.	**COPPER** Cu Isometric
Silver-white, shiny	Silver-white on fresh surface. Gray to black tarnish	10.5	2½–3	Malleable. Usually in irregular grains. May be in wire, plates, branching crystal groups.	**SILVER** Ag Isometric
Gray, shiny	White or steel-gray	14 to 19	4–4½	Malleable. Irregular grains or nuggets. Unusually hard for a metal. Rare.	Platinum Pt Isometric
Silver-white, shiny	Silver-white with reddish tone	9.8	2–2½	Cleavage perfect basal {0001} and rhombohedral {10$\bar{1}$1}. Sectile. Easily fusible in candle flame. When hammered, at first malleable but soon breaks up into small pieces.	Bismuth Bi Rhombohedral
Gold-yellow, shiny	Gold-yellow	15.0 to 19.3	2½–3	Malleable. Irregular grains, nuggets, leaves. Very heavy; specific gravity varies with silver content.	**GOLD** Au Isometric

LUSTER: METALLIC OR SUBMETALLIC
III. Hardness: > 5½. (Cannot be scratched by a knife.)

Streak	Color	G.	H.	Remarks	Name, Composition, Crystal System
		6.0 to 6.2	5½–6	Usually massive. Crystals pseudorthorhombic.	**ARSENOPYRITE** FeAsS Monoclinic
	Silver- or tin- white	6.1 to 6.9	5½–6	Usually massive. Crystals pyritohedral. May be coated with pink nickel bloom.	Skutterudite- Nickel skutterudite (Co,Ni,Fe)As$_3$- (Ni,Co,Fe)As$_3$ Isometric
		6.33	5½	Commonly in pyritohedral crystals with pinkish cast. Also massive.	Cobaltite- Gersdorffite CoAsS—NiAsS Isometric
Black	Pale copper- red. May be silver- white with pink tone	7.5	5–5½	Usually massive. May be coated with green nickel bloom.	**NICCOLITE** NiAs Hexagonal
	Pale brass- yellow	5.0	6–6½	Often in pyritohedrons or striated cubes. Massive granular. Most common sulfide.	**PYRITE** FeS$_2$ Isometric
	Pale yellow to almost white	4.9	6–6½	Frequently in "cock's comb" crystal groups and radiating fibrous masses.	**MARCASITE** FeS$_2$ Orthorhombic
	Black	5.18	6	Strongly magnetic. Crystals octahedral. May show octahedral parting.	**MAGNETITE** Fe$_3$O$_4$ Isometric
Dark brown to black	Black	9.0 to 9.7	5½	Luster pitchy. Massive granular, botryoidal crystals.	Uraninite UO$_2$ Isometric
		4.7	5½–6	May be slightly magnetic. Often associated with magnetite. Massive granular; platy crystals; as sand.	**ILMENITE** FeTiO$_3$ Rhombohedral

LUSTER: METALLIC OR SUBMETALLIC
III. Hardness: $> 5\frac{1}{2}$.
(Cannot be scratched by a knife.) *(Continued)*

Streak	Color	G.	H.	Remarks	Name, Composition, Crystal System
Dark brown to black	Black	3.7 to 4.7	5–6	Compact massive, stalactitic, botryoidal. Associated with other manganese minerals and told by greater hardness.	PSILOMELANE $BaMn''Mn_8'''O_{16}-(OH)_4$ Appears amorphous
		5.3 to 7.3	6	Luster black and shiny on fresh surface. May have slight bluish tarnish. Granular or in stout prismatic crystals.	Columbite-Tantalite $(Fe,Mn)(Nb,Ta)_2O_6$ Orthorhombic
Dark brown	Iron-brown to brown-ish black	7.0 to 7.5	5–5½	Cleavage perfect pinacoidal {010}. With greater amounts of manganese the streak and color are darker.	WOLFRAMITE $(Fe,Mn)WO_4$ Monoclinic
		4.6	5½	Luster pitchy. Frequently accompanied by green oxidation products. Usually in granular masses in peridotites.	CHROMITE $FeCr_2O_4$ Isometric
		5.15	6	Slightly magnetic. Granular or in octahedral crystals. Common only at Franklin, N. J., associated with zincite and willemite.	FRANKLINITE $(Fe,Zn,Mn)-(Fe,Mn)_2O_4$ Isometric
Red-brown, Indian red	Dark brown to steel-gray to black	4.8 to 5.3	5½–6½	Radiating, reniform, massive, micaceous. Rarely in steel-black rhombohedral crystals. Some varieties softer.	HEMATITE Fe_2O_3 Rhombohedral
Pale brown	Brown to black	4.18 to 4.25	6–6½	In prismatic crystals vertically striated; often slender acicular. Crystals frequently twinned. Found in black sands.	RUTILE TiO_2 Tetragonal
Yellow-brown to yellow-ocher	Dark brown to black	3.6 to 4.0	5–5½	Vitreous luster. Usually contains about 15% water while goethite contains 10%.	LIMONITE $FeO(OH)\cdot nH_2O$ Amorphous
Yellow-brown to yellow-ocher	Dark brown to black	4.37	5–5½	Cleavage {010}. Radiating, colloform, stalactitic. Distinguished from limonite by presence of cleavage or crystal form.	GOETHITE $HFeO_2$ Orthorhombic

LUSTER: NONMETALLIC
I. Streak definitely colored.

Streak	Color	G.	H.	Remarks	Name, Composition, Crystal System
Dark red	Dark red to vermilion	8.10	$2\frac{1}{2}$	Cleavage prismatic $\{10\bar{1}0\}$. Usually granular or earthy. Commonly impure and of a dark red or brown color. When pure, translucent or transparent and bright red.	**CINNABAR** HgS Rhombohedral
	Red-brown. Ruby-red when transparent	6.0	$3\frac{1}{2}$–4	Massive or in cubes or octahedrons. May be in very slender crystals. (chalcotrichite). Associated with other oxidized copper minerals such as malachite, azurite, native copper.	**CUPRITE** Cu_2O Isometric
Red-brown, Indian brown	Dark brown to steel-gray to black	4.8 to 5.3	$5\frac{1}{2}$–$6\frac{1}{2}$	Radiating, reniform, massive, micaceous. Rarely in steel-black rhombohedral crystals. Some varieties softer.	**HEMATITE** Fe_2O_3 Rhombohedral
	Deep red to black	5.8	$2\frac{1}{2}$	Cleavage rhombohedral $\{10\bar{1}1\}$. Easily fusible in candle flame. Dark "ruby silver" and shows dark ruby-red color in thin splinters. Associated with other silver minerals.	Pyrargyrite Ag_3SbS_3 Rhombohedral
Bright red	Ruby-red	5.55	2–$2\frac{1}{2}$	Cleavage rhombohedral $\{10\bar{1}1\}$. Easily fusible in candle flame. Light "ruby silver." Associated with pyrargyrite.	Proustite Ag_3AsS_3 Rhombohedral
Pink	Red to pink	2.95	$1\frac{1}{2}$–$2\frac{1}{2}$	Cleavage perfect pinacoidal $\{010\}$. Usually in reniform shapes or as pulverulent or earthy crusts. Found as coatings on cobalt minerals.	Erythrite (cobalt bloom) $Co_3As_2O_8\cdot 8H_2O$ Monoclinic
Yellow-brown to yellow-ocher	Dark brown to black	3.6 to 4.0	5–$5\frac{1}{2}$	Usually hard, with vitreous luster. Usually contains about 15% water while goethite contains 10%.	LIMONITE $FeO(OH)\cdot nH_2O$ Amorphous

LUSTER: NONMETALLIC

I. Streak definitely colored. (*Continued*)

Streak	Color	G.	H.	Remarks	Name, Composition, Crystal System
Yellow-brown to yellow-ocher	Dark brown to black	4.4	5–5½	Cleavage pinacoidal {010}. In radiating fibers, mammillary and stalactitic forms. Rarely in crystals. Definitely distinguished from limonite only by presence of cleavage or crystal form. Usually metallic.	**GOETHITE** HFeO$_2$ Orthorhombic
Brown	Dark brown	7.0 to 7.5	5–5½	Cleavage perfect pinacoidal {010}. With greater amounts of manganese the streak and color are darker.	**WOLFRAMITE** (Fe,Mn)WO$_4$ Monoclinic
	Light to dark brown	3.83 to 3.88	3½–4	In cleavable masses or in small curved rhombohedral crystals. Becomes magnetic after heating in candle flame.	**SIDERITE** FeCO$_3$ Rhombohedral
Light brown	Light to dark brown	3.9 to 4.1	3½–4	Cleavage perfect dodecahedral {110} (6 directions). Usually cleavable granular; may be in tetrahedral crystals. The darker the specimen the higher the percentage of iron. The streak is always of a lighter color than the specimen.	**SPHALERITE** ZnS Isometric
	Brown to black	6.8 to 7.1	6–7	Occurs in twinned crystals. Fibrous, reniform and irregular masses; in rolled grains.	**CASSITERITE** SnO$_2$ Tetragonal
	Reddish brown to black	4.18 to 4.25	6–6½	Crystals vertically striated; often acicular. Twinning common.	**RUTILE** TiO$_2$ Tetragonal
Orange-yellow	Deep red to orange-yellow	5.68	4–4½	Cleavage basal {0001}. Found only at Franklin, N. J., associated with franklinite and willemite.	ZINCITE ZnO Hexagonal
	Bright red	5.9 to 6.1	2½–3	Luster adamantine. In long slender crystals, often interlacing groups. Decrepitates in candle flame.	Crocoite PbCrO$_4$ Monoclinic

Streak	Color	G.	H.	Remarks	Name, Composition, Crystal System
Orange-yellow	Deep red	3.48	$1\frac{1}{2}$–2	Frequently earthy. Associated with orpiment. Fusible in candle flame.	**REALGAR** AsS Monoclinic
	Lemon-yellow	3.49	$1\frac{1}{2}$–2	Cleavage pinacoidal {010}. Luster resinous. Associated with realgar. Fusible in candle flame.	ORPIMENT As_2S_3 Monoclinic
Pale yellow	Pale yellow	2.05 to 2.09	$1\frac{1}{2}$–$2\frac{1}{2}$	Burns with blue flame, giving odor of SO_2. A mass held in the hand close to the ear will be heard to crackle. Crystallized, granular, earthy.	**SULFUR** S Orthorhombic
Light green	Dark emerald-green	3.75 to 3.77	3–$3\frac{1}{2}$	One perfect cleavage {010}. In granular cleavable masses or small prismatic crystals.	Atacamite $Cu_2Cl(OH)_3$ Orthorhombic
		$3.9\pm$	$3\frac{1}{2}$–4	One good cleavage {010}. In small prismatic crystals or granular masses.	Antlerite $Cu_3(SO_4)(OH)_4$ Orthorhombic
	Bright green	3.9 to 4.03	$3\frac{1}{2}$–4	Radiating fibrous, mammillary. Associated with azurite and may alter to it. Effervesces in cold acid.	**MALACHITE** $Cu_2CO_3(OH)_2$ Monoclinic
Light blue	Intense azure-blue	3.77	$3\frac{1}{2}$–4	In small crystals, often in groups. Radiating fibrous, usually as alteration from malachite. Effervesces in cold acid.	**AZURITE** $Cu_3(CO_3)_2(OH)_2$ Monoclinic
		2.12 to 2.30	$2\frac{1}{2}$	Soluble in water. Metallic taste. In crystals, massive, stalactitic	Chalcanthite $CuSO_4 \cdot 5H_2O$ Triclinic
Very light blue	Light green to turquoise blue	2.0 to 2.4	2–4	Massive compact. Associated with oxidized copper minerals.	CHRYSOCOLLA $CuSiO_3 \cdot 2H_2O$ Uncertain
Grayish blue	Very dark blue. Bluish green	2.58 to 2.68	$1\frac{1}{2}$–2	One perfect cleavage {010}. Usually in prismatic crystals.	Vivianite $Fe_3(PO_4)_2 \cdot 8H_2O$ Monoclinic

LUSTER: NONMETALLIC
II. Streak colorless
A. Hardness: $< 2\frac{1}{2}$. (Can be scratched by fingernail.)

Cleavage, Fracture	Color	G.	H.	Remarks	Name, Composition, Crystal System
The micas or related micaceous minerals, which possess such a perfect cleavage that they can be split into exceedingly thin sheets. They may occur as aggregates of minute scales, when the micaceous structure may not be readily apparent. — **Perfect cleavage in one direction**	Pale brown, green, yellow, white	2.76 to 3.0	$2-2\frac{1}{2}$	In foliated masses and scales. Crystals tabular with hexagonal or diamond-shaped outline. Cleavage flakes elastic. Common mica.	**MUSCOVITE** $KAl_2(AlSi_3O_{10})(OH)_2$ Monoclinic
	Usually dark brown, green to black; may be yellow	2.95 to 3	$2\frac{1}{2}-3$	Usually in irregular foliated masses. Crystals have hexagonal outline, but rare. Cleavage flakes elastic.	**BIOTITE** $K(Mg,Fe)_3$ $(AlSi_3O_{10})(OH)_2$ Monoclinic
	Yellowish brown, green, white	2.86	$2\frac{1}{2}-3$	Often in 6-sided tabular crystals; in irregular foliated masses. May show copperlike reflection from cleavage. Occurs in marble.	**PHLOGOPITE** $KMg_3(AlSi_3O_{10})$- $(OH)_2$ Monoclinic
	Green of various shades	2.6 to 2.9	$2-2\frac{1}{2}$	Usually in irregular foliated masses. May be in compact masses of minute scales. Thin sheets flexible but not elastic.	**CHLORITE** Monoclinic
	White, apple-green, gray. When impure, as in soapstone, dark gray, dark green to almost black	2.7 to 2.8	1	Greasy feel. Frequently distinctly foliated or micaceous. Cannot be positively identified by physical tests.	**TALC** $Mg_3(Si_4O_{10})(OH)_2$ Monoclinic
		2.8 to 2.9	1-2		Pyrophyllite $Al_2(Si_4O_{10})(OH)_2$ Monoclinic
	White, gray, green	2.39	$2\frac{1}{2}$	Pearly luster on cleavage face, elsewhere vitreous. Sectile. Commonly foliated massive, may be in broad tabular crystals. Thin sheets flexible but not elastic.	**BRUCITE** $Mg(OH)_2$ Rhombohedral

Cleavage, Fracture	Color	G.	H.	Remarks	Name, Composition, Crystal System
Pinacoidal {010}	Blue, bluish green to colorless	2.58 to 2.68	1½–2	Streak grayish blue. Usually in prismatic crystals.	Vivianite $Fe_3(PO_4)_2 \cdot 8H_2O$ Monoclinic
	Colorless to white	1.75	2–2½	Occurs in crusts and capillary fibers. Soluble in water.	Epsomite $MgSO_4 \cdot 7H_2O$ Orthorhombic
Cubic {100}	Colorless or white	1.99	2	Soluble in water, bitter taste. Resembles halite but usually softer. In granular cleavable masses or cubic crystals.	Sylvite KCl Isometric
{010} perfect, {100} {Ī11} good	Colorless, white, gray. May be colored by impurities	2.32	2	Occurs in crystals, broad cleavage flakes. May be compact massive without cleavage, or fibrous with silky luster.	**GYPSUM** $CaSO_4 \cdot 2H_2O$ Monoclinic
Rhomb. {10Ī1} poor		2.29	1–2	Occurs in saline crusts. Readily soluble in water; cooling and salty taste. Fusible in candle flame.	SODA NITER $NaNO_3$ Rhombohedral
Prismatic {110} seldom seen. F. Conchoidal	Colorless or white	2.09 to 2.14	2	Usually in crusts, silky tufts and delicate acicular crystals. Readily soluble in water; cooling and salty taste. Fusible in the candle flame.	Niter KNO_3 Orthorhombic
{001} perfect; seldom seen. F. earthy	White; may be darker	2.6 to 2.63	2–2½	Generally claylike and compact. When breathed upon gives argillaceous odor. Will adhere to the dry tongue.	**KAOLINITE** $Al_4(Si_4O_{10})(OH)_8$ Monoclinic
Fract. uneven	Pearl-gray or colorless. Turns to pale brown on exposure to light	5.5±	2–3	Perfectly sectile. Translucent in thin plates. In irregular masses, rarely in crystals. Distinguished from other silver halides only by chemical tests.	CERARGYRITE AgCl Isometric

LUSTER: NONMETALLIC

II. Streak colorless

A. Hardness: < 2½. (Can be scratched by fingernail.) (Continued)

Cleavage, Fracture	Color	G.	H.	Remarks	Name, Composition, Crystal System
F. uneven	Pale yellow	2.05 to 2.09	1½–2½	Burns with blue flame, giving odor of SO_2. A mass held in the hand close to the ear will be heard to crackle. Crystallized, granular, earthy.	**SULFUR** S Orthorhombic
	Yellow, brown, gray, white	2.0 to 2.55	1–3	In rounded grains, often earthy and clay-like. Usually harder than 2½.	**BAUXITE** A mixture of Al hydroxides
Seldom seen	White	1.65	1	Usually in rounded masses of fine fibers and acicular crystals.	ULEXITE $NaCaB_5O_9 \cdot 8H_2O$ Triclinic
F. conchoidal	White, gray, yellowish	2.0	2–2½	Fine textured, compact. Smooth feel. When dry will float on water.	Sepiolite $Mg_4(Si_6O_{15})$-$(OH)_2 \cdot 6H_2O$ Uncertain
F. uneven	Apple-green to white	2.2 to 2.8	2–3	In incrustations and earthy masses.	Garnierite $(Ni,Mg)SiO_3 \cdot nH_2O$ Amorphous

LUSTER: NONMETALLIC

II. Streak colorless

B. Hardness: $> 2\frac{1}{2}$, < 3. (Cannot be scratched by fingernail; can be scratched by cent.)

1. Cleavage prominent

Cleavage, Fracture		Color	G.	H.	Remarks	Name, Composition, Crystal System
Perfect cleavage in one direction — See also the minerals of the mica group, p. 478 which may be harder than the fingernail.	{001}	Lilac, grayish white	2.8 to 3.0	$2\frac{1}{2}$–4	Crystals 6-sided prismatic. Usually in small irregular sheets and scales. A pegmatite mineral associated with colored tourmalines.	LEPIDOLITE $K_2Li_3Al_3(AlSi_3O_{10})_2$- $(O,OH,F)_4$ Monoclinic
	{001}	Pink, gray, white	3.0 to 3.1	$3\frac{1}{2}$–5	Usually in irregular foliated masses; folia brittle. Associated with emery.	MARGARITE $CaAl_2(Al_2Si_2O_{10})$- $(OH)_2$ Monoclinic
	{010}	Blue, bluish green to colorless	2.58 to 2.68	$1\frac{1}{2}$–2	Prismatic crystals often in stellate groups. Also fibrous, earthy. Streak grayish blue. A rare mineral.	Vivianite $Fe_3(PO_4)_2 \cdot 8H_2O$ Monoclinic
	{010}	Colorless or white	4.3	$3\frac{1}{2}$	Usually massive, with radiating habit. Effervesces in cold acid.	**WITHERITE** $BaCO_3$ Orthorhombic
	{100}	Red	2.78	$2\frac{1}{2}$–3	Occurs in compact granular or fibrous masses. Occurs with other soluble salts.	Polyhalite $K_2Ca_2Mg(SO_4)_4 \cdot 2H_2O$ Triclinic
	{001}	Pale yellow or gray	2.7 to 2.85	$2\frac{1}{2}$–3	Crystals tabular. Found associated with other salts in salt lake deposits.	Glauberite $Na_2Ca(SO_4)_2$ Monoclinic
Cleavage in 2 directions {001} {100}		Colorless or white to gray	1.95	3	Occurs in cleavable crystalline aggregates.	KERNITE $Na_2B_4O_7 \cdot 4H_2O$ Monoclinic

LUSTER: NONMETALLIC

II. Streak colorless

B. Hardness: > $2\frac{1}{2}$, < 3. (Cannot be scratched by fingernail; can be scratched by cent.)

1. Cleavage prominent. (*Continued*)

Cleavage, Fracture		Color	G.	H.	Remarks	Name, Composition, Crystal System
Cleavage in 3 directions at right angles	Cubic {100}	Colorless, white, red, blue	2.1 to 2.3	$2\frac{1}{2}$	Common salt. Soluble in water, taste salty, fusible in candle flame. In granular cleavable masses or in cubic crystals.	HALITE NaCl Isometric
	Cubic {100}	Colorless or white	1.99	2	Resembles halite, but distinguished from it by more bitter taste and lesser hardness.	Sylvite KCl Isometric
	{001} {010} {100}	Colorless, white, blue, gray, red	2.89 to 2.98	3–3½	Commonly in massive fine aggregates, not showing cleavage; then can be distinguished only by chemical tests.	ANHYDRITE CaSO₄ Orthorhombic
Cleavage in 3 directions not at right angles. Rhombohedral {10$\bar{1}$1}		Colorless, white, and variously tinted	2.72	3	Effervesces in cold acid. Crystals show many forms. Occurs in large masses as limestone and marble. Clear varieties show strong double refraction.	CALCITE CaCO₃ Rhombohedral
		Colorless, white, pink	2.85	3½–4	Usually harder than copper coin. Often in curved rhombohedral crystals with pearly luster. In coarse masses as dolomitic limestone and marble. Powdered mineral will effervesce in cold acid.	DOLOMITE CaMg(CO₃)₂ Rhombohedral
Cleavage in 3 directions. Basal {001} at right angles to prismatic {110}		Colorless, white, blue, yellow, red	4.5	3–3½	Frequently in aggregates of platy or tabular crystals. Pearly luster on basal cleavage. Characterized by high specific gravity for nonmetallic mineral, and thus distinguished from celestite.	BARITE BaSO₄ Orthorhombic

Cleavage, Fracture	Color	G.	H.	Remarks	Name, Composition, Crystal System
Cleavage in 3 directions. Basal {001} at right angles to prismatic {110}	Color-less, white, blue, red	3.95 to 3.97	3–3½	Very similar to barite but lower specific gravity. May be necessary to get crimson strontium flame to distinguish it.	**CELESTITE** $SrSO_4$ Orthorhombic
	Color-less or white. Gray and brown when impure	6.2 to 6.4	3	Adamantine luster. Usually massive but may be in small tabular crystals. Alteration of galena. When massive may need test for SO_4 to distinguish from cerrusite ($PbCO_3$).	**ANGLESITE** $PbSO_4$ Orthorhombic

2. Cleavage not prominent

a. A small splinter is fusible in the candle flame

Color	G.	H.	Remarks	Name, Composition, Crystal System
Colorless or white	1.7±	2–2½	Soluble in water. One good cleavage, seldom seen. In crusts and prismatic crystals. Found only in dry regions. In candle flame swells and then fuses. Sweetish alkaline taste.	**BORAX** $Na_2B_4O_7 \cdot 10H_2O$ Monoclinic
	2.95 to 3.0	2½	Massive. Characterized by peculiar translucent appearance. Fine powder insoluble but becomes nearly invisible when placed in water. Ivigtut, Greenland, only important locality. Pseudocubic parting.	**CRYOLITE** Na_3AlF_6 Monoclinic
	6.55	3–3½	Luster adamantine. In granular masses and platy crystals, usually associated with galena. Effervesces in cold nitric acid. Reduced in candle flame, producing small globules of lead.	**CERUSSITE** $PbCO_3$ Orthorhombic
Colorless, white, red	1.6	1	Bitter taste. Commonly massive granular. In candle flame swells, then fuses. Soluble in water.	Carnallite $KMgCl_3 \cdot 6H_2O$ Orthorhombic
Colorless, yellow, orange, brown	7.0 to 7.2	3½	Luster resinous. In small prismatic crystals. Prism faces may be curved, giving barrel shapes. In granular masses.	Mimetite $Pb_5Cl(AsO_4)_3$ Hexagonal

LUSTER: NONMETALLIC

II. Streak colorless

B. Hardness: $> 2\frac{1}{2}$, < 3. (Cannot be scratched by fingernail; can be scratched by cent.)

2. Cleavage not prominent

b. Infusible in candle flame.

Color	G.	H.	Remarks	Name, Composition, Crystal System
Colorless or white	4.3	$3\frac{1}{2}$	Often in radiating masses; granular; rarely in pseudohexagonal crystals. Effervesces in cold acid.	WITHERITE $BaCO_3$ Orthorhombic
	2.6 to 2.63	$2-2\frac{1}{2}$	Usually compact, earthy. When breathed upon gives an argillaceous odor. The basis of most clays.	KAOLINITE $Al_4(Si_4O_{10})(OH)_8$ Monoclinic
White, gray, yellowish	2.0	$2-2\frac{1}{2}$	Fine textured compact. Smooth feel. When dry will float on water.	Sepiolite $Mg_4(Si_6O_{15})$-$(OH)_2 \cdot 6H_2O$ Uncertain
Colorless, white, blue, gray, red	2.89 to 2.98	$3-3\frac{1}{2}$	Commonly in massive fine aggregates, not showing cleavage, and can be distinguished only by chemical tests.	ANHYDRITE $CaSO_4$ Orthorhombic
Honey-, citron-, or orange-yellow	4.9	$3-3\frac{1}{2}$	Usually found as a coating of fine powder on sphalerite. Rarely in crystals. A rare mineral.	Greenockite CdS Hexagonal
Yellow, brown, gray, white	2.0 to 2.55	$1-3$	Usually pisolitic; in rounded grains and earthy masses. Often impure.	BAUXITE A mixture of aluminum hydroxides
Ruby-red, brown, yellow	6.7 to 7.1	3	Luster resinous. In slender prismatic and cavernous crystals; in barrel-shaped forms.	Vanadinite $Pb_5Cl(VO_4)_3$ Hexagonal
Yellow, green, white, brown	2.33	$3\frac{1}{2}-4$	Characteristically in radiating hemispherical globular aggregates. Cleavage seldom seen.	Wavellite $Al_3(OH)_3(PO_4)_2 \cdot 5H_2O$ Orthorhombic
Olive- to blackish-green, yellow-green, white	2.2	$2-5$	Massive. Fibrous in the asbestos variety, chrysotile. Frequently mottled green in the massive variety.	SERPENTINE $Mg_6Si_4O_{10}(OH)_8$ Monoclinic

C. Hardness: > 3, < 5½. (Cannot be scratched by cent; can be scratched by knife.)

1. Cleavage prominent

Cleavage	Color	G.	H.	Remarks	Name, Composition, Crystal System
{100}	Blue, usually darker at center of crystal. May be white gray or green	3.56 to 3.66	5–7	In bladed aggregates with cleavage parallel to length. Can be scratched by knife parallel to the length of the crystal but not in a direction at right angles to this.	KYANITE Al_2SiO_5 Triclinic
{010}	White, yellow, brown, red	2.1 to 2.2	3½–4	Characteristically in sheaflike crystal aggregates. May be in flat tabular crystals. Luster pearly on cleavage face.	STILBITE $Ca(Al_2Si_7O_{18})\cdot 7H_2O$ Monoclinic
{001}	Colorless, white, pale green, yellow, rose	2.3 to 2.4	4½–5	In prismatic crystals vertically striated. Crystals often resemble cubes truncated by the octahedron. Luster pearly on base, elsewhere vitreous.	APOPHYLLITE $Ca_4K(Si_4O_{10})F\cdot 8H_2O$ Tetragonal
{010}	White, yellow, red	2.18 to 2.20	3½–4	Luster pearly on cleavage face, elsewhere vitreous. Crystals often tabular parallel to cleavage plane. A zeolite, found in cavities in igneous rocks.	HEULANDITE $Ca(Al_2Si_7O_{18})\cdot 6H_2O$ Monoclinic
{010}	Colorless, white	2.42	4–4½	In crystals and in cleavable aggregates. Decrepitates violently in the candle flame.	COLEMANITE $Ca_2B_6O_{11}\cdot 5H_2O$ Monoclinic
{010}	Colorless, white	4.3	3½	Often in radiating crystal aggregates; granular. Rarely in pseudo-hexagonal crystals. Effervesces in cold acid.	WITHERITE $BaCO_3$ Orthorhombic
{010} {110} poor	Colorless, white	2.95	3½–4	Effervesces in cold acid. Falls to powder in the candle flame. Frequently in radiating groups of acicular crystals; in pseudohexagonal twins. Cleavage indistinct.	ARAGONITE $CaCO_3$ Orthorhombic

One cleavage direction

LUSTER: NONMETALLIC
II. Streak colorless
C. Hardness: > 3, < 5½. (Cannot be scratched by cent; can be scratched by knife.)
1. Cleavage prominent. (*Continued*)

Cleavage	Color	G.	H.	Remarks	Name, Composition, Crystal System
{001} {010}	Light blue, green, gray, salmon to clove-brown	3.42 to 3.56	4½–5	Commonly cleavable massive. Found in pegmatites with other lithium minerals.	Triphylite-lithiophilite $Li(Fe,Mn)PO_4$ Orthorhombic
{001} {100}	Colorless, white, gray	2.8 to 2.9	5–5½	Usually cleavable massive to fibrous. Also compact. Associated with crystalline limestone.	WOLLASTONITE $Ca(SiO_3)$ Triclinic
{001} {100}	Colorless, white, gray	2.7 to 2.8	5	Commonly fibrous in radiating aggregates of sharp acicular crystals. Associated with zeolites in cavities in igneous rocks.	Pectolite $Ca_2NaH(SiO_3)_3$ Triclinic
{110}	Colorless, white	2.25	5–5½	In slender prismatic crystals, prism faces vertically striated. Often in radiating groups. A zeolite, found lining cavities in igneous rocks.	NATROLITE $Na_2Al_2Si_3O_{10}·2H_2O$ Monoclinic
{110}	Colorless, white	3.7	3½–4	Occurs in prismatic crystals and pseudohexagonal twins. Also fibrous and massive. Effervesces in cold acid.	STRONTIANITE $SrCO_3$ Orthorhombic
{110}	White, pale green, blue	3.4 to 3.5	4½–5	Often in radiating crystal groups. Also stalactitic, mammillary. Prismatic cleavage seldom seen.	HEMIMORPHITE $Zn_4(Si_2O_7)(OH)_2·H_2O$ Orthorhombic
	White, green, black	3.0 to 3.3	5–6	Crystals usually slender, fibrous, asbestiform. Tremolite (white, gray, violet), actinolite (green) common in metamorphic rocks. Hornblende and arfvedsonite (dark green to black) common in igneous and metamorphic rocks. Cleavage angle characteristic.	AMPHIBOLE GROUP Essentially calcium magnesium silicates Monoclinic

Two cleavage directions

Prismatic at angles of 55° and 125°

Cleavage			Color	G.	H.	Remarks	Name, Composition, Crystal System
Two cleavage directions	Prismatic at nearly 90° angles	Prismatic at angles of 55° and 125°.	Gray, clove-brown, green	2.85 to 3.2	5½–6	An amphibole. Distinct crystals rare. Commonly in aggregates and fibrous massive.	Anthophyllite $(Mg,Fe)_7(Si_8O_{22})$-$(OH)_2$ Orthorhombic
			White, green, black	3.1 to 3.5	5–6	In stout prisms with rectangular cross section. Often in granular crystalline masses. Diopside (colorless, white, green), aegirite (brown, green), augite (dark green to black) are rock-forming minerals. Characterized by rectangular cross section and cleavage.	PYROXENE GROUP Essentially calcium magnesium silicates Monoclinic
			Rose-red, pink, brown	3.58 to 3.70	5½–6	Color diagnostic. Usually massive, cleavable to compact, in imbedded grains; in large rough crystals with rounded edges.	RHODONITE $Mn(SiO_3)$ Triclinic
Three cleavage directions	Rhombohedral {10Ī1} Three directions not at right angles.		Color-less, white, and variously tinted	2.72	3	Effervesces in cold acid. Crystals show many forms. Occurs in large masses as limestone and marble. Clear varieties show strong double refraction.	CALCITE $CaCO_3$ Rhombohedral
			Color-less, white, pink	2.85	3½–4	Often in curved rhombohedral crystals with pearly luster. In coarse masses as dolomitic limestone and marble. Powdered mineral will effervesce in cold acid.	DOLOMITE $CaMg(CO_3)_2$ Rhombohedral
			White, yellow, gray, brown	3.0 to 3.2	3½–5	Commonly in dense compact masses; also in fine to coarse cleavable masses. Effervesces in hot hydrochloric acid.	MAGNESITE $MgCO_3$ Rhombohedral
			Light to dark brown	3.83 to 3.88	3½–4	In cleavable masses or in small curved rhombohedral crystals. Becomes magnetic after heating in the candle flame.	SIDERITE $FeCO_3$ Rhombohedral
			Pink, rose-red, brown	3.45 to 3.6	3½–4½	In cleavable masses or in small rhombohedral crystals. Characterized by its color.	RHODOCROSITE $MnCO_3$ Rhombohedral

LUSTER: NONMETALLIC

II. Streak colorless

C. Hardness: > 3, $< 5\frac{1}{2}$. (Cannot be scratched by cent; can be scratched by knife.)

1. Cleavage prominent. (*Continued*)

Cleavage		Color	G.	H.	Remarks	Name, Composition, Crystal System
Two cleavage directions	{110}	Brown, gray, green, yellow	3.4 to 3.55	5–5½	Luster adamantine to resinous. In thin wedge-shaped crystals with sharp edges. Prismatic cleavage seldom seen.	**SPHENE** (Titanite) $CaTiSiO_5$ Monoclinic
Three cleavage directions	Three directions not at right angles. Rhombo-hedral {10$\bar{1}$1}	Brown, green, blue, pink, white	4.35 to 4.40	5	Usually in rounded botryoidal aggregates and in honeycombed masses. Effervesces in cold hydrochloric acid. Cleavage rarely seen.	**SMITHSONITE** $ZnCO_3$ Rhombohedral
		White, yellow, flesh-red	2.05 to 2.15	4–5	Characteristically in small rhombohedral crystals with nearly cubic angles. A zeolite, found lining cavities in igneous rocks.	**CHABAZITE** $(Ca,Na)_2(Al_2Si_4O_{12})\cdot 6H_2O$ Rhombohedral
	{001} {010} {100}	Color-less, white, blue, gray, red	2.89 to 2.98	3–3½	Commonly in massive fine aggregates, not showing cleavage, and can be distinguished only by chemical tests.	**ANHYDRITE** $CaSO_4$ Orthorhombic
	{001} at rt. an-gles to {110}	Color-less, white, blue, yellow, red	4.5	3–3½	Frequently in aggre-gates of platy or tabu-lar crystals. Pearly luster on basal cleav-age. Characterized by high specific gravity for nonmetallic mineral, and thus distinguished from celestite.	**BARITE** $BaSO_4$ Orthorhombic
		Color-less, white, blue, red	3.95 to 3.97	3–3½	Very similar to barite but lower specific gravity. May be necessary to get crimson strontium flame to distinguish it.	**CELESTITE** $SrSO_4$ Orthorhombic
Four cleavage directions	{111} Oct.	Color-less, violet, green, yellow, pink. Usually has a fine color	3.18	4	In cubic crystals often in penetration twins. Characterized by cleav-age.	**FLUORITE** CaF_2 Isometric

Cleavage		Color	G.	H.	Remarks	Name, Composition, Crystal System
Four cleavage directions	{100} {110}	White, pink, gray, green, brown	2.65 to 2.74	5–6	In prismatic crystals, granular or massive. Commonly altered. Prismatic cleavage obscure.	SCAPOLITE Essentially sodium-calcium aluminum silicate Tetragonal
Six cleavage directions	Dodecahedral {110}	Yellow, brown, white	3.9 to 4.1	3½–4	Luster resinous. Small tetrahedral crystals rare. Usually in cleavable masses. If massive, difficult to determine.	SPHALERITE ZnS Isometric
		Blue, white, gray, green	2.15 to 2.3	5½–6	Massive or in imbedded grains; rarely in crystals. A feldspathoid associated with nepheline, never with quartz.	SODALITE $Na_4(AlSiO_4)_3Cl$ Isometric

2. Cleavage not prominent

Color	G.	H.	Remarks	Name, Composition, Crystal System
Colorless, pale green, yellow	2.8 to 3.0	5–5½	Usually in crystals with many brilliant faces. Occurs with zeolites lining cavities in igneous rocks.	DATOLITE $CaB(SiO_4)(OH)$ Monoclinic
White, pale green, blue	3.4 to 3.5	4½–5	Often in radiating crystal groups. Also stalactitic, mammillary. Prismatic cleavage seldom seen.	HEMIMORPHITE $Zn_4(Si_2O_7)(OH)_2 \cdot H_2O$ Orthorhombic
White, pink, gray, green, brown	2.65 to 2.74	5–6	In prismatic crystals, granular or massive. Commonly altered. Prismatic cleavage obscure.	SCAPOLITE Essentially sodium-calcium aluminum silicate Tetragonal
Colorless, white	2.95	3½–4	Effervesces in cold acid. Falls to powder in the candle flame. Frequently in radiating groups of acicular crystals; in pseudohexagonal twins. Cleavage indistinct.	ARAGONITE $CaCO_3$ Orthorhombic
	2.27	5–5½	Usually in trapezohedrons with vitreous luster. A zeolite, found lining cavities in igneous rocks.	ANALCIME $NaAlSi_2O_6 \cdot H_2O$ Isometric

LUSTER: NONMETALLIC
II. Streak colorless
C. Hardness: > 3, $< 5\frac{1}{2}$. (Cannot be scratched by cent; can be scratched by knife.)
2. Cleavage not prominent. *(Continued)*

Color	G.	H.	Remarks	Name, Composition, Crystal System
Colorless, white	3.7	$3\frac{1}{2}$–4	Occurs in prismatic crystals and pseudohexagonal twins. Also fibrous and massive. Effervesces in cold acid.	**STRONTIANITE** $SrCO_3$ Orthorhombic
	3.0 to 3.2	$3\frac{1}{2}$–5	Commonly in dense compact masses showing no cleavage. Effervesces in hot hydrochloric acid.	**MAGNESITE** $MgCO_3$ Rhombohedral
	4.3	$3\frac{1}{2}$	Often in radiating masses; granular; rarely in pseudohexagonal crystals. Effervesces in cold hydrochloric acid.	**WITHERITE** $BaCO_3$ Orthorhombic
	2.7 to 2.8	5	Commonly fibrous in radiating aggregates of sharp acicular crystals. Associated with zeolites in cavities in igneous rocks.	Pectolite $Ca_2NaH(SiO_3)_3$ Triclinic
	2.25	5–$5\frac{1}{2}$	In slender prismatic crystals, prism faces vertically striated. Often in radiating groups. A zeolite, found lining cavities in igneous rocks. Poor prismatic cleavage.	NATROLITE $Na_2(Al_2Si_3O_{10})2H_2O$ Monoclinic
White, grayish red	2.6 to 2.8	4	May be in rhombohedral crystals. Usually massive granular. Definitely determined only by blowpipe tests. Cleavage pinacoidal, usually obscure.	ALUNITE $KAl_3(OH)_6(SO_4)_2$ Rhombohedral
Colorless, white, yellow, red, brown, green, gray, blue	1.9 to 2.2	5–6	Conchoidal fracture. Precious opal shows internal play of colors. Gravity and hardness less than fine-grained quartz.	**OPAL** $SiO_2 \cdot nH_2O$ Amorphous
Brown, green, blue, pink, white	4.35 to 4.40	5	Usually in rounded botryoidal aggregates and in honeycombed masses. Effervesces in cold hydrochloric acid. Cleavage rarely seen.	**SMITHSONITE** $ZnCO_3$ Rhombohedral

Color	G.	H.	Remarks	Name, Composition, Crystal System
Brown, gray, green, yellow	3.4 to 3.55	5–5½	Adamantine to resinous luster. In thin wedge-shaped crystals with sharp edges. Prismatic cleavage seldom seen.	**SPHENE** (Titanite) $CaTiSiO_5$ Monoclinic
Colorless, white, yellow, red, brown	2.72	3	May be fibrous or fine granular, banded. Effervesces in cold hydrochloric acid. Mexican onyx variety of calcite.	**CALCITE** $CaCO_3$ Rhombohedral
Yellowish to reddish brown	5.0 to 5.3	5–5½	In small crystals or as rolled grains. Found in pegmatites.	Monazite $(Ce,La,Th)PO_4$ Monoclinic
Light to dark brown	3.83 to 3.88	3½–4	Usually cleavable but may be in compact concretions in clay or shale — clay ironstone variety. Becomes magnetic on heating.	**SIDERITE** $FeCO_3$ Rhombohedral
Pale green to brown	3.1 to 3.3	3½–4	Subadamantine luster. Usually in pyramidal crystals, also earthy.	Scorodite $FeAsO_4·2H_2O$ Orthorhombic
White, yellow, green, brown	5.9 to 6.1	4½–5	Luster vitreous to adamantine. Massive and in octahedral-like crystals. Frequently associated with quartz. Will fluoresce.	**SCHEELITE** $CaWO_4$ Tetragonal
Yellow, orange, red, gray, green	6.8±	3	Luster adamantine. Usually in square tabular crystals. Also granular massive. Characterized by color and high specific gravity.	**WULFENITE** $PbMoO_4$ Tetragonal
Colorless, yellow, orange, brown	7.0 to 7.2	3½	Resinous luster. In small hexagonal prisms. Faces often curved, giving barrel shapes. In granular masses. Fuses slowly in candle flame.	Mimetite $Pb_5Cl(AsO_4)_3$ Hexagonal
White, yellow, brown, gray	2.6 to 2.9	3–5	The chief constituent of rock phosphate. Difficult to identify without chemical tests. Occurs massive.	**COLLOPHANE** $Ca_3(PO_4)_2·H_2O$ Amorphous
Yellow, brown, gray, white	2.0 to 2.55	1–3	Usually pisolitic; in rounded grains and earthy masses. Often impure.	**BAUXITE** A mixture of aluminum hydroxides

LUSTER: NONMETALLIC
II. Streak colorless
C. Hardness: > 3, < 5½. (Cannot be scratched by cent; can be scratched by knife.)
2. Cleavage not prominent. (*Continued*)

Color	G.	H.	Remarks	Name, Composition, Crystal System
Green, blue, violet, brown, colorless	3.15 to 3.20	5	Usually in hexagonal prisms with pyramid. Also massive. Poor basal cleavage.	APATITE $Ca_5(F,Cl,OH)(PO_4)_3$ Hexagonal
Green, brown, yellow, gray	6.5 to 7.1	3½–4	In small hexagonal crystals, often curved and barrel-shaped. Crystals may be cavernous. Often globular and botryoidal.	Pyromorphite $Pb_5Cl(PO_4)_3$ Hexagonal
Yellow, green, white, brown	2.33	3½–4	Characteristically in radiating hemispherical globular aggregates. Cleavage seldom seen.	Wavellite $Al_3(OH)_3(PO_4)_2 \cdot 5H_2O$ Orthorhombic
Olive- to blackish green, yellow-green, white	2.2	2–5	Massive. Fibrous in the asbestos variety, chrysotile. Frequently mottled green in the massive variety.	SERPENTINE $Mg_6(Si_4O_{10})(OH)_8$ Monoclinic
Yellow-green, white, blue, gray, brown	3.9 to 4.2	5½	Massive and in disseminated grains. Rarely in hexagonal prisms. Associated with red zincite and black franklinite at Franklin, N. J.	WILLEMITE $Zn_2(SiO_4)$ Rhombohedral
White, gray, blue, green	2.15 to 2.3	5½–6	Massive or in imbedded grains; rarely in crystals. A feldspathoid associated with nepheline, never with quartz. Dodecahedral cleavage poor.	SODALITE $Na_4(AlSiO_4)_3Cl$ Isometric
Deep azure-blue, greenish blue	2.4 to 2.45	5–5½	Usually massive. Associated with feldspathoids and pyrite. Poor dodecahedral cleavage.	Lazurite $(Na,Ca)_4(AlSiO_4)_3(SO_4,S,Cl)$ Isometric

D. Hardness: > 5½, < 7. (Cannot be scratched by knife; can be scratched by quartz.)

1. Cleavage prominent

Cleavage		Color	G.	H.	Remarks	Name, Composition, Crystal System
One cleavage direction	{010}	White, gray, pale lavender, yellowish, greenish	3.35 to 3.45	6½–7	In thin tabular crystals. Luster pearly on cleavage face. Associated with emery, margarite, chlorite.	Diaspore HAlO₂ Orthorhombic
	{010} perfect	Hairbrown, grayish green	3.23	6–7	Commonly in long, slender, prismatic crystals. May be in parallel groups — columnar or fibrous. Found in schistose rocks.	SILLIMANITE Al₂SiO₅ Orthorhombic
	{001}	Yellowish to blackish green	3.35 to 3.45	6–7	In prismatic crystals striated parallel to length. Found in metamorphic rocks and crystalline limestones.	EPIDOTE Monoclinic
	{100}	Blue, usually darker at center of crystal. May be gray or green	3.56 to 3.66	5–7	In bladed aggregates with cleavage parallel to length. Can be scratched by knife parallel to length of crystal but not in a direction at right angles to this.	KYANITE Al₂SiO₅ Triclinic
Two cleavage directions	{001} good {100} poor	White, pale green, or blue	3.0 to 3.1	6	Usually cleavable, resembling feldspar. Found in pegmatites associated with other lithium minerals.	AMBLYGONITE LiAlFPO₄ Triclinic
	{001} good {100}	Colorless, white, gray	2.8 to 2.9	5–5½	Usually cleavable massive to fibrous. Also compact. Associated with crystalline limestone.	WOLLASTONITE CaSiO₃ Triclinic
	{001} {100}	Grayish white, green, pink	3.25 to 3.37	6–6½	In prismatic crystals deeply striated. Also massive, columnar, compact. Luster pearly on cleavage, elsewhere vitreous.	Clinozoisite Ca₂Al₃O(SiO₄)(Si₂O₇)(OH) Monoclinic
	{110}	Colorless, white	2.25	5–5½	In slender prismatic crystals, prism faces vertically striat d Often in r diat ng groups. A zeolite found lining cavities in igneous rocks.	NATROLITE Na₂(Al₂Si₃O₁₀)·2H₂O Monoclinic

LUSTER: NONMETALLIC
II. Streak colorless
D. Hardness: $> 5\frac{1}{2}$, < 7. (Cannot be scratched by knife; can be scratched by quartz.)
1. Cleavage prominent. (Continued)

Cleavage		Color	G.	H.	Remarks	Name, Composition, Crystal System
Two cleavage directions at or nearly 90° angles	{001} {010}	Colorless, white, gray, cream, red, green	2.54 to 2.56	6	In cleavable masses or in irregular grains as rock constituents. May be in crystals in pegmatite. Distinguished with certainty only with the microscope. Green amazonstone is microcline.	ORTHOCLASE (Monoclinic) MICROCLINE (Triclinic) $K(AlSi_3O_8)$
	{001} {010}	Colorless, white, gray, bluish. Often shows a beautiful play of colors	2.62 (albite) to 2.76 (anorthite)	6	In cleavable masses or in irregular grains as a rock constituent. On the better cleavage can be seen a series of fine parallel striations due to albite twinning; these distinguish it from orthoclase.	PLAGIOCLASE Various combinations of albite, $Na(AlSi_3O_8)$ and anorthite, $Ca(Al_2Si_2O_8)$ Triclinic
	{110}	White, gray, pink, green	3.15 to 3.20	$6\frac{1}{2}$–7	In flattened prismatic crystals, vertically striated. Also massive cleavable. Pink variety, kunzite; green, hiddenite. Found in pegmatites. Frequently shows good {100} parting.	SPODUMENE $LiAl(Si_2O_6)$ Monoclinic
	{110}	White, green, black	3.1 to 3.5	5–6	In stout prisms with rectangular cross section. Often in granular crystalline masses. Diopside (colorless, white, green), aegirite (brown, green), augite (dark green to black) are rock-forming minerals. Characterized by rectangular cross section and cleavage.	PYROXENE GROUP Essentially calcium magnesium silicates Monoclinic
	{110}	Gray-brown, green, bronze-brown, black	3.2 to 3.5	$5\frac{1}{2}$	Crystals usually prismatic but rare. Commonly massive, fibrous, lamellar. Fe may replace Mg and mineral is darker.	ENSTATITE $Mg_2(Si_2O_6)$ Orthorhombic

Cleavage			Color	G.	H.	Remarks	Name, Composition, Crystal System
Two cleavage directions	at 55° and 125° angles	at or nearly 90° angles	{110}	Rose-red, pink, brown	3.58 to 3.70	5½–6	Color diagnostic. Usually massive; cleavable to compact; in imbedded grains; in large rough crystals with rounded edges.	RHODONITE Mn(SiO₃) Triclinic
			{110}	White, green, black	3.0 to 3.3	5–6	Crystals usually slender fibrous asbestiform. Tremolite (white, gray, violet) and actinolite (green) are common in metamorphic rocks. Hornblende and arfvedsonite (dark green to black) are common in igneous rocks. The group is characterized by its broad cleavage angle.	AMPHIBOLE GROUP Essentially calcium magnesium silicates Monoclinic
			{110}	Gray, clove-brown, green	2.85 to 3.2	5½–6	An amphibole. Distinct crystals rare. Commonly in aggregates and fibrous massive.	Anthophyllite (Mg,Fe)₇(Si₈O₂₂)-(OH)₂ Orthorhombic
			{110}	Brown, gray, green, yellow	3.4 to 3.55	5–5½	Luster adamantine to resinous. In thin wedge-shaped crystals with sharp edges. Prismatic cleavage seldom seen.	SPHENE (Titanite) CaTiO(SO₄) Monoclinic
	Six cleavage directions, dodecahedral		{110}	Blue, gray, white, green	2.15 to 2.3	5½–6	Massive or in imbedded grains; rarely in crystals. A feldspathoid associated with nepheline, never with quartz.	SODALITE Na₄Al₃Si₃O₁₂Cl Isometric

2. Cleavage not prominent

Color	G.	H.	Remarks	Name, Composition, Crystal System
Colorless	2.26	7	Occurs as small crystals in cavities in volcanic rocks. Difficult to determine without optical aid.	Tridymite SiO₂ Pseudohexagonal
	2.27	5–5½	Usually in trapezohedrons with vitreous luster. A zeolite, found lining cavities in igneous rocks.	ANALCIME Na(AlSi₂O₆)H₂O Isometric
Colorless or white	2.32	7	Occurs in spherical aggregations in volcanic rocks. Difficult to determine without optical aid.	Cristobalite SiO₂ Pseudoisometric

LUSTER: NONMETALLIC
II. Streak colorless
D. Hardness: $> 5\frac{1}{2}$, < 7. (Cannot be scratched by knife; can be scratched by quartz.)
2. Cleavage not prominent. *(Continued)*

Color	G.	H.	Remarks	Name, Composition, Crystal System
Colorless, yellow, red, brown, green, gray, blue	1.9 to 2.2	5–6	Conchoidal fracture. Precious opal shows internal play of colors. Gravity and hardness less than fine-grained quartz.	OPAL $SiO_2 \cdot nH_2O$ Amorphous
Gray, white, colorless	2.45 to 2.50	$5\frac{1}{2}$–6	In trapezohedral crystals embedded in dark igneous rock. Does not line cavities as analcime does.	LEUCITE $K(AlSi_2O_6)$ Pseudoisometric
Colorless, pale green, yellow	2.8 to 3.0	5–$5\frac{1}{2}$	Usually in crystals with many brilliant faces. Occurs with zeolites lining cavities in igneous rocks.	DATOLITE $CaB(SiO_4)(OH)$ Monoclinic
Colorless, white, pale yellow	2.97 to 3.02	7	In prismatic crystals resembling topaz but distinguished by lack of cleavage. Also in irregular masses and indistinct crystals. A rare mineral.	Danburite $CaB_2Si_2O_8$ Orthorhombic
White, gray, light to dark green, brown	2.65 to 2.74	5–6	In prismatic crystals, granular or massive. Commonly altered. Prismatic cleavage obscure.	SCAPOLITE Essentially sodium-calcium aluminum Silicate Tetragonal
Colorless, white, smoky, amethyst. Variously colored when impure	2.65	7	Crystals usually show horizontally striated prism with pyramid.	QUARTZ SiO_2 Rhombohedral
Colorless, gray, greenish, reddish	2.55 to 2.65	$5\frac{1}{2}$–6	Greasy luster. A rock constituent, usually massive; rarely in hexagonal prisms. Poor prismatic cleavage. A feldspathoid.	NEPHELINE $(Na,K)AlSiO_4$ Hexagonal
White, gray, yellow, green	2.9 to 3.0	7	Commonly in small isolated cubic crystals, less often in groups.	Boracite $Mg_3B_7O_{13}Cl$ Pseudoisometric

Color	G.	H.	Remarks	Name, Composition, Crystal System
Light yellow, brown, orange	3.1 to 3.2	6–6½	Occurs in disseminated crystals and grains. Commonly in crystalline limestones.	Chondrodite $Mg_5(SiO_4)_2(F,OH)_2$ Monoclinic
Light brown, yellow, red, green	2.65	7	Luster waxy to dull. Commonly colloform. May be banded or lining cavities.	**CHALCEDONY** SiO_2 Cryptocrystalline quartz
Blue, bluish green, green	2.6 to 2.8	6	Usually appears amorphous in reniform and stalactitic masses.	TURQUOISE $CuAl_6(PO_4)_4(OH)_8 \cdot 4H_2O$ Triclinic
Apple-green, gray, white	2.8 to 2.95	6–6½	Reniform and stalactitic with crystalline surface. In subparallel groups of tabular crystals.	**PREHNITE** $Ca_2Al_2Si_3O_{10}(OH)_2$ Orthorhombic
Yellow-green, white, blue, gray, brown	3.9 to 4.2	5½	Massive and in disseminated grains. Rarely in hexagonal prisms. Associated with red zincite and black franklinite at Franklin, N. J.	WILLEMITE Zn_2SiO_4 Rhombohedral
Blue, violet, pink	3.26 to 3.36	7	Occurs in aggregates of fibrous and felted masses. Imperfect cleavage parallel to length of fibers. Resembles tourmaline. Poor {100} cleavage.	Dumortierite $Al_8BSi_3O_{19}(OH)$ Orthorhombic
Olive to grayish green, brown	3.27 to 3.37	6½–7	Usually in disseminated grains in basic igneous rocks. May be massive granular.	**OLIVINE** $(Mg,Fe)_2(SiO_4)$ Orthorhombic
Black, green, brown, blue, red, pink, white	3.0 to 3.25	7–7½	In slender prismatic crystals with triangular cross section. Crystals may be in radiating groups. Found usually in pegmatites. Black most common, other colors associated with lithium minerals.	**TOURMALINE** Rhombohedral
Green, brown, yellow, blue, red	3.35 to 4.45	6½	In square prismatic crystals vertically striated. Often columnar and granular massive. Found in crystalline limestones.	IDOCRASE (Vesuvianite) Tetragonal

LUSTER: NONMETALLIC
II. Streak colorless
D. Hardness: $> 5\frac{1}{2}$, < 7. (Cannot be scratched by knife; can be scratched by quartz.)
2. Cleavage not prominent. (*Continued*)

Color	G.	H.	Remarks	Name, Composition, Crystal System
Clove-brown, gray, green, yellow	3.27 to 3.35	$6\frac{1}{2}$–7	In wedge-shaped crystals with sharp edges. Also lamellar.	AXINITE $Ca_2(FeMn)Al_2(BO_3)$-$(Si_4O_{12})(OH)$ Triclinic
Red-brown to brownish black	3.65 to 3.75	7–$7\frac{1}{2}$	In prismatic crystals; commonly in cruciform penetration twins. Frequently altered on the surface and then soft. Found in schists.	STAUROLITE $Fe_2Al_4(SiO_4)_2(OH)_2$ Orthorhombic
Reddish brown, flesh-red, olive-green	3.16 to 3.20	$7\frac{1}{2}$	Prismatic crystals with nearly square cross section. Cross section may show black cross (chiastolite). May be altered to mica and then soft. Found in schists.	ANDALUSITE Al_2SiO_5 Orthorhombic
Brown, gray, green, yellow	3.4 to 3.55	5–$5\frac{1}{2}$	Luster adamantine to resinous. In thin wedge-shaped crystals with sharp edges. Prismatic cleavage seldom seen.	SPHENE (Titanite) $CaTiO(SiO_4)$ Monoclinic
Yellowish to reddish brown	5.0 to 5.3	5–$5\frac{1}{2}$	In isolated crystals, granular. Commonly found in pegmatites.	Monazite $(Ce,La,Di)PO_4$ Monoclinic
Brown to black	6.8 to 7.1	6–7	Rarely in prismatic crystals, twinned. Fibrous, giving reniform surface. Rolled grains. Usually gives light brown streak.	CASSITERITE SnO_2 Tetragonal
Reddish brown to black	4.18 to 4.25	6–$6\frac{1}{2}$	In prismatic crystals vertically striated; often slender acicular. Crystals frequently twinned. A constituent of black sands.	RUTILE TiO_2 Tetragonal
Brown to pitch-black	3.5 to 4.2	$5\frac{1}{2}$–6	Crystals often tabular. Massive and in imbedded grains. An accessory mineral in igneous rocks.	Allanite Monoclinic

Color	G.	H.	Remarks	Name, Composition, Crystal System
Blue, rarely colorless	2.60 to 2.66	$7-7\frac{1}{2}$	In imbedded grains and massive, resembling quartz. Commonly altered and foliated; then softer than a knife.	Cordierite $Mg_2Al_3(AlSi_5O_{18})$ Orthorhombic (Pseudohexagonal)
Deep azure-blue, greenish blue	2.4 to 2.45	$5-5\frac{1}{2}$	Usually massive. Associated with feldspathoids and pyrite. Poor dodecahedral cleavage.	LAZURITE $(Na,Ca)_4(AlSiO_4)_3$-(SO_4,S,Cl) Isometric
Azure-blue	3.0 to 3.1	$5-5\frac{1}{2}$	Usually in pyramidal crystals, which distinguishes it from massive lazurite. A rare mineral.	LAZULITE $MgAl_2(OH)_2(PO_4)_2$ Monoclinic
Blue, green, white, gray	2.15 to 2.3	$5\frac{1}{2}-6$	Massive or in imbedded grains; rarely in crystals. A feldspathoid associated with nepheline, never with quartz. Poor dodecahedral cleavage.	SODALITE $Na_4(AlSiO_4)_3Cl$ Isometric

E. Hardness: > 7. (Cannot be scratched by quartz.)

1. Cleavage prominent

Cleavage		Color	G.	H.	Remarks	Name, Composition, Crystal System
One cleavage direction	{001}	Colorless, yellow, pink, bluish, greenish	3.4 to 3.6	8	Usually in crystals, also coarse to fine granular. Found in pegmatites.	TOPAZ $Al_2(SiO_4)(F,OH)_2$ Orthorhombic
	{010}	Brown, gray, greenish gray	3.23	6-7	Commonly in long slender prismatic crystals. May be in parallel groups, columnar or fibrous. Found in schistose rocks.	SILLIMANITE Al_2SiO_5 Orthorhombic
Two cleavage directions	{110}	White, gray, pink, green	3.15 to 3.20	$6\frac{1}{2}-7$	In flattened prismatic crystals, vertically striated. Also massive cleavable. Pink variety, kunzite; green, hiddenite. Found in pegmatites. Frequently shows good {100} parting.	SPODUMENE $LiAl(Si_2O_6)$ Monoclinic
Three cleavage directions	{010} {110}	Colorless, pale blue, gray	3.09	8	Commonly in tabular or prismatic crystals in schists.	Lawsonite $CaAl_2(Si_2O_7)(OH)_2\cdot H_2O$ Orthorhombic

LUSTER: NONMETALLIC
II. Streak colorless
E. Hardness: > 7.   (Cannot be scratched by quartz.)
1. Cleavage prominent. *(Continued)*

Cleavage	Color	G.	H.	Remarks	Name, Composition, Crystal System
Four cleavage directions {111}	Colorless, yellow, red, blue, black	3.5	10	Adamantine luster. In octahedral crystals, frequently twinned. Faces may be curved.	Diamond C Isometric
No cleavage. Rhombohedral and basal parting.	Colorless, gray, blue, red, yellow, brown, green	3.95 to 4.1	9	Luster adamantine to vitreous. Parting fragments may appear nearly cubic. In rude barrel-shaped crystals.	**CORUNDUM** Al_2O_3 Rhombohedral

2. Cleavage not prominent

Color	G.	H.	Remarks	Name, Composition, Crystal System
Colorless, white, smoky, amethyst. Variously colored when impure	2.65	7	Crystals usually show horizontally striated prism with pyramid.	**QUARTZ** SiO_2 Rhombohedral
Colorless, white, pale yellow	2.97 to 3.02	7	In prismatic crystals resembling topaz but distinguished by lack of cleavage. Also in irregular masses and indistinct crystals. A rare mineral.	Danburite $Ca(B_2Si_2O_8)$ Orthorhombic
White, colorless	2.97 to 3.0	$7\frac{1}{2}$-8	In small rhombohedral crystals. A rare mineral.	Phenacite $Be_2(SiO_4)$ Rhombohedral
White and almost any color	3.95 to 4.1	9	Luster adamantine to vitreous. Parting fragments may appear nearly cubic. In rude barrel-shaped crystals.	**CORUNDUM** Al_2O_3 Rhombohedral

Color	G.	H.	Remarks	Name, Composition, Crystal System
Red, black, lavender, blue, green, brown	3.6 to 4.0	8	In octahedrons; twinning common. Associated with crystalline limestones.	**SPINEL** $MgAl_2O_4$ Isometric
Bluish green, green, yellow, pink, colorless	2.75 to 2.8	$7\frac{1}{2}$–8	Commonly in hexagonal prisms terminated by the base; pyramid faces are rare. Crystals large in places. Poor basal cleavage.	**BERYL** $Be_3Al_2(Si_6O_{18})$ Hexagonal
Yellowish to emerald-green	3.65 to 3.8	$8\frac{1}{2}$	In tabular crystals frequently in pseudohexagonal twins. Found in pegmatites.	CHRYSOBERYL $BeAl_2O_4$ Orthorhombic
Green, brown, blue, red, pink, white, black	3.0 to 3.25	7–$7\frac{1}{2}$	In slender prismatic crystals with triangular cross section. Crystals may be in radiating groups. Found usually in pegmatites. Black most common, other colors associated with lithium minerals.	**TOURMALINE** Rhombohedral
Green, gray, white	3.3 to 3.5	$6\frac{1}{2}$–7	Massive, closely compact. Poor prismatic cleavage at nearly 90° angles. A pyroxene.	Jadeite $NaAl(Si_2O_6)$ Monoclinic
Olive to grayish green, brown	3.27 to 3.37	$6\frac{1}{2}$–7	Usually in disseminated grains in basic igneous rocks. May be massive granular.	**OLIVINE** $(Mg,Fe)_2(SiO_4)$ Orthorhombic
Green, brown, yellow, blue, red	3.35 to 3.45	$6\frac{1}{2}$	In square prismatic crystals vertically striated. Often columnar and granular massive. Found in crystalline limestones.	IDOCRASE (Vesuvianite) Tetragonal
Dark green	4.55	$7\frac{1}{2}$–8	Usually in octahedrons characteristically striated. A zinc spinel.	Gahnite $ZnAl_2O_4$ Isometric
Reddish brown to black	6.8 to 7.1	6–7	Rarely in prismatic crystals twinned. Fibrous, giving reniform surface. Rolled grains. Usually gives light brown streak.	**CASSITERITE** SnO_2 Tetragonal

LUSTER: NONMETALLIC
II. Streak colorless
E. Hardness: > 7. (Cannot be scratched by quartz.)
2. Cleavage not prominent. *(Continued)*

Color	G.	H.	Remarks	Name, Composition, Crystal System
Reddish brown, flesh-red, olive-green	3.16 to 3.20	$7\frac{1}{2}$	Prismatic crystals with nearly square cross section. Cross section may show black cross (chiastolite). May be altered to mica and then soft. Found in schists.	ANDALUSITE Al_2SiO_5 Orthorhombic
Clove-brown, green, yellow, gray	3.27 to 3.35	$6\frac{1}{2}$–7	In wedge-shaped crystals with sharp edges. Also lamellar.	AXINITE $Ca_2(Fe,Mn)Al_2(BO_3)\text{-}(Si_4O_{12})(OH)$ Triclinic
Red-brown to brownish black	3.65 to 3.75	7–$7\frac{1}{2}$	In prismatic crystals; commonly in cruciform penetration twins. Frequently altered on the surface and then soft. Found in schists.	STAUROLITE $Fe_2Al_9O_7(SiO_4)_4(OH)$ Orthorhombic
Brown, red, gray, green, colorless	4.68	$7\frac{1}{2}$	Usually in small prisms truncated by the pyramid. An accessory mineral in igneous rocks. Found as rolled grains in sand.	ZIRCON $ZrSiO_4$ Tetragonal
Usually brown to red. Also yellow, green, pink	3.5 to 4.3	$6\frac{1}{2}$–$7\frac{1}{2}$	Usually in dodecahedrons or trapezohedrons or in combinations of the two. An accessory mineral in igneous rocks and pegmatites. Commonly in metamorphic rocks. As sand.	GARNET $A_3B_2(SiO_4)_3$ Isometric

MINERALS ARRANGED ACCORDING TO
INCREASING SPECIFIC GRAVITY

G.	Name	G.	Name	G.	Name
0.917	Ice	2.6–2.79		3.0–3.1	Lazulite
1.6	Carnallite			3.0–3.2	Magnesite
1.7	Borax	2.55–2.65	Nepheline	3.0–3.1	Margarite
1.75	Epsomite	2.6–2.63	Kaolinite	3.0–3.25	Tourmaline
1.95	Kernite	2.62	Albite	3.0–3.3	Tremolite
1.96	Ulexite	2.60–2.66	Cordierite	3.09	Lawsonite
1.99	Sylvite	2.58–2.68	Vivianite	3.1–3.2	Autunite
		2.65	Oligoclase	3.1–3.2	Chondrodite
2.0–2.19		2.65	Quartz	3.15–3.20	Apatite
		2.69	Andesine	3.15–3.20	Spodumene
2.0–2.55	Bauxite	2.6–2.8	Alunite	3.16–3.20	Andalusite
2.0–2.4	Chrysocolla	2.6–2.8	Turquois	3.18	Fluorite
2.0	Sepiolite	2.71	Labradorite		
2.05–2.09	Sulfur	2.65–2.74	Scapolite	3.2–3.39	
2.05–2.15	Chabazite	2.72	Calcite		
1.9–2.2	Opal	2.6–2.9	Chlorite	3.1–3.3	Scorodite
2.09–2.14	Niter			3.2	Hornblende
2.1–2.2	Stilbite	2.62–2.76	Plagioclase	3.23	Sillimanite
2.16	Halite	2.6–2.9	Collophane	3.2–3.3	Diopside
2.12–2.30	Chalcanthite	2.74	Bytownite	3.2–3.4	Augite
2.18–2.20	Heulandite	2.7–2.8	Pectolite	3.25–3.37	Clinozoisite
		2.7–2.8	Talc	3.26–3.36	Dumortierite
2.2–2.39		2.70–2.85	Glauberite	3.27–3.35	Axinite
		2.76	Anorthite	3.27–4.37	Olivine
2.12–2.30	Chalcanthite	2.75–2.8	Beryl	3.2–3.5	Enstatite
2.0–2.4	Chrysocolla	2.78	Polyhalite		
2.2–2.65	Serpentine			3.4–3.59	
2.25	Natrolite	2.8–2.99			
2.26	Tridymite			3.27–4.27	Olivine
2.27	Analcime	2.6–2.9	Collophane	3.3–3.5	Jadeite
2.29	Soda niter	2.8–2.9	Pyrophyllite	3.35–3.45	Diaspore
2.30	Cristobalite	2.8–2.9	Wollastonite	3.35–3.45	Epidote
2.30	Sodalite	2.85	Dolomite	3.35–3.45	Idocrase
2.3	Graphite	2.86	Phlogopite	3.4–3.5	Hemimorphite
2.32	Gypsum	2.76–3.1	Muscovite	3.45	Arfvedsonite
2.33	Wavellite	2.8–2.95	Prehnite	3.40–3.55	Aegirite
2.3–2.4	Apophyllite	2.8–3.0	Datolite	3.4–3.55	Sphene
2.39	Brucite	2.8–3.0	Lepidolite	3.48	Realgar
		2.89–2.98	Anhydrite	3.42–3.56	Triphylite
		2.9–3.0	Boracite	3.49	Orpiment
2.4–2.59		2.95	Aragonite	3.4–3.6	Topaz
		2.95	Erythrite	3.5	Diamond
2.0–2.55	Bauxite	2.8–3.2	Biotite	3.45–3.60	Rhodochrosite
2.2–2.65	Serpentine	2.95–3.0	Cryolite	3.5–4.3	Garnet
2.42	Colemanite	2.97–3.00	Phenacite		
2.42	Petalite			3.6–3.79	
2.4–2.45	Lazurite	3.0–3.19			
2.45–2.50	Leucite			3.27–4.37	Olivine
2.2–2.8	Garnierite	2.97–3.02	Danburite	3.5–4.2	Allanite
2.54–2.57	Microcline	2.85–3.2	Anthophyllite	3.5–4.3	Garnet
2.57	Orthoclase	3.0–3.1	Amblygonite	3.6–4.0	Spinel

G.	Name	G.	Name	G.	Name
3.56–3.66	Kyanite	4.6	Chromite	5.85	Pyrargyrite
3.58–3.70	Rhodonite	4.58–4.65	Pyrrhotite		
3.65–3.75	Staurolite	4.7	Ilmenite	6.0–6.49	
3.7	Strontianite	4.75	Pyrolusite		
3.65–3.8	Chrysoberyl	4.6–4.76	Covellite	5.9–6.1	Crocoite
3.75–3.77	Atacamite	4.62–4.73	Molybdenite	5.9–6.1	Scheelite
3.77	Azurite	4.68	Zircon	6.0	Cuprite
				6.07	Arsenopyrite
3.8–3.99		4.8–4.99		6.0–6.2	Polybasite
				6.2–6.3	Stephanite
3.7–4.7	Psilomelane	4.6–5.0	Pentlandite	6.2–6.4	Anglesite
3.6–4.0	Spinel	4.6–5.1	Tetrahedrite-Tennantite	5.3–7.3	Columbite
3.6–4.0	Limonite			6.33	Cobaltite
3.83–3.88	Siderite	4.89	Marcasite		
3.5–4.2	Allanite	4.9	Greenockite		
3.5–4.3	Garnet			6.5–6.99	
3.9	Antlerite	5.0–5.19			
3.9–4.03	Malachite			6.5	Skutterudite
3.95–3.97	Celestite	5.02	Pyrite	6.55	Cerussite
		4.8–5.3	Hematite	6.78	Bismuthinite
4.0–4.19		5.06–5.08	Bornite	6.5–7.1	Pyromorphite
		5.15	Franklinite	6.8	Wulfenite
3.9–4.1	Sphalerite	5.0–5.3	Monazite	6.7–7.1	Vanadinite
4.02	Corundum	5.18	Magnetite	6.8–7.1	Cassiterite
3.9–4.2	Willemite				
		5.2–5.39		7.0–7.49	
4.2–4.39				7.0–7.2	Mimetite
				7.0–7.5	Wolframite
4.1–4.3	Chalcopyrite	5.4–5.59		7.3	Argentite
3.7–4.7	Psilomelane				
4.18–4.25	Rutile	5.5	Millerite	7.5–7.99	
4.3	Manganite	5.5±	Cerargyrite		
4.3	Witherite	5.55	Proustite	7.4–7.6	Galena
4.37	Goethite			7.3–7.9	Iron
4.35–4.40	Smithsonite	5.6–5.79		7.78	Niccolite
4.4–4.59		5.5–5.8	Chalcocite	>8.0	
4.4	Stannite	5.68	Zincite		
4.43–4.45	Enargite	5.7	Arsenic	8.0–8.2	Sylvanite
4.5	Barite	5.5–6.0	Jamesonite	8.10	Cinnabar
4.55	Gahnite	5.3–7.3	Columbite	8.9	Copper
4.52–4.62	Stibnite			9.0–9.7	Uraninite
				9.35	Calaverite
		5.8–5.99		9.8	Bismuth
4.6–4.79				10.5	Silver
				15.0–19.3	Gold
3.7–4.7	Psilomelane	5.8–5.9	Bournonite	14–19	Platinum

SUBJECT INDEX

MINERAL INDEX

Name, p.	Composition	Xl. Sys.	G.	H.	Remarks
Acadialite, 509					See chabazite
Acanthite, 247	Ag_2S	Mon	7.2–7.3	$2–2\frac{1}{2}$	Low temp. Ag_2S
Achroite, 427					Colorless tourmaline
Acmite, 439	$NaFe'''(Si_2O_6)$	Mon	3.5	$6–6\frac{1}{2}$	A pyroxene
Actinolite, 445	$Ca_2(Mg,Fe)_5(Si_8O_{22})$- $(OH)_2$	Mon	3.0–3.2	5–6	An amphibole
Adularia, 491					See orthoclase
Aegirite, 439	$NaFe'''(Si_2O_6)$	Mon	3.40–3.55	$6–6\frac{1}{2}$	A pyroxene
Aenigmatite, 413	$(Na,Ca)_4(Fe'',Fe''',$ $Mn,Ti,Al)_{13}(Si_2O_7)_6$	Tric	3.75	$5\frac{1}{2}$	Cl$\{110\}$
Agate, 482					See quartz
Alabandite, 252	MnS	Iso	4.0	$3\frac{1}{2}–4$	Black
Alabaster, 366					See gypsum
Albite, 495	$Na(AlSi_3O_8)$—$Ab_{90}An_{10}$	Tric	2.62	6	A feldspar
Alexandrite, 311					Gem chrysoberyl
Allanite, 419	$X_2Y_3O(SiO_4)(Si_2O_7)$- (OH)	Mon	3.5–4.2	$5\frac{1}{2}–6$	Brown-black
Allemontite, 235	$AsSb$	Hex	5.8–6.2	3–4	One cleavage
Almandite, 403	$Fe_3Al_2(SiO_4)_3$	Iso	4.25	7	A garnet
Altaite, 252, 274	$PbTe$	Iso	8.16	3	Tin-white
Alumstone, 369					See alunite
Alunite, 369	$KAl_3(OH)_6(SO_4)_2$	Rho	2.6–2.8	4	Usually massive
Amalgam, 229					See silver
Amazonstone, 494					Green microcline
Amblygonite, 378	$LiAlFPO_4$	Tric	3.0–3.1	6	Fusible at 2
Amethyst, 481					Purple quartz
Amphibole, 443					A mineral group
Analcime, 507	$Na(AlSi_2O_6)H_2O$	Iso	2.27	$5–5\frac{1}{2}$	A feldspathoid
Anatase, 297	TiO_2	Tet	3.9	$5\frac{1}{2}–6$	Adamantine luster
Anauxite, 462		Mon	2.6	2	Si-rich kaolinite
Andalusite, 406	Al_2SiO_5	Orth	3.16–3.20	$7\frac{1}{2}$	Infusible
Andesine, 499	$Ab_{70}An_{30}$—$Ab_{50}An_{50}$	Tric	2.69	6	Plagioclase feldspar
Andradite, 403	$Ca_3Fe_2(SiO_4)_3$	Iso	3.75	7	A garnet
Anglesite, 362	$PbSO_4$	Orth	6.2–6.4	3	Cl $\{001\}$ $\{110\}$
Anhydrite, 363	$CaSO_4$	Orth	2.89–2.98	$3–3\frac{1}{2}$	Cl$\{100\}$ $\{010\}$ $\{001\}$
Ankerite, 339	$CaCO_3 \cdot (Mg,Fe,Mn) CO_3$	Rho	2.95–3	$3\frac{1}{2}$	Cl $\{10\bar{1}1\}$
Annabergite, 383	$Ni_3(AsO_4)_2 \cdot 8H_2O$	Mon	3.0	$2\frac{1}{2}–3$	Nickel bloom. Green
Anorthite, 495	$Ab_{10}An_{90}$—$CaAl_2Si_2O_8$	Tric	2.76	6	Plagioclase feldspar
Anorthoclase, 494	$K(AlSi_3O_8)$—Na- $(AlSi_3O_8)$	Tric	2.58	6	A feldspar
Anthophyllite, 443	$(Mg,Fe)_7(Si_8O_{22})(OH)_2$	Orth	2.85–3.2	$5\frac{1}{2}–6$	An amphibole
Antigorite, 463					See serpentine
Antimony, 234	Sb	Rho	6.7	3	Cl $\{0001\}$
Antlerite, 364	$Cu_3(OH)_4SO_4$	Orth	$3.9\pm$	$3\frac{1}{2}–4$	Green
Apatite, 373	$Ca_5(F,Cl,OH)(PO_4)_3$	Hex	3.15–3.20	5	Cl $\{0001\}$ poor
Apophyllite, 460	$Ca_4K(Si_4O_{10})_2F \cdot 8H_2O$	Tet	2.3–2.4	$4\frac{1}{2}–5$	Cl $\{001\}$
Aquamarine, 425					See beryl
Aragonite, 344	$CaCO_3$	Orth	2.95	$3\frac{1}{2}–4$	Cl $\{010\}$ $\{110\}$
Arfvedsonite, 446	$Na_3Mg_4Al(Si_8O_{22})$- $(OH,F)_2$	Mon	3.45	6	An amphibole

MINERAL INDEX

MINERAL INDEX

Name, p.	Composition	XI. Sys.	G.	H.	Remarks
Brittle mica, 472	....	......	......	.....	See margarite
Brochantite, 365	$Cu_4(OH)_6SO_4$	Mon	3.9	$3\frac{1}{2}$–4	Cl {010}. Green
Bromyrite, 325	AgBr	Iso	5.9	1–$1\frac{1}{2}$	Sectile
Bronzite, 436	$(Mg,Fe)_2(Si_2O_6)$	Orth	$3.3\pm$	$5\frac{1}{2}$	See enstatite
Brookite, 297	TiO_2	Orth	3.9–4.1	$5\frac{1}{2}$–6	Adamantine luster
Brucite, 314	$Mg(OH)_2$	Rho	2.39	$2\frac{1}{2}$	Cl {0001}
Bytownite, 499	$Ab_{30}An_{70}$—$Ab_{10}An_{90}$	Tric	2.74	6	Plag. feldspar
Cairngorm stone, 481	....	......	....	....	See quartz
Calamine, 415	....	......	....	....	See hemimorphite
Calaverite, 274	$AuTe_2$	Mon	9.35	$2\frac{1}{2}$	Fusible at 1
Calcite, 334	$CaCO_3$	Rho	2.72	3	Cl {10$\bar{1}$1}
Californite, 420	....	......	....	....	See idocrase
Cancrinite, 502	$(Na,K)_{6-8}Al_6Si_6O_{24}\cdot$ $(CO_3)_{1-2}\cdot2$–$3H_2O$	Hex	2.45	5–6	A feldspathoid
Capillary pyrites, 259	....	......	....	....	See millerite
Carnallite, 328	$KMgCl_3\cdot6H_2O$	Orth	1.6	1	Deliquescent
Carnelian, 482	....	......	....	....	Red chalcedony
Carnotite, 383	$K_2(UO_2)_2(VO_4)_2\cdot nH_2O$	Orth	4.1	Soft	Yellow
Cassiterite, 299	SnO_2	Tet	6.8–7.1	6–7	Luster adamantine
Cat's-eye, 481	....	......	....	....	See chrysoberyl and quartz
Celestite, 361	$SrSO_4$	Orth	3.95–3.97	3–$3\frac{1}{2}$	Cl {001} {110}
Celsian, 491	$BaAl_2Si_2O_8$	Mon	3.37	6	A feldspar
Cerargyrite, 324	AgCl	Iso	$5.5\pm$	2–3	Perfectly sectile
Cerussite, 347	$PbCO_3$	Orth	6.55	3–$3\frac{1}{2}$	Effer. in HNO_3
Chabazite, 509	$(Ca,Na)_2(Al_2Si_4O_{12})\cdot$ $6H_2O$	Rho	2.05–2.15	4–5	Cubelike crystals
Chalcanthite, 369	$CuSO_4\cdot5H_2O$	Tric	2.12–2.30	$2\frac{1}{2}$	Soluble in water
Chalcedony, 482	....	......	....	....	Cryptocryst. quartz
Chalcocite, 248	Cu_2S	Orth	5.5–5.8	$2\frac{1}{2}$–3	Imperfectly sectile
Chalcopyrite, 255	$CuFeS_2$	Tet	4.1–4.3	$3\frac{1}{2}$–4	Brittle. Yellow
Chalcotrichite, 288	....	......	....	....	Fibrous cuprite
Chalk, 337	....	......	....	....	See calcite
Chalybite, 341	....	......	....	....	See siderite
Chert, 483	SiO_2	.....	2.65	7	Cryptocryst. quartz
Chessylite, 349	....	......	....	....	See azurite
Chiastolite, 406	....	......	....	....	See andalusite
Chloanthite, 275	....	......	....	....	Nickel skutterudite
Chlorite, 473	$Mg_3(Si_4O_{10})(OH)_2\cdot$ $Mg_3(OH)_6$	Mon	2.6–2.9	2–$2\frac{1}{2}$	Cl {001}
Chloritoid, 472	$(Fe,Mg)_2(Al_4Si_2O_{10})$– $(OH)_4$	Mon	3.5	6–7	Brittle mica
Chondrodite, 410	$Mg_5(SiO_4)_2(F,OH)_2$	Mon	3.1–3.2	6–$6\frac{1}{2}$	Yellow-red
Chromite, 310	$FeCr_2O_4$	Iso	4.6	$5\frac{1}{2}$	Luster submetallic
Chrysoberyl, 311	$BeAl_2O_4$	Orth	3.65–3.8	$8\frac{1}{2}$	Crystals tabular
Chrysocolla, 429	$CuSiO_3\cdot2H_2O$	?	2.0–2.4	2–4	Bluish green
Chrysolite, 400	....	......	....	....	See olivine
Chrysoprase, 482	....	......	....	....	Green chalcedony

MINERAL INDEX

Name, p.	Composition	Xl. Sys.	G.	H.	Remarks
Chrysotile, 463	....	Rho	....	.....	Serpentine asbestos
Cinnabar, 262	HgS	Rho	8.10	$2\frac{1}{2}$	Red
Cinnamon stone, 403	....	....	....	.....	See grossularite
Citrine, 481	....	....	....	.....	See quartz
Clay ironstone, 341	....	....	....	.....	See siderite
Cleavelandite, 498	....	....	....	.....	White, platy albite
Cliachite, 317	Al(OH)$_3$	Amor	2.5±	1–3	See bauxite
Clinochlore, 473	....	....	....	.....	See chlorite
Clinoenstatite, 436	Mg$_2$(Si$_2$O$_6$)	Mon	3.19	6	Prismatic cl.
Clinoferrosilite, 436	Fe$_2$(Si$_2$O$_6$)	Mon	3.6	6	A pyroxene
Clinohumite, 411	Mg$_9$(SiO$_4$)$_4$(F,OH)$_2$	Mon	3.1–3.2	6	See chondrodite
Clinozoisite, 417	Ca$_2$Al$_3$(SiO$_4$)(Si$_2$O$_7$)(OH)	Mon	3.25–3.37	6–$6\frac{1}{2}$	Crystals striated
Cobaltite, 270	CoAsS	Iso	6.33	$5\frac{1}{2}$	In pyritohedrons
Cogwheel ore, 282	....	....	....	.....	See bournonite
Colemanite, 357	Ca$_2$B$_6$O$_{11}$·5H$_2$O	Mon	2.42	4–$4\frac{1}{2}$	Cl {010} perfect
Collophane, 374	....	....	....	.....	See apatite
Columbite, 312	(Fe,Mn)Nb$_2$O$_6$	Orth	5.3–7.3	6	Luster submetallic
Common mica, 467	....	....	....	.....	See muscovite
Common salt, 320	....	....	....	.....	See halite
Copper, 229	Cu	Iso	8.9	$2\frac{1}{2}$–3	Malleable
Copper glance, 248	....	....	....	.....	See chalcocite
Copper nickel, 259	....	....	....	.....	See niccolite
Copper pyrites, 255	....	....	....	.....	See chalcopyrite
Cordierite, 426	Mg$_2$Al$_3$(AlSi$_5$O$_{18}$)	Orth	2.60–2.66	7–$7\frac{1}{2}$	Blue
Corundum, 290	Al$_2$O$_3$	Rho	4.02	9	Rhomb. parting
Cotton-balls, 356	....	....	....	.....	See ulexite
Covellite, 261	CuS	Hex	4.6–4.76	$1\frac{1}{2}$–2	Blue
Cristobalite, 485	SiO$_2$	Tet?	2.30	7	In volcanic rocks
Crocidolite, 446	Na$_3$Fe$_3$''Fe$_2$'''(Si$_8$O$_{23}$)-(OH)	Mon	3.2–3.3	4	Blue asbestos
Crocoite, 364	PbCrO$_4$	Mon	5.9–6.1	$2\frac{1}{2}$–3	Orange-red
Cryolite, 325	Na$_3$AlF$_6$	Mon	2.95–3.0	$2\frac{1}{2}$	White
Cummingtonite, 444	(Mg,Fe)$_7$(Si$_8$O$_{22}$)(OH)$_2$	Mon	2.85–3.2	6	An amphibole
Cuprite, 287	Cu$_2$O	Iso	6.0	$3\frac{1}{2}$–4	In red crystals
Cyanite, 407	....	....	....	.....	See kyanite
Cymophane, 312	....	....	....	.....	See chrysoberyl
Danaite, 272	(Fe,Co)AsS	Mon	5.9–6.2	$5\frac{1}{2}$–6	See arsenopyrite
Danburite, 499	Ca(B$_2$Si$_2$O$_8$)	Orth	2.97–3.02	7	In crystals
Datolite, 411	CaB(SiO$_4$)(OH)	Mon	2.8–3.0	5–$5\frac{1}{2}$	Usually in crystals
Demantoid, 403	....	....	....	.....	Green andradite
Diallage, 436	....	....	....	.....	See diopside
Diamond, 240	C	Iso	3.5	10	Adamantine luster
Diaspore, 303	AlO(OH)	Orth	3.35–3.45	$6\frac{1}{2}$–7	Cl {010} perfect
Diatomaceous earth, 486	....	....	....	.....	See opal
Diatomite, 486	....	....	....	.....	See opal
Dichroite, 426	....	....	....	.....	See cordierite
Dickite, 462	Al$_4$(Si$_4$O$_{10}$)$_3$(OH)$_{12}$-3H$_2$O	Mon	2.6	2–$2\frac{1}{2}$	Clay mineral

MINERAL INDEX

Name, p.	Composition	Xl. Sys.	G.	H.	Remarks
Digenite, 249	Cu_9S_5	Iso	5.6	$2\frac{1}{2}$–3	Like chalcocite
Diopside, 436	$CaMg(Si_2O_6)$	Mon	3.2–3.3	5–6	A pyroxene
Dioptase, 429	$Cu_6(Si_6O_{18})\cdot6H_2O$	Rho	3.3	5	Green
Dolomite, 338	$CaMg(CO_3)_2$	Rho	2.85	$3\frac{1}{2}$–4	Cl $\{10\bar{1}1\}$
Dry-bone ore, 343	. . . .	. . . .	. . . .	. . . .	See smithsonite
Dumortierite, 413	$(Al,Fe)_7O_3(BO_3)(SiO_4)_3$	Orth	3.26–3.36	7	Radiating
Edenite, 447	$Ca_2NaMg_5(AlSi_7O_{22})$-$(OH,F)_2$	Mon	3.0	6	See hornblende
Electrum, 226	. . . .	. . . .	. . . .	. . . .	See gold
Eleolite, 502	. . . .	. . . .	. . . .	. . . .	See nepheline
Embolite, 325	$Ag(Cl,Br)$	Iso	5.3–5.4	1–$1\frac{1}{2}$	Sectile
Emerald, 425	. . . .	. . . .	. . . .	. . . .	See beryl
Emery, 291	. . . .	. . . .	. . . .	. . . .	Corundum with magnetite
Enargite, 281	Cu_3AsS_4	Orth	4.43–4.45	3	Cl $\{110\}$
Endlichite, 377	. . . .	. . . .	. . . .	. . . .	See vanadinite
Enstatite, 435	$Mg_2(Si_2O_6)$	Orth	3.2–3.5	$5\frac{1}{2}$	A pyroxene
Epidote, 417	$Ca_2(Al,Fe)Al_2O(SiO_4)$-$(Si_2O_7)(OH)$	Mon	3.35–3.45	6–7	Cl $\{001\}$
Epsomite, 368	$MgSO_4\cdot7H_2O$	Orth	1.75	2–$2\frac{1}{2}$	Bitter taste
Epsom salt, 368	. . . .	. . . .	. . . .	. . . .	See epsomite
Erythrite, 382	$Co_3(AsO_4)_2\cdot8H_2O$	Mon	2.95	$1\frac{1}{2}$–$2\frac{1}{2}$	Pink. Cobalt bloom
Essonite, 403	. . . .	. . . .	. . . .	. . . .	See grossularite
Euclase, 426	$B_2Al_2(SiO_4)_2(OH)_2$	Mon	3.1	$7\frac{1}{2}$	Cl $\{010\}$
Eucryptite, 438	$Li(Al,Si)_2O_4$	Hex	2.67	. . . .	Spodumene alter.
Fahlore, 280	. . . .	. . . .	. . . .	. . . .	See tetrahedrite
Fayalite, 401	Fe_2SiO_4	Orth	4.14	$6\frac{1}{2}$	See olivine
Feather ore, 283	. . . .	. . . .	. . . .	. . . .	See jamesonite
Feldspar, 487	. . . .	. . . .	. . . .	. . . .	A mineral group
Feldspathoid, 500	. . . .	. . . .	. . . .	. . . .	A mineral group
Ferberite, 386	$FeWO_4$	Mon	7.0–7.5	5	See wolframite
Fergusonite, 314	$R'''(Nb,Ta)O_4$	Tet	5.8	$5\frac{1}{2}$–6	Brown-black
Ferrosilite, 436	$Fe_2(Si_2O_6)$	Orth	3.6	6	A pyroxene
Fersmannite, 413	$Ca_4Na_2Ti_4Si_3O_{18}F_2$	Mon	3.44	$5\frac{1}{2}$	Brown
Fibrolite, 407	. . . .	. . . .	. . . .	. . . .	See sillimanite
Flint, 483	SiO_2	. . . .	2.65	7	Cryptocryst. qtz.
Flos ferri, 345	. . . .	. . . .	. . . .	. . . .	See aragonite
Fluorite, 325	CaF_2	Iso	3.18	4	Cl octahedral
Forsterite, 401	Mg_2SiO_4	Orth	3.2	$6\frac{1}{2}$	See olivine
Fowlerite, 441	. . . .	. . . .	. . . .	. . . .	Zinc-bearing rhodonite
Franklinite, 310	(Fe,Zn,Mn)-$(Fe,Mn)_2O_4$	Iso	5.15	6	At Franklin, N. J.
Freibergite, 280	. . . .	. . . .	. . . .	. . . .	Argentiferous tetrahedrite
Gadolinite, 426	$Y_2Fe''Be_2(SiO_4)_2O_2$	Mon	4.0–4.5	$6\frac{1}{2}$–7	Black
Gahnite, 307	$ZnAl_2O_4$	Iso	4.55	$7\frac{1}{2}$–8	Green octahedrons
Galaxite, 307	$MnAl_2O_4$	Iso	4.03	$7\frac{1}{2}$–8	Mn spinel

MINERAL INDEX

Name, p.	Composition	Xl. Sys.	G.	H.	Remarks
Galena, 250	PbS	Iso	7.4–7.6	$2\frac{1}{2}$	Cl cubic
Garnet, 401	$A_3''B_2'''(SiO_4)_3$	Iso	3.5–4.3	$6\frac{1}{2}$–$7\frac{1}{2}$	In crystals
Garnierite, 464	$(Ni,Mg)SiO_3 \cdot nH_2O$	Amor	2.2–2.8	2–3	Green
Gaylussite, 350	$Na_2Ca(CO_3)_2 \cdot 5H_2O$	Mon	1.99	2–3	Fusible at 1
Gedrite, 444	. . . .	. . . .	. . . .	. . . .	See anthophyllite
Geocronite, 283	$Pb_5(Sb,As)_2S_8$	Orth	6.4±	$2\frac{1}{2}$	. . . .
Gersdorffite, 270	NiAsS	Iso	5.9	$5\frac{1}{2}$	See cobaltite
Geyserite, 486	. . . .	. . . .	. . . .	. . . .	See opal
Gibbsite, 304, 317	$Al(OH)_3$	Mon	2.3–2.4	$2\frac{1}{2}$–$3\frac{1}{2}$	Basal cl.
Glauberite, 359	$Na_2Ca(SO_4)_2$	Mon	2.70–2.85	$2\frac{1}{2}$–3	Cl {001}
Glauconite, 471	$K_2(Mg,Fe)_2Al_6(Si_4O_{10})_3$-$(OH)_{12}$	Mon	2.3±	2	In green sands
Glaucophane, 446	$Na_2Mg_3Al_2(Si_8O_{22})$-$(OH,F)_2$	Mon	3.0–3.2	6–$6\frac{1}{2}$	An amphibole
Gmelinite, 510	$(Na,Ca)_6Al_6(Al,Si)$-$Si_{13}O_{40} \cdot 20H_2O$	Rho	2.1±	$4\frac{1}{2}$	A zeolite
Goethite, 304	$HFeO_2$	Orth	4.37	5–$5\frac{1}{2}$	Cl {010}
Gold, 225	Au	Iso	15.0–19.3	$2\frac{1}{2}$–3	Yellow. Soft
Graphite, 244	C	Hex	2.3	1–2	Black. Platy
Gray copper, 280	. . . .	. . . .	. . . .	. . . .	See tetrahedrite
Green copper carbonate, 349	. . . .	. . . .	. . . .	. . . .	See malachite
Greenockite, 257	CdS	Hex	4.9	3–$3\frac{1}{2}$	Yellow-orange
Grossularite, 403	$Ca_3Al_2(SiO_4)_3$	Iso	3.53	$6\frac{1}{2}$	A garnet
Gypsum, 366	$CaSO_4 \cdot 2H_2O$	Mon	2.32	2	Cl {010}{100}{011}
Halite, 320	NaCl	Iso	2.16	$2\frac{1}{2}$	Cl cubic. Salty
Halloysite, 462	$Al_4(Si_4O_{10})(OH)_8$	Amor	2.0–2.2	1–2	A clay mineral
Harmotome, 511	$Ba(Al_2Si_6O_{16}) \cdot 6H_2O$	Mon	2.45	$4\frac{1}{2}$	A zeolite
Hastingsite, 447	$Ca_2NaMg_4Al_3Si_6O_{22}$-$(OH,F)_2$	Mon	3.2	6	See hornblende
Hauynite, 503	$(Na,Ca)_{6-8}Al_6Si_6O_{24}$·-$(SO_4)_{1-2}$	Iso	2.4–2.5	$5\frac{1}{2}$–6	A feldspathoid
Heavy spar, 359	. . . .	. . . .	. . . .	. . . .	See barite
Hectorite, 462	$(Mg,Li)_6Si_8O_{20}(OH)_4$	Mon	2.5	1–$1\frac{1}{2}$	Li montmorillonite
Hedenbergite, 437	$CaFe(Si_2O_6)$	Mon	3.55	5–6	A pyroxene
Heliotrope, 482	. . . .	. . . .	. . . .	. . . .	Green and red chalcedony
Hematite, 292	Fe_2O_3	Rho	5.26	$5\frac{1}{2}$–$6\frac{1}{2}$	Red streak
Hemimorphite, 415	$Zn_4(Si_2O_7)(OH)_2 \cdot H_2O$	Orth	3.4–3.5	$4\frac{1}{2}$–5	Cl {110}
Hercynite, 307	$FeAl_2O_4$	Iso	4.39	$7\frac{1}{2}$–8	Iron spinel
Hessite, 274	Ag_2Te	Iso	8.4	$2\frac{1}{2}$–3	. . . .
Heulandite, 510	$Ca(Al_2Si_7O_{18}) \cdot 6H_2O$	Mon	2.18–2.20	$3\frac{1}{2}$–4	Cl {010} perfect
Hiddenite, 437	. . . .	. . . .	. . . .	. . . .	Green spodumene
Holmquistite, 446	. . . .	. . . .	. . . .	. . . .	Lithium-bearing glaucophane
Hornblende, 446	$Ca_2Na(Mg,Fe'')_4$-$(Al,Fe''',Ti)_3Si_8O_{22}$-$(O,OH)_2$	Mon	3.2	5–6	An amphibole
Horn silver, 324	. . . .	. . . .	. . . .	. . . .	See cerargyrite
Huebnerite, 386	$MnWO_4$	Mon	7.0	5	See wolframite

MINERAL INDEX

Name, p.	Composition	Xl. Sys.	G.	H.	Remarks
Humite, 411	$Mg_7(SiO_4)_3(F,OH)_2$	Orth	3.1–3.2	6	See chondrodite
Hyacinth, 405					See zircon
Hyalite, 486					Globular, colorless opal
Hyalophane, 491	$(K,Ba)(Al,Si)_2Si_2O_8$	Mon	2.8	6	See orthoclase
Hydrozincite, 344	$2ZnCO_3\cdot3Zn(OH)_2$	Mon	3.6–3.8	$2–2\frac{1}{2}$	Secondary mineral
Hypersthene, 436	$(Mg,Fe)_2(Si_2O_6)$	Orth	3.4–3.5	5–6	A pyroxene
Ice, 289	H_2O	Hex	0.917	$1\frac{1}{2}$	
Iceland spar, 335					See calcite
Iddingsite, 401	$H_8Mg_9Fe_2Si_3O_{14}(?)$	Orth	3.5–3.8	3	After olivine
Idocrase, 419	$Ca_{10}(Mg,Fe)_2Al_4(SiO_4)_5(Si_2O_7)_2(OH)_4$	Tet	3.35–3.45	$6\frac{1}{2}$	Prismatic crystals
Illite, 463					Micalike clay mineral
Ilmenite, 295	$FeTiO_3$	Rho	4.7	$5\frac{1}{2}–6$	Slightly magnetic
Ilvaite, 416	$CaAl_2(Si_2O_7)(OH)_2\cdot H_2O$	Orth	4.0	$5\frac{1}{2}–6$	Black
Indicolite, 429					See tourmaline
Iodobromite, 325	$Ag(Cl,Br,I)$	Iso	5.71	$1–1\frac{1}{2}$	Sectile
Iodyrite, 325	AgI	Hex	5.5–5.7	$1–1\frac{1}{2}$	Sectile
Iolite, 426					See cordierite
Iridium, 233	Ir	Iso	22.7	6–7	A platinum metal
Iridosmine, 233	Ir,Os	Rho	19.3–21.1	6–7	See platinum
Iron, 233	Fe	Iso	7.3–7.9	$4\frac{1}{2}$	Very rare
Iron pyrites, 267					See pyrite
Jacinth, 405					See zircon
Jacobsite, 309	$MnFe_2O_4$	Iso	5.1	$5\frac{1}{2}–6\frac{1}{2}$	A spinel
Jade, 438, 445					See nephrite and jadeite
Jadeite, 438	$NaAl(Si_2O_6)$	Mon	3.3–3.5	$6\frac{1}{2}–7$	Green. Compact
Jamesonite, 283	$Pb_4FeSb_6S_{14}$	Mon	5.5–6.0	2–3	Feather ore
Jargon, 405					See zircon
Jarosite, 370	$KFe_3(OH)_6(SO_4)_2$	Rho	3.2±	3	Yellow-brown
Jasper, 483					See quartz
Kainite, 324	$MgSO_4\cdot KCl\cdot 3H_2O$	Mon	2.1	3	
Kaliophilite, 501	$K(AlSiO_4)$	Hex	2.61	6	See nepheline
Kaolin, 462					Clay minerals
Kaolinite, 461	$Al_4(Si_4O_{10})(OH)_8$	Mon	2.6–2.65	$2–2\frac{1}{2}$	Earthy
Kernite, 355	$Na_2B_4O_7\cdot 4H_2O$	Mon	1.95	3	Cl {001} {100}
Krennerite, 274	$AuTe_2$	Orth	8.62	2–3	Basal cl.
Kunzite, 437					Pink spodumene
Kyanite, 407	Al_2SiO_5	Tric	3.56–3.66	5–7	Blue. Bladed
Labradorite, 499	$Ab_{50}An_{50}—Ab_{30}An_{70}$	Tric	2.71	6	Plag. feldspar
Lamprophyllite, 413	$CaNa_3Ti_3Si_3O_{14}(OH,F)$	Mon?	3.45	4	Platy
Lapis lazuli, 503					See lazurite
Larsenite, 401	$PbZnSiO_4$	Orth	5.9	3	Olivine group
Laumontite, 508	$(Ca,Na)_7Al_{12}(Al,Si)_2Si_{26}O_{80}\cdot 25H_2O$	Mon	2.28	4	A zeolite

MINERAL INDEX

Name, p.	Composition	Xl. Sys.	G.	H.	Remarks
Lawsonite, 416	$CaAl_2(Si_2O_7)(OH)_2 \cdot H_2O$	Orth	3.09	8	In gneisses and schists
Lazulite, 378	$MgAl_2(OH)_2(PO_4)_2$	Mon	3.0–3.1	$5-5\frac{1}{2}$	Blue
Lazurite, 503	$(Na,Ca)_4(AlSiO_4)_3-$ (SO_4,S,Cl)	Iso	2.4–2.45	$5-5\frac{1}{2}$	Pyrite associated
Lechatelierite, 484	SiO_2	Amor	2.2	6–7	Fused silica
Lepidocrocite, 306	$FeO(OH)$	Orth	4.09	5	Red
Lepidolite, 471	$K_2Li_3Al_3(AlSi_3O_{10})_2-$ $(OH,F)_4$	Mon	2.8–3.0	$2\frac{1}{2}-4$	A mica
Leucite, 500	$K(AlSi_2O_6)$	.....	2.45–2.50	$5\frac{1}{2}-6$	In trapezohedrons
Limonite, 316	$FeO(OH) \cdot nH_2O$	Amor	3.6–4.0	$5-5\frac{1}{2}$	Streak yellow-brown
Linnaeite, 276	Co_3S_4	Iso	4.8	$4\frac{1}{2}-5\frac{1}{2}$	....
Lithia mica, 471	....	.....	.....	.....	See lepidolite
Lithiophilite, 373	$LiMnPO_4$	Orth	3.5	5	See triphylite
Lodestone, 309	....	.....	.....	.....	See magnetite
Magnesiochromite, 311	$MgCr_2O_4$	Iso	4.2	$5\frac{1}{2}$	A spinel
Magnesioferrite, 309	$MgFe_2O_4$	Iso	4.5	$5\frac{1}{2}-6\frac{1}{2}$	A spinel
Magnesite, 340	$MgCO_3$	Rho	3.0–3.2	$3\frac{1}{2}-5$	Commonly massive
Magnetic pyrites, 258	....	.....	.....	.....	See pyrrhotite
Magnetite, 308	Fe_3O_4	Iso	5.18	6	Strongly magnetic
Malachite, 349	$Cu_2CO_3(OH)_2$	Mon	3.9–4.03	$3\frac{1}{2}-4$	Green
Manganite, 315	$MnO(OH)$	Orth	4.3	4	Prismatic crystals
Mangano-tantalite, 313	$MnO(Ta,Cb)_2O_5$	Orth	6.6±	$4\frac{1}{2}$	See columbite
Marcasite, 270	FeS_2	Orth	4.89	$6-6\frac{1}{2}$	White iron pyrites
Margarite, 472	$CaAl_2(Al_2Si_2O_{10})(OH)_2$	Mon	3.0–3.1	$3\frac{1}{2}-5$	A brittle mica
Marialite, 505	$(Na,Ca)_4Al_3(Al,Si)_3Si_6-$ $O_{24}(Cl,CO_3,SO_4)$	Tet	2.60±	$5\frac{1}{2}-6$	See scapolite
Martite, 293	....	.....	.....	.....	See hematite
Meerschaum, 473	....	.....	.....	.....	See sepiolite
Meionite, 505	$(Ca,Na)_4Al_3(Al,Si)_3Si_6-$ $O_{24}(Cl,CO_3,SO_4)$	Tet	2.69	$5\frac{1}{2}-6$	See scapolite
Melaconite, 288	....	.....	.....	.....	See tenorite
Melanite, 403	Black andradite	Iso	3.7	7	A garnet
Melanterite, 271	$FeSO_4 \cdot 7H_2O$	Mon	1.90	2	Green-blue
Menaccanite, 295	....	.....	.....	.....	See ilmenite
Meneghinite, 283	$Pb_{13}Sb_7S_{23}$	Orth	6.36	$2\frac{1}{2}$	
Mercury, 223	Hg	.....	13.6	0	Fluid. Quicksilver
Mica, 467					A mineral group
Microcline, 493	$K(AlSi_3O_8)$	Tric	2.54–2.57	6	A feldspar
Microlite, 314	$Ca_2Ta_2O_7$	Iso	5.48–5.56	$5\frac{1}{2}$	Ore of tantalum
Microperthite, 490	....	.....	.....	.....	Microcline and albite
Millerite, 259	NiS	Rho	5.5±0.2	$3-3\frac{1}{2}$	Capillary crystals
Mimetite, 376	$Pb_5Cl(AsO_4)_3$	Hex	7.0–7.2	$3\frac{1}{2}$	Like pyromorphite
Mispickel, 272	....	.....	.....	.....	See arsenopyrite
Molybdenite, 273	MoS_2	Hex	4.62–4.73	$1-1\frac{1}{2}$	Black. Platy

MINERAL INDEX

Name, p.	Composition	Xl. Sys.	G.	H.	Remarks
Monazite, 372	$(Ce,La,Y,Th)PO_4$	Mon	5.0–5.3	$5-5\frac{1}{2}$	Parting $\{001\}$
Monticellite, 401	$CaMgSiO_4$	Orth	3.2	5	See olivine
Montmoril- lonite, 462	$(Al,Mg)_8(Si_4O_{10})_3$- $(OH)_{10} \cdot 12H_2O$	Mon	2.5	$1-1\frac{1}{2}$	A clay mineral
Moonstone, 491	. . . .	. . . .	. . . .	. . . .	See albite and orthoclase
Morganite, 425	. . . .	. . . .	. . . .	. . . .	See beryl
Mullite, 408	$Al_6Si_2O_{13}$	Orth	3.23	6–7	Cl $\{100\}$
Muscovite, 467	$KAl_2(AlSi_3O_{10})(OH)_2$	Mon	2.76–3.1	$2-2\frac{1}{2}$	Cl $\{001\}$ perfect
Nacrite, 462	$Al_4(Si_4O_{10})(OH)_8$	Mon	2.6	$2-2\frac{1}{2}$	See kaolinite
Nagyagite, 274	$Pb_5Au(Te,Sb)_4S_{5-8}$	Mon?	7.4	$1-1\frac{1}{2}$	. . . .
Natroalunite, 370	. . . .	. . . .	. . . .	. . . .	Soda alunite
Natrolite, 508	$Na_2(Al_2Si_3O_{10}) \cdot 2H_2O$	Mon	2.25	$5-5\frac{1}{2}$	Cl $\{110\}$ perfect
Nepheline, 501	$(Na,K)(AlSiO_4)$	Hex	2.55–2.65	$5\frac{1}{2}-6$	Greasy luster
Nephrite, 445	. . . .	. . . .	. . . .	. . . .	See tremolite
Neptunite, 413	$(Na,K)(Fe'',Mn,Ti)$- Si_2O_6	Mon	3.23	5–6	Black
Niccolite, 259	$NiAs$	Hex	7.78	$5-5\frac{1}{2}$	Copper-red
Nickel bloom, 383	. . . .	. . . .	. . . .	. . . .	See annabergite
Nickel iron, 233	Ni,Fe	Iso	7.8–8.2	5	In meteorites
Nickel skutterudite, 275	$(Ni,Co,Fe)As_3$	Iso	6.5 ± 0.4	$5\frac{1}{2}-6$	Tin white
Niter, 352	KNO_3	Orth	2.09–2.14	2	Saltpeter
Nontronite, 462	$Fe(AlSi)_8O_{20}(OH)_4$	Mon	2.5	$1-1\frac{1}{2}$	Clay mineral
Norbergite, 411	$Mg_3(SiO_4)_1(F,OH)_2$	Orth	3.1–3.2	6	See chondrodite
Noselite, 503	$Na_4Al_3Si_3O_{12}SO_4$	Iso	$2.3\pm$	6	A feldspathoid
Octahedrite, 297	. . . .	. . . .	. . . .	. . . .	See anatase
Oligoclase, 499	$Ab_{90}An_{10}$—$Ab_{70}An_{30}$	Tric	2.65	6	Plag. feldspar
Olivine, 400	$(Mg,Fe)_2SiO_4$	Orth	3.27–4.37	$6\frac{1}{2}-7$	Green rock mineral
Onyx, 483	. . . .	. . . .	. . . .	. . . .	Layered chalcedony
Opal, 485	$SiO_2 \cdot nH_2O$	Amor	1.9–2.2	5–6	Conch. fracture
Orpiment, 264	As_2S_3	Mon	3.49	$1\frac{1}{2}-2$	Cl $\{010\}$. Yellow
Orthite, 419	. . . .	. . . .	. . . .	. . . .	See allanite
Orthoclase, 490	$K(AlSi_3O_8)$	Mon	2.57	6	A feldspar
Ottrelite, 472	$(Fe'',Mn)(Al,Fe''')_2$- $Si_3O_{10} \cdot H_2O$	Mon	3.5	6–7	A brittle mica
Palladium, 233	Pd	Iso	11.9	$4\frac{1}{2}-5$	See platinum
Paragonite, 469	$NaAl_2(AlSi_3O_{10})(OH)_2$	Mon	2.85	2	Like muscovite
Pargasite, 447	$Ca_4Na_2Mg_9Al_4Si_{13}O_{44}$- $(OH,F)_4$	Mon	3–3.5	$5\frac{1}{2}$	See hornblende
Patronite, 377	. . . .	. . . .	. . . .	. . . .	An ore of vanadium
Peacock ore, 249	. . . .	. . . .	. . . .	. . . .	See bornite
Pearceite, 277	$(Ag,Cu)_{16}As_2S_{11}$	Mon	6.15	3	Tabular crystals
Pectolite, 442	$Ca_2NaH(SiO_3)_3$	Tric	2.7–2.8	5	Crystals acicular
Penninite, 473	. . . .	. . . .	. . . .	. . . .	See chlorite
Pentlandite, 260	$(Fe,Ni)_9S_8$	Iso	4.6–5.0	$3\frac{1}{2}-4$	In pyrrhotite

MINERAL INDEX

Name, p.	Composition	Xl. Sys.	G.	H.	Remarks
Peridot, 400	. . . .	. . . .	. . . .	. . . . .	Gem olivine
Perovskite, 297	$CaTiO_3$	Iso	4.03	$5\frac{1}{2}$	Yellow
Perthite, 490	. . . .	. . . .	. . . .	. . . . .	Microcline and albite
Petalite, 504	$Li(AlSi_4O_{10})$	Mon	2.4	$6–6\frac{1}{2}$	Good cleavage
Petzite, 274	$(Ag,Au)_2Te$	Iso?	8.7–9.0	$2\frac{1}{2}–3$	. . . .
Phenacite, 399	$Be_2(SiO_4)$	Rho	2.97–3.00	$7\frac{1}{2}–8$	In pegmatites
Phillipsite, 511	$KCa(Al_3Si_5O_{16})\cdot6H_2O$	Mon	2.2	$4\frac{1}{2}–5$	A zeolite
Phlogopite, 470	$KMg_3(AlSi_3O_{10})(OH)_2$	Mon	2.86	$2\frac{1}{2}–3$	Brown mica
Phosgenite, 348	$Pb_2Cl_2CO_3$	Tet	6.0–6.3	3	Fusible at 1
Phosphorite, 375	. . . .	. . . .	. . . .	. . . . .	Phosphate rock
Picotite, 306	. . . .	. . . .	. . . .	. . . . .	See spinel
Piedmontite, 418	Mn'' epidote	Mon	3.4	$6\frac{1}{2}$	Reddish brown
Pinite, 469	. . . .	. . . .	. . . .	. . . . .	See muscovite
Pitchblend, 301	. . . .	. . . .	. . . .	. . . . .	See uraninite
Plagioclase, 495	$Ab_{100}An_0—Ab_0An_{100}$	Tric	2.62–2.76	6	A feldspar series
Plagionite, 283	$Pb_5Sb_8S_{17}$	Mon	5.56	$2\frac{1}{2}$	. . . .
Platinum, 231	Pt	Iso	14–19	$4–4\frac{1}{2}$	As grains in placers
Pleonaste, 306	. . . .	. . . .	. . . .	. . . . .	See spinel
Plumbago, 244	. . . .	. . . .	. . . .	. . . . .	See graphite
Polianite, 297	MnO_2	Tet	5.0	$6–6\frac{1}{2}$	Steel-gray
Pollucite, 501	$Cs_4Al_4Si_9O_{26}\cdot H_2O$	Iso	2.9	$6\frac{1}{2}$	Colorless
Polybasite, 277	$Ag_{16}Ab_2S_{11}$	Mon	6.0–6.2	2–3	Pseudorhombohedral
Polyhalite, 366	$K_2Ca_2Mg(SO_4)_4\cdot2H_2O$	Tric	2.78	$2\frac{1}{2}–3$	Bitter taste
Potash feldspar, 491	. . . .	. . . .	. . . .	. . . . .	See orthoclase
Potash mica, 467	. . . .	. . . .	. . . .	. . . . .	See muscovite
Powellite, 385	$CaMoO_4$	Tet	4.23	$3\frac{1}{2}–4$	Fluoresces
Prase, 483	. . . .	. . . .	. . . .	. . . . .	See quartz
Prehnite, 421	$Ca_2Al_2(Si_3O_{10})(OH)_2$	Orth	2.8–2.95	$6–6\frac{1}{2}$	Tabular crystals
Prochlorite, 473	. . . .	. . . .	. . . .	. . . . .	See chlorite
Proustite, 279	Ag_3AsS_3	Rho	5.55	$2–2\frac{1}{2}$	Light ruby silver
Pseudoleucite, 501	. . . .	. . . .	. . . .	. . . . .	See leucite
Pseudowollastonite, 442	. . . .	. . . .	. . . .	. . . . .	See wollastonite
Psilomelane, 316	$BaMn''Mn^4_8O_{16}(OH)_4$	Orth	3.7–4.7	5–6	Botryoidal
Purple copper ore, 249	. . . .	. . . .	. . . .	. . . . .	See bornite
Pyrargyrite, 278	Ag_3SbS_3	Rho	5.85	$2\frac{1}{2}$	Dark ruby silver
Pyrite, 267	FeS_2	Iso	5.02	$6–6\frac{1}{2}$	Crystals striated
Pyrochlore, 314	$(Na,Ca)_2(Nb,Ti)-$ $(O,F)_7$?	Iso	4.3±	5	Infusible
Pyrolusite, 297	MnO_2	Tet	4.75	1–2	Sooty
Pyromorphite, 375	$Pb_5Cl(PO_4)_3$	Hex	6.5–7.1	$3\frac{1}{2}–4$	Adamantine luster
Pyrope, 402	$Mg_3Al_2(SiO_4)_3$	Iso	3.51	7	A garnet
Pyrophyllite, 465	$Al_2(Si_4O_{10})(OH)_2$	Mon	2.8–2.9	1–2	Smooth feel
Pyroxene, 434	. . . .	. . . .	. . . .	. . . . .	A mineral group
Pyrrhotite, 258	$Fe_{1-x}S$	Hex	4.58–4.65	4	Magnetic
Quartz, 478	SiO_2	Rho	2.65	7	No cleavage

MINERAL INDEX

Name, p.	Composition	Xl. Sys.	G.	H.	Remarks
Ramsayite, 413	$Na_2Ti_2Si_2O_9$	Orth	3.43	6	From Kola
Rasorite, 355					See kernite
Realgar, 263	AsS	Mon	3.48	$1\frac{1}{2}$–2	Cl {010}. Red
Red copper ore, 287					See cuprite
Red ocher, 293					See hematite
Rhodochrosite, 342	$MnCO_3$	Rho	3.45–3.6	$3\frac{1}{2}$–$4\frac{1}{2}$	Cl {10$\bar{1}$1}. Pink
Rhodolite, 403	$3(Mg,Fe)O\cdot Al_2O_3\cdot 3SiO_2$	Iso	3.84	7	See garnet
Rhodonite, 441	$Mn(SiO_3)$	Tric	3.58–3.70	$5\frac{1}{2}$–6	Pink
Riebeckite, 446	$Na_3Fe_3''Fe_2'''(Si_8O_{22})(OH)_2$	Mon	3.44	4	An amphibole
Rock crystal, 481					See quartz
Rock salt, 320					See halite
Roscoelite, 378	$K_2V_4Al_2Si_6O_{20}(OH)_4$	Mon	2.97	$2\frac{1}{2}$	Vanadium mica
Rubellite, 429					See tourmaline
Ruby, 290					Red gem corundum
Ruby copper, 287					See cuprite
Ruby silver, 278					See pyrargyrite and proustite
Rutile, 296	TiO_2	Tet	4.18–4.25	6–$6\frac{1}{2}$	Adamantine luster
Saltpeter, 352					See niter
Sanidine, 491					See orthoclase
Saponite, 462	$(Mg,Al)_6(Si,Al)_8O_{20}(OH)_4$	Mon	2.5	1–$1\frac{1}{2}$	Clay mineral
Sapphire, 290					Blue gem corundum
Satin spar, 367					Fibrous gypsum
Scapolite, 505	Various	Tet	2.65–2.74	5–6	Cl {010} {110}
Scheelite, 387	$CaWO_4$	Tet	5.9–6.1	$4\frac{1}{2}$–5	Cl {011}
Schorlite, 427					See tourmaline
Scolecite, 509	$Ca(Al_2Si_3O_{10})\cdot 3H_2O$	Mon	2.2±	5–$5\frac{1}{2}$	A zeolite
Scorodite, 379	$FeAsO_4\cdot 2H_2O$	Orth	3.1–3.3	$3\frac{1}{2}$–4	Green to brown
Scorzalite, 378	$FeAl_2(OH)_2(PO_4)_2$	Mon	3.35	$5\frac{1}{2}$–6	
Selenite, 366					See gypsum
Semseyite, 283	$Pb_9Sb_8S_{21}$	Mon	5.8	$2\frac{1}{2}$	
Sepiolite, 473	$Mg_4(Si_6O_{15})(OH)_2\cdot 6H_2O$	Mon?	2.0	2–$2\frac{1}{2}$	Meerschaum
Sericite, 469					Fine-grained muscovite
Serpentine, 463	$Mg_6(Si_4O_{10})(OH)_8$	Mon	2.2	2–5	Green to yellow
Siderite, 341	$FeCO_3$	Rho	3.83–3.88	$3\frac{1}{2}$–4	Cl {10$\bar{1}$1}
Sillimanite, 407	Al_2SiO_5	Orth	3.23	6–7	Cl {010} perfect
Silver, 228	Ag	Iso	10.5	$2\frac{1}{2}$–3	White, malleable
Silver glance, 247					See argentite
Skutterudite, 275	$(Co,Ni,Fe)As_3$	Iso	6.5±0.4	5	Tin white
Smaltite, 276					See skutterudite
Smithsonite, 343	$ZnCO_3$	Rho	4.35–4.40	5	Reniform
Soapstone, 466					See talc
Sodalite, 502	$Na_4(AlSiO_4)_3Cl$	Iso	2.15–2.3	$5\frac{1}{2}$–6	Usually blue
Sodamicrocline, 494					See microcline
Soda niter, 351	$NaNO_3$	Rho	2.29	1–2	Cooling taste
Spathic iron, 341					See siderite
Specular iron, 293					See hematite

MINERAL INDEX

Name, p.	Composition	Xl. Sys.	G.	H.	Remarks
Sperrylite, 232	$PtAs_2$	Iso	10.50	6–7	See platinum
Spessartite, 403	$Mn_3Al_2(SiO_4)_3$	Iso	4.18	7	A garnet
Sphalerite, 252	ZnS	Iso	3.9–4.1	$3\frac{1}{2}$–4	Cl {110} 6 directions
Sphene, 412	$CaTiO(SiO_4)$	Mon	3.40–3.55	5–$5\frac{1}{2}$	Wedge-shaped xls
Spinel, 306	$MgAl_2O_4$	Iso	3.6–4.0	8	In octahedrons
Spodumene, 437	$LiAl(Si_2O_6)$	Mon	3.15–3.20	$6\frac{1}{2}$–7	Cl {110}. Part {100}
Stannite, 256	Cu_2FeSnS_4	Tet	4.4	4	Easily fusible
Staurolite, 409	$Fe_2Al_9O_7(SiO_4)_4(OH)$	Orth	3.65–3.75	7–$7\frac{1}{2}$	In cruciform twins
Steatite, 466	. . . .	. . . .	. . . . . .	. . . .	See talc
Stephanite, 277	Ag_5SbS_4	Orth	6.2–6.3	2–$2\frac{1}{2}$	Pseudohexagonal
Stibnite, 264	Sb_2S_3	Orth	4.52–4.62	2	Cl {010} perfect
Stilbite, 510	$Ca(Al_2Si_7O_{18})\cdot7H_2O$	Mon	2.1–2.2	$3\frac{1}{2}$–4	Sheaflike aggregates
Stolzite, 385	$PbWO_4$	Tet	7.9–8.3	$2\frac{1}{2}$–3	Cl {001} {011}
Stromeyerite, 249	$(Ag,Cu)_2S$	Orth	6.2–6.3	$2\frac{1}{2}$–3	. . . .
Strontianite, 347	$SrCO_3$	Orth	3.7	$3\frac{1}{2}$–4	Efferv. in HCl
Sulfur, 236	S	Orth	2.05–2.09	$1\frac{1}{2}$–$2\frac{1}{2}$	Burns with blue flame
Sunstone, 499	. . . .	. . . .	. . . . . .	. . . .	See oligoclase
Sylvanite, 275	$(Au,Ag)Te_2$	Mon	8.0–8.2	$1\frac{1}{2}$–2	Cl {010} perfect
Sylvite, 323	KCl	Iso	1.99	2	Cl cubic perfect
Talc, 466	$Mg_3(Si_4O_{10})(OH)_2$	Mon	2.7–2.8	1	Greasy feel
Tantalite, 312	$(Fe,Mn)Ta_2O_6$	Orth	6.5±	6	See columbite
Tennantite, 280	$(Cu,Fe,Zn,Ag)_{12}As_4S_{13}$	Iso	4.6–5.1	3–$4\frac{1}{2}$	In tetrahedrons
Tenorite, 288	CuO	Tric	6.5	3–4	Black
Tephroite, 401, 442	$Mn_2(SiO_4)$	Orth	4.1	6	See olivine
Tetrahedrite, 280	$(Cu,Fe,Zn,Ag)_{12}Sb_4S_{13}$	Iso	4.6–5.1	3–$4\frac{1}{2}$	In tetrahedrons
Thenardite, 359	Na_2SO_4	Orth	2.68	$2\frac{1}{2}$	In saline lakes
Thomsonite, 508	$(Ca,Na)_6Al_8(Al,Si)_2$-$Si_{10}O_{40}\cdot12H_2O$	Orth	2.3	5	A zeolite
Thorianite, 303	ThO_2	Iso	9.7	$6\frac{1}{2}$	Poor cleavage
Thorite, 406	$Th(SiO_4)$	Tet	5.3	5	Usually hydrated
Thulite, 417	. . . .	. . . .	. . . . . .	. . . .	Rose-red zoisite
Tiger's-eye, 481	. . . .	. . . .	. . . . . .	. . . .	See quartz
Tin, 223	Sn	Tet	7.3	2	Very rare
Tin stone, 299	. . . .	. . . .	. . . . . .	. . . .	See cassiterite
Titanic iron ore, 295	. . . .	. . . .	. . . . . .	. . . .	See ilmenite
Titanite, 412					See sphene
Topaz, 408	$Al_2(SiO_4)(F,OH)_2$	Orth	3.4–3.6	8	Cl {001} perfect
Torbernite, 382	$Cu(UO_2)_2(PO_4)_2$-8–$12H_2O$	Tet	3.22	2–$2\frac{1}{2}$	Green
Tourmaline, 426	$XY_3Al_6(BO_3)_3(Si_6O_{18})$-$(OH)_4$	Rho	3.0–3.25	7–$7\frac{1}{2}$	Trigonal section
Travertine, 337	. . . .	. . . .	. . . . . .	. . . .	See calcite
Tremolite, 444	$Ca_2Mg_5(Si_8O_{22})(OH)_2$	Mon	3.0–3.3	5–6	Cl {110} perfect
Tridymite, 484	SiO_2	Orth	2.26	7	In volcanic rocks
Triphylite, 373	$LiFePO_4$	Orth	3.42–3.56	$4\frac{1}{2}$–5	Cl {001} {010}
Troilite, 258	. . . .	. . . .	. . . . . .	. . . .	See pyrrhotite
Trona, 350	$Na_3H(CO_3)_2\cdot2H_2O$	Mon	2.13	3	Alkaline taste

MINERAL INDEX

Name, p.	Composition	Xl. Sys.	G.	H.	Remarks
Troostite, 399	. . . .	. . . .	. . . .	. . . . .	Manganiferous willemite
Tufa, 337	. . . .	. . . .	. . . .	. . . . .	See calcite
Turgite, 306	$2Fe_2O_3 \cdot H_2O$	. . . . .	4.2–4.6	$6\frac{1}{2}$	Red streak
Turquoise, 380	$CuAl_6(PO_4)_4$- $(OH)_8 \cdot 4H_2O$	Tric	2.6–2.8	6	Blue-green
Tyuyamunite, 384	$Ca(UO_2)_2(VO_4)_2 \cdot nH_2O$	Orth	3.7–4.3	2	Yellow
Ulexite, 356	$NaCaB_5O_9 \cdot 8H_2O$	Tric	1.96	1	"Cotton-balls"
Uralian emerald, 404	. . . .	. . . .	. . . .	. . . . .	See andradite
Uralite, 447	. . . .	. . . .	. . . .	. . . . .	See hornblende
Uraninite, 301	UO_2	Iso	9.0–9.7	$5\frac{1}{2}$	Pitchy luster
Uvarovite, 403	$Ca_3Cr_2(SiO_4)_3$	Iso	3.45	$7\frac{1}{2}$	Green garnet
Vanadinite, 377	$Pb_5Cl(VO_4)_3$	Hex	6.7–7.1	3	Luster resinous
Variscite, 382	$Al(PO_4) \cdot 2H_2O$	Orth	2.57	$3\frac{1}{2}$–$4\frac{1}{2}$	Green, massive
Verde antique, 464	. . . .	. . . .	. . . .	. . . . .	See serpentine
Vermiculite, 471	. . . .	Mon	2.4	$1\frac{1}{2}$	Altered biotite
Vesuvianite, 419	. . . .	. . . .	. . . .	. . . . .	See idocrase
Vivianite, 382	$Fe_3(PO_4)_2 \cdot 8H_2O$	Mon	2.58–2.68	$1\frac{1}{2}$–2	Cl {010} perfect
Wad, 299	. . . .	. . . .	. . . .	. . . . .	Manganese ore
Wavellite, 380	$Al_3(OH)_3(PO_4)_2 \cdot 5H_2O$	Orth	2.33	$3\frac{1}{2}$–4	Radiating aggregates
Wernerite, 505	. . . .	. . . .	. . . .	. . . . .	See scapolite
White iron pyrites, 270	. . . .	. . . .	. . . .	. . . . .	See marcasite
White mica, 467	. . . .	. . . .	. . . .	. . . . .	See muscovite
Willemite, 399	Zn_2SiO_4	Rho	3.9–4.2	$5\frac{1}{2}$	From Franklin, N. J.
Witherite, 346	$BaCO_3$	Orth	4.3	$3\frac{1}{2}$	Efferv. in HCl
Wolframite, 385	$(Fe,Mn)WO_4$	Mon	7.0–7.5	5–$5\frac{1}{2}$	Cl {010} perfect
Wollastonite, 442	$Ca(SiO_3)$	Tric	2.8–2.9	5–$5\frac{1}{2}$	Cl {001} {100}
Wood tin, 299	. . . .	. . . .	. . . .	. . . . .	See cassiterite
Wulfenite, 387	$PbMoO_4$	Tet	6.8±	3	Orange-red
Wurtzite, 253	ZnS	Hex	3.98	4	See sphalerite
Yellow copper ore, 255	. . . .	. . . .	. . . .	. . . . .	See chalcopyrite
Zeolite, 506	. . . .	. . . .	. . . .	. . . . .	A mineral group
Zinc blende, 252	. . . .	. . . .	. . . .	. . . . .	See sphalerite
Zincite, 289	ZnO	Hex	5.68	4–$4\frac{1}{2}$	At Franklin, N. J.
Zinc spinel, 307	. . . .	. . . .	. . . .	. . . . .	See gahnite
Zinkenite, 283	$Pb_6Sb_{14}S_{27}$	Hex	5.3	3–$3\frac{1}{2}$	. . . .
Zircon, 404	$ZrSiO_4$	Tet	4.68	$7\frac{1}{2}$	In small crystals
Zoisite, 417	$Ca_2Al_3(SiO_4)_3(OH)$	Orth	3.3	6	See clinozoisite

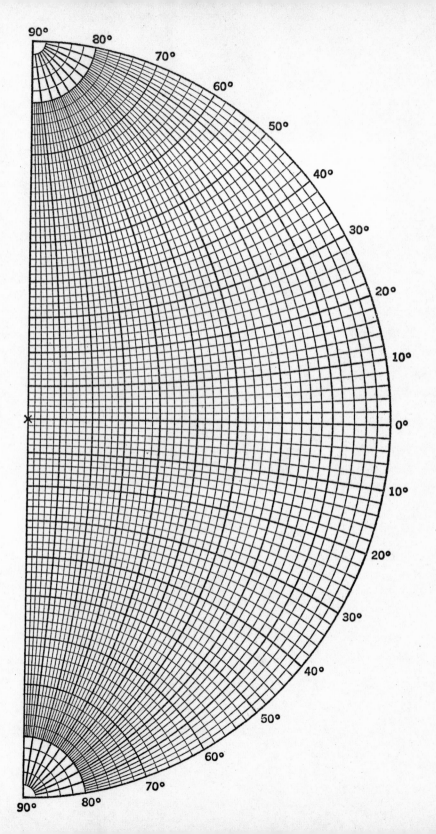